CONSTRUCTION TECH STUDIES

D1578236

CONSTRUCTION TECH STUDIES

BUILDING AND
CIVIL ENGINEERING
CLAIMS IN
PERSPECTIVE

THIRD EDITION

BUILDING AND CIVIL ENGINEERING
CLAIMS IN PERSPECTIVE

THIRD EDITION

G A HUGHES OBE, FRICS
J N BARBER MA, LLB, MICE, FCIArb, Barrister

Longman
Scientific &
Technical

Longman Scientific & Technical,
Longman Group UK Limited,
Longman House, Burnt Mill, Harlow,
Essex CM20 2JE, England
and Associated Companies throughout the world.

First published 1983
Second edition 1985
Third edition 1992

ISBN 0 582 059356

British Library Cataloguing in Publication Data
A catalogue record for this book is available from
the British Library

Set by 4 in 10/12 Compugraphic Times

Printed and Bound in Great Braitain
at the Bath Press, Avon

Contents

Introduction

'Claims' — a term likely to arouse the emotions of the most matter-of-fact architect, engineer or quantity surveyor, a chill of apprehension or a thrill of anticipation (according to one's point of view) in any contractor, and yet what are they? Claims for payment, or additional payment, yes, but what is there about them that makes them different from 'ordinary payments' yet apparently so difficult to define? Some say they concern only matters for which the contract provides, yet do not explain how other matters are to be brought to attention. Others say they concern only matters outwith the contract, thus ignoring the disputes that arise about valuation of variations and the like. Some consider they are ploys indulged in only by unscrupulous contractors, whilst some contractors regard them as a defence mechanism against shortcomings (real or imagined) of the employer's professional advisers, or fate in the shape of unexpected circumstances. Others consider they are the means of rescuing a contractor from an injudicious (real or inadvertent) tender. They cannot be all these things, so what then can they be? If there is this difference of opinion about what they are, is it small wonder that there is difficulty of communication in dealing with them?

Do they represent a problem? There is no point in going to great lengths merely to resolve a definition if that is all there is to it. Too many of us in the construction industry know from our own experience that claims occur, that they divert considerable resources in terms of staff at the expense of ongoing construction. They cause budgetary difficulties and financial embarrassment to our employers. They cause financial difficulties, restriction of cash flow, loss of liquidity or worse to contractors (and sub-contractors in their turn). To the extent that they represent a legitimate but unestablished entitlement they cost an incredible amount to finance over long periods, which, if the contractors in question are able to stay in business, means inevitably a charge on the industry falling ultimately on the employer. There have been conferences and seminars and symposia galore on the subject, which suggests there is no lack of concern.

On a more formal level, the Harris Working Party (Contracting in Civil Engineering since Banwell) said that the problem of claims was 'probably the most difficult and controversial matter affecting relations in the industry'. In the Banwell Report which preceded Harris it was said '... it would be to the benefit of the whole industry if the impact of claims was substantially reduced'. In his book on engineering law, Max Abrahamson refers (p 393) to an informal Discussion by F R Oliver (ICE, 5 October 1972) and says 'Some of the statistics about the prevalence of claims given at that discussion are frightening'. From other evidence also, I am inclined to agree. There seems, however, no real idea of the size of the problem. In terms of money owed by employers to contractors it is unlikely to be less than $£10^8$ and could be around $£10^9$, taking building and civil engineering together. From this, it is not very diffiuclt to calculate the financial drain at recent high overdraft rates. One can also get some idea of the enormous cost in staff time which must be involved.

So, claims are the symptoms of a problem. What causes them, are they avoidable or unavoidable? It has been said that 'Claims are a fact of life' and 'Claims are here to stay', which in the context of seeming to be unwelcome conveys an air of resignation, a suggestion that the cause cannot be diagnosed, much less treated. It has also been said that 'More than a quarter of the money paid by employers to contractors is now based on negotiations which take place after the contract is signed'. As a statement that is probably true but it does nothing to indicate either cause or remedy. If claims represent a situation which is unacceptable and avoidable, then it follows that some fault lies somewhere and it should not be beyond the wit of those of us who purport to serve the construction industry to do something about it. If they are unavoidable, then at least we should equip ourselves to deal with them efficiently and expeditiously and minimize the cost in terms of both money and staff resources. An engineer has been defined as a man who can construct a facility for sixpence that any fool can construct for a shilling (or did all that go out with decimalization?) and quantity surveyors have claimed that giving value for money is one of their prime objectives (or does that stop with cost planning?). In either case it is to be hoped that these are not mere platitudes.

So far as avoidability is concerned, this must lie primarily in the production of the design and the contract documents. These must portray properly what is required to be done and the physical context in which it is to be achieved, and all this in the realization that another party is committing himself to translate these documentary depictions into physical reality for a price. But this is no more than the architect, engineer and quantity surveyor are paid to do. The counterpart is of course a properly prepared tender, and this requires corresponding skill and probity on the part of the contractor. It has been said that some contractors price their tenders low deliberately so as to secure the work with the intention of making good their losses by way of a claim. If true, it seems an incredibly risky way of doing business. The opportunity is unpredictable (unless architects, engineers and quantity surveyors can be relied upon to be consistently incompetent); the outcome is unreliable in fact and time. In addition to proper documentation and tendering, administration of the contract during construction must be properly observed by both sides. Of course there are unscrupulous people on both sides of the fence, but the actions and attitudes of a few should not be allowed to cloud the main issues. Surely it is possible to distinguish between good and bad claims and, if we are professionally competent as we should be, deal with them as they deserve?

To the extent that claims are unavoidable, then it should be part of our stock-in-trade to have the skill and knowledge to deal with them as with any other problem our professions require. We should know the principles upon which the various liabilities and responsibilities of each party and their agents are determined, so as to be able to discern how the terms of the contract or of contract law apply to the circumstances met with or vice versa. We should recognize that in the nature of the construction industry some events and situations are unavoidable and unforeseeable. We should recognize the economic advantages to the employer that risks should be allocated and not all thrust upon the contractor; and once they have been allocated we should not cavil at placing them where they belong, whether it be employer or contractor. Contract conditions have changed over the years in this matter of allocating risks and it is no longer appropriate to apply the mental attitude of half a century ago (when the contractor was expected to take all risks) to the situation today, where that is no longer the case. Then engineers, at least, had the authority, tacit or assumed, to mitigate hardships and dispense 'justice'. That is no longer the case and the fact must be recognized.

So far as this book is concerned, it is intended to deal with claims as they are currently met with. In pointing to the solution of any given case, opportunity will be taken where appropriate to indicate how the situation may have been avoided. In a work such as this it is not possible to do more than present a very small sample — hopefully representative — of the various categories which will illustrate basic principles. There is always the difficulty in giving a worked example that the solution is applicable only to the facts related. Every contract differs, every situation differs. To be of any help, therefore, the principles involved in each case need to be indicated. Needless to say, the cases themselves are fictitious, at least so far as their presentation is concerned, and are necessarily simplified but they all derive from real life and some from reported cases.

No reason is seen why 'claims' should arouse such a depth of emotion and irrational antipathy so that judgment is clouded and justice thrown to the winds. There is no necessity for architects, engineers or quantity surveyors to feel personally insulted that a contractor should presume to enter a claim (if there is implied criticism and the cap fits, it may be uncomfortable to wear). By the same token, there is no necessity for contractors to regard architects, engineers and quantity surveyors as being of questionable legitimacy if they say 'No' to a badly constructed or ill-founded claim. If a contractor is expected to quote chapter and verse in justification of his claim, is it not reasonable to expect the professions to do a little better than give a monosyllabic 'No' in response? Comment has been made that this sort of treatment often conveys indecisiveness rather than decisiveness and prompts a contractor to persist rather than desist.

If anything can be done to reduce significantly the burden of claims, then contractors, employers and the rest of us concerned must benefit significantly. Not only are there the direct and obvious benefits of saving money and staff resources, there are also the side-effect benefits on the work itself as regards quality, efficiency, and, not least, the climate in which it is carried out.

It is hoped that this book may make some small contribution to put the subject in perspective. If there seems to be criticism here and there, may it be taken as intended — as constructive? Even professionals can make mistakes and the law does not require perfection to avoid a charge of negligence. However, that does not allow us to become resigned about a situation which it is within our capacity to improve.

Voorthuizen
Holland 1983

Preface to third edition

The opportunity has been taken, while revising and bringing the book up to date, to examine more closely the legal and contractual framework within which claims are to be avoided, asserted and assessed. This is not intended to detract from the central purpose of the book, which is still to put the subject of claims in perspective, but rather (continuing the metaphor), by filling in the background, to lend greater clarity to the main subject and improve the balance of the picture.

For example, consider the question — for whose benefit are claims provisions inserted in construction contracts? Most construction professionals now instinctively respond that the provisions exist for the benefit of contractors — the 'road to riches' syndrome. Some will suggest that claims provisions are for the benefit of the employer in attracting lower tender prices. Others may say the provisions are to make the contract 'fair'.

All three views have some substance, but they overlook the origin of the contractual provisions invoked by claims. The origin was to satisfy two essential aims of employers: to keep the contract in place whatever eventualities might arise, and to allow the employer or his agent to order variations. Invalidating or exceeding the contract was found both embarrassing and expensive for an employer, and forms of contract evolved to overcome problems exposed by the courts.

A further aim of employers, historically, was that the involvement of lawyers and courts in contentious matters should be minimized. Claims-based provisions were introduced to enable what would be breaches of contract to be dealt with by internally administered remedies. At one time, employers reserved the additional advantage that the decision of the employer's appointee, the engineer or architect, on such matters was virtually beyond challenge in the courts.

The aim of making construction contracts fair, although supported by ancient and respectable advocates including Aristotle and St Thomas Aquinas,[1] was put on one side during the great construction boom of the Industrial Revolution. Forms of contract of that era showed scant regard for fairness and they were upheld by the courts without objection, even with righteous enthusiasm. It was near the end of the nineteenth century before any trend towards fairness again became noticeable. The trend can be observed over the past century in decisions of the courts, in Acts of Parliament, and in the standard forms of contract. The situation now exists that contracts that are not fair may even overreach themselves and defeat their own object.

---

1. 'To sell dearer or to buy cheaper than a thing is worth is in itself unjust and unlawful', Saint Thomas Aquinas, *Summa Theologica*.

Satisfying the aim of fairness increases the likelihood of adjustment of price and time, but it does not entail the inevitable sacrifice of the employer's other objective, that works should be completed on time and within budget. What it does entail is that greater care and effort is needed in pre-contract preparation to achieve that objective. An appreciation of claims is thus as important to pre-contract preparation as it is to contract administration or post-contract clearing up.

Understanding of the general legal and contractual framework is not a substitute for understanding of the realities of construction, of finance and of costs. The two aspects go hand in hand. Indeed, reality and the law begin to merge. The recent attitude of the courts in commercial contracts is to discourage 'excessive semantic and syntactical analysis', in favour of business common sense. This does not mean that the written terms of a contract are to be disregarded, but that they are presumed to have been agreed between responsible, prudent and experienced persons. Whether or not such a presumption is justified, it is a healthy approach and one that may help to restore the perception of claims to proper proportions.

G A Hughes	J N Barber
Voorthuizen	Stanmore
Holland 1991	UK 1991

ACKNOWLEDGEMENTS

I am indebted to John Barber who has made amendments to bring this book up to date and has made this third edition possible. He is particularly well fitted to undertake the task, being qualified as civil engineer, barrister and arbitrator. He practises as a consulting engineer, dealing with a wide variety of projects and problems world-wide, and his contribution to this edition is much appreciated.

G A Hughes

We are grateful to the following for permission to reproduce copyright material:

Butterworths for an extract from *Law of Contract* by Cheshire, Fifoot & Furmston (12th Edition, 1991); the Controller of Her Majesty's Stationery Office for extracts from *GC/Works/1* (2nd Edition) & extracts from *GC/Works/1* (3rd Edition); The Institution of Civil Engineers for an extract from the article 'The Conditions of Engineering Contracts' by E Rimmer from *Institution of Civil Engineers Journal* Vol 11 (1939) & an extract from the article 'Rate Fixing in Civil Engineering Contracts' by C Haswell from *Proceedings of The Institution of Civil Engineers* Vol 24 (1963); Sweet & Maxwell Ltd for an extract from *Handbook of Arbitration Practice* by Bernstein (2nd Edition, 1990) & an extract from *The Judge as Juror: The Judicial Determination of Factual Issues* by Bingham; Thomas Telford Publications, on behalf of The Institution of Civil Engineers, for extracts from *Institution of Civil Engineers Arbitration Procedure*, extracts from *Institution of Civil Engineers Conditions of Contract* (5th Edition) & extracts from *Institution of Civil Engineers Conditions of Contract* (6th Edition), copyright The Institution of Civil Engineers, Federation of Civil Engineering Contractors & Association of Consulting Engineers.

Table of statutes

Table of cases

List of abbreviations

AC	Appeal Cases
A/E/QS	Architect/Engineer/Quantity Surveyor
All ER	All England Law Reports
BLR	Building Law Reports
B/Q	Bill(s) of Quantities
Ch	Chancery
CESMM	Civil Engineering Standard Method of Measurement 1976
CESMM2	Civil Engineering Standard Method of Measurement (2nd Edition) 1985
Const LJ	Construction Law Journal
C/W	Clerk of Works
EoT	Extension of Time
FIDIC4	FIDIC Conditions of Contract for Works of Civil Engineering Construction, Fourth Edition 1987
GC/Wks 1 Ed 2	General Conditions of Government Contract for Building and Civil Engineering Works (Edition 2) 1977
GC/Wks 1 Ed 3	General Conditions of Government Contract for Building and Civil Engineering Works (Edition 3) December 1989, Revised 1990
ICE Form	Conditions of Contract for use with Works of Civil Engineering Construction ('ICE Conditions')
ICE4	ICE Conditions, 4th ed (1955)
ICE5	ICE Conditions, 5th ed (1973), Revised June 1979*
ICE6	ICE Conditions, 6th ed (1991)
ICLR	International Construction Law Review
JCT Form	'Standard Form' of building contract
JCT 63/77	'Standard Form' of building contract, 1963 ed, 1977 Revision
JCT 80	'Standard Form' of building contract, 1980 edition*
Lloyd's Rep	Lloyd's Law Reports
MLR	Minimum Lending Rate
MMRB	Method of Measurement for Road and Bridge Works
M of M	Method of Measurement
PM	Project Manager
QB	Queen's Bench
RE	Resident Engineer
RSC	Rules of Supreme Court
SGA	Sale of Goods Act 1979
SGSA	Supply of Goods and Services Act 1982

---

* References to later amendments of ICE5 and JCT 80 are made in the text

SI	Site Investigation
SMM6	Standard Method of Measurement for Building Works Edition 6
SMM for CEQ	Standard Method of Measurement for Civil Engineering Quantities
SO	Superintending Officer
SU	Statutory Undertaker
T & P	Time and Progress
UCTA	Unfair Contract Terms Act 1977
VI	Variation Instruction
VO	Variation Order
WLR	Weekly Law Reports

Chapter 1
Definition and classification of claims

GENERALLY

There are so many different opinions as to what constitutes a claim that the first essential in trying to get this problem in perspective is to construct a definition which is comprehensive, comprehensible, and acceptable both to those who for whatever reason produce claims and to those who have to examine and report them. It should present no procedural difficulties and should not prejudge any issue. Let us look then at some ideas current on the subject and see whether any are tenable and either from them or criticisms of them try to construct such a definition.

CURRENT USAGES

Of the three major Forms of Contract, JCT, ICE and GC/Wks 1, only the ICE Form recognizes claims in Clause 52(4) as being concerned with seeking 'a higher rate or price' for varied work or '. . . additional payment pursuant to any (other) Clause . . .'. Payments due in accordance with the contract are dealt with in Clause 60(1), which requires the contractor to submit a statement showing what he considers he is entitled to and which the engineer is required to certify. GC/Wks 1 Ed2 uses the word 'claims' in Condition 40(3) as referring to requests for monthly payment of advances on account. All these forms use the term 'claims' to refer to claims against the employer by third parties (e.g. ICE Clauses 22(1), 28(1), 29(2) and 30(2); JCT Clause 20.1 and GC/Wks 1 Ed2 Conditions 47 and 48). ICE does use the word in a somewhat wider sense in Clause 65(3), where it is stipulated that determination shall be 'without prejudice to the claims of either party in respect of any antecedent breach thereof'. This is not qualified as to whether it refers to matters for which the contract provides or otherwise and therefore must include both.

Contractual

Although the word 'claim' is used sparingly in standard conditions of contract, claims are often (and properly) made in respect of matters for which the conditions make express provision, e.g. ICE5 Clauses 52(1), 55(2), 56, 58, 59 etc as well as 7(3), 13(3), 14(6), 27(6), 31(2) and 42(1). It matters not that the latter group is in respect of circumstances which are in the nature of breaches of contract.[1] That they are provided for in the contract means that they fall to be dealt with under the contract. JCT 80 Clauses 3, 13.5, 13.7, 14.2 etc. are similar. Such claims are often referred to as 'contractual' but this term is somewhat imprecise. The better description is 'claims under the contract'. But it does not follow that only matters within the immediate compass of the clauses of the contract are legitimately claims.

Let us look at a case where a contractor is dissatisfied with a quantity surveyor's valuation of varied work.

Contractor to Architect   *4 April 1975*

> *We must draw your attention to our claim for higher rates in connection with Variation No 10, together with the consequential effect on other work. The Quantity Surveyor has valued this work at prices in the Bill of Quantities but we contend these are insufficient and take no account of the effect of the variation on other work as provided under Clause 13.5.5.*
>
> *Will you please give this matter your urgent attention as the amount of money now involved is substantial?*

Architect to Contractor   *1 May 1975*

> *I refer to your letter of 4 April and have had a report from the Quantity Surveyor on the matter of valuation of Variation No 10.*
>
> *The QS has valued the work in accordance with Clause 13.5 and it is for you to make representations to him if you are not satisfied. The clause in question makes no provision for claiming anything further and clearly this is not a matter coming within the provisions of Clause 26.*
>
> *The Conditions of Contract make no provision for such claims and there would seem to be no alternative but to leave the matter until after Practical Completion.*

Naive? Maybe, but there are those who try variations on this theme that nothing outside the conditions of contract can have any effect. What about common law rights and remedies?

---

1. For example, ICE5 Clause 7(3) provides compensation for failure by the engineer to perform an implied obligation to issue at a time reasonable in all the circumstances drawings or instructions reasonably requested by the contractor. The engineer's failure would constitute a breach of the obligation.

> *We regret we cannot accept the decision contained in your letter of May 1st. We have already made representations to the Quantity Surveyor but without effect. We agree that it is not a matter under Clause 26.*
>
> *We are not prepared to leave the matter until after Practical Completion; the amount of money involved is large and the cost of financing is high. Are we to understand that the third paragraph of your letter refers to arbitration? If so, we cannot agree.*
>
> *We must formally notify you of our intention to claim the additional cost of finance in respect of the sum due to us until payment is received.*

Although there is no express provision as to what will happen in the event that the QS's valuation is unacceptable, clearly the contractor cannot be precluded from expressing his opinions and notifying his intentions. Quantity surveyors are fallible and can make mistakes at times. The architect is doing his client disservice in not grasping the nettle. The contractor could be wrong and the QS right, but the matter must be thrashed out and either rejected (with reasons) or accepted in whole or part. The architect's veiled reference to arbitration is unhelpful and somewhat pointless. If some further payment is eventually found to be due, how would the architect and quantity surveyor explain the finance costs? (Or would they try to refuse payment?)[2].

Extra-contractual   Let us look at the converse. There are those who contend that claims can only be in respect of matters for which there is no provision in the contract. Take a case where an engineer is dilatory in giving an extension of time. On completion of the work the engineer may feel somewhat affronted to receive the following letter:

> *Contractor to Engineer*   *30 September 1974*
>
> *We herewith formally submit our claim amounting to £42,000 for acceleration of the work to complete by 31 August last. Full details of the calculations of this claim are attached. We should be glad if you would include a substantial payment on account thereof in the next Certificate.*

One can imagine the engineer irately phoning the RE and demanding an explanation. The RE would hotly deny giving any instructions to accelerate and the engineer, who is perhaps more familiar with ICE4 than with ICE5, would write:

> *Engineer to Contractor*   *4 October 1974*
>
> *I refer to your letter of 30 September and am at a loss to understand on what grounds you base this extravagant claim. No instructions were issued by the RE or myself to accelerate the work and the claim is accordingly rejected.*

If the contractor knows his stuff he will point out the provisions of Clause 44 of the Conditions but he may be more inclined to write on the following lines:

> *Contractor to Engineer*   *11 October 1974*
>
> *With reference to your letter of 4 October we would point out that we have made several applications for an extension of time but have received none.*

---

2. See Chapter 11.

We were therefore of the view that we were under obligation to complete the work by the contract date and took steps to increase our plant and work overtime in order to achieve this. We therefore consider ourselves entitled to be reimbursed the extra cost.

Now, it does not matter whether he was justified (he could have assumed he would eventually get an extension of time), he considers himself entitled and nothing can prevent him entering a claim. Whether he gave proper notice, whether he can prove his case is not relevant at this point. He thinks he is entitled and so makes a claim.

So, again we come to the conclusion that it matters nothing what the nature of the claim may be or whether it is justified or not. If the contractor considers he is entitled, he cannot be prevented from saying so.

Let us look now at the situation in which a contractor is suffering from interference by another contractor on an adjacent site by the latter's blasting operations. When our contractor tendered there was no indication that the work was about to commence on the adjacent site, though it is probably one of the matters he might have ascertained by enquiry. His own work entailed no blasting. Work is in progress and he is obliged to suspend operations at times as there is danger to his men.

Contractor to Engineer   2 June 1975

We have to inform you that because of blasting operations on the adjacent site, we have to suspend operations two or three times per day with a consequent loss of output and delay.

As soon as blasting is complete we intend submitting a claim for the additional cost involved and for extension of time as this situation could not have been foreseen when we tendered.

Engineer to Contractor   5 June 1975

I note that you are having to suspend operations because of blasting on the adjacent site. I must point out that this is in no way the responsibility of the Employer.

I would suggest that you should either seek an injunction against the adjacent contractor and/or inform him of your intention to claim your additional costs from him. This claim should include liquidated damages which will be recovered from you in the event of delay as I see no grounds for awarding an extension of time.

As a general rule, non-foreseeability does not provide grounds for extra payment or relief from contractual obligations, except insofar as there is express provision in the contract.[3] Nor is there any implied warranty[4] by the employer that a contractor will be free from interference by third parties for whom the employer is not responsible.[5]

The engineer is right to point out the limits on the employer's responsibility, but the further comments on the contractor's actions in relation to the third party contractor are gratuitous. The engineer is unnecessarily exposing the limitations of his knowledge of the law. It may be open for the contractor to seek an injunction against the adjacent contractor, but the legal situation is complex. The basis of the potential claim against the adjacent contractor would

---

3. *British Movietonews v London & District Cinemas Ltd* [1952] AC 166.
4. 'Warranty' is used in the legal sense of a promise or undertaking, the breach of which gives rise to entitlement to financial compensation.
5. *Porter v Tottenham UDC* [1915] 1 KB 776.

be in tort, possibly in nuisance, negligence or breach of statutory duty. The contractor might well seek the co-operation of the employer, as the owner of the site, in pursuing an injunction. The contractor might alternatively seek the assistance of the statutory authorities to improve control of the blasting. The liquidated damages mentioned might not be recoverable from the adjacent contractor.[6] The engineer would have done better to restrain his enthusiasm and recommend the contractor to obtain legal advice.

The main point at issue here is that whether a claim is based on grounds within or outwith the contract, at least there must be reason why the employer is liable. He may be at fault or it may be a matter for which he has accepted liability or for which he may be liable in law. If he is not, then no claim will lie against him.

On the other hand, inability of the contractor to recover as damages from the third party the liquidated damages for which the contractor would be liable to the employer under the contract on account of the delay, might be considered justification to grant an extension of time on the grounds of 'other special circumstances'.

Why the distinction?

It may be asked, does the distinction between contractual and extra-contractual claims matter? What is its significance? If the contractor considers he has an entitlement or a right to compensation, he is entitled to say so and his saying so is, in terms of ordinary English usage and common convenience, referred to as a claim.

There are two points. The first is that every entitlement or right must be matched by a corresponding obligation, liability or detriment.[7] As illustrated in the last example, the claimant, if he wishes to pursue his entitlement or right, must identify correctly who bears the obligation, liability or detriment.

The second point is to identify whose function it is to respond to a claim in terms of investigation, recording facts and adducing arguments, and who has the power and duty to decide by determining issues and making awards in respect of the claim. This is relevant for the claimant in that he needs to address his claim to the appropriate person in a form which is suitable. It is also relevant to the person who has the function of responding and/or deciding since he needs to appreciate the existence and scope of his powers and duties.

It is a separate matter how the person is paid for exercising these duties of responding and deciding. It comes as a shock to some contractors to learn that under traditional fee-scale arrangements, consulting engineers are not paid extra for fighting and rejecting claims. On the contrary, fee-scale arrangements commonly mean that the engineer is paid a percentage of the amount which he awards and certifies for payment to the contractor under the contract, but he receives nothing if he rejects the claim. Different arrangements apply if the claim goes to arbitration: normally the consulting engineer is then reimbursed on a time basis. The Standard Form of Agreement for the appointment of a quantity surveyor, on the other hand, provides that the quantity surveyor shall be entitled to be paid by the employer for additional services such as 'investigation of the validity of contractor's claims'.

Architects, engineers and quantity surveyors appointed to act under the contract have powers and duties imposed upon them by the contract conditions — but only those defined. These include the valuation of variations (JCT 80 Clause 13.4, ICE Clause 52, GC/Wks 1 — Ed 2 Cond 9), matters affecting the regular progress of the work (JCT 80 Clause 26, ICE Clauses 7, 14, 31, 42 etc, GC/Wks 1 — Ed 2 Cond 53) or whatever, and in connection with claims on such matters they are required both to respond and to decide. The A/E/QS is required to respond by investigating the claim, keeping or agreeing records, examining the submission, and adducing any contrary arguments. This should be regarded as separate

---

6. *Archital Luxfer v Dunning* [1989] 5 Const LJ 47.
7. A contractor's entitlement to extension of time gives rise to a corresponding detriment: the reduction in the employer's right to liquidated damages.

from the decision on the claim, which will comprise both a decision on the principles and a decision on amount or 'quantum' (if any). The decision leads to the issue of a certificate if any money is due.

In some cases the Conditions of Contract may specifically provide for claims to be resolved by agreement rather than by unilateral decision of the A/E/QS, for example, in settling rates for extra work. The power to decide only arises in such cases if there is a failure to agree.

There are, as we have seen, other matters for which no provision for adjustment is made under the contract. In the absence of general powers of decision, the architect, engineer or quantity surveyor has no implied authority to settle such matters or bind the employer. No doubt in most cases, the employer will look to the architect, engineer or quantity surveyor to respond and to provide advice, he may expect reports as to the validity of the claim and its value, and recommendations as to settlement, but any settlement or arrangement made without his express authority will not be binding.[8]

The position is complicated by the ICE and FIDIC forms of contract where the engineer is conferred with a further power to decide on matters in dispute. Under the relevant provisions (ICE Clause 66, FIDIC Clause 67), all disputes which are to be referred to an arbitrator must first be referred back to the engineer. It follows that the engineer has power at that stage to decide any matter which the arbitrator could decide. According to a recent decision,[9] this means that the engineer has power to decide on certain extra-contractual claims, if referred to him under this clause. He does not, however, have such power prior to such reference, and a claim can only be referred if there is a difference or dispute between the employer and the contractor. Accordingly, extra-contractual claims should be dealt with initially by the employer.

The guiding principle is that claims should be dealt with on the basis of their nature and the relevant power in the contract to deal with them. There should be no question of their being dealt with according to whether the reason for them is obvious or not or a ready explanation available or not. Should that be attempted and any 'agreement' with the contractor be upset by reason of other matters in dispute being referred to the employer, or arbitration proceedings supervene, then any 'accommodation' resorted to as a matter of convenience may well cause embarrassment if not actual difficulty.[10]

The distinction is also relevant to claims taken to arbitration or litigation. There the power to determine issues and make awards is known as 'jurisdiction'. The jurisdiction of an arbitrator derives from the arbitration clause in the contract, coupled with his appointment and the reference to him of specific matters. The arbitrator must deal with all matters put before him. If he deals with matters outside his jurisdiction, his decision may be set aside as void. His decision may also be set aside as void if he attempts to investigate the claim independently: he is limited to considering the evidence put before him.[11]

The jurisdiction of a court depends on the matters referred to it by the issue of a writ and exchange of pleadings. In *Northern Regional Health Authority v Crouch*[12] it was held that a court did not have jurisdiction to exercise powers conferred on an arbitrator by a contract such as the JCT Form to 'open up, review and revise any certificate, opinion or decision' of the architect. The Court of Appeal held that such powers involved an element

8. *Sharpe v San Paulo Rly* [1873] LR 8 Ch App 597.
9. *Ashville Investments Ltd v Elmer Contractors Ltd* [1989] QB 488; cf *Fillite (Runcorn) Ltd v Aqua-Lift* [1989] 45 BLR 27. See Humphrey Lloyd QC, 'An expanded power to decide? The effect of two cases on the engineer's power under Clause 67 of the FIDIC Conditions' [1988] ICLR 326.
10. In *Sharpe v San Paulo Rly* [1873] LR 8 Ch App 597, the engineer had entered into an arrangement with the contractor to make adjustments to stations on the railway line as compensation for the quantity of earthworks being double that scheduled by the engineer. The Privy Council held that the employer was not bound by the arrangement.
11. *Fox v PG Wellfair* [1981] 2 Lloyd's Rep 514.
12. *Northern Regional Health Authority v Derek Crouch Construction* [1984] QB 644.

of contract-making and were therefore outside the powers of a court. Such jurisdiction may, however, now be conferred on a court by agreement of the parties.[13]

A court will also decline to deal with a case, if one party objects, on the basis that there is an arbitration clause in the contract and the matter is within the scope of the arbitration clause.[14]

Ploys by the unscrupulous

Continuing with the nature of claims, there have been suggestions, not entirely without justification, that they are ploys indulged in by unscrupulous contractors to turn a more or less dishonest penny. It is mooted that some contractors price their tenders low deliberately so as to secure work, with the intention of making good their losses and making a profit by way of claims. No doubt there are unscrupulous people on both sides of the fence, and the architect, engineer or quantity surveyor must be alert to any ploys. Attitudes on both sides may well be coloured by the degree of trust each has in his opposite number and by the degree of knowledge and experience encountered.

The possibility that some claims are tainted by dishonesty does not mean that this is the general case, nor does it justify the dismissal of all claims as spurious. If risks are apportioned between employer and contractor it is unreasonable to expect tenderers to allow in their prices for those risks which the employer has shouldered. And where there are provisions for adjustment through claims, and particularly where there are notice requirements for the submission of claims, then claims and notice of claim must be expected. Not all claims that are submitted will be soundly based, as one might wish in an ideal world. Not all claims will be properly argued and documented. But there is nothing inherently dishonest or unscrupulous in the submission of claims.

Defence mechanism

The counter argument to the foregoing is that claims are some sort of defence mechanism by long-suffering contractors against the incompetence or inhumanity of architects, engineers and quantity surveyors. This in turn is about as true as the generalization about unscrupulous contractors, but in the same way there is perhaps that germ of truth which sparks the canard. Those of us who prepare contract documents must be presumed to know our trade, to know what contracts provide for, what they mean and the circumstances, both physical and commercial, in which they operate. We must be expected to be able to administer those contracts similarly.

PROPER USAGE

We have looked at some of the things which a claim may represent and at some which it may not. Justification or lack of it should not be confused with whether a contractor may claim; to attempt to do that would be to prejudge the issue. Whatever the merits or otherwise, the architect, engineer or quantity surveyor would be wise to encourage the contractor to keep him informed of anything which is happening or has happened involving the possibility of additional expense. In some cases work in hand may be concerned or affected and the architect or engineer may be able to take remedial action (if he or the employer is at fault), or avoiding or mitigating action (if the cause is one for which the employer has accepted the risk).

In addition, the contractor is in many cases specifically required to give notice and could well jeopardize his position if he failed to do so.

Definition

As regards defining the term 'claim', therefore, would it not be sensible, indeed is it not necessary, to get back to essentials and use something like the dictionary definition of the word as applied to the circumstances of the construction industry — namely, that it is:

   (a) a demand or, if something less strong (?provocative) is preferred, a request or application for something to which

---

13. Courts and Legal Services Act 1990 s100.
14. Arbitration Act 1950 s4.

(b) a contractor (including quite scrupulous ones) considers, believes or contends (rightly or wrongly) he is entitled but in respect of which

(c) agreement has not yet been reached?

Such a definition would have the merit at least of including anything actual or potential when trouble or expense is likely to be involved, about which the architect, engineer or quantity surveyor should, in the employer's interests, be informed. It would leave those people free to exercise their powers under the contract if such permit or otherwise to refer the matter to the employer (with or without advice) seeking instructions. It would enable the architect or engineer to take remedial, avoiding or mitigating action if appropriate or to inform the contractor that in his opinion it is the contractor's responsibility (and why). At this stage it does not matter whether the basis of the claim lies within or outwith the contract. The proposed definition would not preclude any contention of believed entitlement or demand a categorization which could be self-destructive. It leaves to be dealt with in an appropriate manner any frivolous claims made by an unscrupulous contractor.

For the purpose of this book, therefore, the word 'claim' will be used to mean simply a request, demand, application for payment or notification of presumed entitlement to which the contractor, rightly or wrongly at that stage, considers himself entitled and in respect of which agreement has not yet been reached. It will generally be spelt with a small 'c'.

Classification by type   Having arrived at a definition, it is necessary to look at the various types of claim and consider some of the terms frequently used in connection with them (again without unanimity as to what is meant) and try to arrive at some reasoned basis for such terms. Claims fall into three main categories.

Claims under the contract

These claims (sometimes loosely referred to as 'contractual') concern matters which have a basis in the contract itself where particular provision can be quoted as giving rise to entitlement. For example, the measurement of work done (ICE Clauses 55, 56 and 57; GC/Wks 1 Ed 2 Cond 10); the measurement and valuation of variations (JCT 63/77 Clause 11, JCT 80 Clause 13, ICE Clause 52, GC/Wks 1 Ed 2 Cond 9); delay arising from various causes (ICE Clauses 7, 14, 31, 42 etc.) or disturbance (JCT 80 Clause 26) etc., clearly come in this category. Generally such clauses define the basis of valuation to be adopted and stipulate who (architect, engineer or quantity surveyor) is to do what.

Common law, equitable and statutory remedies

These are sometimes referred to rather imprecisely as 'extra-contractual'. In the absence of express contractual provisions dealing with entitlements and adjustments, common law remedies may be available. These include damages for breach of contract; payment on a *quantum meruit* where there was no formal contract or the contract has been exceeded, repudiated, or frustrated; equitable remedies including rectification, rescission, or injunction; damages under the Misrepresentation Act 1967; and damages in tort (although remedies in tort will rarely be granted where the parties are in a contractual relationship).[15] The basis of these remedies and their availability is explained in Chapter 2. The essential point is that a party wishing to benefit from a common law remedy must assert his right by claiming it, but the architect, engineer or quantity surveyor has no implied authority (except in some cases under ICE Clause 66, FIDIC Clause 67) to settle such claims.

Ex gratia

This is where a contractor is seeking something more tangible than sympathy but where he has no contractual provision to rely upon, where there has been no breach or tort by

---

15. *Greater Nottingham Co-op Soc Ltd v Cementation Piling & Foundations Ltd* [1989] QB 71; *William Hill v Bernard Sunley* [1982] 22 BLR 1; *Tai Hing Cotton Mill v Liu Chong Hing Bank* [1986] AC 80.

the employer and the contractor is seeking, as the term suggests, some payment as an act of grace. It may be that the contractor underestimated the cost when tendering, that the execution of the work proved more difficult than he expected or that risks were higher than he allowed for; in short, that his costs were greater than the payment due. By seeking payment on an *ex gratia* basis the contractor is tacitly admitting that he has no entitlement for further payment, either contractual or extra-contractual. Some employers may be prepared to be generous or they may consider it to be in their business interests to help, but local and central government authorities are rarely in a position to take this view.

On the other hand, where an employer settles a claim, which has a basis in the contract or at law, by means of a payment expressed to be '*ex gratia*', he is simply settling the claim. In such circumstances, the words '*ex gratia*' do not carry a necessary or even a probable implication that the agreement is to be without legal effect.[16]

Basis must be decided

The basis of a claim is what it is. It needs to be identified and addressed. It is up to the party claiming to assert a valid and relevant basis of claim. If there are alternative bases of claim available, he should put them forward — judgments by panels of judges in the Court of Appeal or House of Lords demonstrate that even the most eminent legal minds can reach the same conclusion by different routes — but it is not enough for the claimant merely to state facts and hope that the architect, engineer, quantity surveyor, arbitrator or judge will be moved by sympathy to find an appropriate basis of entitlement.

Conversely the architect, engineer or quantity surveyor ought to deal with the claims as submitted, addressing all arguments and not confining his reply to those arguments which he can readily refute. Where any claim or part of a claim is outside his powers under the contract he should either refer it directly to the employer or back to the contractor to take up with the employer.

Instances have been known where an architect, engineer or quantity surveyor has incorrectiy dubbed a claim 'extra-contractual' where he preferred not to deal with it — perhaps with the thought that the contractor would be disinclined to pursue it directly with the employer — or has sought to deal with a claim on some spurious basis, perhaps because he thought it would be less embarrassing to himself or that the explanation would be more acceptable to the employer than the correct basis. Such manipulation should not be resorted to, if only for the reason that should settlement not be reached the contractor might then be obliged to shift his ground to the correct basis — particularly if the matters have to be taken to arbitration or litigation. Conversely, a contractor may wish to avoid blaming the architect or engineer or even the employer for breach (it sounds too unkind, not to say provocative). He would, however, be unwise to fudge the issue by using euphemisms or choosing a contractual ground which was inappropriate. Nor should an architect, engineer or quantity surveyor take exception if circumstances over which they had no control have put the employer in breach. If the matter was within their control, they should not expect the contractor to accept the consequences.

Classification by subject

Claims may also be classified according to their subject-matter. The categories need to be basic, logical and generally applicable. It is submitted that the following, or any combination of them, meet those requirements:

1. Concerning the existence or applicability of the contract.
2. Concerning contract documentation.
3. Concerning the execution of the work.
4. Concerning payment.
5. Concerning prolongation (delay and disruption).
6. Concerning default, determination, forfeiture, etc.

---

16. *Edwards v Skyways Ltd* [1964] 1 WLR 349.

Existence of contract

Matters outside scope of contract — Most claims concern matters within the scope of a valid contract, but situations arise where the existence or validity of the contract is challenged, to escape from the commitment of onerous conditions or to obtain more advantageous entitlements. This covers two scenarios:

(a) That a binding contract was never established initially. For a binding contract to come into existence, certain requirements must be satisfied. There must be agreement, 'consideration' and intention to create legal relations. Problems commonly occur with the issue of letters of intent, submission of qualified or alternative tenders, revocation of tenders, and work being started or even finished prior to resolution of outstanding matters. If agreement is not concluded on the intended contract, the contract will not apply, but the contractor will usually be entitled to reasonable payment for work actually performed. If agreement is eventually reached, the contract refers back to the start of the work. These matters will be further discussed, with examples, in Chapter 4.

(b) That a contract has ceased to bind. Once a binding contract has been established, there may still be challenges to its validity. A contract may be declared void by a court, for example, on account of 'economic duress'; or it may be rescinded, for example, for misrepresentation; or it may be held to have been 'frustrated', in which case it is treated at common law[17] as brought to an end. Such events rarely happen with standard forms of contract, which are deliberately drafted to keep the contract in place, but one needs to be aware of the possibilities. These matters will be further discussed, with examples, in Chapter 2.

Documentation

Generally — Assuming the contract is valid, the actual contract documents applicable to that contract and the actual words used in the documents will have a substantial, if not controlling, effect on any claim. Most generalizations one may make regarding building and civil engineering contracts can be negated by specific or *ad hoc* provisions. No matter what should have been said, they must be interpreted on what they say. No matter what one would have liked them to say ('... surely they cannot mean that ...'), they must be construed[18] as they stand. No matter what difficulty compliance with the provisions of the contract may involve, they will determine what the obligations and responsibilities of the parties are. In formulating a claim or examining one, the relevant provisions of the contract, even of so-called standard documents, should not be assumed. Printed documents have different editions; *ad hoc* amendments are often made; documents that one might assume should exist or be incorporated ('... they cannot possibly have forgotten to include that ...') should be checked.

Shortcomings — Documents are prepared by people, and people are fallible. After a contract is in being, matters may be discovered which should have been included. They cannot be added unilaterally by one or other party later; once a contract is let documents cannot be amended except by agreement between the parties. Pre-tender correspondence may inadvertently be omitted or not given effect; a covering letter to a tender containing important information may not have been referred to in the tender itself; post-tender correspondence may not be referred to in the acceptance. Conflicts between offers, counter-offers and acceptances must be resolved according to legal rules. Documents such as method statements, if incorporated in the contract documents, may be unintentionally promoted to the status of contractual stipulations.

---

17. The common law position in the event of frustration is now subject to the Law Reform (Frustrated Contracts) Act 1943 as well as any contractual provisions.
18. To 'construe' a contract is to ascertain its proper or correct legal meaning and significance. The process of construing is, confusingly, known as 'construction'.

Implied terms — The express words of the contract documentation may also be supplemented by 'implied terms', implied by common law or statute. Terms may be implied as standard implied terms, applicable to a class of contracts, or as specific implied terms required for an individual contract. In addition to knowing the terms that will be implied as standard, it is equally important to be aware of the terms which will not be implied. Also express terms may be excluded or their effect may be limited by common law or statute; for example, penalty clauses or clauses restricting liability for misrepresentation.

Ambiguities and discrepancies — Ambiguities and discrepancies can arise between documents, or within a given document. The legal rules for construing contracts operate to resolve ambiguities, but the answer provided by the rules might not be satisfactory as regards what is actually to be built. A discrepancy might even invalidate the contract if it could not be resolved. Accordingly, most forms of contract provide powers to resolve ambiguities and discrepancies as regards work to be executed, but subject to possible adjustment of entitlement to payment. Errors or alleged errors in Bills of Quantities are a prolific source of argument, if not dispute or possibly claim, raising the question 'What is an error?' That is a question more difficult to answer than might be supposed.

These matters will be further discussed, with examples, in Chapter 5.

Execution of the Work

Supply of information/delay in giving — The British practice of letting contracts on a minimum of information has strong disadvantages. 'For Heaven's sake let us get that contract let — we can supply the rest of the details while the job is under way', has a chorus which runs 'for Heaven's sake get that detail out and those bending schedules away before the contractor is brought to a standstill'. The concession (for that is what it amounts to) of letting the contract on less than full information carries with it severe obligations to supply that information in good time (and whose opinion matters in that connection?).

Variations/proper payment — Variations are commonplace and there is a tendency not to appreciate the disruptive effect that a relatively minor variation can have on the work. Some tend to be rather major in character and one may perhaps need to consider whether they are properly within the ambit of the relevant clause. That problem might be of relatively academic importance if there were not a tendency on the part of some architects, engineers and quantity surveyors to apply bill rates where the verbal description of the work is the same but the circumstances in which it is carried out are by no means the same.

Risks/responsibility for — Modern conditions of contract allocate risks likely to be met in the course of the work to one party or the other. Some risks are insurable; for example, damage to the work by fire, or damage to third parties. Clear allocation of risk enables appropriate insurance to be effected; it can also define the risk insured. Other risks such as ground conditions, weather, or price inflation are not insurable and must be regarded as commercial risks. The arguments for risk allocation include considerations of fairness,[19] the limited ability of contractors to bear risk in view of the low profit/turnover ratios in construction, and relative abilities of the parties to carry out investigations in advance.[20] On the other side, employers can point to their need for reliable budgetary control and the dangers that risk-sharing provisions will be exploited.[21] There are special difficulties where risk is allocated to one party up to a certain level, with the excess risk then switched to the other party. Definition of the switch-over level by means of a test of 'foreseeability' provides considerable scope for argument, but this may be unavoidable in the quest for an acceptable balance.

19. See Rimmer E J 1939 The conditions of engineering contract. *ICE Journal* **11**: 13.
20. See Uff J, Capper P (eds) 1989 *Construction Contract Policy, Improved Procedures and Practice* Centre of Construction Law and Management, King's College, London.
21. See Duncan Wallace I N QC 1986 *Construction Contracts, Principles and Policies* Chapter 23, Sweet & Maxwell, London. Also published [1983] ICLR p. 16.

Defects — Rights, powers and liability in relation to defective work pass through a number of stages on construction contracts. Up until substantial completion, the architect or engineer is usually empowered by the Conditions of Contract to reject work which does not comply with the contract requirements — he may order its removal and replacement. After substantial completion, most Conditions of Contract provide a further period where the architect or engineer may order defective work to be rectified, this right being secured by a retention fund. The contractor is bound to complete all such rectification work before a final certificate is issued and the retention fund released. The contractor also has the right to enter the site and carry out such rectification work. Once the final certificate is issued, the engineer or architect is usually *functus officio*, he ceases to have any powers under the contract. The contractor will still be liable in damages for any breaches of contract discovered subsequently up till the end of the statutory limitation period prescribed by the Limitation Act 1980, or Latent Damage Act 1986 where applicable. (He may also be liable in tort or through collateral warranties to subsequent owners; that is, however, outside the scope of this book.) Claims by the contractor can arise as to whether, prior to the final certificate, the engineer or architect was justified in rejecting or requiring rectification of work.

These matters will be further discussed in Chapter 6, with examples.

Payment

Valuation of contract work — This is a matter concerning only measure and value contracts, as in lump-sum contracts the contract sum is already fixed and is adjusted by addition and deduction. Problems in this category are usually centred on the applicability of B/Q descriptions to the work as executed (including perhaps errors or deficiences in such description which are also referred to under 'Documentation' above) and the question of whether or not the B/Q price applies to increased or decreased quantities.

Valuation of varied work — This is a most prolific source of claims and disputes and these generally centre upon whether the work in question is similar in all respects both as regards its character and the conditions under which it is executed. This matter of similarity is fundamental and includes time, timing, sequences, relationship to other work being done concurrently and everything else which could cause a difference of cost compared with work which might otherwise be similar so far as the tendered prices are concerned.

Other provisions for payment — Here are included matters which are in the nature of breach of contract by the employer, such as delay in supplying information etc. (see Clause 26 of JCT 80; Clauses 7, 13, 14, 31, 42 of ICE and Condition 53 of GC/Wks 1 Ed 2). Although provision is made for adjustment in the contract the analogy of breach and the corresponding remedy of damages is often reflected[22] in Conditions of Contract by excluding entitlement to profit. Delay in this sense is not to be confused with extra time for extra work which may be involved in variations.

These matters will be further discussed in Chapter 7, with examples.

Prolongation

Extensions of time — Securing timely completion is an important part of any construction contract. The primary means of doing so is to make completion by a given date a term of the contract, thus entitling the employer to damages (usually fixed as liquidated damages) for failure to complete by that date. This entitlement would be lost entirely, however, in the event of any delay caused by the employer, unless the contract provides specifically for adjustment of the date for completion by means of extension of time. To enable extension of time to be given in case of delay by the employer, each cause must be specifically and individually spelt out and cannot be swept up under the umbrella of 'delays such as fairly

---

22. This analogy is not always adopted. For example, in the Hong Kong Government General Conditions of Contract (1985 Edition), profit is excluded on delay and disruption claims but not on other damage-type entitlements.

entitle'. Provisions for extensions of time were thus introduced to safeguard the employer's position, but they were later enlarged as part of the framework of risk allocation. While extensions of time are primarily concerned with relief from liquidated damages, there is an inevitable relationship with claims for delay and disruption costs, where the cause of delay gives entitlement to both time and money. Entitlement to extension of time does not, however, of itself provide any entitlement to additional payment.

Delay for which the employer is responsible — If delay occurs for which the employer is responsible and if in consequence the contractor incurs extra cost, then generally the contractor will be entitled to reimbursement. Responsibility in this context is concerned generally with acts or omissions of the employer or his agents but it may also include certain matters, such as unforeseen ground conditions, for which the employer accepts financial responsibility. Generally, too, the contractor will have to demonstrate or prove the damage he has suffered and no profit will be included. The assessment of overheads to which a contractor may be entitled as a result of delay raises difficult questions. Again it is necessary to distinguish delay from extra time for extra work. One problem in this connection is how to deal with overlapping delays and the relative effects of those delays for which the employer is responsible and those for which he is not. Extension of time is concerned with delays which occur on the critical path, or a path that has become critical. Delay to any operations not on the critical path and therefore not involving an extension of time can, if extra cost is involved, provide legitimate grounds for claim.

Delay is of two kinds: one where work is stopped when it is comparatively easy to calculate the cost, the other (and the more usual) where work is slowed down. In the latter cases it will be necessary to assess the delay in terms 'as if' stopped (e.g. where work continues but certain items of plant are idle) or in terms of the reduction of productivity (as where an item of plant is working to reduced capacity). Such delay may also cause work to be done out of sequence or otherwise uneconomically and thus involve 'disruption' or 'loss of productivity' as well as costs arising simply from prolongation. Claims may also be made for costs incurred in overcoming delays. In the USA these are known as 'constructive acceleration claims'.

Delay for which the employer is not responsible — Generally, in such cases the contractor will not be entitled to compensation, unless the contract explicitly provides entitlement.[23] It is not enough for the contractor to say that such circumstances were not, or could not have been, foreseen when tendering. Such matters as exceptionally inclement weather, strikes, etc., may give the contractor an entitlement to extension of time (dependent upon the terms of the relevant particular clause) but not to compensation. An exception may occur if some antecedent cause for which the employer is responsible pushes a contractor into a period of inclement weather which he otherwise would not have encountered or where work would otherwise have reached a stage where the weather would have had less or no effect.

These matters will be further discussed in Chapter 8, with examples.

Default

This is a category which includes failure to complete within the stipulated time (for which provision is made for liquidated damages) and failure to comply with the specification (for which provision is made for rejection). These remedies are also backed up by the rather more drastic sanction of determination in default.

Liquidated damages — There is much misunderstanding about the recoverability of liquidated damages. The fact is that provided the contractor is entitled to no, or no further, extension of time and provided the damages are a genuine pre-estimate of the loss likely to be incurred as a result of delay, then the employer is entitled to recover the liquidated damages in respect of the period of delay. There must be a date from which liquidated

---

23. For example, Clause 12 of the ICE Conditions.

damages can run and whether this can be set retrospectively will depend upon the terms of the relevant clause. Clearly an extension of time cannot be given until the cause of delay has ceased, but beyond that there can be doubt and it is always wise to give an extension of time as early as is feasible and to review the time situation periodically, say every 3 months, to ensure not only that there is a date from which liquidated damages can run but also that the contractor knows his responsibility as regards completion and has a target to which to work.

Rejection — Time and money are only two aspects of a contract. The third aspect is quality or compliance with the specification and drawings. If defects are not discovered during construction but appear later, the employer will be thrown back on seeking to recover common law damages as compensation. Conditions of Contract contain powerful provisions, however, to enable inspection and testing of the works during construction, and rejection of work which does not comply with the contract. Claims can arise in connection with the exercise of powers under these provisions.

Determination — These clauses are not a frequent source of claims. It is, however, most important to ensure that there is entitlement to determine, and that the requirements of the relevant provisions are followed precisely if the right to determine is exercised, as wrongful determination can lead to substantial claims. Termination of the contractor's employment may also arise in the event of frustration, outbreak of war, or through the exercise of special powers of determination.

These matters will be further discussed in Chapter 9, with examples.

COMMON LAW BACKGROUND

Before coming to particular categories of claim in detail, we review in Chapter 2 the common law background of contracts and claims generally and, in Chapter 3, the life cycle of claims. Construction contracts do not exist in isolation; they cannot be considered without reference to the general legal framework from which their power to bind the parties is derived and within which they must consequently be applied.

Particular note should be taken of the warning that this book assumes that the general legal framework is English law. While many features of English law are shared with other countries, and decisions of English courts are accepted as good authority in many countries, this should not be presumed.[24]

We also examine the range of common law and equitable remedies for a different reason. Such remedies are largely overridden in construction contracts by express secondary obligations, but the standard forms of contract reflect their common law origins in their approach. The courts therefore look to the common law rules for assistance in interpreting the express provisions.

LIFE CYCLE OF CLAIMS

Few claims go on to the stage of adjudication by a court or arbitrator, but that is the ultimate and conclusive stage in the possible life cycle of a claim, the end of the line. What may happen in that final stage also exerts an influence on all the earlier stages. Accordingly we start Chapter 3 with an examination of the processes of litigation and arbitration. We also consider the earlier stages of notification and presentation of a claim.

No claim arises for consideration or adjudication unless the contractor gives due notification and proceeds to assert an entitlement. It is up to the contractor to make out his entitlement and to show that his claim is justified within the terms of the contract. The presentation of claims is a matter both of skill and attitude. Recognizing claim situations and taking appropriate action are key functions of any professional directly involved in construction.

---

24. See Max Abrahamson, Checklist for Foreign Laws — FIDIC Forms in Context, [1988] 5 ICLR 266.

Finally, in Chapter 12, we consider the processes of adjudication and negotiation. The role of the architect, engineer or quantity surveyor in adjudicating on claims is rather different from the role of a judge or arbitrator. The A/E/QS has the duty to collect and agree relevant facts on behalf of the employer, and to consider what arguments are available against the contractor's claim, before he can adjudicate. Also unlike the arbitrator or judge, the claim may involve his own acts or omissions.

STANDPOINT

In this book, claims are studied from the viewpoints of both protagonists, the contractor on the one hand and the architect, engineer or quantity surveyor on the other. This does not signify any overall bias. Nor does it mean that the interests of their backers, that is, the sub-contractors and the employer, are forgotten. Each side ought to understand and respect the other's position as well as his own, in order to avoid acrimony and promote constructive attitudes. Claims are, after all, merely ancillary to the principal objectives in construction, which are to get the works completed satisfactorily and on time, and provide prompt and proper payment. We should keep those objectives in mind when approaching and dealing with claims.

Chapter 2
Contracts and common law

INTRODUCTION

In dealing with claims, one has to work on the basis of the background law. One is constrained to arrive at decisions which are in accordance with that law so that, if challenged, they would be upheld in the courts. The following chapter provides a brief introduction to those areas of law that are relevant to building and civil engineering claims. It is not intended as a comprehensive treatise. The intention is to provide an overview and a guide to the main principles and concepts which will be referred to in the later chapters. In addition, certain questions — such as the liability of the architect, engineer or quantity surveyor towards the contractor — are examined in greater detail.

GENERALLY

On most construction projects, the contract documentation is extensive. It is tempting to assume that the parties' rights, duties and obligations can always be discerned merely by reading what is written and shown on drawings in the documentation. It is indeed the aim of construction contracts generally (and international construction contracts particularly) to provide a comprehensive framework of rules and to define not only the primary obligations, but also secondary obligations which arise in the event of non-fulfilment of the primary ones. Construction contracts provide internally administered means of variation, enforcement and adjudication, to minimize the need for reference to the courts.

Nevertheless, the essence of a contract is its recognition and enforceability by the courts. Ultimately, the application of a contract is a matter of whether the court would recognize the contract as valid, which documents it would find as forming part of the contract, how the court would interpret the written terms of the contract, whether it would imply or exclude any terms, what evidence it would admit or require, and what remedies it would grant. It follows from the nature of a contract as a legal document that the 'correct' interpretation and application is that which would be adopted by a judge.[1] Construction disputes may often be referred to arbitration instead of the courts, but an arbitrator is equally bound to apply the law.

In England and Wales and in most Commonwealth countries, the judges administer justice and adjudicate on contracts according to a combination of statute law and 'common law'; that is, the law developed by judges in cases over the years. Common law is accordingly sometimes called 'case law'. Statute law is the law laid down in Acts of Parliament and subsidiary legislation. Statute law overrides the common law where there is any difference, but in the commercial field there are few interventions by legislation. Accordingly we start with an explanation of the common law, where to find it, and how to use it.

In addition, the in-built systems of variation, compensation, enforcement and adjudication in standard forms of contract often borrow ideas from the common law, and the courts refer

---

1. This is subject to the qualification made by the Court of Appeal in *Northern Regional Health Authority v Derek Crouch Construction* [1984] 1 QB 644, that a court will not assume the special powers conferred by a contract on an arbitrator to open up, review and revise the decision of an architect, engineer or quantity surveyor. Such powers can, however, now be conferred on the court by agreement between the parties: Courts and Legal Services Act 1990 s100.

to the common law to interpret the contract. Thus in *Wraight v PH & T Holdings*,[2] it was held that the words 'direct loss and/or damage', which appeared in the JCT form of contract, should be given the same meaning there as they have at common law in a case of breach of contract. Care is required, however, to avoid unsound analogies. For example in *Panamena v Frederick Leyland*,[3] a ship surveyor appointed to certify time and materials used in the repair of a ship refused to issue certificates without proof that the amounts used were reasonably necessary. Perhaps he believed that the common law doctrine of mitigation applied, but the House of Lords held that he was wrong.

It is an essential feature of the law that the courts or an arbitration tribunal will always come to a decision on any dispute submitted to them. That decision will be final and binding on the parties named in the submission,[4] subject to any right of appeal to a higher court. Reference to the courts or arbitration is thus a means to overcome prevarication or uncertainty. Since the legal process usually takes at least a year and some times two or three or more, it can be prudent to initiate legal proceedings at an early stage when it is clear that a dispute will not otherwise be resolved.

Enthusiasm for the ability of the legal process to provide solutions should, however, be qualified by a realization of its limitations and drawbacks. As explained by Hart,[5] the concept of law is that it provides rules as to what *ought* to be done, coupled with sanctions administered by the State to enforce those rules. In civil (in the sense of non-criminal) matters, the sanctions available are generally limited to awarding compensation after the event, and then enforcing the award, if necessary, by seizure or attachment of assets. The court does not fulfil the original non-financial objectives of the parties. For example, it does not produce a building on time, nor does it rectify defects. The court does not itself investigate the dispute, it merely decides between the evidence and arguments presented by the parties. Nor does the court guarantee that the award or judgment will be satisfied; that depends on the party held liable having sufficient assets available and within the jurisdiction, against which the judgment can be enforced.

There are other significant factors against use of the legal process, including the legal costs and time-span involved in obtaining a decision. But, as any military strategist will confirm, the best means of avoiding battle is to be prepared and to be seen to be prepared.

SOURCES OF LAW

Common law The two main legal systems around the world, apart from communist and Islamic countries, are classified as 'common law' and 'civil law'. The civil law system, which has its roots in Roman law, is found in most continental European countries and their former colonies. Civil law rules are generally to be found in 'Codes', which set down principles of law. It is characteristic of the civil law systems that the courts apply the principles of law as written in the Codes and that, in determining facts, they adopt an inquisitorial role. The witnesses are questioned primarily by the judge rather than by the parties' representatives.

The common law, on the other hand, has its roots in the Norman Conquest of England in 1066. The new King set up central courts at Westminster to replace the independent local Saxon courts, but he did not seek to impose a complete set of new laws. Subject to any new laws enacted by the King, the judges were to apply the laws of the old local courts, gradually resolving any differences to produce a law of common application. Hence it was called the common law. In theory at least, the judges did not make new laws, they merely declared the existing law. This led to the doctrine of 'judicial precedent': once a judge had decided a particular question of law, the point was to be regarded as settled and, subject

---

2. *Wraight v PH & T Holdings* [1968] reported at 13 BLR 26. It was cited with approval and followed by the Court of Appeal in *Minter v WHTSO* [1981] 13 BLR 1.
3. *Panamena Europea Navigacion v Frederick Leyland & Co* [1947] AC 428.
4. The doctrine of *res judicata* or issue estoppel prevents a party disputing the same point in subsequent arbitration or litigation against the same party. The decision does not, however, necessarily bind other parties.
5. Hart H L A 1961 *The Concept of Law*. Oxford University Press.

to review by higher courts, the first judge's decision was to be followed by other judges subsequently confronted with the same point.[6] The first decision was regarded as a 'precedent'.

In addition, the common law courts adopted an adversarial system of deciding questions of fact, requiring the parties to produce the evidence to prove their case. The court's function was to weigh the evidence impartially, with the claimant or 'plaintiff' in a civil case required to adduce evidence to prove any allegations of fact on a 'balance of probabilities'. Questions of fact were decided by juries, with questions of law decided by the judges. Juries are no longer used in civil cases (except in certain cases involving fraud or defamation) but the distinction between questions of fact and questions of law survives. Decisions on questions of fact are not regarded as having any value as precedents.[7] The distinction raises some difficulties but there are a number of established rules. For example, the interpretation of a contract is a question of law;[8] what is 'reasonable' is a question of fact, but the test for reasonableness is a question of law.

Common law rules are thus to be found in the previous decisions of judges, which are reported in the law reports,[9] in so far as the decision has not been overruled or reversed by a superior court. The order of superiority corresponds to the appeal process. Thus judgments of the Court of Appeal override those of the High Court; judgments of the House of Lords override those of either Court of Appeal or High Court. On certain matters, the House of Lords may in turn be overridden by the European Court. Some parts of decisions are regarded as 'binding', while others are regarded as merely 'persuasive', with various degrees of persuasiveness.[10] Where a court comprises several judges, as in the Court of Appeal or House of Lords, only points agreed by the majority are binding. Textbooks will tell you which cases are relevant, what parts of a decision are binding, and whether cases have been either superseded or endorsed, but it is important to appreciate that the primary source of the common law remains the reports of the decisions themselves in law reports. Textbooks (including this one) are a guide but they should not be regarded as authority for their statements of the law beyond the cases that they cite.

Equity

The term 'common law', in the sense of judge-made law, is also used to cover rules of 'equity', derived from the Court of Chancery which was once very separate from the Common Law Courts. The Court of Chancery was established by the King in 1474 to hear appeals from the Common Law Courts; initially the Chancellor administered justice solely on the basis of conscience, to relieve the shortcomings of the common law rules and procedures, and the hardships which resulted. This developed into a separate set of principles referred to as rules of equity. In due course these rules became settled and the doctrine of judicial precedent came to apply to equity as to the common law. In 1875, the jurisdictions of the Court of Chancery and the Common Law Courts were merged in a new Supreme Court of Judicature, which administers both common law and equity. The distinction is said to be a thing of the past, but certain aspects are still important. Where there is conflict, the rules of equity prevail. There is, however, no equitable jurisdiction to rewrite an improvident contract.[11]

---

6. The decision of a High Court Judge at first instance is, however, only persuasive and not binding on other High Court Judges.
7. *Qualcast (Wolverhampton) Ltd v Haynes* [1959] AC 743.
8. In *'The Hadjitsakos'* [1975] 1 Lloyd's Rep 356, Lord Denning MR said 'I venture to think that we have gone too far in saying that the interpretation of a written document is a question of law', but the majority of the Court of Appeal disagreed. In *Hosier & Dickinson Ltd v P & M Kaye Ltd* [1972] 1 WLR 146 Lord Reid commented on the 'far-reaching effects' of any decision as to the meaning of a clause of a standard form of contract.
9. A judicial decision still provides a precedent although it has not been reported in the law reports, the only requirement for citation being that it is supported by the note of a barrister or (since 1990) solicitor who was present in court. The Courts and Legal Services Act 1990 s115 has conferred authority on reports of cases made by solicitors. Computerized systems now enable access to many unreported cases, but the courts prefer to limit argument to reported cases.
10. For a full explanation of the doctrine of precedent, refer to a text book on the English Legal System, such as Walker and Walker, *The English Legal System*. Butterworth & Co, London. 7th edn, 1992.
11. *Clea Shipping v Bulk Oil* [1984] 1 All ER 129.

Statute

In addition to common law (in the broad sense), the courts also apply 'statute law', that is, law enacted by the legislature. In England and Wales, this comprises Acts of Parliament, together with subsidiary legislation, published as Statutory Instruments, made under powers conferred by Acts of Parliament.[12] Since the accession of the UK to the European Community, statute law also includes European Community legislation. Fortunately, the amount of statute law affecting commercial aspects of construction is very limited. Textbooks are again useful as a guide to relevant statutes and to discover whether the statutes have been brought into force, and whether they have been repealed or amended.[13] Where a statute has been interpreted by the courts, that interpretation itself assumes the force of law.

Many other countries share the English common law or its roots. Some, such as Hong Kong,[14] apply English common law as it is. Others — such as Canada, Singapore, Malaysia, India, Nigeria and Australia and even the USA — have evolved their own law from English common law roots. Cases from other common law jurisdictions may be cited as persuasive precedents and this helps to minimise divergence. Provisions for appeal from many Commonwealth jurisdictions to the Privy Council have helped to unify the common law. Since the Judicial Committee of the Privy Council and the Judicial Committee of the House of Lords comprise the same individuals, their decisions are regarded as equivalent.[15]

Scotland and Northern Ireland are separate 'law districts'; they have their own separate legal systems and, in many areas of law, separate legislation. The Scots legal system is partly a civil law system, but the House of Lords is the ultimate court of appeal for all the law districts and many House of Lords decisions are equally applicable to England, Wales, Scotland and Northern Ireland.

Fortunately, the concept of a contract is equally familiar to civil law systems. Indeed, the development of the English law of contract was greatly influenced by the French law of Obligations. International standard forms of contract are, however, predominantly of common law origins.

Local law

This book has been written primarily in the context of common law and statute law as they stand in England and Wales. Where contracts are subject to English law, either because the works are situated within the jurisdiction[16] or because the contract stipulates (as it may) that English law shall apply, then English cases and statutes are directly relevant.[17] In other jurisdictions, due account must be taken of any local law and the acceptance of English judicial decisions as law should not be presumed.[18]

CONSTRUCTION LAW

The law is conventionally divided into topics according to their legal provenance: the law of contract, the law of tort, the law of property and so forth. The law relevant to building and civil engineering, sometimes called 'construction law' or 'building law', cuts across these divisions. It is principally concerned with the law of contract, but it also involves

---

12. Acts of Parliament include Private Acts and Hybrid Acts, in addition to the Public Acts. Subsidiary legislation also includes autonomic legislation made by independent statutory bodies, such as local authorities or port authorities, under powers conferred by their statutes.
13. Unlike Hong Kong, which has an excellent system for up-dating statutes and consolidating amendments, UK statutes are only gradually being consolidated. Some help is available from Statutes in Force, published by HMSO.
14. Application of English Law Ordinance (Cap 88) s3.
15. Privy Council decisions are often more readily understood since only a single judgment is normally delivered by the five members. In House of Lords cases, it may be necessary to sift through five separate and sometimes conflicting judgments to extract the law.
16. The word 'jurisdiction' is used here as meaning a geographical area where an autonomous legal system exists. It does not necessarily conform with political boundaries. For example, in Australia and the USA, the separate states constitute separate jurisdictions, but there is also a federal jurisdiction dealing with certain matters. 'Jurisdiction' is also used to mean the power to decide matters and enforce orders relating to disputes submitted.
17. There are various other reasons why English Law might apply, for example, if England is stipulated as the place for arbitration proceedings.
18. In *Mitsui Construction v A-G of Hong Kong* [1986] 33 BLR 1, at p 18, Lord Bridge warned against excessive reliance on interpretation of similar phrases in other forms of contract in other jurisdictions.

other topics including tort, restitution, property and equity (which are all part of 'substantive' law) and evidence, civil procedure and arbitration law (which are all part of 'adjectival' or procedural law). The distinction between substantive and adjectival law is important because a court will always apply its own adjectival or procedural law in dealing with a case, but it may apply the substantive law of another country if appropriate. In this chapter, we look at substantive law. Adjectival law is dealt with in Chapter 3.

Each legal topic may also be divided into two aspects: the existence and nature of rights or duties; and the remedies which will be granted in the event of those rights being infringed[19] or duties not being performed. We look first at the existence and nature of the rights and duties, then at the remedies available to enforce them.

Contract

A contract is an agreement between two parties which is, or would be, recognized by a court as legally binding on those parties. A contract may be regarded to some extent as private law — Standard Forms of Contract have even been likened to private legislation — but a contract does not bind or confer rights on persons who are not parties to the contract. This is the doctrine of 'privity of contract', which is a central factor affecting the way construction projects are set up, as construction projects commonly involve numerous separate organizations. Contractual links are established between the organizations to produce an overall contractual framework, but the organizations will not all be linked directly to each other by contract. They may be linked indirectly through contractual chains. The effect of the doctrine is that rights and obligations can only be pursued in contract through unbroken contractual chains, without jumping links. If one party in the chain becomes insolvent or the contracts in the chain are not 'back-to-back',[20] then, subject to any assignment of the right of action in the case of insolvency, the possibility of pursuing rights and obligations may be defeated. In some situations, collateral contracts (for example, directly between employer and sub-contractor) can be used to overcome problems.

Cross-links are also established, with powers and duties conferred on appointed persons to act or make decisions under a contract, although they are not themselves parties to that contract.

Special problems can occur where organizations are involved in projects without adequate contractual links. For example, utility undertakers often become involved acting under statutory powers or duties.

The courts do not interfere in contractual relations unless and until called upon to do so by one of the parties. In that event, a court will pronounce on such matters as whether a contract exists, what are its terms and how they apply to a particular situation, in order to determine the parties' respective rights. These aspects are considered in greater detail in Chapter 4 below. A court will also (if called upon) grant 'remedies' to cure certain situations, principally where a term of the contract has been breached, but also where, for example, the written contract does not state correctly the agreement of the parties, or the contract has been exceeded or invalidated for some reason. These aspects are considered below.

Tort

'Tort' is derived from the Latin 'tortum', meaning injury or wrong. The law of tort is concerned with civil wrongs; more specifically, it is concerned with breaches of duties and/or the protection of rights imposed or recognized by law independent of contract. It is therefore not subject to the doctrine of privity of contract. Historically torts, such as trespass, nuisance, conversion and defamation (libel and slander), were concerned mainly with protection of rights. Recent developments in tort have been directed more towards breaches of duty as a basis of liability. Such duties may be specific (for example, to provide guard rails and toe boards complying with specified dimensions around a working platform if a person is

---

19.   This is reflected in the legal maxim *ubi jus ibi remedium* — where there is a right there is a remedy.
20.   For example, if a main contract excluded design liability, the employer would be unable to pursue a specialist sub-contractor through the contractual chain in respect of design.

liable to fall a distance of more than 6 feet 6 inches from it[21]) or they may consist simply of a duty to exercise due skill and care. To give rise to tortious liability, the duty must be owed towards a specific person or class of persons.

Duties giving rise to potential liability are imposed by statute, by common law, or by a combination of statute and common law. Statutory torts are created, for example, by the Occupier's Liability Act 1984 or the Defective Premises Act 1972, which expressly provide entitlement to damages on the basis of breach of duty. Both the Acts are based on negligence rather than specific duties. Other statutes, such as the Factories Act, impose specific duties which are subject to the criminal law, but have been held by the courts as also giving rise to private rights to damages in tort.

Negligence

While the torts based on statute are of great significance in construction work, they are of limited relevance to construction contract claims. More relevant in this context is the common law tort of negligence. It is particularly relevant on two counts; firstly because of the possibility that the architect, engineer or quantity surveyor, though not a party to the employer's contract with the contractor, might be liable to the contractor in negligence; or that the employer might be vicariously[22] liable to the contractor for such negligence. (The possible corollary, less frequently discussed, is that the contractor might be similarly liable in negligence to the engineer, architect or quantity surveyor.) Secondly, there is the possibility of tort providing directly enforceable rights and obligations between employer and sub-contractor, or between main contractor and sub-sub-contractor. As the law is in a state of flux on these questions, it is necessary to examine the legal background in some detail.

The common law on negligence developed in its present generalised form from a House of Lords decision in 1932, *Donoghue v Stevenson*,[23] otherwise known as the case of the snail in the ginger beer bottle. The plaintiff was a young lady who claimed she had suffered illness after drinking part of the contents of a bottle of ginger beer which had been purchased for her by a friend. On pouring the remainder of the bottle into her tumbler, she had found it contained a decomposed snail. The bottle was opaque so that the presence of the snail was not discoverable until the bottle was emptied into the tumbler: there was accordingly no possibility of intermediate inspection. The plaintiff had no remedy in contract against the café owner, as she was not a party to the contract of sale, nor had the café owner been negligent. Instead, the plaintiff sued the manufacturer of the ginger beer in tort. It was held that the manufacturer could be liable to the plaintiff in tort, on the basis of breach of a 'duty of care' owed by the manufacturer to the plaintiff. The duty of care arose out of the proximity of the relationship, there being no possibility of intermediate inspection to interrupt it. Lord Atkin, in a much-quoted judgment, said the law did not grant a remedy in respect of every injury suffered by every person as a result of a negligent act or omission, and he propounded a principle, known as the 'neighbour' principle, to determine whether the law would grant a remedy in any particular situation or relationship:

> 'Rules of law arise which limit the range of complainants and the extent of their remedy. The rule that you are to love your neighbour becomes in law: You must not injure your neighbour, and the lawyer's question: Who is my neighbour? receives a restricted reply. You must take reasonable care to avoid acts or omissions which you can reasonably foresee would be likely to injure your neighbour. Who then, in law, is my neighbour? The answer seems to be persons who are so closely and directly affected by my act that I ought reasonably to have them in contemplation as being so affected when I am directing my mind to the acts or omissions which are called in question.'

---

21. The duty is imposed by s28 of the Construction (Working Place) Regulations 1966; it is recognized as giving rise to liability in tort to a person who is injured as a consequence of a breach of the regulation.
22. 'Vicarious' liability is where one person is liable for the acts or omissions of another.
23. *Donoghue v Stevenson* [1932] AC 562.

Onto this case have been grafted a number of further principles. Two particular developments or principles need mention here. The first is the development of the tort of negligent misstatement and the doctrine of reliance, following the decision of the House of Lords in *Hedley Byrne v Heller*.[24] The facts of that case are that the plaintiffs, who were advertising agents, had sought a report from the defendants, who were bankers, on the financial position of one of their clients. The bank had said by phone they believed the client 'to be respectably constituted and considered good for its normal business engagements'. In a subsequent letter the bank reaffirmed this view. It was found the bank had been negligent in giving this advice. It was held by the House of Lords that in situations where it was clear that the enquirer was relying on the person giving the information, a duty of care arose, which could give rise to liability independent of contract. On the particular facts of the case, it was held that the liability was effectively excluded by an exclusion clause in the banker's letter, but the principle was established. It has been developed in a number of cases and reconfirmed by the House of Lords in *Caparo v Dickman*.[25]

The second principle is that liability for negligence in tort does not extend to 'pure economic loss', except in the case of negligent misstatement. Thus, in *Spartan Steel & Alloys v Martin*,[26] the defendants, while excavating a trench, had negligently cut through an electric cable. It was held that the plaintiffs, who owned a factory served by the cable, could recover damages from the defendants in respect of the 'melt' in their furnace at the time, but not in respect of the loss of profit on four further melts that could have been carried out during the period while the supply was interrupted. Such further loss of profit was pure economic loss rather than a consequence of the physical damage.

Between 1972 and 1990, there were a large number of cases which greatly expanded the scope of tortious liability, but then restored it close to its original position. Many of the cases are no longer to be regarded as good law, so only a limited awareness is needed. The expansion started with the Court of Appeal decision in *Sadie Dutton v Bognor Regis UDC*[27] in 1972. This was supported and elaborated by the House of Lords in *Anns v Merton*[28] in 1977. In both cases, local authorities were held liable to the owners of properties which had suffered subsidence. The owners were held entitled to recover the cost of putting their properties into sound structural condition, although the only physical damage was cracking. The duty of care arose from the statutory power of the local authorities under the Public Health Act 1936 to approve plans and make inspections during construction. A passage in the judgment of Lord Wilberforce in *Anns* was taken as establishing a very broad principle. He propounded a two-stage test:

> 'First one has to ask whether as between the alleged wrongdoer and the person who has suffered damage there is a sufficient relationship of proximity or neighbourhood such that, in the reasonable contemplation of the former, carelessness on his part may be likely to cause damage to the latter, in which case a prima facie duty of care arises. Secondly, if the first question is answered affirmatively, it is necessary to consider whether there are any considerations which ought to negative, or to reduce or limit the scope of the duty or the class of person to whom it is owed or the damages to which a breach of it may give rise.'

On the basis of this two-stage test, the scope of tort was extended to the point in *Junior Books v Veitchi*[29] in 1983, when the House of Lords held that a building owner was entitled to recover damages directly from a nominated flooring sub-contractor in negligence, in respect of dusting of the floor. This decision apparently shocked the system so much that

---

24. *Hedley Byrne & Co Ltd v Heller & Partners* [1964] AC 465.
25. *Caparo Industries plc v Dickman* [1990] 2 AC 605.
26. *Spartan Steel & Alloys v Martin & Co (Contractors) Ltd* [1973] 1 QB 27.
27. *Dutton v Bognor Regis UDC* [1972] 1 QB 373.
28. *Anns v Merton London Borough Council* [1978] AC 728.
29. *Junior Books v Veitchi* [1983] 1 AC 520.

the expansion went into reverse for 7 years, culminating in 1990 with a specially convened seven strong House of Lords in *Murphy v Brentwood DC*[30] which declared that *Anns* had been wrongly decided and that all the cases based on *Anns* must be regarded as unsound. The broad statement of principle by Lord Wilberforce gave way to a more cautious approach expounded first in Australia[31] that:

> 'The law should develop novel categories of negligence incrementally and by analogy with established categories rather than by a massive extension of a prima facie duty of care.'

A number of principles have been restored and reinforced, particularly the rule against recovery of pure economic loss.[32] The imposition of a duty of care should depend not only on reasonable foresight and proximity, but also on considerations of policy and whether it is just and reasonable to impose liability.[33]

Concurrent liability in tort and contract

One factor to be taken into consideration in deciding both the existence and the scope of any duty or liability is the existence of a contract or contractual framework. The old division between tort and contract was stated in 1898 in *Turner v Stallibrass*[34] as follows:

> 'The rule of law on the subject, as I understand it, is that, if in order to make out a cause of action it is not necessary for the plaintiff to rely on a contract, the action is one founded on tort; but, on the other hand, if, in order successfully to maintain his action, it is necessary for him to rely upon and prove a contract, the action is one founded upon contract.'

In 1962, in *Scruttons v Midland Silicones*,[35] the House of Lords held that stevedores, sued by consignees for negligently damaging a drum of chemicals, could not take the benefit of a clause in the contract between the consignees and the carrier, contained in the bill of lading, limiting the amount of damages. In a strong dissenting judgment, however, Lord Denning (who was then in the House of Lords) pointed out that the duty of care only arose out of the stevedores' contract with the carrier.

Subsequently, a closer, less exclusive relationship between contract and tort has emerged — and partly retreated. At one time, developments in the tort of negligence appeared to be merging with the law of contract, to supplement contractual obligations or to overcome difficulties caused by the doctrine of privity of contract. There are three situations:

1. Liability between parties in direct contract.

2. Liability between parties forming part of a contractual chain (e.g. between employer and sub-contractor), or part of a contractual framework (e.g. between A/E/QS and main contractor or sub-contractor).

3. Liability to a third party outside a contractual framework, but where the duty arises in contract.

The third situation is of interest in construction,[36] but it is not relevant to the claims discussed in this book.

---

30. *Murphy v Brentwood DC* [1991] 1 AC 398.
31. *Sutherland Shire Council v Heyman* [1985] 60 ALR 1.
32. *D & F Estates v Church Commissioners* [1989] AC 177.
33. For a fuller discussion of these topics, see Powell J QC 'Tortious liability and economic loss' in *Legal Obligations in Construction*. Centre of Construction Law and Management, King's College, London, 1992.
34. *Turner v Stallibrass* [1898] 1 QB 56 per AL Smith LJ.
35. *Scruttons v Midland Silicones* [1962] AC 446.
36. For example, could an adjacent property owner who had suffered subsidence due to ground-water lowering, rely on a specification requirement to maintain ground water levels?

As between parties in direct contract, concurrent liability in tort and contract has been established as possible,[37] but the courts have then moved to a view that the rules governing the relationship are to be presumed to be contained in the contract. In *Tai Hing Cotton Mill v Liu Chong Hing Bank*,[38] the Privy Council rejected a claim in tort, stating:

> 'Their Lordships do not believe that there is anything to the advantage of the law's development in searching for a liability in tort where the parties are in a contractual relationship ... when the task will be to identify a duty arising from the proximity and character of the relationship between the parties, their Lordships believe it to be correct in principle and necessary for the avoidance of confusion in the law to adhere to the contractual analysis: on principle because it is a relationship in which the parties have, subject to a few exceptions, the right to determine their obligations to each other, and for the avoidance of confusion because different consequences do follow according to whether liability arises from contract or tort, e.g. in the limitation of action.'

This approach was applied strictly by the Court of Appeal in *Greater Nottingham Co-op v Cementation Piling & Foundations*,[39] where the employer had entered into a collateral contract with the piling sub-contractor. Since the collateral contract did not mention a duty to exercise skill and care, no such duty would be imposed in tort.

As between parties who are not in direct contract but are part of a contractual chain or framework, the position is less clear. In *Junior Books v Veitchi*,[40] a nominated sub-contractor was held liable to the employer in tort essentially for breach of the specification. The status of the decision as a precedent has fluctuated. It has been described as a decision that might 'no longer usefully be cited',[41] only to be revived as a possible application of the principle in *Hedley Byrne*.[42] One point in the *Junior Books* judgments concerns the relevance of the contracts in the chain to the duties in tort between the parties. Lord Fraser held[43] that the contracts were relevant. He said: 'A duty not to produce a defective article sets a standard which is less easily ascertained because it has to be judged largely by reference to the contract.'

There has also been an important development in regard to the effect of the contractual framework on insurance arrangements. In *Norwich CC v Harvey*,[44] the Court of Appeal upheld a decision that subcontractors were entitled to rely, in relation to works carried out under the JCT Form of Contract, on the employer's obligation to insure against fire. Accordingly they were not to be held liable in negligence to the employer for causing damage by fire.

Liability of engineer, architect or quantity surveyor

For many years, following *Chambers v Goldthorpe*,[45] engineers and architects were considered to be immune from suit in negligence in respect of certification, on the grounds that they were acting as quasi-arbitrators. This decision was overruled by the House of Lords in 1972 in *Sutcliffe v Thackrah*,[46] where it was held that an architect was liable to the employer in contract for negligently certifying defective work. The possibility of the A/E/QS being liable to the contractor for failure to certify was suggested, but in *Pacific Associates v Baxter*,[47] the Court of Appeal held that the contractor could not recover damages in

---

37. *Bagot v Stevens Scanlan & Co* [1966] 1 QB 197; *Esso Petroleum v Mardon* [1976] QB 801; *Midland Bank Trust v Hett, Stubbs & Kemp* [1979] Ch 384.
38. *Tai Hing Cotton Mill v Liu Chong Hing Bank* [1986] AC 80.
39. *Greater Nottingham Co-op v Cementation Piling & Foundations* [1989] QB 71.
40. *Junior Books v Veitchi* [1983] 1 AC 520.
41. *D & F Estates v Church Commissioners* [1989] AC 177.
42. See *Murphy v Brentwood DC* [1991] 1 AC 398.
43. *Junior Books v Veitchi* [1983] 1 AC 520 at p 533.
44. *Norwich CC v Harvey* [1989] 1 WLR 828.
45. *Chambers v Goldthorpe* [1901] 1 KB 624.
46. *Sutcliffe v Thackrah* [1974] AC 727.
47. *Pacific Associates v Baxter* [1990] 1 QB 993.

negligence against the engineer because the contractual framework already catered for the situation. The contractor had brought an action against the engineer, after compromising arbitration proceedings against the employer, alleging that the engineer had acted negligently and in breach of a duty to act fairly and impartially by not certifying the contractor's claims. The reasoning of the three judgments varies. Purchas LJ followed the policy that:[48]

> 'Where the parties have come together against a contractual structure which provides for compensation in the event of a failure of one of the parties involved, the court will be slow to superimpose an added duty of care beyond that which was in the contemplation of the parties at the time that they came together.'

He concluded that as there were contractual provisions in the contract which afforded an avenue enabling the contractor to recover from the employer, there was no basis for imposing a duty of care on the engineer in favour of the contractor which would be effectively the same as the provisions under the contract.

The same conclusion was reached by the two other members of the court, but with varying degrees of reliance on the existence of a clause in the contract which excluded liability on the engineer. The effectiveness of the clause appears to have turned on the fact that it was contained in a contract document prepared and issued by the engineer (in the same way as the exclusion clause on the bank reference in *Hedley Byrne*), rather than its contractual effect. Russell LJ also expressed the view that there was a difference between certification and contract preparation, as follows:[49]

> 'I entertain no doubt but that the engineer, when they prepared tenders and contract documents, held themselves out as experts on whom the contractor was entitled to rely in the administration of the contract. Throughout its operation it was plainly contemplated that the engineer would supervise the activities of the contractor and would bring to bear their expertise, as well as fairness, in determining the extent of the work to be certified.'

The decision has been followed in Hong Kong,[50] but emphasis was placed on the availability of recourse against the employer through the contract. The corollary may be that if the contract provides no recourse (as is sometimes found with *ad hoc* amendments to standard forms), then the A/E/QS may be liable to the contractor or even a sub-contractor.

Restitution

The law of 'restitution', otherwise called quasi-contract, also imposes obligations independent of contract, but on the basis of unjust enrichment rather than breach of duty. In particular, where one person has carried out work for another person in the absence of a contract, but with the common expectation that payment would be made, restitution or quasi-contract will impose an obligation to pay a reasonable price, known legally as a '*quantum meruit*'. Such an obligation may arise in quasi-contract either where there never was a contract or where work is carried out after a contract has been rendered void for some reason.

An obligation to pay on a *quantum meruit* can also arise under an implied contract, that is, a contract implied by law by virtue of the conduct of the parties where there is no express agreement as to price.[51] The distinction between an implied contract and quasi-contract, and their respective consequences, was clarified in *British Steel Corp v Cleveland Bridge*

---

48. *Pacific Associates v Baxter* [1990] 1 QB 993.
49. Ibid at p 1036.
50. *Leon Engineering & Construction v Ka Duk Investment Co Ltd* [1989] 47 BLR 139.
51. The use of implied contracts may be partly replaced by the introduction of the implied term in s15 of the Supply of Goods and Services Act 1982, but with the same result. This provides

> '1. Where, under a contract for the supply of a service, the consideration for the service is not determined by the contract, left to be determined in a manner agreed by the contract or determined by the course of dealing between the parties, there is an implied term that the party contracting with the supplier will pay a reasonable charge.
> 2. What is a reasonable charge is a question of fact.'

Engineering.[52] In that case, the parties had proceeded with the supply and acceptance of steel nodes for a building project while still in disagreement on a number of terms of the draft contract. They actually completed the supply and acceptance without having resolved their disagreements. It was held that there was no contract; that the supplier, British Steel, was entitled to be paid the value of the nodes supplied on the basis of quasi-contract; but that Cleveland Bridge could not recover damages for late delivery as the right to damages depended on the existence of a contract. Generally, the courts prefer to find that a contract exists where parties have proceeded with work. The crucial factor appears to be whether there is express disagreement to contradict the existence of a contract.

The meaning of a *quantum meruit* and the basis of evaluation are considered below.

Law of property

The law of property is an extensive and complex subject. Fortunately only a very limited part normally impinges on construction contracts. Property transactions relating to land required for a project are, or should be, completed before the construction contracts are let. If matters do arise involving such transactions, they are best left to specialist lawyers.

Certain concepts from the law of property are, however, an essential part of construction contracts. It is largely a matter of terminology: words are used in senses that are different from their popular usage. In particular, 'property' itself in the legal sense does not mean the physical subject-matter of land or goods, but the proprietary interest or right in the subject matter which is recognized by the law. The law of property is concerned with defining such rights or interests, and providing means for their creation, division or superposition, transfer, protection and extinction.

Classification of property

The law of property has its origins in feudal times, when power depended on land. The courts then were much concerned with actions related to land, which were known as 'real' actions. One classification of property is accordingly into 'real property' and 'personal property', the former being interests in land, the latter being interests in goods and 'choses in action'. (Choses in action are things such as cheques and bills of exchange — a 'chose' is a 'thing'.) For historical reasons, however, leasehold interests in land were classified as personal property.

The terms real and personal property are still used, but the tendency is to adopt a classification into 'immovable' and 'movable' property. Immovable property concerns all interests in land and things attached to land. Movable property concerns everything else. Construction is largely about the conversion of movable property into immovable property. Such conversion is subject to the legal principle that 'what is joined to the soil becomes part of the soil'.[53] For example, in *Sumpter v Hedges*,[54] it was held that the owner of the land was not bound to pay for the partly-completed building, although he proceeded to complete it, but he was bound to pay for the unfixed materials which he used.

Degrees of interest

The law relating to immovable property is now to be found mostly in statute, particularly the Law of Property Act 1925, but the concepts still reflect feudal origins. There is no absolute ownership of land in England and Wales, there are only interests in land. The principal interests are known as 'estates', as in freehold or leasehold estate. An estate in land, unless otherwise limited, extends to the skies and to the depths;[55] hence the problems in construction with matters such as oversailing cranes and ground anchors.

Secondary interests can also exist in land, including 'charges' and 'easements'. A 'charge' is a right to recover money through the sale of an interest in land, or to recover money

52. *British Steel Corporation v Cleveland Bridge Engineering* [1984] 1 All ER 504.
53. This is a translation of the Latin maxim *quicquid plantatur solo, solo cedit.*
54. *Sumpter v Hedges* [1898] 1 QB 673.
55. This is a translation of the Latin maxim *cuius est solum, eius est usque ad caelum et ad inferos.*

in the event of its sale.[56] An 'easement' is a right to a physical benefit from or over land (such as an easement of support or an easement of light), or to physical presence on, under or over the land (such as an easement of access or for a pipeline or for an oversailing crane). An easement is protected by law as an interest, as distinct from a mere licence. This means, for example, that an easement will be protected by the granting of an injunction or an order for specific performance. Easements are often referred to in construction contracts.

Licence

The right of a contractor to be on a site does not amount to an interest; it is a 'licence'. 'A licence in connection with land while entitling the licensee to use the land for the purposes authorized by the licence does not create an interest in the land.'[57] The question occurs from time to time whether the contractor's licence is revocable by the employer at will. In *Hounslow LBC v Twickenham Garden Developments*,[58] it was held that the licence was not revocable at will, but the more popular view appears to be that the courts will not enforce the contractor's licence except in damages.[59]

Possession

A separate but associated concept is that of possession. Possession does not necessarily imply physical contact. In law, possession is a matter of rights over the subject-matter and freedom from interference in its use. There are obviously degrees of possession of a site, but generally a party who grants possession to another warrants freedom from interference. There appears to be little case-law on the subject, but Canadian cases have used the concept of possession to resolve some problems over utility undertakers.[60]

Property in goods

With movable property, the law allows for ownership, but it also allows for concurrent interests. There are two levels of interest: 'general property',[61] which corresponds to title, and 'special property' which is any lesser interest. Vesting provisions in construction contracts allow for the transfer of property without physical movement of the subject matter.

The risk of loss or damage to goods may be split from the property in the goods. Contracts should clarify where the risk lies at any time[62] to allow for effective insurance.

Equity

The law of equity differed from the old common law in that, firstly, it was based on conscience. Secondly, because the Court of Chancery granted remedies *in personam* rather than *in rem* (that is, the court acted by applying coercion to the person directly rather than by seizing 'things'), it could deal with problems differently. In particular this allowed the development of the concept of a 'trust'. The bulk of the law of equity is concerned with trusts, which are only of peripheral interest to construction contracts. The possibility of relevance should not be overlooked, however — some use has been made of trusts to deal with problems over retention funds and payments for sub-contractors.

The remainder of the law of equity is interspersed with the common law, particularly in the law of contract. For example, the doctrines of commercial duress and rectification originate in equity. These are now treated as part of the common law, but special considerations arise because of the equitable origins.

---

56. One form of charge on land is a mortgage.
57. *Street v Mountford* [1985] AC 809.
58. *Hounslow LBC v Twickenham Garden Developments* [1971] Ch 233.
59. *Surrey Heath BC v Lovell Construction* [1988] 42 BLR 25; see also *Tara Civil Engineering v Moorfield Developments* [1989] 46 BLR 72.
60. See Duncan Wallace I N 1986 *Construction Contracts Principles and Policies* para 4–14. Sweet & Maxwell, London.
61. Sale of Goods Act 1979 s61 defines 'property' to mean 'the general property in goods and not merely a special property'.
62. Sale of Goods Act 1979 s20 provides 'Unless otherwise agreed, the goods remain at the seller's risk until the property in them is transferred to the buyer'.

A separate subject, whose relationship to equity is more in its name than its origins, is 'equitable estoppel'. This has developed into the broader heading of 'conventional estoppel' which is dealt with in Chapter 5.

COMMON LAW AND EQUITABLE REMEDIES

Generally

The end product of any legal proceedings is to provide a remedy. In most cases, one is concerned with financial compensation. Both laymen and lawyers talk loosely of all common law remedies yielding payment of money as 'damages', but there are a number of such remedies distinct from damages in its narrow legal sense, including 'debt', and the restitutionary remedy of a *quantum meruit*. The common law also provides certain other remedies such as 'rescission' for fraudulent misrepresentation, the right to repudiate a contract for breach of condition, and the equitable remedies including injunction and specific performance. The rules concerning remedies are worthy of examination not only for their direct application, but also for their relevance as analogies where remedies are provided under the contract.

Debt

Debt is an old common law action, to recover a fixed or ascertained sum that is due. Thus an action to enforce payment on an engineer's certificate would be an action in debt. The distinction between debt and damages can be important. For example, in debt, it is not necessary to prove a loss, only to prove the sum due; a claim in debt is not subject to any requirement of mitigation; and the law against penalties does not apply.

Non-payment of a debt does not entitle the unpaid contractor to repudiate the contract and cease performance, unless either the right to do so is stipulated in the contract[63] or the employer manifests a clear intention not to be bound by the contract. The contractor who stopped work otherwise for late payment could find himself liable in damages for late completion or non-completion; he should seek his remedy through the courts, possibly using the Order 14 procedure.[64]

Damages

'Damages', in law, means monetary compensation recoverable by a claimant from a defendant for loss or damage suffered by the claimant and flowing from a breach by the defendant of a legal duty or obligation. The term is used to cover damages for breach of contract, misrepresentation, tort, and even damages for breach of trust. The rules applicable are distinct, though often similar, for the various categories.

In tort, damages are to be assessed on the basis of restoring the injured person, so far as possible, to the position he would have been in but for the tort. Special rules apply. For example, management time may be recoverable, but it must be strictly proved — a percentage addition is not sufficient.[65]

In contract, damages are recoverable for breach of a term of the contract, that is, for non-compliance with, or non-fulfilment of, an undertaking contained in the contract. The undertaking may be absolute — a warranty that some outcome will be provided or achieved — or an undertaking to perform a duty with reasonable skill, care and diligence. In the latter situation, damages are said to be fault-based, but the amount of damages still depends on the loss or damage suffered, not the degree of fault.

Proof of loss

Entitlement to damages requires that the claimant has suffered loss or damage as a result of the breach — 'exemplary damages', to punish the party in breach, are rarely available. To recover damages, a claimant must first prove the undertaking alleged to be breached and the breach alleged. Secondly he must prove that the loss or damage, as claimed, flowed

---

63. For example, under Clause 69 of FIDIC 4 or Clause 28.1 of JCT 80, Private Edition only. JCT 80 provides only for determination, rather than suspension, for non-payment.
64. See Chapter 3.
65. *Tate & Lyle v GLC* [1983] 2 AC 509.

from the alleged breach and that it falls within categories or heads of damage accepted by the law as recoverable — the law will not recognize loss or damage which is too 'remote'. Thirdly, except in so far as the courts will act on a conjectural assessment, the claimant must prove the measure, that is the amount or value, of the loss or damage.

To discharge the burden of proof, the claimant is required to prove any question of fact necessary to the claim on a 'balance of probabilities', by adducing evidence (subject to assistance by any legal presumption). Every link in the chain of causation must be proved. If the chain of causation is broken by the intervention or action of the claimant or a third party, or if the defendant's act merely provided the occasion for the event causing the loss or damage, there is no liability.[66]

Remoteness of damage

The rule on remoteness of damage in contract is that damages for breach of contract are only recoverable in so far as the consequences which flowed from the breach were in the presumed or actual contemplation of the parties at the time of contract. The law is encapsulated in three leading cases which merit detailed study. The first is *Hadley v Baxendale*.[67] The facts of the case are that the claimants or 'plaintiffs' (referred to in shorthand as P) were millers at Gloucester. The mill crank shaft broke and P sent it by the defendant D, a common carrier, to the makers at Greenwich to provide a pattern for a replacement. In breach of contract, D delayed the delivery of the shaft and the mill was kept idle longer than necessary. It was found as fact that D was only told 'the article to be carried was the broken shaft of a mill and that the plaintiffs were the millers of the mill'. The classic statement of the law on remoteness was made by Alderson B:

> 'Where two parties have made a contract which one of them has broken, the damages which the other party ought to receive in respect of such breach of contract should be such as may fairly and reasonably be considered either arising naturally, i.e. according to the usual course of things, from such breach of contract itself, or such as may reasonably be supposed to have been in the contemplation of both parties, at the time they made the contract, as the probable result of the breach of it.'

On the facts, it was held that the plaintiffs could not recover as damages from the defendant the loss of profit suffered due to the mill standing idle. The loss was too remote.

The two 'limbs' or 'rules' in *Hadley v Baxendale* are commonly referred to as 'general' and 'special' damages. The rules were amplified by the Court of Appeal in the second leading case, *Victoria Laundry (Windsor) Ltd v Newman Industries*.[68] The Laundry entered into a contract with Newman Industries, for them to supply and install a large second-hand boiler. The boiler was damaged while being dismantled and delivery was delayed for 5 months. The Laundry claimed loss of profit: (a) £16 per week on account of new laundry customers, there being an unsatisfied demand for laundry services at that time, and (b) £262 a week which they could and would have earned under dyeing contracts with the Ministry of Supply. Asquith LJ, delivering the sole judgment of the Court, derived the following propositions:

> '1) . . . the governing purpose of damages is to put the party whose rights have been violated in the same position, so far as money can do so, as if his rights had been observed . . .
> 2) In cases of breach of contract the aggrieved party is only entitled to recover such part of the loss actually resulting as was at the time of the contract reasonably foreseeable as liable to result from the breach.
> 3) What was at that time reasonably so foreseeable depends on the knowledge

---

66. *Quinn v Burch Bros (Building) Ltd* [1966] 2 QB 370.
67. *Hadley v Baxendale* [1854] 9 Ex 341.
68. *Victoria Laundry (Windsor) Ltd v Newman Industries* [1949] 2 KB 528.

then possessed by the parties or, at all events, by the party who later commits the breach.

4) For this purpose, knowledge 'possessed' is of two kinds; one imputed, the other actual. Everyone, as a reasonable person, is taken to know the 'ordinary course of things' and consequently what loss is liable to result from a breach of contract in that ordinary course. This is the subject-matter of the 'first rule' in *Hadley v Baxendale*. But to this knowledge, which a contract-breaker is assumed to possess whether he actually possesses it or not, there may have to be added in a particular case knowledge which he actually possesses, of special circumstances outside the 'ordinary course of things', of such a kind that a breach in those special circumstances would be liable to cause more loss. Such a case attracts the operation of the 'second rule' so as to make additional loss also recoverable.

5) In order to make the contract-breaker liable under either rule it is not necessary that he should actually have asked himself what loss is liable to result from a breach. As has often been pointed out, parties at the time of contracting contemplate not the breach of the contract, but its performance. It suffices that, if he had considered the question, he would as a reasonable man have concluded that the loss in question was liable to result . . .

6) Nor, finally, to make a particular loss recoverable, need it be proved that upon a given state of knowledge the defendant could, as a reasonable man, foresee that a breach must necessarily result in that loss. It is enough if he could foresee it was likely so to result . . . '

On the facts, the court concluded that the special dyeing contracts were not within the contemplation of the parties at the time of contract so the plaintiff could not recover the loss of anticipated profit. The plaintiff was entitled, however, to recover 'some general (and perhaps conjectural) sum for loss of business in respect of dyeing contracts to be reasonably expected'.

In the third case, *The 'Heron II'*,[69] these rules were endorsed by the House of Lords, including the basis of entitlement to general damages. Lord Reid observed: 'There was nothing new in holding that damages should be estimated on a conjectural basis'.

Measure of damages

The measure of damages for breach of contract is based on the concept of '*restitutio in integrum*' — where a party sustains a loss by reason of a breach of contract, he is to be placed so far as money can do it, in the same situation with respect to damages as if the contract had been performed.[70] The claimant's loss is to be judged on the basis of the defendant's strict contractual liability, not the plaintiff's expectation. 'A defendant is not liable in damages for not doing that which he is not bound to do.'[71] Where the contract permits a range of performance, the measure of damages is to be assessed on the basis of an implied term that the defendant's performance would be reasonable in all the circumstances.[72]

In general, the measure of damages is to be assessed as at the date when the cause of action accrued, but special rules have been evolved regarding recovery of the cost of repair or replacement of construction work following defective performance, the date at which repair or replacement costs should be assessed, and whether credit must be given for any betterment involved.[73]

---

69. *The 'Heron II', Czarnikow v Koufos* [1969] 1 AC 350.
70. *Robinson v Harman* [1848] 1 Ex 855.
71. *Abrahams v Reiach* [1922] 1 KB 477.
72. *Paula Lee v Robert Zehil* [1983] 2 All ER 390.
73. See Duncan Wallace I N 1986 *Construction Contracts Principles and Policies*, Chapters 9 to 13, for a review of this topic. Sweet & Maxwell, London.

Mitigation

The right to recover pecuniary loss naturally flowing from a breach of contract is qualified by a requirement of mitigation — the claimant has a duty to take all reasonable steps to mitigate the loss consequent on the breach and is debarred from claiming any part of the damage which is due to his neglect to take such steps.[74] The requirement is subject to limitation: the claimant is not required to embark on a course of action that is risky or might cause loss of reputation.[75] And it can work the other way — if the claimant incurs loss or expense by taking reasonable steps attempting to mitigate the effects of the breach, he is entitled to recover this further loss or expense.[76] The onus of proving failure to mitigate rests on the defendant.[77]

Liquidated damages

The parties to a contract can agree the measure of damages in advance against specific eventualities such as late completion. The fixed amount so agreed is known as 'liquidated damages'. Such agreement will be enforced by the courts even though it is not the actual loss or damage suffered. But the law will not enforce a 'penalty'.[78] If the amount of liquidated damages is excessive relative to the likely damage foreseeable at the time of contract, it will be treated as a penalty. The courts will not be bound by the description given in the contract as to whether a stipulation is a penalty or liquidated damages.[79] The essence of liquidated damages is that it is a genuine covenanted pre-estimate of damage. It is no obstacle to the sum stipulated being a genuine pre-estimate of damage that the consequences of the breach are such as to make a precise pre-estimation almost an impossibility; on the contrary, it has been held that that is just the situation when it is probable that pre-estimated damage was the true bargain between the parties.[80] Nor is it an obstacle to recovery of liquidated damages that, in the event, the actual loss or damage suffered turns out to be substantially greater or less than the amount stipulated. The onus of showing that a stipulation is a penalty lies upon the defendant.[81]

Exclusion and limitation clauses

A contract can exclude or limit the amount of liability for specific breaches of contract by express stipulation, but exclusion clauses are interpreted strictly '*contra proferentem*', that is, against the party that inserted the provision. There are also special rules about exclusion clauses in the Unfair Contract Terms Act 1977, which apply not only to consumer contracts but also where one party deals 'on the other's written standard terms of business'. Subsection 3(2) of the Act provides, in such cases, so far as relevant:

> 'As against that party, the other cannot by reference to any contract term, when himself in breach of contract, exclude or restrict any liability of his in respect of the breach ... except in so far as ... the contract term satisfies the requirement of reasonableness.'

Limitation clauses are treated with less hostility than exclusion clauses.[82]

Contributory negligence

In tort, there is statutory provision for reduction of the amount of damages recoverable, on the grounds of contributory negligence by the claimant.[83] The defence of contributory negligence by the claimant is not available in cases of breach of contract, however, except

---

74. *British Westinghouse v Underground Electric Railways* [1912] AC 673; cf *Hussey v Eels* [1990] 2 QB 227.
75. *Dunkirk Colliery v Lever* [1878[9 ChD 20.
76. *Wilson v United Counties Bank* [1920] AC 102.
77. *Roper v Johnson* [1873] LR 8 CP 167; *Strutt v Whitnell* [1975] 1 WLR 870.
78. *Dunlop v New Garage & Motor Co* [1915] AC 79.
79. Ibid.
80. Ibid.
81. *Robophone v Blank* [1966] 1 WLR 1428.
82. *Ailsa Craig v Malvern Fishing* [1983] 1 WLR 964.
83. Law Reform (Contributory Negligence) Act 1945.

in the limited situation where the defendant's liability in contract is the same as his liability in the tort of negligence independent of the existence of any contract.[84]

Liability for sub-contractors

A main contractor is fully liable for breaches of the main contract caused by his sub-contractors or suppliers, save that the contractor will only be liable for the quality and not the fitness for purpose of goods specified by name.[85] Liability for nominated sub-contractors may be negatived if the employers settle the terms of the sub-contract[86] but, if the main contractor accepts a nomination and settles the terms of the sub-contract, the fact of nomination has limited effect.

Quantum meruit

Liability in damages is distinct from liability to pay on a '*quantum meruit*' for work performed. *Quantum meruit* is legal Latin, which may be translated as 'what it deserves' or 'what it is worth' or, as expressed in statutes, 'a reasonable price having regard to the circumstances of the case'.[87] An obligation to pay on a *quantum meruit* may be imposed by law:

(a) as an implied term in a fresh contract where the amount payable has not been stipulated;

(b) as an implied term in an implied substitute contract where the obligation under an existing contract is varied or exceeded, or the original contract is frustrated, or void for mistake, or wrongfully repudiated;[88]

(c) in quasi-contract, where there is no contract (or, possibly, where an existing contract has been frustrated or wrongfully repudiated or is void for mistake) but the work has been performed for the defendant at his request and with the common expectation that payment would be made.

Quantum meruit should not be taken as a synonym for 'cost-plus'. It is based more on the concept of market price or 'fair commercial price'.[89] The difficult question concerns the relevance of prices in an existing or void contract to the determination of a *quantum meruit*. Where a contract is void, then the contract does not exist. Therefore, on principle, it cannot be applied as a limit on the amount of a *quantum meruit*.[90] Nevertheless, the existence of previous agreements, unconcluded agreements or even frustrated agreements may be taken as providing evidence of the market price.

In *Way v Latilla*,[91] although the facts of the case are rather specialised, Lord Atkin and Lord Wright both set out principles of general application. Lord Atkin said:[92]

'That, in fixing a salary basis, the court may pay regard to the previous conversation of the parties was decided by the Court of Exchequer in 1869, in *Scarisbrick v Parkinson*, where the terms of an agreement, invalid under the Statute of Frauds, were held to be admissible as evidence in a *quantum meruit*. This seems to me to be good law, and to give effect to a principle which has been adopted regularly by the courts not only in fixing remuneration for services but also in fixing prices, sums due for use and occupation, and, indeed, in all

---

84. *Forsikrings Vesta v Butcher* [1989] AC 852.
85. *Young & Marten v McManus Childs* [1969] 1 AC 454.
86. *Gloucestershire CC v Richardson* [1969] 1 AC 480.
87. For example, Sale of Goods Act 1979 s8; Supply of Goods & Services Act 1982 s15.
88. Payment on a *quantum meruit* is not recoverable merely because there has been a breach of contract which would have entitled the party to repudiate the contract if, in fact, the party elected to continue with and complete the work: *Morrison-Knudsen Co Ltd v British Columbia Hydro & Power Authority* 85 DLR (3d) 186 [1978], also reported [1991] 7 Const LJ 227.
89. *The 'Saronikos'* [1986] 2 Lloyd's Rep 277.
90. *Rover International v Cannon Film Sales (No 3)* [1989] 1 WLR 912.
91. *Way v Latilla* [1937] 3 All ER 759; see also *British Steel Corporation v Cleveland Bridge* [1984] 1 All ER 504.
92. *Way v Latilla* [1937] 3 All ER 759 at p 764.

cases where the court has to determine what is a reasonable reward for the consideration given by the claimant.'

Lord Wright said:[93]

> 'The idea of such a fee being excluded, it follows that the question of the amount to which the appellant is entitled is left at large, and the court must do the best it can to arrive at a figure which seems to it fair and reasonable to both parties, on all the facts of the case. One aspect of the facts to be considered is found in the communings of the parties while the business was going on. Evidence of this nature is admissible to show what the parties had in mind, however indeterminately, with regard to the basis of remuneration. On those facts, the court may be able to infer, or attribute to the parties, an intention that a certain basis of payment should apply.'

Where there is a valid contract but the contract is exceeded, the position is different. The employer is then bound to pay reasonable remuneration for work done outside the original contract and, for the rest of the work done, to pay according to the terms of the contract so far as applicable.[94] In 'The Hadjitsakos',[95] referring to a contract for the charter of a ship, Sir John Pennycuick emphasized the difference:

> 'In the broadest terms, once one accepts that the *quantum meruit* basis is to be applied then upon that basis the implied term must be to pay remuneration according to the provisions of the charter with such modifications as have become requisite by reason of the circumstances prevailing . . . The position is wholly different from that which arises in the simple case where services are rendered without the remuneration being specified and where the implied term is merely reasonable remuneration.'

A claim on a *quantum meruit*, either in quasi-contract or under a substitute contract, may be pleaded, if available, as an alternative to a claim in damages. Thus in *Thorn v London Corporation*,[96] it was held that there was no implied warranty that the works could be constructed according to the method of construction indicated by the Engineer on the drawings and the claim for damages for breach of warranty failed. The court indicated, however, that a claim on a *quantum meruit* might well have succeeded, on the grounds that the contractor had built something outside the contemplation of the contract.

Where work is commenced at the request, or on the instructions, of the employer (for example, by a letter of intent) but the overall contract is not concluded, the contractor will normally be entitled to recover payment in quasi-contract or under an implied contract covering work specifically instructed. It is open to either side to terminate the work before the overall contract is concluded — there is no commitment to continue and complete the whole of the Works. If a full contract is subsequently concluded, it will be taken to refer back to and include the work carried out in anticipation of the contract; a *quantum meruit* cannot be claimed for that part of the work performed before the contract was agreed.[97]

Where work is carried out on the basis of quasi-contract, if the work done is defective or different from the specification, only the real value can be recovered as a *quantum meruit*.[98] This is important as there can be no recovery of damages for breach of contract in quasi-contract — by definition there is no contract to breach.

Equitable remedies

In addition to the common law remedies described, there also exist equitable remedies formerly granted by the Court of Chancery and directed at the person. These include

---

93. *Way v Latilla* [1937] 3 All ER 759 at p 766.
94. *Steven v Bromley* [1919] 2 KB 722; *The 'Hadjitsakos'* [1975] 1 Lloyd's Rep 356.
95. *The 'Hadjitsakos'* [1975] 1 Lloyd's Rep 356 at p 370.
96. *Thorn v London Corporation* [1876] 1 App Cas 120.
97. *Trollope & Colls v Atomic Power Constructions* [1963] 1 WLR 333.
98. *Farnsworth v Garrard* [1807] 1 Camp 38; *Dakin v Lee* [1916] 1 KB 566. See also *Crown House Engineering v AMEC Projects Ltd* [1989] 48 BLR 32.

rescission (as mentioned below in relation to misrepresentation) to delete a contract; rectification, to correct the written terms of a contract; specific performance, to order the performance of a contract; injunction, to require a person to do or refrain from doing some act; Mareva injunctions, to restrain a person from transferring assets out of the jurisdiction; and Anton Piller orders, to permit premises to be entered and searched.

Although the equitable and common law jurisdictions were fused in 1875, equitable remedies are discretionary and are still subject to equitable doctrines and maxims. For example, there is the doctrine of 'laches' — equity will not grant a remedy if the party has delayed or has not taken an opportunity to seek the remedy. Equity will not act in vain — an order for specific performance will not be granted if this would entail supervision by the courts, for example, of the performance of works. Equity will not assist a volunteer — a party who takes on obligations for no consideration cannot obtain compensation in equity. He who comes unto equity must come with clean hands — equitable remedies will only be granted to those who have fulfilled their own obligations.

Set-off

While damages or a debt must generally be claimed and proved before they can be recovered through the courts, the situation is different where the party which has suffered the loss or damage is sitting on money due to the other party. The law recognizes a right to withhold money in respect of a justified claim from a payment otherwise due. This is called a right of set-off.

The exercise of a right of set-off is a very practical matter. It does not involve the courts or arbitration unless and until the party to whom the payment is otherwise due commences legal proceedings to pursue the payment. The right of set-off is then to be pleaded, both in diminution of the payment due and as a counterclaim if it exceeds the payment due.[99] The existence of a right of set-off will provide grounds to resist an application for summary judgment.[1] It allows a special order to be made as to costs.[2] Where the non-payment would otherwise provide grounds for the other party to repudiate the contract, it provides grounds for denying the right to repudiate.[3]

There are three categories of set-off:

1. The right to set off mutual liquidated debts. This is a common law right with statutory origins.

2. The right to abatement or extinction of the price, on account of nonconformance, defects or defective performance in goods[4] or work of construction.[5]

3. The right to set off an entitlement to damages against a claim in debt or damages connected with the same subject matter.[6]

Regarding Category 2, the right to withhold part payment in respect of defective construction work was established in *Mondel v Steel*.[7] It represented a relief from the rule that a building contractor could recover nothing until he had completed the entire contract.

The main practical effect of the right of set-off in all three categories is in relation to costs. This is illustrated by *Hanak v Green*,[8] where a building owner sued a builder for

---

99. RSC O18 r17.

1. *Aries Tanker Corp v Total Transport Ltd, The 'Aries'* [1977] 1 WLR 185; but the defendant may be required to pay the amount claimed into court as a condition of leave to defend.
2. RSC O15 r2; *Hanak v Green* [1958] 2 QB 9.
3. *Santiren Shipping v Unimarine SA* [1981] 1 All ER 340.
4. Sale of Goods Act 1979 s53(1).
5. *Mondel v Steel* [1841] 8 M & W 858; *Young v Kitchin* [1878] 3 ExD 127; *Gilbert-Ash (Northern) v Modern Engineering (Bristol)* [1974] AC 689.
6. *Hanak v Green* [1958] 2 QB 9; *Young v Kitchin* [1878] 3 ExD 127.
7. *Mondel v Steel* [1841] 8 M & W 858.
8. *Hanak v Green* [1958] 2 QB 9.

£266 for breach of contract for failure to complete or properly complete certain items of work. The builder counterclaimed or claimed by way of set-off:

(a) on a *quantum meruit* in respect of extra work done outside the contract;
(b) on the ground of loss caused by the owner's refusal to admit the builder's workmen;
(c) for trespass to the builder's tools.

The builder's set-off and counterclaim exceeded the claim by £10. Initially, he was ordered to pay the costs of the owner's claim. He appealed on the question of costs, and the Court of Appeal held that his counterclaim was a valid set-off, and that it extinguished the claim so that a special order as to costs should be made.

Where a right of set-off is relied upon as grounds to resist repudiation, it is not necessary that the amount of the set-off should be accurate, but it must be 'a reasonable assessment made in good faith'.[9] The right to set-off may be excluded by contractual stipulation.[10]

A set-off is not available to stop payment on a promissory note or bill of exchange.[11] At one time, a series of decisions in the Court of Appeal held that the certificate of an A/E/QS was to be treated as equivalent to a promissory note or bill of exchange, but this was overruled by the House of Lords in *Gilbert Ash v Modern Engineering*.[12] It was held that the normal rights of set-off do apply against the certificate of an A/E/QS.

Different rules of set-off apply in bankruptcy situations.[13]

Interest

A party who has obtained a judgment or arbitration award is entitled under statute[14] to recover interest automatically on the amount awarded, from the date of the judgment or award.

A court also has a statutory power[15] (which is discretionary but ought normally to be exercised) to award interest prior to the date of the judgment or award, on any amount which was claimed in the action and which is either the subject of an award or was paid over before the judgment or award. The rate of interest and the commencement date are discretionary but only simple interest can be awarded. There is no statutory power to award interest on monies paid over before the date of commencement of the action. Similar statutory powers are conferred on arbitrators.[16]

Alternatively, interest or financing charges may be claimed as 'special damages' within the second limb of *Hadley v Baxendale*, if it can be shown that these were within the contemplation of the parties at the time of contract as likely to flow from a breach of contract.[17] It appears that, in construction contracts, it will be readily inferred that the parties at the time of contract contemplated the likelihood of financing charges being incurred by a contractor.[18]

Limitation periods

Since 1623, legislation has provided limitation periods to protect defendants from stale claims. The statutory provisions are procedural, although their effect is substantive. They allow a defendant to raise as a defence, in the event of a claim, that the proceedings were commenced after the relevant statutory limitation period had expired. The limitation defence

---

9. *Santiren Shipping v Unimarine SA* [1981] 1 All ER 340; *The 'Nanfri'* [1979] AC 757; [1978] QB 927.
10. *Hong Kong and Shanghai Banking Corporation v Kloeckner & Co AG* [1990] 2 QB 514.
11. *Fielding and Platt Ltd v Najjar* [1969] 1 WLR 357.
12. *Gilbert Ash (Northern) v Modern Engineering (Bristol)* [1974] AC 689; overruling *Dawnays v FG Minter* [1971] 1 WLR 1205.
13. Bankruptcy Act 1914 s31; see *Chitty on Contracts* 26th edn, paras 1354, 1355. Sweet & Maxwell, London.
14. Judgments Act 1838 s17; Administration of Justice Act 1970; Arbitration Act 1959 s20.
15. Supreme Court Act 1981 s22A, as inserted by the Administration of Justice Act 1982.
16. Arbitration Act 1950 s19A, as inserted by the Administration of Justice Act 1982; *President of India v La Pintada Cia Navegacion SA* [1985] AC 104.
17. *Wadsworth v Lydall* [1981] 1 WLR 598.
18. *IMCC v Karl O Helm* [1986] 1 Lloyd's Rep 81; *Minter v WHTSO* [1981] 13 BLR 1.

must be pleaded. Because it is procedural, the statute only curtails the remedy, not the right. For example, if a claim were paid after the expiry of the limitation period without proceedings being commenced, the payment would still be valid.

The current law on limitation periods is to be found in the Limitation Act 1980 and the Latent Damage Act 1986. The principal provisions affecting contractual claims are s5 and s8(1) of the 1980 Act. s5 provides

> 'An action founded on a simple contract shall not be brought after the expiration of six years from the date on which the cause of action accrued.'

Section 8(1) provides in identical terms for an action 'upon a specialty' with a limitation period of 12 years. A 'specialty' is a contract under seal or executed as a deed.[19] Further time limits are provided against other situations. For example, s10 deals with claims for contribution.

The Limitation Act applies to arbitration as well as litigation. Arbitration proceedings must therefore be commenced within the statutory limitation period. There is no relief because negotiations were in progress at the time the period expired.

A separate time limit applies where equitable remedies are sought, for example, where rescission of a contract is sought on account of economic duress. The equitable doctrine of 'laches' requires a party to seek such equitable remedy as early as possible, otherwise the remedy may be denied.[20] The doctrine does not apply to claims for rectification.

EXTRA-CONTRACTUAL RELIEF

The law generally upholds freedom of contract, particularly in commercial transactions. It does not grant relief merely because the contract was improvident or because expectations are not fulfilled. There are, however, certain situations where the law will grant extra-contractual relief, based on holding the contract either brought to an end or void *ab initio* through the doctrines of frustration or mistake; or providing relief outside the contract on the basis of misrepresentation; or it may rescind a contract on the grounds of economic duress.

The application of these doctrines to provide relief in practice is presently quite rare,[21] but this is largely due to the provisions written into modern forms of construction contract to provide relief. Not only have the situations calling for extra-contractual relief become fewer, but also the attitudes of the courts hardened as forms of contract became more equitable. In some forms of contract, the contractual provisions appear to anticipate the relief that would be granted at common law and emulate the common law approach to evaluating the relief, but insist that the contract remains binding and is not vitiated as it might have been at common law.

Frustration

If events occur to create a situation which is outside the contemplation of the contract, so that the obligations under the contract cannot be fulfilled or cannot be fulfilled as contemplated by the contract, the contract may cease to apply. It is treated as 'frustrated' and no longer binding in regard to unfulfilled primary obligations. Entitlement to payment or compensation in respect of work performed prior to the frustrating event is now governed by statute[22] or by explicit contractual provision. If the contractor continues to perform work after the frustrating event at the request of the employer, he is entitled to payment for such work performed after the contract was frustrated on a *quantum meruit*.[23]

---

19. Law of Property (Miscellaneous Provisions) Act 1989.
20. *North Ocean Shipping v Hyundai* [1979] QB 705.
21. But for trends in Australia see 'Quantum Meruit in Australia' DS Jones & RT Varghese [1991] 8 ICLR p 40.
22. Law Reform (Frustrated Contracts) Act 1943.
23. *Lodder v Slowey* [1904] AC 442; *Rover International v Cannon Film Sales (No 3)* [1989] 1 WLR 912.

For a number of years, following *Bush v Whitehaven Trustees*[24] the courts used this approach to provide relief from harsh terms on construction contracts. The courts relieved contractors from hardship by holding the contract frustrated when conditions turned out to be different from what they had expected at the time of tender. In *Davis Contractors v Fareham UDC*,[25] however, the House of Lords held this generous interpretation to be unjustified in relation to mere expectations and warned that relief against unforeseen conditions could only be dealt with by explicit provisions in the contract.

As Viscount Simon explained in *British Movietonews v London & District Cinemas*:[26]

'The parties to an executory contract are often faced in the course of carrying it out, with a turn of events which they did not wholly anticipate — a wholly abnormal rise or fall in prices, a sudden depreciation of currency, an unexpected obstacle to execution or the like. Yet this does not in itself affect the bargain they have made.'

In the absence of explicit contractual provisions for relief, the obligations of the parties are unaffected by their unwritten expectations. The position is different, however, if the expectations are written into the contract. In that case, the existing contract may cease to bind the parties. As Viscount Simon continued:

'If on the other hand, a consideration of the terms of the contract, in the light of the circumstances existing when it was made, shows that they never agreed to be bound in a fundamentally different situation which has now unexpectedly emerged, the contract ceases to bind at that point — not because the Court in its discretion thinks it just and reasonable to qualify the terms of the contract, but because on its true construction it does not apply in that situation.'

Mistake

The heading 'Mistake' refers to situations where one or both parties is or are under a misapprehension of present fact at the time of contract. In very limited situations the law will hold the contract to be void on the grounds of a mistake. The consequence of the contract being void is that neither party is bound by the contract — either party may decline to proceed further. If a contractor submits a claim that the contract is void for mistake, it must be open to the employer to accept that claim and terminate the work forthwith — the contractor may not both assert that the contract is void and insist on the right to complete. If the contract is void but parties nevertheless do proceed, the contractor will be entitled to claim payment on a *quantum meruit*, either in quasi-contract or under an implied substitute contract.

Mistake situations can be divided into three categories:

1. *Unilateral mistake* — Where the mistake is such that the parties are at cross-purposes, or where the mistaken belief of one party is known to the other party.

2. *Common mistake* — Where the parties share the same misapprehension. This includes cases where one party knows of the mistake but is unaware of, or does not consider, its significance.[27]

3. *Rectification* — Where the written contract does not accord with the previously negotiated agreement of the parties, the courts may grant 'rectification' of the written contract.

There is some disagreement about terminology. Category 2, labelled as 'common mistake' in accordance with one school of thought, is termed 'mutual mistake' by another school;

---

24. *Bush v Whitehaven Trustees* [1888] Hudson's BC 4th Ed Vol 2 122.
25. *Davis Contractors v Fareham UDC* [1956] AC 696.
26. *British Movietonews v London & District Cinemas* [1952] AC 166.
27. *Bell v Lever Bros* [1932] AC 161.

the first school reserves 'mutual mistake' to describe the sub-division of Category 1 where the parties are at cross-purposes. Both usages are found in the law reports.

Unilateral mistake

Where there is unilateral mistake as to a fundamental assumption on which a contract is based, the contract may be held void on the ground that there never was true agreement. Such relief will not lightly be granted. At common law, only fundamental mistake is material.[28] Equity also provides relief but, in *Tamplin v James*,[29] Baggalay LJ observed that 'Where there has been no misrepresentation and where there is no ambiguity in the terms of the contract, the defendant cannot be allowed to evade the performance of it by the simple statement that he has made a mistake'.

The cases show relief granted in four main situations of unilateral mistake. In all situations, the mistake must be one of fact. The first situation is where the parties have been at cross-purposes as to a material fact.[30] The second is where there has been mistake as to the identity of the other party contracting, where the first party did not intend to enter, and would not have entered, into a contract with that person.[31] The third is where a party signing a contract document has been misled as to the nature of the document, in which case the plea of '*non est factum*' may apply.[32] The fourth situation is where there is a mistake by the offeror in his tender, and the mistake is known to the other party when he purports to accept. An offer contained in a tender may not validly be accepted where it was or ought clearly to have been apparent that the tender was based upon a serious mistake, for example, as to the units of measurement in calculating the totals.[33]

There is a distinction between the various situations of unilateral mistake, as to the relevant test applicable. Where the mistake is known to one party, the test is subjective as to the belief of the mistaken person. Where the parties are at cross-purposes, the test is objective — what a reasonable person would have understood from the agreement as expressed.

Common mistake

The rules relating to unilateral mistake are essentially extensions of the rules on formation of contract and the need for agreement. Where the parties share a common misapprehension, the position is different, as there is clearly agreement. In very limited situations, the law will hold that a contract is rendered void by common mistake: either void *ab initio* at common law, or voidable (liable to be set aside subject to conditions) in equity.

One situation where a contract will readily be held void, both at common law and in equity, is where the subject matter of the contract has ceased to exist, unknown to the parties, before the time of contract.[34] This would apply, for example, to a contract to repair a building if the building had, unknown to the parties, been destroyed by fire prior to the contract being agreed.

Many cases can be dealt with, however, on the basis of construction of the contract rather than holding the contract void for mistake. In an Australian case, *McRae v Commonwealth Disposals Commission*,[35] the Commission had invited tenders for the purchase of a sunken tanker which did not, in fact, exist. The successful tenderer incurred substantial costs before this was discovered. The Commission argued that they had mistakenly believed, as did the

---

28. *Kennedy v Panama Royal Mail Co* [1867] LR 2 QB 580.
29. *Tamplin v James* [1880] 15 ChD 215.
30. *Raffles v Wichelhaus* [1864] 2 H & C 906.
31. *Cundy v Lindsay* [1878] 3 App Cas 459; cf *Citibank NA v Brown Shipley & Co* [1991] 2 All ER 690.
32. *Saunders v Anglia Building Society* [1971] AC 1004.
33. *Hartog v Colin and Shields* [1939] 3 All ER 566. See also Canadian cases, e.g. *Belle River Community Arena Inc v Kaufmann Co Ltd* [1978] 87 DLR (3d) 761. But for subsequent backlash developments in Canada, see Percy 'Radical Developments in the Law of Tenders' [1988] 4 Const LJ 171.
34. *Couturier v Hastie* [1856] 5 HL Cas 673; *Pritchard v Merchants' and Tradesmen's Mutual Life Society* [1858] 3 CBNS 622.
35. *McRae v Commonwealth Disposals Commission* [1951] 84 CLR 377.

tenderers, that the tanker existed, and that the contract was therefore void for mistake. It was held, however, that the Commission had no reasonable grounds for its belief; that the contract was not void; and that the successful tenderer was entitled to recover his abortive costs on the basis of an implied warranty as to the existence of the tanker.

The most difficult, but important, group of cases concern common mistake as to a fundamental assumption on which the contract was based. In the leading case, *Bell v Lever Bros*[36] the following proposition was accepted by the majority of the House of Lords:

> 'Whenever it is to be inferred from the terms of the contract or from its surrounding circumstances that the consensus has been reached upon the basis of a particular contractual assumption which is not true, the contract can be set aside: i.e. it is void *ab initio* if the assumption is of present fact and it ceases to bind if the assumption is of future fact when that assumption is shown to be untrue'.

It was emphasized that the assumption must be a fundamental one. The proposition was explained by Lord Atkin that 'if the contract expressly or impliedly contains a term that a particular assumption is a condition of the contract, the contract is avoided if the assumption is not true'. He equated the test with that for frustration, and emphasized the reluctance of the law to hold contracts void for mistake:[37]

> 'It is of paramount importance that contracts should be observed, and that if parties honestly comply with the essentials of the formation of contracts — i.e. agree in the same terms on the same subject matter — they are bound, and must rely on the stipulations of the contract for protection from the effect of facts unknown to them.'

The rules to be extracted from *Bell v Lever Bros* are obscured by lack of unanimity amongst the judges, but the position has been clarified by Steyn J in *Associated Japanese Bank v Credit du Nord*.[38] He prefaced his judgment with a comment:

> 'Throughout the law of contract two themes regularly recur: respect for the sanctity of contract and the need to give effect to the reasonable expectations of honest men. Usually, these themes work in the same direction. Occasionally they point to opposite solutions.'

The case concerned a guarantee relating to the lease-back of four machines, which, in fact, did not exist. Steyn J identified the crucial test from *Bell v Lever Bros* as Lord Atkin's statement:[39]

> '... a mistake will not affect assent unless it is the mistake of both parties, and is as to the existence of some quality which makes the thing without the quality essentially different from the thing as it was believed to be.'

He also quoted Lord Thankerton's statement that common mistake 'can only properly relate to something which both (parties) must necessarily have accepted in their minds as an essential and integral part of the subject-matter'. He commented:[40]

> 'Logically, before one can turn to the rules as to mistake, whether at common law or in equity, one must first determine whether the contract itself, by express or implied condition precedent or otherwise, provides who bears the risk of the relevant mistake. It is at this hurdle that many pleas of mistake will fail or

36. *Bell v Lever Bros* [1932] AC 161.
37. Ibid at p 226.
38. *Associated Japanese Bank v Credit du Nord* [1989] 1 WLR 255.
39. Ibid at p 265; *Bell v Lever Bros* [1932] AC 161 at p 218.
40. *Associated Japanese Bank v Credit du Nord* [1989] 1 WLR 255 at p 268.

prove to have been unnecessary. Only if the contract is silent on the point is there scope for invoking mistake.'

He also raised the question of grounds for belief:[41]

> 'What happens if the party who is seeking to rely on the mistake had no reasonable grounds for his belief? An extreme example is that of the man who makes a contract with minimal knowledge of the facts to which the mistake relates but is content that it is a good speculative risk. In my judgment a party cannot be allowed to rely on a common mistake where the mistake consists of a belief which is entertained by him without any reasonable grounds for belief: cf *McRae v Commonwealth Disposals Commission*. That is not because principles such as estoppel or negligence require it, but simply because policy and good sense dictate that the positive rules regarding common mistake should be so qualified.'

Rectification

Where a written contract does not correspond to the agreement negotiated between the parties, the court may amend the written contract under the equitable power of 'rectification'. The burden of proving the common and continuing intention rests on the party seeking rectification. Convincing evidence is required, but oral evidence is admissible. The doctrine of laches does not apply.

Misrepresentation

Remedies for breach of contract depend on the breach of a term of the contract, but not all statements made in the course of negotiating a contract become terms of the contract. Those which do not become terms of the contract are regarded as 'mere representations'. Such representations may, however, have had a substantial effect on the price or the agreement to accept a risk. In construction the question of representations is particularly relevant to site conditions or the existence of services.

The basic rule is that where an agreement is reduced to writing, the written agreement is taken as a full record of the terms of the contract agreed between the parties. A representation may become incorporated as a term of the contract if there is evidence of an intention by one party or the other that there should be contractual liability in respect of the accuracy of the statement.

At common law, liability outside of contract could be imposed for 'mere representations' only in case of fraud.[42] In that case, the common law conferred both a right to rescind the contract (that is, to treat it as never having existed) and to recover damages in tort for fraud. Where the misrepresentation was non-fraudulent (whether negligent or innocent), equity permitted rescission of the contract, but conferred no right to damages. It also required as a condition for granting rescission that the parties could be substantially restored to the position pertaining before the contract was made.

The Misrepresentation Act 1967 introduced a new statutory right to damages for negligent misrepresentation and a statutory discretion to award damages for innocent misrepresentation. The right to rescission in both cases was also made discretionary. The burden of proving negligence in this context does not rest on the claimant — the Act requires the person who made the misrepresentation to prove 'that he had reasonable ground to believe and did believe up to the time the contract was made that the facts represented were true' to avoid liability. The measure of damages under these provisions is in tort rather than for breach of contract.

A representation is a statement of fact, past or present. Statements of opinion, intention or law are not considered as representations, unless they imply the existence of past or present

---

41. *Associated Japanese Bank v Credit du Nord* [1989] 1 WLR 255 at p 268.
42. *Derry v Peek* [1889] 14 App Cas 337 .

facts, for example, that reasonable grounds existed for the opinion or that there were no known contrary facts.

In general, silence cannot amount to a representation except where the party is under a duty to disclose facts. With insurance and other contracts subject to the doctrine of 'uberrimae fides' (utmost good faith), there is a positive duty to disclose known facts — failure to do so entitles the insurer to rescind the contract. With any contract, where a positive representation has been made, there is a duty to disclose subsequent changes which occur before the contract is made. Failure to do so will amount to a misrepresentation.[43] A partial representation, where non-disclosure of a fact distorts a positive representation, may constitute a misrepresentation.[44] The question has been considered in the Australian courts whether an employer had a duty to disclose information to tenderers.[45] The courts concluded that the essential question was whether, in any particular case, the employer had accepted or assumed any responsibility for giving the information; there was no generally implied assumption of responsibility. Changes in standard forms of construction contract which have introduced a duty of disclosure[46] could lead to liability for misrepresentation if contractual provisions for relief are inadequate.

At common law, disclaimers may exclude responsibility for information supplied, in the absence of fraud, but this is now subject to the requirement of reasonableness in the Misrepresentation Act 1967 (as amended). Thus at common law:[47]

'Such a clause (excluding liability) would be a good protection against any mistake or miscalculation, but fraud vitiates every contract and every clause in it.'

The Misrepresentation Act 1967 s3 (as substituted by the Unfair Contract Terms Act 1977) provides:

'If a contract contains a term which would exclude or restrict —

(a) any liability to which a party to a contract may be subject by reason of any misrepresentation made by him before the contract was made; or

(b) any remedy available to another party to the contract by reason of such a misrepresentation, that term shall be of no effect except in so far as it satisfies the requirement of reasonableness as stated in section 11(1) of the Unfair Contract Terms Act 1977; and it is for those claiming that the term satisfies that requirement to show that it does.'

Unlike some parts of UCTA, this clause applies to all contracts. s11(1) and Schedule 2 of UCTA set out guidelines by which reasonableness is to be judged.

If there is an actionable misrepresentation as to site conditions, the measure of damages is not a *quantum meruit* but an indemnity against obligations necessarily created by the contract, that is the extra expense which had been incurred.[48]

Economic duress

Situations can arise where one party seeks to impose a change which is not in accordance with the original contract and to obtain agreement to the variation by threat of non-payment or non-completion. If the variation is agreed in response to such threats, it may be set aside by the courts (assuming it is not void in any event for lack of consideration) on the grounds of economic duress.[49]

43. *Traill v Baring* [1864] 33 LJ Ch 521.
44. *Goldsmith v Rodger* [1962] 2 Lloyd's Rep 249.
45. *Dillingham Construction Pty Ltd v Downs* [1972] 13 BLR 97.
46. For example, ICE6 Clause 11(1) and FIDIC4 Clause 11.1
47. *Boyd & Forrest v Glasgow & SW Railway* [1915] SC (HL) 20.
48. Ibid.
49. *Pao On v Lau Yiu* [1980] AC 614.

An agreement to accept less or pay more than stipulated in the original contract is only binding in law if it represents a fresh contract to vary the original contract. The fresh contract must itself be supported by consideration — past consideration, such as performance of the original promise, is no consideration.[50] Fresh consideration may, however, be provided by comparatively minor acts or promises[51] or even a 'pragmatic benefit'.[52]

The doctrine of economic duress has its origins in rules whereby a contract could be set aside either for duress — usually physical threats to the person or to goods — or 'undue influence', where the parties to the contract were within a family, professional, religious or trustee-type relationship. In *D & C Builders v Rees*,[53] the question arose as to the effect of commercial intimidation. A small firm of builders in dire financial straits was pushed by the wife of the house-owner to accept £300 in settlement of a debt of £480 which was due. She threatened to pay nothing if they declined. Lord Denning MR was prepared to hold that such an agreement could be binding in equity as an estoppel, but it was not binding because it was induced by the threat: 'No person can insist on a settlement procured by intimidation'.

In *North Ocean Shipping v Hyundai*,[54] Mocatta J reviewed the cases and concluded that there was a doctrine of commercial duress and that 'a threat to break a contract may amount to such economic duress . . . If there has been such a form of duress leading to a contract for consideration, I think that contract is a voidable one which can be avoided and the excess money paid under it recovered.' It is, however, an equitable doctrine, subject to the doctrine of 'laches'. The party subjected to commercial duress could either affirm or avoid the contract once the duress ceased. As the plaintiff in that case had not taken steps to set aside the variation until some considerable time after the duress ceased, he was held to have affirmed it.

In *Pao On v Lau Yiu*,[55] the Privy Council agreed there was a doctrine of commercial duress, but held that 'commercial pressure is not enough, there must be a coercion of will so as to vitiate consent'. In *Williams v Roffey Bros and Nicholls*,[56] the Court of Appeal recognized the possible application of the doctrine of economic duress, but as the sub-contractor in that case would have been financially incapable of completing the work if the main contractor had not agreed to the extra payment, the warning that work would be stopped was not a threat.

50. *Stilk v Myrick* [1809] 2 Camp 317.
51. *North Ocean Shipping v Hyundai* [1979] QB 705.
52. *Williams v Roffey Bros & Nicholls (Contractors) Ltd* [1991] 1 QB 1.
53. *D & C Builders v Rees* [1966] 2 QB 617.
54. *North Ocean Shipping v Hyundai* [1979] QB 705.
55. *Pao On v Lau Yiu* [1980] AC 614.
56. *Williams v Roffey Bros & Nicholls (Contractors) Ltd* [1991] 1 QB 1.

Chapter 3
The life cycle of a claim

THE FOUR PHASES OF A PROJECT

A building or civil engineering project can commonly span 5, 10 or more years from the initial concept until settlement of the final account and/or resolution of all claims. This considerable time span has four significant phases relative to the life cycle of claims which might arise on the project:

Phase 1 Pre-tender — from initial concept up to invitation of tenders

Phase 2 Contract formulation — preparation and submission of tenders, tender assessment, pre-contract negotiations and contract formulation

Phase 3 Construction — during construction up to substantial completion

Phase 4 Post-completion — settlement of outstanding matters after substantial completion.

Pre-tender

The phase leading up to invitation of tenders is often protracted, with permissions or approvals to be obtained, property or easements to be acquired, and finance to be arranged or fitted within annual budgets. During this phase, the employer's requirements are defined, site investigations and design are carried out, and contract documentation is prepared including specifications, drawings and bills of quantities. Arrangements are made to invite competitive tenders, or to select a single contractor for negotiations. Prequalification of tenderers is commonly undertaken, either for the specific project or for general listing.

There is often pressure from the employer at this stage to shorten the time being taken in detailed preparation or to restrict the expenditure on investigation. The employer may be unwilling or unable fully to define his requirements, or the architect or engineer may fail to extract or clarify the requirements. Availability of information, compatibility of design elements, and completeness of contract documentation and requirements are likely to suffer, giving rise to the possibility of claims in subsequent phases.

Contract formulation

Phase 2 is relatively short. Once the contract documentation is completed, a contract may be negotiated direct with a single contractor, or tenders may be invited. Competitive tendering is common, particularly for public works. Apart from any other benefits of competition, it avoids problems of explaining agreements over price or choice of contractor.

Despite the enormous effort devoted by contractors to tendering, almost always without any payment, it does not follow that the contractor who has prepared the 'best' tender will be awarded the contract. On the contrary, as the contract will normally be awarded to the lowest bidder, the prudent tenderer is unlikely to become the successful contractor. Success in some cases follows from ingenuity in devising methods of construction, but more frequently the successful tenderer will be the one who has taken the most optimistic view of progress and other eventualities, or has made a mistake.

Whether competitive tendering leads to inadequate prices and claims-hungry contractors depends essentially on the market. A contractor's aim in tendering is to find the 'market' price, that is, to bid just below all other tenderers, subject to an assessment that it is feasible to carry out the work at that price and make a profit. If the market is depressed, prudence in regard to such feasibility can go by the board as contractors struggle to maintain a satisfactory work-load and cash flow. (This phenomenon is not limited to contractors: it can be observed equally with architects, consulting engineers and quantity surveyors when subject to fee competition.) The wisdom of accepting a tender which is clearly inadequate is doubtful, but it can be difficult to convince the guardians of the purse strings that a low bid should be rejected. Statistical analysis can provide some assistance in identifying whether a very low bid should be regarded as an outlier.

The aim of minimizing both the need and potential for claims may well lead an employer to a strategy of ensuring, so far as possible, that the prospective contractor knows what he is expected to do and the conditions in which he will have to do it, and that he is fixed with that knowledge, before the contract price is settled. For example, some employers make use of sample finishes at pre-contract stage to establish the standards expected. As the time typically allowed for tendering limits the practicability of investigations by tenderers, the employer ought to arrange for relevant investigations to be carried out beforehand and the information provided to tenderers. Investigations ought to be conducted to provide the data required for planning of construction as well as the design of the permanent works. Some employers even invite prospective tenderers to participate in settling the investigation programme for this purpose. There is commonly a meeting arranged during the tender period to allow questions and answers before bids are submitted; greater advantage could often be taken on both sides to use the opportunity to clarify matters and resolve problems. Conditions of Contract which allow for generous extra payment in the event of unforeseen circumstances or changes during construction do not provide any incentive to tenderers to investigate or discover what will be encountered, nor to deal with shortcomings in the design, at time of tender. Some forms of contract (e.g. the BPF System[1]) seek to adjust the balance, but it is largely a matter of attitude.

After tenders have been received, they are assessed before one is accepted. The assessment can be based on price alone, but other factors affecting finance or value for money, such as cash flow projections or technical proposals, may also be taken into account for the purposes of comparison. Qualifications or alternative bids must be dealt with. The lowest few tenderers should be asked to explain specific low or high rates,[2] deal with arithmetical errors in the bid, submit detailed method statements (if required) and clarify any other matters. Acceptance of the tender, having resolved any differences, leads to a contract, prepared in the light of the facts as they are known to the parties and the events in prospect, to cater for events as they occur and circumstances as they are encountered (see Figure 3.1).

Most invitations to tender stipulate that the employer shall not be bound to accept the lowest or any tender. The significance of such a reservation has been highlighted by two recent cases. In *Harvela Investments v Royal Trust Co of Canada*,[3] tenders were invited for the purchase of shares. One tenderer submitted a bid of '$2.1 million or $101,000 in excess of any other offer expressed as a fixed monetary amount'. His 'referential' bid was accepted by the vendor. Another tenderer, whose fixed monetary offer would otherwise have been the highest, brought an action against the vendors. The House of Lords held that the vendors, by inviting sealed tenders for the shares without any reservation, had assumed a binding obligation to enter into a contract with the tenderer submitting the highest fixed price tender. Referential bids could not be considered.

In *Blackpool & Fylde Aero Club Ltd v Blackpool BC*,[4] the local authority had invited tenders for the operation of pleasure flights from Blackpool Airport. The incumbent Aero Club was invited to bid and it submitted a bid which would have been successful, but the

---

1. The British Property Federation System of building design and construction, known as the 'BPF System', was first published in 1983. It seeks to overcome these problems by adopting a more integrated approach to the design and construction process.
2. The possibility exists that a contract might be held void for mistake if an employer knowingly accepted a tender which contained an obvious error, without giving the tenderer an opportunity to withdraw or correct the error, see page 40 *supra*.
3. *Harvela Investments v Royal Trust Co of Canada* [1986] AC 207.
4. *Blackpool & Fylde Aero Club Ltd v Blackpool BC* [1990] 1 WLR 1195.

Figure 3.1

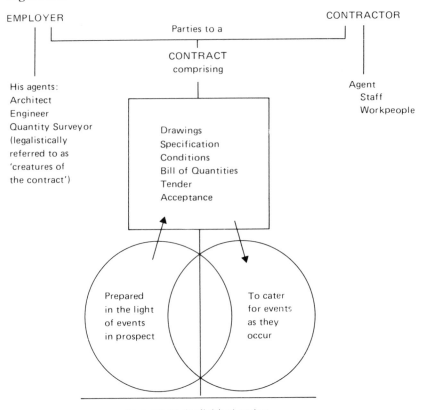

bid was rejected on the grounds that it was submitted after the deadline set by the invitation of tenders. It later transpired that the bid had in fact been submitted in time; the tender box had been emptied early. The Aero Club brought an action against the local authority, who had by then awarded the concession to another tenderer. The local authority sought to rely on a reservation in the invitation of tenders that 'The Council do not bind themselves to accept all or any part of any tender'. The Court of Appeal held that, notwithstanding the reservation, the invitation to tender gave rise to a binding obligation to give proper consideration to tenders which conformed with the conditions of tender, and the local authority was accordingly liable to the Aero Club in damages.

Construction

The construction phase is usually planned to last somewhere between 3 months and 3 years. During this phase, events will occur and circumstances will be encountered, which may give rise to claims. Possession of parts of the site, due to be provided by the employer to enable construction, may be delayed. Rarely does construction proceed according to the contract drawings and specification without variations, or instructions to clarify or amplify requirements. There may be disagreement as to whether or not an instruction constitutes a variation. There will also be interaction between contractor and supervisor in supervision, enforcement and the keeping of records.

Any claims in respect of matters for which the contract makes provision for adjustment should, if possible, be settled as they arise during this phase; amounts agreed should be included in periodic payments. Claims in respect of matters for which the contract makes no provision for adjustment should not be put on one side, but reported to the employer with recommendations with a view to reaching a settlement.

The construction phase is significant contractually under most Standard Forms in marking the duration of certain responsibilities for the works, rights of indemnity against third party claims, powers of the engineer or architect, and provision of security against default or defective performance. Such security is provided through retention funds, vesting of plant or requirements for bonds or sureties.

Post-completion

Substantial completion accordingly marks a significant change in contractual relationships and obligations. Responsibility for care of the works is transferred. Powers to order variations or the removal of defective work lapse. Partial release is made of the retention fund, and liability to liquidated damages ceases to accrue. Most standard forms provide a further period of 12 months during which the reduced retention fund is withheld to cover rectification of defects and the contractor is entitled to carry out all rectification work. The fund is only fully released on completion of all rectification work ordered by the architect or engineer at the end of the period, which is commonly called the 'maintenance period' or 'defects liability period'. Both names are misleading as there is no duty to maintain in the sense of providing for the employer's use of the works, nor does liability for defects cease when the period expires. The obligation in ICE5 Clause 8 to 'construct, complete and maintain' can mean no more than maintain the work in the state in which the specification requires it to be handed over at completion although it may have been constructed at an earlier date. In ICE6, the reference to 'maintain' has been omitted and the period has been more accurately renamed as the 'defects correction period'. Liability for loss or damage suffered due to defective work continues until the relevant statutory limitation period expires; only the obligation to correct defects ceases with the issue of the maintenance or defects correction certificate.

Most standard forms provide that settlement of the final account should take place within a few months after the end of the maintenance period.[5] Once the final certificate is issued, the powers of the architect, engineer and quantity surveyor under the contract come to an end.

If disputes go to arbitration, the final phase can be prolonged by several years.

THE SEVEN STAGES OF CLAIMS

Seedbed

Most claims relate to conditions encountered or events which occur during the construction phase. They come to life during that phase, but the first stage in the life cycle of claims is already complete at the end of phase 1 when tenders are invited or, at latest, after phase 2 when the parties enter into a contract. The seeds of claims and the nutrients essential for their development are contained in the contract documentation and the information supplied or not supplied pre-contract. The greatest opportunity to prevent claims comes to an end once tenders are invited and the contract is let. The life cycle of claims could beneficially be completed by feedback of the lessons learnt into the seedbed of pre-contract preparation.

The seedbed has two elements within the control of the employer and his professional team. The first is the effort expended in pre-contract preparation as regards reliability and completeness of information, design and documentation. The second is the policy of risk allocation adopted through the choice of Form of Contract and any *ad hoc* amendments. The two elements combine in practice to influence or control, for any given project, the level of tender prices and, subject to the further effect of events and factors occurring during construction, the number of claims that will be submitted, the final out-turn price and the eventual time to complete the works.

Taking pre-contract preparation first, the degree of thoroughness determines, at tender stage, the reliability and adequacy of information disclosed regarding site and ground conditions; the completeness of the scope of work and design details; and the extent of ambiguities and discrepancies in the contract documents. At tender stage, tenderers rely on the information provided — they have virtually no means of assessing its reliabilty except, perhaps, previous experience with the same employer and/or professional team. If fuller

---

5. e.g. JCT 80 Clause 30.8 (as amended by Amendment 4: 1987); GC/Wks 1 Ed 3 Condition 49; ICE6 Clause 60(4).

pre-contract preparation discloses the existence of more difficult conditions or more completely describes the employer's requirements, this will tend to increase the level of tender prices, but will reduce the potential for claims. Conversely, inadequate tender preparation will tend to reduce tender prices, but increase the potential for claims. Furthermore, if matters do not become apparent or discrepancies are not resolved or requirements are not stated until construction is in progress, the eventual encounters or instructions are likely to cause delay, disruption and reduced efficiency — it is more economical to carry out works and deal with difficulties if they are instructed or identified well in advance. Poor pre-contract preparation thus leads to increased costs, increased claims, increased final out-turn price, increased difference between tender and out-turn price, and delayed completion dates. Poor pre-contract preparation leads to lower tender prices, but any advantage is merely an illusion.

The other element is risk allocation policy. Acceptance by the employer of a higher degree of risk should reduce tender prices, but will allow a greater increase in the price through claims if the pre-contract preparation has been poor. A lower degree of employer risk may be expected to reduce the increase in price through claims, but the initial tender price is likely to be higher. In practice, the effect of contract policy on tender prices depends on the perception of the risk allocation by tenderers, based on their experience with the particular Standard Form; non-standard forms will usually provoke extra caution and marking up of the tender price, whatever their actual terms. The effect is also subject to market conditions, rather than objective assessment of risks.

The drafting or choice of Conditions of Contract might therefore depend on the confidence of the employer in the pre-contract preparation. A policy of sharing risks fairly can provide him with either the most satisfactory or the least satisfactory outcome, depending on the pre-contract preparation effort expended. A risk-sharing contract with adequate pre-contract preparation will attract a low tender price which will be reflected in a low out-turn price. A risk-sharing contract with poor pre-contract preparation will also attract a low tender price — almost certainly lower than if the preparation had been adequate — but the advantage will be merely an illusion. The out-turn price will be inflated by claims. A policy of low employer risk, on the other hand, may save him from the worst effects of inadequate pre-contract preparation, but it will not obtain the full benefits for him of good preparation.[6] Contractors will include a premium in tenders where the Conditions of Contract are harsh, and that premium will not be reduced by improved pre-contract preparation by the employer.

There are, however, practical limits on the employer's choice of risk allocation policy to avoid the effects of inadequate pre-contract preparation. Excessively harsh risk allocation may lose the benefit of the contract for the employer altogether, either by the contractor becoming insolvent or through intervention of the common law. The low profit margins used in the construction industry as a result of the system of stage payments, make contractors vulnerable to risk. Bringing in a new contractor is invariably expensive, time consuming and unsatisfactory as regards responsibility for defects. If the common law intervenes to provide extra-contractual relief, the employer may find the eventual price much higher than would have been obtained with a more equitable contract. Harsh Conditions of Contract may also deter competitive bids from contractors who would be most reliable in terms of resources, experience and financial stability. These factors tend to militate against the use of harsh forms of contract and encourage the adoption of more equitable Conditions, but the implications for pre-contract preparation of adopting an equitable form of contract should not be forgotten.

The final out-turn price ought also to take account of the cost of dealing with claims submitted, whether or not justified, but this has tended to be hidden, unless the matter goes

---

6. The ICE New Engineering Contract, according to the documents issued for consultation, adopts a policy of shifting risk onto the employer to provide an incentive to the employer to ensure satisfactory pre-contract preparation. The alternative view is that an employer should only adopt such a form of contract if he is confident of the adequacy of the pre-contract preparation.

to arbitration, by the standard Conditions of Engagement of architects, engineers and quantity surveyors in so far as they are based on a blanket percentage fee.

An additional important question is whether the Conditions of Contract provide incentives effectively to motivate the contractor to make full use of his expertise and overcome difficulties expeditiously. This depends also on relationships and attitudes, but the employer may well be advised to adopt a policy of accepting those risks which are problematical as to the likelihood of their occurrence, in which case he will pay only for those which eventuate and then only the cost in actually meeting them. He may well be advised to choose to put upon the contractor risks where the likelihood of occurrence is reasonably foreseeable and/or where the contractor, by reason of his practical experience, is more capable of finding an economical solution and can be expected to make a reasonable allowance in his tender.

Whatever policy of risk allocation is adopted and whatever pre-contract preparation is undertaken, the position becomes fixed when the parties enter into a contract.

Germination and notification

Once the contract has come into existence, the life cycle goes on to the second stage: an event occurs, a circumstance is encountered, which combines with the contract documentation to stimulate a claim, possibly to create or germinate a valid claim. The stimulus is recognized and translated into notification.

Notification can lead to mitigation of the effects of the event or circumstance; it is also a cue for extra records to be kept and agreed. The giving of timely notice is commonly stipulated to be a pre-condition to entitlement (or failure to do so a reason for partial disentitlement) to ensure both that the opportunity for mitigation is not missed and that records are kept.

Not every claim that is notified is valid. The stimulus to submit a claim may be a perceived imbalance, a shortfall in income or an overspend in costs — indicating a 'need' to claim. It is not, however, a necessary criterion for entitlement under the contract that the contractor should have suffered a shortfall, nor is suffering a shortfall of itself grounds for extra entitlement, although it may seem to provide 'moral' grounds for claiming.

Presentation

The third stage of a claim is its presentation by the contractor. It is up to the contractor to make out his claim, in terms of the contract, the events and the records. He cannot expect the architect, engineer or quantity surveyor to do the job for him, nor to assume that spasmodic correspondence which may have taken place will be accepted as constituting a claim. The contractor needs to set out clearly that a certain matter is the subject of a claim (with the amount involved) and refer to relevant correspondence, discussions etc.

Some forms of contract also provide for the contractor's entitlements to be reduced (for example, by reduction of billed rates) where justified by changes in quantity or nature of the work. In practice, such provisions are rarely invoked, except as a response to a claim by a contractor or where defective work is involved. There is little incentive to any independent consultant to initiate such a claim under the usual arrangements since it may result in a reduction of his own fees. Nevertheless, the principle of mutuality in claims should not be forgotten.

Examination

At stage four the claim is considered by the A/E/QS and some negotiation may take place. Although he will already have been alerted by notice from the contractor of the circumstances or events giving rise to the claim and the expectation of its submission, the A/E/QS cannot consider the claim fully until it is presented. During the intervening period he will have been able to ensure that adequate and reliable records were kept. He may have been able to deal with some causes of the claim, for example, by increasing his own resources to speed up the supply of drawings or prompting the employer to provide possession of parts of the site — it is one of the potential benefits of the conventional contracting system that the A/E/QS is often in a position to mitigate as well as adjudicate on claims.

Correspondence between contractor and A/E/QS at this stage may help to identify whether there is a basis of claim and what are the significant questions to be addressed, but the A/E/QS ought clearly to be acting throughout this stage on behalf of the employer, investigating the facts and considering the legal and contractual arguments opposed to the contractor's contentions. It is only after consideration of the employer's side that he can proceed to making a decision.[7]

This stage may also include negotiation of agreements: some standard forms expressly empower the A/E/QS to make agreements with the contractor on specific categories of claim, such as the value of variations. In those cases it is only if agreement cannot be reached that the A/E/QS goes on to the next stage of making a decision. In attempting to reach agreement the A/E/QS is negotiating on behalf of the employer. He ought clearly to be on the opposite side of the negotiating table, not seeking to hold a balance (although he would be foolish to refuse to agree a settlement that he would subsequently have to award by decision). It is open to the A/E/QS to refer to the employer for his input, so long as the A/E/QS is not, and does not regard himself as, bound by the employer's comments in regard to any decisions involving a discretion.[8] There is no reason why the employer should not actually insist on being consulted, but the contractor is not affected by such a requirement unless he has notice of it.

Decision

Where the contract does not provide for such agreements or where agreement is not reached, the claim proceeds to stage five, the initial decision of the A/E/QS. The law recognizes two classes of decision: those that are regarded as purely administrative decisions and those involving the exercise of a discretion. Confusion is often generated because a legal discretion is not the same as a practical discretion. For example, a decision whether timber is of fair quality is probably regarded by the law as purely administrative,[9] even if the specification refers to the opinion of the A/E/QS; the construction professional would probably say he had a discretion in that he could overlook minor defects. Certification of payment for work performed in accordance with the contract is generally an administrative duty. In *Sutcliffe v Thackrah*[10] there is ample guidance that in certifying payment for work so performed the A/E/QS is required to exercise his professional skill and knowledge as it should be exercised and to act honestly; he is not employed to be unfair to the contractor, but no question of impartiality arises.

Where a legal discretion is involved, for example, in assessing entitlement to extension of time for completion, the position of the A/E/QS is different. He has to take on a dual role. He has to consider the evidence and arguments on both sides as a judge or arbitrator, but unlike a judge or arbitrator, he also has to supply the evidence and arguments on one side. It is not (contrary to popular belief) a free discretion; he is bound to apply objective standards.

Three difficult questions arise, which are also relevant to stage six:

1. Does the A/E/QS have any duty to consider evidence or arguments favourable to the contractor which have not been advanced by him?

2. Is it proper for the A/E/QS to refer claims to the employer before reaching a decision?

3. Should the A/E/QS put to the contractor for comment, before reaching a decision, any matters which either the employer or the A/E/QS himself has raised against the contractor's submission, and which the A/E/QS expects to take into consideration in reaching his decision?

The answers to these questions are considered below and in Chapter 12.

---

7. ICE6 Clause 2(8) has introduced a new provision that 'The Engineer shall . . . act impartially within the terms of the Contract having regard to all the circumstances'. It is submitted that this provision ignores the essential duality of the Engineer's role. It is only in exercising a discretion that the Engineer ought to be impartial.
8. *Panamena Europea Navigacion v Frederick Leyland & Co* [1947] AC 428.
9. *Hillas v Arcos* [1932] 147 LT 503.
10. *Sutcliffe v Thackrah* [1974] AC 727.

Reference back

The next stage, stage six, can occur only with certain forms of contract[11] which provide that, if the contractor or employer is dissatisfied with a decision of the A/E/QS and wishes to dispute it, he must refer the matter back to the A/E/QS for reconsideration and a final decision before he can refer the matter to independent arbitration. Both administrative and discretionary decisions can be referred. An administrative decision can thus be promoted to a quasi-arbitral decision involving a discretion.

This reference back to the A/E/QS is a relic of earlier times when the architect or engineer was stipulated to act as final arbitrator on any dispute. The sixth stage may now, additionally or alternatively, include forms of alternative dispute resolution: mediation, conciliation, adjudication, or reference to an independent expert. It is sometimes stipulated that the decision of the A/E/QS or the recommendation of the mediator shall be binding unless referred to arbitration within a fixed period.[12]

Arbitration/litigation

Stage seven is the final stage — arbitration or litigation. The claim cannot proceed beyond this stage — a court or arbitrator will always give a definitive answer, enforceable as a judgment. Once an award has been given and any appeal procedure has been exhausted, the courts will not allow the matter to be re-opened. It will be treated as *res judicata*.

It is not necessary that a claim should progress through all seven stages. The potential for some claims can be avoided at stage one, before the contract documentation is finalized. At stage two, many claims wither and die as the events unfold. Others proceed to stage three. Thereafter, a claim may yield fruit, or wither and die, at any stage.

It is important to recognize the different stages. Too often, claims are considered as purely a post-contract phenomenon rather than partly a consequence of pre-contract preparation. Too often, reluctance to progress from stage four to stages five, six and seven creates a festering stalemate. The essence of legal and contractual procedure is irresistible progress.

IMPLICATIONS AND REQUIREMENTS OF LEGAL PROCEDURE

The stages of evaluation, negotiation and decision are considered later in Chapter 12. In this chapter we look at the seedbed of claims, and at germination, notification and presentation, but we start at what may seem the wrong end by examining first the implications of litigation and arbitration. The ultimate stage has important lessons and repercussions for earlier stages, not least the importance of recording facts in contemporaneous documents and the dangers involved in being economical with the truth. It also dispels the myth that frivolous claims and unjustified rejections are a nuisance created by construction contracts, although one might conclude that the means contained in construction contracts to deter frivolous claims or promote the speedy and just settlement of valid claims, are less effective than the procedures available to the courts.

Litigation

Although most construction contracts contain arbitration clauses, which effectively prevent many claims being referred to the courts, it is instructive to examine first the process of litigation (as proceedings through the courts are termed). The rules of procedure described are those applicable to the High Court,[13] including the 'Official Referees', the judges to whom most construction disputes are referred. High Court rules also form the basis of much of arbitration procedure, either inescapably by rule of law or optionally by choice as a model.

High Court procedure is governed primarily by the 'Rules of Supreme Court' ('RSC'). These comprise some 113 'Orders' subdivided into 'rules', relating to matters such as pleadings, costs and special procedures. They have the force of law, as they are made under

---

11. For example, ICE5, ICE6, FIDIC4. GC/Wks 1 Ed 3 Condition 59 provides for an adjudicator. A provision for matters to be referred back to the Engineer for his final decision has been introduced in the 1985 Edition of the Hong Kong Government Conditions of Contract as Clause 86.
12. For example ICE5 or ICE6 Clause 66, FIDIC4 Clause 67.1.
13. The High Court is the main court dealing with civil, as distinct from criminal, matters. Civil claims involving small sums of money are dealt with in the County Courts which have separate rules.

statutory powers. Lawyers refer to the 'White Books' — two thick and expensive volumes, revised bi-annually, which contain not only the text of the Rules, but also commentary and references to cases interpreting the Rules. Non-lawyers will rarely need to refer to the Rules in detail but should be aware of their existence and authority.

Procedure in the High Court is also subject to the law of evidence, which is supplied by the common law and various statutes including the Civil Evidence Acts of 1968 and 1972. The law of evidence governs the burden of proof and other matters such as what evidence is admissible or inadmissible, what presumptions may be relied upon, and how facts may be proved.

It is a fundamental right under the English legal system, implicit in the Rules of Supreme Court, that any person may commence civil legal proceedings making a claim against another person, and he is then entitled to have that other person either respond and dispute the claim, or judgment be entered against him. Rarely, for example, if the claimant has been declared a 'vexatious litigant' or the intended defendant is resident outside the jurisdiction, leave of the court is required. Otherwise, the right is virtually unrestricted. The right to commence proceedings does not signify that the claim is justified or even arguable, but once proceedings have been commenced the claim cannot just be ignored.

Proceedings are commenced generally by service of a writ, a simple and inexpensive process. The standard printed form is filled in with details of the parties and the nature of the claim, then 'issued' by paying the fee to have the writ sealed and stamped in the court registry. It is 'served', normally, by sending the sealed copy with a photocopy to the other party's solicitors. The writ must either be endorsed with a statement of claim, setting out the nature of the claim and its grounds, or it must be followed by a separate statement of claim. Preparation of the writ must be carried out by a solicitor if the claimant is a firm or company.

There are a number of rules to discourage frivolous claims. A defendant (the party against whom the writ is issued) can seek an order to have the action struck out on the grounds that the statement of claim discloses no cause of action against him or that the proceedings are vexatious or frivolous. Very rarely, a defendant can have an action struck out if the plaintiff (as the claimant is called in litigation) does not pursue the claim. If the case proceeds to a hearing, the burden of proving the claim rests on the plaintiff and the legal costs of the other party will be awarded against him if he fails to prove it. Meanwhile, however, the defendant must acknowledge service of the writ[14] and must enter a defence[15] in reply to every claim, otherwise the plaintiff may obtain a default judgment against him. Generally, the law exhibits greater concern to compel a party to participate in the legal process, than to deter unjustified claims.

Rights of defendant

The rights of a defendant are protected in so far as he is entitled to have the matter determined at trial, providing he takes the required steps of acknowledging service of the writ, entering a defence, and complying with orders. Subject to the procedures for summary judgment and interim payments contained in RSC Orders 14 and 29, described below, a defendant will rarely be required to make any payment to the plaintiff before judgment, even though the matter may take 1, 2 or more years to come to trial.

Order 14

The right of the defendant to have the matter determined at trial is subject to the right of the plaintiff to summary judgment in clear-cut cases. RSC Order 14 provides a speedy

---

14. Acknowledging service of a writ merely involves ticking the relevant box on a printed form and returning it to the plaintiff's solicitor.
15. The defendant may either 'deny' or 'not admit' those facts which he disputes. He may also set up affirmative defences, e.g. limitation or failure to mitigate.

process, whereby a plaintiff may serve a summons, immediately after service of the Statement of Claim, returnable before a Master. (To 'return' a summons is to appear in response to it; a Master is a judicial official of the High Court who deals with all 'interlocutory' or preliminary matters.) The Order 14 hearing, held in Chambers (that is, with the public excluded), is based solely on affidavit evidence (written statements sworn under oath) and legal argument. No oral evidence is heard. If the plaintiff satisfies the Master that the defendant can have no triable defence, he will be awarded immediate judgment (subject to a right of appeal to a judge in chambers). In borderline cases, the Master may grant leave to defend subject to conditions. An engineer's or architect's certificate is an example of what might be accepted as showing no triable defence, but such a certificate is not proof against a claim to set-off,[16] nor against challenge to the validity of the certificate. In the latter case, the employer must be able to show, as grounds for leave to defend, that, in good faith and on reasonable material, the certificate is open to challenge; a mere requirement to investigate the certificate is not enough.[17] Judgment will not be given under Order 14 where complex issues are involved which require full-scale argument. The procedure is not to be used simply to by-pass the normal wait for a full hearing.[18]

Order 29

The courts and legislature have traditionally been reluctant, except in the clear-cut cases covered by RSC Order 14, to acknowledge the needs of claimants to obtain some payment before conclusion of the hearing, which may be several years after commencement of legal proceedings. This was changed by the Administration of Justice Act 1969, which introduced a power for the rules committee of the High Court to make rules of court enabling interim payments to be ordered in respect of anticipated awards of damages, debt or other sum which a defendant, or defendant to a counter-claim, might be held liable to pay. Initially rules were made enabling payments to be made in personal injury cases and actions for possession of land. But, in 1980,[19] these were replaced by more general rules, issued as Order 29 Part II, comprising rules 9 to 18. Under the new rules, an application for interim payment may be made separately or in conjunction with a summons for summary judgment under Order 14.[20] As with Order 14, the application is made at a hearing with only documentary evidence sworn on affidavit. Order 29 rule 11(1) provides, so far as relevant:

'If, on the hearing of an application under rule 10 in an action for damages, the Court is satisfied —

(a) that the defendant against whom the order is sought (in this paragraph referred to as "the respondent") has admitted liability for the plaintiff's damages; or
(b) that the plaintiff has obtained judgment against the respondent for damages to be assessed; or
(c) that, if the action proceeded to trial, the plaintiff would obtain judgment for substantial damages against the respondent . . .

the Court may, if it thinks fit . . ., order the respondent to make an interim payment of such amount as it thinks just, not exceeding a reasonable proportion of the damages which in the opinion of the Court are likely to be recovered by the plaintiff after taking into account any relevant contributory negligence and any set-off, cross-claim or counterclaim on which the respondent may be entitled to rely.'

Rule 12 provides in similar terms in respect of sums other than damages. In particular, Rule 12(c) provides:

'If, on the hearing of an application under rule 10, the Court is satisfied — . . .

---

16. *Gilbert Ash (Northern) v Modern Engineering (Bristol)* [1974] AC 689.
17. *R M Douglas Construction v Bass Leisure Ltd* [1990] 53 BLR 119.
18. *John Mowlem plc v Carlton Gate Development Co Ltd* [1990] 51 BLR 104; *Home and Overseas Insurance v Mentor Insurance* [1989] 3 All ER 74.
19. SI 1980/1010.
20. RSC O29 r10(2).

(c) that, if the action proceeded to trial the plaintiff would obtain judgment against the defendant for a substantial sum of money apart from any damages or costs, the Court may, if it thinks fit, and without prejudice to any contentions of the parties as to the nature or character of the sum to be paid by the defendant, order the defendant to make an interim payment of such amount as it thinks just, after taking into account any set-off, cross-claim or counterclaim on which the defendant may be entitled to rely.'

The fact that an interim payment has been ordered is not to be pleaded or disclosed at the hearing.[21] The Court may, on final judgment or discontinuance of the action, order repayment of part or all the interim payment.[22] The provision for ordering repayment also refers to interim payments made voluntarily — that probably refers to payments made voluntarily after an application under rule 10, but it may also be open to the parties to agree that a payment made on account shall be deemed to be an interim payment for this purpose.

The availability of interim payment under Order 29 is somewhat restricted by the apparent imposition of a high onus of proof on the claimant to satisfy the court as to the probable success at trial, while the defendant or respondent need only demonstrate a likelihood that the counterclaim will succeed as set-off or cross-claim.[23] At trial, by comparison, the parties bear an equal burden of proof in relation to their respective claims and counterclaims.

Denial of justified claims

For many years, there were financial advantages to an unscrupulous defendant in denying justified claims up to the start of the hearing. No interest was payable on the amount withheld, provided payment was made before judgment, unless the parties had stipulated such interest in their contract. Legal costs would probably have to be paid up to the date of settlement, but so long as these were less than the interest saved, there was still an advantage. Commonly, payment would be made shortly before commencement of the hearing when costs were about to escalate.

At common law, 'mediaeval abhorrence of usury' led the courts not to grant interest as damages, although entitlement to interest on judgment debts (i.e. amounts actually awarded) from the date of the judgment was long established. Legislation intervened, initially with 'Lord Tenterden's Act' of 1833 and later with the Law Reform (Miscellaneous Provisions) Act 1934, to give judges power to include interest in their awards up to the date of judgment on amounts actually awarded. This provided an incentive to either settle or make part payment before the award, but it did not provide an incentive to settle or make payments on account any earlier.

The position has been radically altered by the Administration of Justice Act 1982. This has given judges and arbitrators powers to award interest where payment has been made prior to judgment but after commencement of proceedings. Interest on payments made before judgment accrues up to the date of payment. The Act still excludes interest on payments made before legal proceedings are commenced.[24] The result of this is to remove the financial incentive to postpone settlement of justified claims, and to encourage payment before the commencement of proceedings. The commencement of proceedings has gained an added significance.

Payments into court

From the other side, what can a defendant do to settle an exaggerated claim? Provision

---

21. RSC O29 r15.
22. RSC O29 r17.
23. *Shanning International v George Wimpey International Ltd* [1989] 1 WLR 981; see also *Smallman Construction Ltd v Redpath Dorman Long Ltd* [1988] 47 BLR 15; *British and Commonwealth Holdings plc v Quadrex Holdings Inc* [1989] QB 842; *Crown House Engineering v Amec Projects Ltd* [1989] 48 BLR 32; *Andrews v Schooling* [1991] 1 WLR 783.
24. *President of India v La Pintada* [1985] AC 104.

is made in the rules[25] for a defendant to make a 'payment into court', which the plaintiff is entitled to take out in full and final settlement of his claim (or part of his claim if separate parts are involved). Time limits apply for the plaintiff to accept the payment in; thereafter he must obtain an order of the court. The plaintiff taking such a payment in full and final settlement of his whole claim before commencement of the hearing will also be entitled automatically to his legal costs down to the date of the payment in.[26]

The incentive for the plaintiff to take the payment in settlement, even if it does not quite match his expectations or aspirations, lies in rules on entitlement to legal costs. The general rule is that 'costs follow the event': a successful plaintiff will be awarded his costs as part of the judgment; an unsuccessful plaintiff will have to pay the defendant's costs. But success in this context is judged taking into account any payment into court. If the plaintiff fails to beat the amount of the payment in, he will have to bear not only his own costs from the effective date of payment in, but also the defendant's costs incurred after that date.[27] As costs can exceed the value of the original claim, this is a powerful incentive to each side respectively to make and accept realistic offers. The rules are equally applicable to counterclaims.

The course of proceedings

After service of a writ, proceedings in the High Court have three distinct phases. These are exchange of pleadings, preparation for trial, and the trial itself. Each phase has features of practical significance for everyday working, which are described below.

The legal process can also include further stages including appeal to a higher court and enforcement of the judgment, but these are of marginal relevance, save to note that enforcement of a judgment is the ultimate means for the law to assert its power. The power of the law depends on the feasibility of enforcement. In civil cases, enforcement depends on there being assets within the jurisdiction against which the judgment can be enforced. If there are such assets, the law is relentless in the support of rights, but the law does not supply the wherewithal. As it is said, a penniless defendant, a 'man of straw', is not worth powder and shot.

Such considerations lead to provisions in construction contracts to provide security on the employer's side. Performance bonds, vesting of plant and material, and retention funds all provide means of immediate enforcement. On the contractor's side, stage payments coupled with ready enforceability of certificates provide safeguards. The provision of bonds is expensive, however, and it is open to abuse.

Pleadings

The first phase of proceedings is concerned with establishing details of each party's case and identifying what are the points in issue. This is done through the exchange of 'pleadings'. The plaintiff must serve a Statement of Claim, and the defendant, if he wishes to defend the action, must serve a Defence. Together these form the essential pleadings. Further pleadings may be exchanged. Commonly the plaintiff will serve a Reply. The defendant may seek Further and Better Particulars of the Statement of Claim; the plaintiff may seek Further and Better Particulars of the Defence. Each must provide the Further and Better Particulars sought. Further exchanges are permitted but rarely used.

Time limits are laid down for the various stages of pleadings, particularly service of the Defence. In practice, the limits are not rigidly observed but their existence does provide a means of enforcing progress. A party may apply for judgment to be entered or the action

---

25. RSC O22.
26. RSC O62 r10(2), see also *Hudson v Elmbridge BC* [1991] 4 All ER 55 and *Hodgson v Guardall Ltd* [1991] 3 All ER 823.
27. The effective date is some days after the actual date of payment in, to allow a reasonable time for consideration of the offer.

to be struck out, as appropriate, on the grounds that the other party has not complied with the time limits.

It is not intended to suggest that claims ought to be formulated as legal pleadings by a contractor for submission to the A/E/QS, nor that the A/E/QS should respond in legal format. But the objectives of legal pleadings are relevant to claims at any level, and the basic discipline can be adopted with advantage to all concerned. The objectives are to identify all the points in issue, to ensure that there exists a valid basis of claim or defence, and to allow each party to know the nature of the case he has to answer. Points raised on either side must be answered and not ignored. Achievement of these objectives should promote the settlement of justified claims and discourage the pursuit of unjustified claims. It should also minimize the dissipation of effort pursuing matters not in dispute, and avoid a party being taken by surprise.

Parties do not always share an interest in resolving matters, so discipline is imposed on pleadings by the rules of procedure, set out in RSC Order 18. The principal rules, which may be considered as of wider potential application, are as follows:

r7(1) '. . . every pleading must contain, and contain only, a statement in a summary form of the material facts on which the party pleading relies for his claim or defence, as the case may be, but not the evidence by which those facts are to be proved, and the statement must be as brief as the nature of the case admits.'

r7(2) '. . . the effect of any document or the purport of any conversation referred to in the pleading must, if material, be briefly stated.'

r11 'A party may by his pleading raise any point of law.'

r12(1) '. . . every pleading must contain the necessary particulars of any claim, defence or other matter pleaded . . .'

r13(1) '. . . any allegation of fact made by a party in his pleading is deemed to be admitted by the opposite party unless it is traversed by that party in his pleading . . .'

r13(2) 'A traverse may be made either by a denial or by a statement of non-admission and either expressly or by necessary implication.'

r13(3) '. . . a general denial of such allegations, or a general statement of non-admission of them, is not a sufficient traverse of them.'

r15(1) 'A statement of claim must state specifically the relief or remedy which the plaintiff claims . . .'

r19(1) 'The Court may at any stage of the proceedings order to be struck out or amended any pleading . . . on the ground that
(a) it discloses no reasonable cause of action or defence, as the case may be; or
(b) it is scandalous, frivolous or vexatious; or
(c) it may prejudice, embarrass or delay the fair trial of the action; or
(d) it is otherwise an abuse of the process of the court;
and may order the action to be stayed or dismissed or judgment to be entered accordingly, as the case may be.'

Unlike pleadings, a contractor's submission of a claim must also present the evidence on which his claim is to be judged. But how much easier to adjudicate on a claim when the grounds of claim are clearly stated. How much less aggrieved a contractor should be when he is given a detailed response to his claim, rather than a blank rejection.

Preparation for trial

After the close of pleadings, the parties must prepare for trial. Part of the preparation will be done by the parties separately: preparation of proofs of evidence, preparation of experts' reports, and research into any points of law. But the most significant activities require interaction between the parties. They are 'discovery' and, at a later time, exchange of experts' reports.

Discovery is a process which comes as a shock to the uninitiated. Its practical significance can be devastating, particularly where a party has been economical with the truth, or indiscreet, or allowed his decisions to be influenced by extraneous considerations. Each party is required to provide to the other a list of all documents (including records in virtually any form) relevant to the matters in issue, which are or have been in his possession, custody or power.[28] He must subsequently allow the other party to inspect and copy the documents. A party's refusal to do so can result in his claim being struck out or judgment being entered against him, as the case may be.

The fact that a document is adverse to a party's case does not relieve him of the obligation to disclose it. On the contrary, a document is considered 'relevant' (which is the criterion for disclosure) if 'it is reasonable to suppose it contains information which may ... enable the (other) party either to advance his own case or damage the case of his adversary or which may fairly lead him to a train of inquiry which may have either of these two consequences'.[29]

The practice of discovery was developed by the Court of Chancery, at a time when the parties could not personally give evidence, 'to put the parties on their conscience to disclose their relevant documents to one another in advance of the hearings'. The practice was retained by the Supreme Court of Judicature Act 1873 when the Court of Chancery was merged with the common law courts. The aim of discovery is now also to 'dispose fairly of the case or for saving costs'.[30] An order for discovery is discretionary, and the court will consider that aim in deciding on any specific orders. (It has been commented by a continental lawyer that the practice of discovery gives the lie to the popular statement that the common law system is not inquisitorial.)

The only relief against giving inspection of documents is for various classes of 'privileged' documents. These classes are very limited, and relate mainly to 'legal professional privilege' which attaches to communications between a party and his lawyer, or other documents prepared by others for the party's lawyer for the purposes of the litigation or arbitration. There is no privilege for documents just because they are marked 'confidential internal memo', nor for commercially sensitive documents such as tender make-ups. Privilege is granted in respect of some Government documents on grounds of national security.

Current practice is also to require the exchange of experts' reports and proofs of evidence of other witnesses in commercial disputes before the hearing. This only applies to reports of experts whom the parties intend to call at the hearing. A party is not required to call every expert that he may have consulted, nor to disclose the reports of experts who are not called — such reports will normally be privileged.

The trial

It is, of course, possible for the parties to compromise their dispute at any time prior to trial or, indeed, during the trial. Very few cases actually go through to judgment. Nevertheless, cases are generally settled in anticipation of what would happen at trial.

An important distinction is made at trial between 'questions of fact' and 'questions of law'. Questions of fact are required to be proved by evidence unless admitted, and the plaintiff has the burden of proving facts on a balance of probabilities. What questions of fact have to be proved should be clear from the pleadings — whatever is alleged in the statement of claim and either disputed or not admitted in the defence must be proved. As Lord Justice

---

28. RSC O24 r1(1).
29. *Compagnie Financiere v Peruvian Guano Co* [1882] 11 QBD 55.
30. RSC O24 r8.

Bingham has said: 'The mills of civil litigation may grind slowly, yet they grind exceeding small.'

Questions of law are to be decided by the judge after hearing argument on both sides. A judge must decide the facts on the evidence submitted — he may not supply evidence to himself — but he is not so restricted in regard to questions of law. A judge is bound, generally, by the 'rules of natural justice', which are principally that each party must be heard, and that a party is entitled to know the case he has to answer.

Conduct of trials is also influenced by lawyers' rules of professional conduct, some of which may appear rather curious to construction professionals. In regard to facts, a lawyer may not put forward what he knows to be false, but he is under no duty to investigate the truth of any evidence. On the contrary, he is precluded from expressing any personal belief in the truth of any fact or the validity of any point of law submitted. But in relation to questions of law, a lawyer is bound to assist the court by drawing attention to any legal precedents contrary to his case, as well as those in its favour.

Common law procedure is often labelled adversarial in that each party is bound to produce its own evidence and to argue its own case. Each party's witnesses are open to cross-examination by the other side, to test their evidence and credibility. Evidence is not limited to witnesses' oral testimony, it also includes documents submitted as evidence, and 'real evidence'. Real evidence comprises objects or documents which are themselves evidence of some fact. For example a concrete beam with a crack is evidence that the beam is cracked, but a judge is more limited than an arbitrator as to the conclusions he may draw from real evidence without the assistance of expert opinion. Certain types of evidence may be disallowed as 'inadmissible', particularly 'hearsay' evidence (that is, evidence based on second-hand knowledge), but the strict rules may be relaxed by agreement of the parties.[31]

Perhaps the most significant aspect of the trial is the weight attached by judges and arbitrators to contemporaneous documents as evidence. Lord Justice Bingham has commented,[32]

'letters or minutes written well before there was any breath of dispute may throw a very clear light on (the parties') knowledge and intentions at a particular time.'

Similarly Ronald Bernstein QC has commented, in a guide to judging questions of fact:[33]

'What people did and wrote and said at the time of an event is less subject to vicissitudes of recollection than oral evidence given from memory before you, several years after the event. In particular, contemporaneous documents are much more reliable in general than subsequent recollection of events.'

This is very strong reason for parties to ensure that all relevant or potentially relevant facts are recorded in contemporaneous documents, whether in letters, minutes of meetings, photographs, progress charts or diaries. It is the key reason for keeping full and accurate diaries of events as they occur on site during construction. It is also a strong reason not to leave any disputed statement uncontradicted. If allegations of fact in a document are not accepted, then they should be refuted immediately in writing.

Arbitration

Recognition by the courts

Arbitration is a private system of dispute resolution. It is, like a contract, established by agreement between two parties. It binds only those parties and only in regard to issues within the scope of the arbitration agreement. Its significance, compared with other private systems

---

31. Civil Evidence Act 1968 s1(1).
32. Bingham T, 1985, The Judge as Juror: the Judicial Determination of Factual Issues. *Current Legal Problems 1985*. Stevens & Sons, London.
33. Bernstein R, 1987, Handbook of Arbitration Practice, para 17.4.1. Sweet & Maxwell, London.

of dispute resolution, is that it is recognized and supported by statute as an alternative to litigation. The courts will 'stay' an action on a dispute where an arbitration agreement exists, unless the parties waive the right to object.[34] Unlike a contract, an arbitration agreement does not require to be supported by consideration, but it must be in writing to come within the statutes.[35]

An arbitration agreement may be part of a contract. Those contained in all the main standard forms[36] are agreements in writing to refer future disputes to arbitration and therefore, in England and Wales, within the scope of the Arbitration Acts 1950 and 1979. (Scotland and Northern Ireland have separate arbitration laws.) Once the Arbitration Acts apply, they create a comprehensive, legally enforceable framework. For example, the appointed arbitrator is protected from dismissal without leave of the court;[37] he has certain powers to give procedural orders and make awards, including awards of interest and costs;[38] and his awards are enforceable through the courts in the same manner as a judgment or order of the court.[39] The Acts also provide powers for the courts to intervene, on applicaton of one of the parties, for example, to appoint an arbitrator if the parties cannot agree,[40] to issue subpoenas for witnesses to attend,[41] to grant the arbitrator special powers,[42] or to remove the arbitrator for misconduct.[43] Following the Arbitration Act 1979, an arbitrator's award is close to final. Appeal is only available on questions of law and then only by agreement of the parties[44] or by leave of the court in very restricted situations.[45]

The first Arbitration Act was enacted in 1698, but the major developments were in the nineteenth century. The earlier statutes have all now been superseded by the Arbitration Acts of 1950, 1975 and 1979 (as amended[46]), but mention should be made, in the context of construction claims, of changes effected by the Arbitration Act 1934. Prior to the 1934 Act, it was possible for the architect or engineer appointed under a contract also to be named as the sole and final arbitrator on any disputes arising in connection with the contract. It was common practice to do so at one time, despite the protests of builders and civil engineering contractors that they should have a right to independent arbitration.[47] The 1934 Act finally stopped the practice. Old cases on the role of the architect or engineer must be read in the light of this change.

Jurisdiction

The power of an arbitrator to give orders, decide issues and make an award in respect of a dispute is known as his 'jurisdiction'. A party is not bound to submit to arbitration of a dispute outside the arbitrator's jurisdiction and, more significantly, an award made by an arbitrator outside his jurisdiction may be set aside in the High Court as void.

The extent of an arbitrator's jurisdiction is derived from, and limited by, the arbitration agreement and the reference, and it depends on the words of the agreement. The Standard Forms mostly confer very broad jurisdiction. For example, under ICE5 Clause 66, it covers 'a dispute or difference of any kind whatsoever . . . between the Employer and the Contractor in connection with or arising out of the Contract or the carrying out of the Works including

---

34. Arbitration Act 1950 s4.
35. Arbitration Act 1950 s32; Arbitration Act 1979 s7(1)(e).
36. JCT 63/77 Clause 35; JCT 80, Art 5 of the Agreement or Clause 41 of the Conditions as amended by Amendment 4: 1987 or Amendment 6: 1988; ICE5 and ICE6 Clause 66; FIDIC3 and FIDIC4 Clause 67; GC/Wks 1 Ed 2 Condition 61; GC/Wks 1 Ed 3 Condition 60.
37. Arbitration Act 1950 s1.
38. Ibid ss12(1), 12(2), 12(3), 14, 15, 16, 18(1) and 19A.
39. Ibid s25.
40. Ibid s10 (as amended by Courts & Legal Services Act 1990 s101).
41. Arbitration Act 1950 s12(4).
42. Arbitration Act 1979 s5.
43. Arbitration Act 1950 s23.
44. Arbitration Act 1979 s1.
45. *Antaios Cia Naviera v Salen Rederierna, The 'Antaios'* [1985] AC 191.
46. In particular, by the Administration of Justice Act 1982 and Courts and Legal Services Act 1990. The Arbitration Act 1975 is mostly concerned with non-domestic arbitrations and enforcement of foreign arbitral awards.
47. See Royce N, 1985 Producing a Standard Form of Contract, 1 Const LJ 255.

any dispute as to any decision opinion instruction direction certificate or valuation of the Engineer (whether during the progress of the Works or after their completion and whether before or after the determination abandonment or breach of the Contract)'. The phrase 'in connection with' means that the scope is not limited to claims under the contract but extends to extra-contractual matters such as rectification.[48] JCT 80 is similarly broad. GC/Wks 1 Ed 3 Condition 60 refers to 'disputes, differences or questions between the Authority and the Contractor arising out of or relating to the Contract ...'.

The 1950 Act provides broad general powers[49] to an arbitrator, once appointed, together with specific powers to administer oaths and examine witnesses on oath or affirmation,[50] to make interim awards,[51] to order specific performance,[52] to correct slips in his award,[53] to award costs,[54] and to award interest down to the date of the award.[55] These powers have been amplified by the Courts as including the power to order pleadings and discovery,[56] and to order inspection of property.[57]

In general, where parties refer a dispute to arbitration in England, they impliedly agree that the arbitration is to be conducted in all respects with the law of England, unless the agreement or reference provides otherwise;[58] but not all powers available to judges are available to arbitrators. For example, an arbitrator has no implied power to order concurrent hearings,[59] nor to issue a writ for default in compliance with an order,[60] nor to commit a witness for contempt.[61]

An arbitrator also lacks the peremptory powers of a judge to award judgment or dismiss a claim for failure by one of the parties to comply with an order or time limit. In *Bremer Vulkan v South India Shipping Corp Ltd*,[62] the House of Lords also held that an arbitrator did not have the power of a judge to strike out an arbitration for want of prosecution. This lack of power to expedite proceedings with a reluctant party has been partly cured by the Arbitration Act 1979 and the Courts and Legal Services Act 1990. Section 5 of the Arbitration Act 1979 provides that, on the application of the arbitrator or of any party to the reference, the High Court may make an order extending the powers of the arbitrator

> 'to continue with the reference in default of appearance or of any other act by one of the parties in like manner as a judge of the High Court might continue with proceedings in that court where a party fails to comply with an order of that court or a requirement of rules of court.'

The value of Section 5 is reduced, however, by the delay and cost involved in making an application to the court. An application would normally be made by one of the parties; an arbitrator would be ill-advised personally to seek such powers as he might be unable to recover the costs of doing so. The Courts and Legal Services Act s102, inserting a new section 13A into the Arbitration Act 1950, has introduced a further power for an arbitrator to make an award dismissing a claim directly for want of prosecution.

48. *Ashville Investments Ltd v Elmer Contractors Ltd* [1989] QB 488; cf *Fillite (Runcorn) v Aqua-Lift* [1989] 45 BLR 27. An arbitrator may also have jurisdiction to deal with claims for a *quantum meruit* where the contract has been exceeded: *Gibraltar Government v Kenney* [1956] 2 QB 410.
49. Arbitration Act 1950 s12(1).
50. Ibid s12(1).
51. Ibid s14.
52. Ibid s15.
53. Ibid s17.
54. Ibid s18.
55. Ibid s19A, as inserted by Administration of Justice Act 1982.
56. *Kursell v Timber Operators* [1923] 2 KB 202.
57. *The 'Vasso'* [1983] 1 WLR 838.
58. *Chandris v Isbrandtsen-Moller* [1951] 1 KB 240.
59. *Oxford Shipping Co v Nippon Yusen Kaisha* [1984] 3 All ER 835.
60. *Bremer Vulkan Schiffbau und Maschinenfabrik v South India Shipping Corp Ltd* [1981] AC 909.
61. Ibid.
62. Ibid.

Under s12(6) of the 1950 Act, the Court has powers to make orders in support of the arbitration process, including orders for security for costs, interrogatories, securing the amount in dispute in the reference, and authorizing persons to enter land or buildings in the possession of a party to the reference, or authorizing samples to be taken or observations to be made or experiments to be tried.

Misconduct

The courts have no general power to supervise arbitrations, but they have powers, if called upon by one of the parties, to remove an arbitrator for 'misconduct'[63] or to remit an award to him.[64] Misconduct does not necessarily entail any 'moral turpitude', it may involve any procedural or other misconduct which is such as to lead one or both the parties to doubt the likelihood of a fair hearing.[65]

Appeals

Prior to the 1979 Act, the courts could also readily be asked by a party to review an arbitration award under the 'case stated' procedure, but the procedure was being abused as a delaying tactic. It was stopped by the 1979 Act, which introduced in its place a limited right of appeal on questions of law, requiring leave of the court unless both parties consent. The requirement for leave has been interpreted very restrictively by the House of Lords[66] in the name of commercial needs. This has an unfortunate side-effect, however, of virtually stopping the development of a body of case-law on construction contracts. Disputes on construction contracts must generally be referred to arbitration. Construction arbitration awards themselves are currently not published or regarded as having any value as precedents in the UK[67] so, unless an appeal is heard, the potential contribution of the proceedings to resolving future uncertainty and providing clarification and guidance is lost.

Arbitration rules

A recent trend, reflecting concern over arbitrator's powers to control proceedings, has been to introduce procedural rules for construction arbitrations. The ICE Arbitration Procedure was introduced in 1983 and the JCT Arbitration Rules in 1988.

These rules can have a significant impact beyond merely enhancing the arbitrator's powers of control. For example, ICE5 Clause 66 stipulates as a pre-condition to arbitration that the specific dispute should have been referred first to the Engineer for his decision under Clause 66, but Rule 4.2 of the ICE Arbitration Procedure (1983) states:

> 'Once his appointment is completed the Arbitrator shall have jurisdiction over any issue connected with or necessary to the determination of any dispute or difference already referred to him whether or not the connected issue has first been referred to the Engineer for his decision under Clause 66(1) of the ICE Conditions of Contract.'

This has been interpreted by the Courts as permitting considerable leeway in introducing new issues.[68]

Unlike the Rules of Supreme Court, which provide statutory powers to High Court judges, arbitration rules depend for their authority on incorporation in the arbitration agreement. Arbitration rules are not binding if not agreed by both parties.[69] The Standard Forms have

---

63. Arbitration Act 1950 s23.
64. Arbitration Act 1950 s22.
65. *Modern Engineering (Bristol) v Miskin* [1981] 1 Lloyd's Rep 135.
66. *Antaios Cia Naviera v Salen Rederierna, The 'Antaios'* [1985] AC 191. As a response, consent to appeal questions of law to the courts is written into some arbitration agreements e.g. JCT 80 Amendment 4:1987 or Amendment 6: 1988 Clause 41.6.
67. In some other countries, e.g. the Netherlands, selected arbitral awards are reported, see Barber J N 'The Potential for Reporting Arbitral Awards', [1987] 4 ICLR 213.
68. *Mid-Glamorgan CC v Land Authority of Wales* [1990] 49 BLR 61.
69. *Pratt v Swanmore Builders and Baker* [1980] 1 BLR 37.

been amended to stipulate agreement to the rules: ICE5 was amended in the 1986 Reprint while JCT 80 was amended by Amendment 6: 1988. ICE6 also provides for automatic application of subsequent revisions to the rules, JCT 80 allows for application of revisions by agreement.

A weakness of the arbitration rules is that the sanctions available to arbitrators to enforce compliance with orders made under the rules are still limited without reference to the court. The rules themselves provide few sanctions. The orders do not amount to awards and are therefore not directly enforceable through the courts. If an application is made to the High Court under the Arbitration Act 1979 Section 5, the court might review the scope of the rules before granting the additional powers to the arbitrator. Arbitration rules may be subject to considerations of public policy,[70] and they may be interpreted restrictively by the courts, in so far as they conflict with principles applied by the courts themselves.[71] It might be held that the parties cannot confer some powers on an arbitrator.[72]

Evidence

In theory, the rules of evidence apply in arbitration as in court proceedings.[73] The Civil Evidence Act 1968 is expressly stated to apply to arbitration proceedings: parties wishing to disregard the strict rules of evidence ought to enter into an agreement to do so.[74] Arbitration rules may include such an agreement. Arguably, agreement not to apply the strict rules of evidence may be inferred from absence of objection at the hearing. The rule of practice in the courts that a document must be read aloud before it constitutes evidence does not, however, apply in arbitration.

As in court proceedings, each party at an arbitration hearing presents its case in turn. There are occasionally suggestions that arbitrators ought to adopt an inquisitorial approach (compared with the adversarial system), but essentially it is for the parties to put before the arbitrator such evidence and such arguments as they wish to be taken into account. ICE5 Clause 66(5)(a) and ICE6 Clause 66(8)(b) specifically provide that neither party shall be limited in the proceedings before the arbitrator to the evidence or arguments put before the engineer for the purpose of obtaining his Clause 66 decision.

Evidence includes not only oral testimony and written documents, it may also include 'real evidence', for example, the building or site itself which is the subject matter of a dispute. An arbitrator is entitled, by virtue of his expertise, to draw conclusions from inspection of real evidence, where a judge would be obliged to rely on expert testimony.[75]

Litigation and arbitration compared

The choice between litigation and arbitration has become a significant issue again following the Courts and Legal Services Act 1990. The decision of the Court of Appeal in *Northern Regional Health Authority v Derek Crouch*[76] in 1984 made it impossible for a judge to act under a contractual provision for the opening up and review of the decision of an engineer or architect. All such matters therefore had to be referred to arbitration. It is, however, now possible with the agreement of the parties under the Courts and Legal Services Act 1990 s100 for a judge to take on the special powers conferred on an arbitrator.

Arbitration offers a number of potential advantages over litigation. These include speed and convenience, in that the arbitrator will sit to suit the convenience of the parties, rather than the parties waiting for a judge; privacy, in that the public are excluded; the arbitrator's

---

70. This is implied in *Henry Bath & Son v Birgby Products* [1962] 1 Lloyd's Rep 389.
71. For example, in relation to ordering security for costs.
72. In *Kursell v Timber Operators* [1923] 2 KB 202, it was said that the parties could not by agreement confer on an arbitrator power to commit for contempt or to order the issue of a writ of *habeas corpus ad testificandum*.
73. *Re Enoch & Zaretsky Boch* [1910] 1 KB 327.
74. Civil Evidence Act 1968 s1(1) and s18.
75. See Barber J N 1988 Real evidence and expert arbitrators. *Arbitration* **54**, 34.
76. *Northern Regional Health Authority v Derek Crouch Construction* [1984] QB 644.

specialist expertise, which should enable him to assimilate the evidence more quickly and reach a better-informed decision on the specialist matters; and potential savings in costs, in that legal representation is not compulsory, documents need not be read to the tribunal, and the arbitrator's expertise should reduce the need for expert evidence.[77]

On the other hand, the parties must pay for the services of the arbitrator and the room for the hearing, whereas a judge and courtroom come for a nominal fee. There is no procedure for summary judgment in arbitration.[78] The achievement of speed and savings in costs depends on the attitudes of the parties; an arbitrator lacks all the procedural powers of a judge to compel progress and compliance with orders: obstructive behaviour by the parties may require reference to the courts for assistance which loses the benefit of avoiding the courts. Where non-specialist lawyers are employed as advocates, the advantage of the arbitrator's specialist knowledge may be reduced, although lawyer representation may be better skilled and experienced at dealing with witnesses and arguing the law.

Attempts to cure the drawbacks of arbitration and improve its potential for speed and cost-effectiveness have been made by the introduction of the rules of arbitration procedure and stipulating in the standard forms of contract that such rules should apply.[79] Some of the procedures, such as documents-only arbitrations or special procedures for experts, offer great potential. Other provisions, such as ordering security for costs or for the award, are of doubtful effectiveness in the absence of powers of enforcement.

There is some scope for combining arbitration and litigation to obtain the advantages of both, for example, by initiating parallel court and arbitration proceedings. This allows application for summary judgment under Order 14,[80] with reference to arbitration if the application fails. The current position on offers of settlement in arbitration is less satisfactory than the rules on payment into court in court proceedings. In Hong Kong, this has been overcome by providing for payments into court in relation to arbitration proceedings.[81]

Costs

Despite the intention that arbitration should be an economical means of dispute resolution, the costs involved can be horrendous, sometimes exceeding the amount in dispute. While costs can be significantly reduced by co-operation, they also provide the incentive to compromise or settle disputes. The general rule in arbitration is the same as in litigation — the successful party is entitled to be awarded his costs, comprising his assessed costs of the proceedings, that is, of legal representation, expert witnesses and document production. In addition, the costs of the award — the fees payable to the arbitrator, the costs of the room and the costs of transcripts (if any) — will be awarded against the unsuccessful party. A party will not, however, recover any costs of his own staff time, nor any compensation for the disruption involved in pursuing the dispute. Furthermore, by reason of rules for assessing the costs recoverable, it is common that a party will only recover some two-thirds or three-quarters of his actual legal costs.

The power of the arbitrator to award costs is contained in s18 of the 1950 Act. It is stated to be a discretion but the discretion must be exercised in accordance with established rules, and reasons given for any departure.[82] An arbitrator may specifically award against a party any costs which have been unnecessarily incurred or thrown away as a result of the acts or omissions of the party or his representative.

---

77. In practice, legal representation and expert evidence are both fairly common in arbitration.
78. The ICE Arbitration Rules provide for 'summary awards' but this suffers from the drawback that the arbitrator himself is required to reach a preliminary conclusion. In the High Court, applications for summary judgment are heard by a Master, not by the trial Judge.
79. ICE Arbitration Rules (1983) and ICE6 Clause 66; JCT Arbitration Rules (1988) and JCT 80 Clause 41.9, inserted by Amendment 6: 1988.
80. *Tradax v Cerrahogullari* [1981] 3 All ER 344; see *R M Douglas Construction v Bass Leisure Ltd* [1990] 53 BLR 119 for a review of later developments.
81. Supreme Court Ordinance (Cap 4) s54(2)(j) and Hong Kong Rules of the Supreme Court O73 rr11—18.
82. *The 'Erich Schroeder'* [1974] 1 Lloyd's Rep 192.

Success in the context of costs must take account of any offer made (the equivalent of payment into court in litigation), provided the offer includes an offer to pay costs down to the date of the offer.[83] If the claimant persists in pursuing his claim after an offer and fails to beat it, he will be entitled to his costs against the respondent up to the date of the offer, but will normally have to bear both his own costs and the costs of the respondent incurred thereafter.

Some arbitration rules provide that, under certain procedures, the parties shall normally bear their own costs and share the arbitrator's costs equally,[84] or that they should not be entitled to costs of any legal representation.[85] Such provisions may, however, be invalid under the Arbitration Act 1950 s18(3).

Interest

Interest is automatically payable on an arbitration award from the date of the award.[86] Interest may also be payable for periods prior to the award. An arbitrator has a discretion[87] (which should normally be exercised), to include in his award simple interest at such rate as he thinks fit:

> '(a) on any sum which is the subject of the reference but which is paid before the award, for such period ending not later than the date of the payment as he thinks fit; and
> (b) on any sum which he awards, for such period ending not later than the date of the award as he thinks fit.'

Third parties and counter-claims

This description of litigation and arbitration procedure has been limited to the case of a plaintiff or claimant claiming against the defendant or respondent. In practice, the defendant may have a separate counter-claim against the plaintiff, or may wish to claim contribution or an indemnity from a third party (such as a sub-contractor or supplier). Litigation procedure allows not only counter-claims, but also third party claims to be joined in a single action. The rules of procedure apply equally to counter-claims as to claims, but with the parties' roles reversed.

In arbitration, counter-claims are permitted, but it is not usually possible for third parties to be joined, nor for arbitration hearings to be consolidated without the consent of all the parties.[88] The JCT 80 Conditions and ICE Arbitration Procedure make some provision for joinder of third parties or ordering of concurrent hearings, as does the Arbitration Ordinance in Hong Kong,[89] but success has apparently been limited. Alternative approaches, such as permitting a sub-contractor to pursue a claim in the name of the main contractor, are usually adopted to overcome such problems.

GERMINATION AND NOTIFICATION

Generally

From much of what one hears at seminars and conferences and reads in textbooks one might be forgiven for assuming that claims are a phenomenon that just appears — like blight on potatoes. This is, of course, not so and the importance of this fact is that early recognition of a claim or potential claim may make it possible to deal with it in its embryo stage and so avoid the massive document that might otherwise land on one's desk at a later stage of the job, together with all the problems that then go with it. Of course, with the best

---

83. *Tramountana Armadora v Atlantic Shipping Co* [1978] 2 All ER 870.
84. For example, ICE Arbitration Procedure (1983) Rule 21.1.
85. For example, ICE Arbitration Procedure (1983) Rule 23.
86. Arbitration Act 1950 s20.
87. Arbitration Act 1950 s19A, as inserted by Administration of Justice Act 1982.
88. *Oxford Shipping Co v Nippon Yusen Kaisha* [1984] 3 All ER 835.
89. JCT 80 Art 5.1.4 of the Agreement or Clause 41.2.1 of the Conditions under Amendment 4: 1987 or Amendment 6: 1988; ICE Arbitration Procedure (1983) Rule 7; Arbitration Ordinance (Cap 341) s6B.

will in the world, this sad state of affairs cannot always be avoided. There will probably always be intractable situations compounded of physical difficulties, documents defective in the sense that they do not cater properly for the event in question, and difficulties of personality on both sides. But they will very rarely appear suddenly without some prior warning which it is up to us to recognize. A very great deal can be done to avoid such situations by recognizing the potentiality for a claim, not feeling resentful that a contractor should seek what are to him his just dues (even if he proves to be wrong or has no case) and endeavouring to solve problems as they arise.

If some event occurs which gives rise to cost or expense beyond what was expected, then, in the nature of things, it is likely to be the contractor who first appreciates the possibility. It is therefore not unreasonable to expect him to take the initiative and inform the architect, engineer or quantity surveyor at the appropriate level. If that is right then it is unfair and unreasonable to complain if the contractor gives such notice; it is wrong to condemn him for being 'claims conscious' or on that evidence alone to suspect his motives.

The happening of an event to be notified

If troubles arise in connection with earthworks and material being excavated is found to be unsuitable for constructing embankments as expected and specified, it may not be immediately apparent to the contractor that he should notify the engineer's representative that some action under Clause 12 of the ICE Conditions is warranted. It may not be immediately apparent to the engineer's representative that there is anything more than inclement weather causing trouble or that what he thought was ineptitude on the part of the contractor's staff could possibly be a 'design' fault in seeking to use this material at all. The main preoccupation of both sides is to get the job built; difficulties are an inherent risk of the construction industry and it may well be some time before the contractor realises the full implications of the situation and thinks in terms of a 'claim' and therefore the necessity of a notice under such as Clause 12 of the ICE Conditions. In such circumstances when has the event causing the claim happened?

In one sense it has 'happened' when the excavation in question started, but in terms of a claim it cannot be said to have happened until one side or the other (usually the contractor) has become aware of the situation or could reasonably be expected to have become aware of it as being something possibly warranting a claim. In this case one is referring to physical circumstances which are making themselves apparent in the course of the work. More plant, more men, lack of progress, different methods; any or all of these can call attention to the fact that there is trouble and should be alerting someone to correlate these with the contractor's liability under the contract and from that to a view that there may be an entitlement to additional payment.

Delay

Delay in construction contracts is not an uncommon occurrence, but even the existence of it is not always apparent unless someone is alert to the situation and is constantly monitoring progress against programme. Failure to issue a drawing after it has been requested, failure to nominate a sub-contractor by the required date, the impact of a variation order altering work actually in progress — all these are relatively obvious. With most jobs of any size there are usually periodic progress meetings at which substantive delay may become apparent, but it must not be forgotten that it is necessary to translate instances of delay into terms of (a) whose responsibility they are and (b) their impact on the work, before one can determine whether a claim is likely to be involved or not.

Clearly if the delay in question has been caused by the contractor then he will be unable to claim additional cost. If, however, it has been caused by the employer (or his agents or another of his contractors), then it may well give rise to an entitlement. If such delay lies on the critical path then the contractor could be entitled to an extension of time as well. If it has been caused by an event such as exceptionally inclement weather, then the contractor may be entitled to an extension of time but to no payment. Then again it is not unusual to find one cause overlapping another and the problem then arises as to which supervenes.

This problem is dealt with in more detail in Chapter 8. Suffice it to say here that the matter is one which requires constant attention by both sides. Each must be aware of the rights and liabilities of the other. There must be some working arrangement between them whereby progress and delay can be monitored.

It must not be overlooked that all this is, in a way, secondary to the main object of the exercise, namely to achieve physical progress on the Works. This will be the main pre-occupation of both contractor and RE/CW staff but it is in this very situation that they must be alert to the potentiality of claims if they are not to be rudely awakened when it is too late to do anything about it and additional cost and expense have been incurred.

Interim payment signals

So much for the more tangible indications of claims. There is, however, another area in which the possibility of claim may make itself apparent and that is in the course of preparing statements for interim payments and in the preparation of final accounts.

There are some people on both sides of the fence who seem to think that almost anything will do by way of statements for interim payments; statements are only approximate, there will be another coming along in a month's time, staff is really too busy on other things to spend too much time on them. Those who subscribe to this idea are heading for trouble and ignoring a valuable indicator of potential genuine claim situations, or alternatively are liable to be misled by a substantial gap between expenditure and income to think there is need for a claim when actually contract work or variations are undermeasured.

The first indications to a contractor that something may be amiss can be a significant discrepancy between expenditure and money certified for payment. He may try to account for the shortfall but estimates of undermeasurement are notoriously unreliable and in any case tend to follow the event rather belatedly. The contractor may therefore be precipitated into looking for grounds for claim where either no necessity exists or where the amount claimed may be grossly overstated. Such a situation tends to give a contractor a reputation of being 'claims conscious' and tends to discredit a genuine claim when one arises.

Consider the situation where on a M£2 contract, the contractor had admittedly substantial delay and consequent disruption for which the employer was responsible. His costs on completion of the work showed a shortfall of something like £750,000 compared with certificates, even after allowing for retentions. He had already submitted an interim claim for additional costs attributable to delay and disruption which he then updated to cover his losses. The cost of delay in itself is not easy to assess but disruption is notoriously difficult to evaluate. A consultant QS was called in to advise the employer in connection with the claim but not the final account, which remained with the employer's site staff. The consultant asked both the engineer and the contractor how the final measurement and preparation of the final account were progressing and was told by both that these were well up to date. In face of that information it was not unreasonable to consider the claim at its face value, to try to establish the extent of delay and disruption and evaluate it. When all the costs of delay had been assessed, there remained a disruption element amounting to some 40 per cent loss of productivity of labour (and something similar on plant). If true, this would have meant that throughout the whole period of the contract four out of ten men were effectively doing nothing at all, or maybe eight out of ten working at half capacity. It is difficult to believe that such a situation is possible. One would have expected such a state of affairs to have been obvious from almost casual observation, and even with labour difficulties being what they are one would have expected the contractor to mitigate the damage and discharge some of the men until the cause of the trouble was remedied. In fact the final account took a further year to complete and the pick-up, compared with the interim payments, accounted for more than half the so-called loss of productivity. But what a tragedy! The contractor appeared rather stupid if not actually dishonest. The engineer's staff were not exactly covered with glory. The contractor stood out of money he was entitled to — at very considerable cost in terms of bank charges — and his liquidity was reduced to vanishing point.

It is clear then that it is in everybody's interests to maximize interim payments to a contractor within his contract entitlement. In addition to obviating the sort of situation indicated above, this affords the opportunity to keep a check on the out-turn of quantities (detecting possible errors in lump-sum contracts and increase or decrease in the case of measure and value contracts), initiating discussion on rates and prices for varied work and providing a reasonably reliable financial statement for both employer and contractor. There is much advantage to be gained from interim valuations being prepared jointly by contractor and QS staff.

That process can be supplemented to further advantage if work on the final measurement and definitive agreement on rates for varied work, etc, is also proceeded with concurrently and as close up behind completed work as possible. This above all will reveal those matters where a contractor considers that proposed rates and prices for varied work are insufficient, and investigation may demonstrate that he is or is not entitled to something more (a 'claim' being disposed of before it is formulated). Investigation may reveal that something further is involved — and this may be the moment when the need for claiming something (perhaps by way of 'loss and expense caused by matters materially affecting regular progress of the Works') has reasonably become apparent. The value of starting work on the final account as soon as there is completed permanent work to measure cannot be overstated. The objective of completing the final account within the maintenance period (at most 12 months) is well within the bounds of possibility and the effect on the claims situation can be substantial.

One further point on the matter of both interim statements for payments on account and the preparation of final accounts is that the work is expedited and the staff effort involved is reduced if both measurement and rate-fixing are done jointly by the contractor and A/E/QS staff.

Notices

This, then, is how claims really and usually originate, where matters of difference begin with discussion, proceed at times with correspondence, are the subject of negotiation in the course of everyday business and to some extent at least get themselves settled without the big artillery being brought in on either side. It is submitted that rather more could be dealt with in the same way if we applied our minds to doing so. Of course there is a welter of other work going on; the main effort of the contractor is to get the job done, of the architect or engineer to produce outstanding information in time to avoid causing delay (perhaps with an employer who cannot make up his mind as to what he wants and is reluctant to pay for the privilege), and of the quantity surveyor to produce estimates for variations, check interim statements for payment on account, measure work before it is covered up and so on. There are occasions when the contractor gives every indication of exploiting loopholes or interpreting events to bolster a claim, with the A/E/QS fighting a defensive action. All these problems can be dealt with better if both sides know their job, know what they and the other party to the contract are entitled to, know where they and the job stand as regards interim and final accounts; and know the consequences of putting off dealing with claims until they can be put off no longer. In short, if they accept that whilst construction is one half of the equation, payment is the other, and the latter is not a trivial factor to be dealt with when time permits.

Having said that, it is clear that the contractor must give notice of an intention to claim as soon as possible. Just what this means is not always easy to define, the point being: when does the claim arise, or rather when does the necessity to enter a claim become apparent? Conditions of Contract in the past have attempted to stipulate that notice shall be given 'immediately upon the happening' of the event giving rise to the claim. ICE 4 was penal in this connection, particularly as regards Clause 12 which stipulated that 'the cost of all work done or Constructional Plant used by the Contractor prior to giving such notice . . . shall be deemed to have been covered in the rates and prices . . .'

GC/Wks 1 continues the hard line of ICE4. In Edition 2, Condition 53(3) states, somewhat legalistically, 'It shall be a condition precedent to the Contract Sum being increased . . . that the Contractor, immediately upon becoming aware . . . shall have given notice to the SO'. Edition 3 puts it more directly in Condition 46: 'The Contract Sum shall not be increased

... unless the Contractor immediately upon becoming aware ... has given notice to the PM ...'.

Later editions of the ICE Conditions have adopted a more reasonable line. The fifth edition, in Clause 52(4), requires 'notice in writing ... as soon as reasonably possible after the happening of the events giving rise to the claim'. The sixth edition has added an apparent limit: '... as soon as may be reasonable and in any event within 28 days after the happening of the events giving rise to the claim', but in both editions the consequence of failure to notify is that 'the Contractor shall be entitled to payment in respect thereof only to the extent that the Engineer has not been prevented from or substantially prejudiced by such failure in investigating the said claim'. The approach of FIDIC4 is similar. Clause 53.1 requires notice 'within 28 days after the event giving rise to the claim has first arisen'. The consequence of failure depends, under Clause 53.4, on the extent of contemporary records. JCT 80, in Clause 26.1.1, requires that '... the Contractor's application shall be made as soon as it has become, or should reasonably have become apparent to him that the regular progress of the Works ... has been or was likely to be affected'. The consequence of failure to notify is not stipulated.

Thus the conditions of contract all seem to recognise that a claim situation does not occur at a clearly defined point in time and is not always instantly recognized. Notices of intention to claim are amongst the many other notices required from the contractor. It follows, however, that if the contractor is required to give notice, with the implication, if not the express statement, that failure to do so may damage or preclude his entitlement, then neither the architect, engineer or quantity surveyor is entitled to complain or criticize if the contractor does as he is required. No doubt there are cases where notice is given unreasonably or even frivolously, but this is not the general case, commercial considerations such as not antagonising the employer or his professional advisers usually providing sufficient disincentive.

Far from discouraging notice, architects, engineers and quantity surveyors should indeed encourage it. That is not the same thing as encouraging the making of specious or ill-founded claims, but whenever there is the possibility of a claim the A/E/QS must be informed if they are to take remedial action (if that is possible and the fault lies with them or their employer, or if it is a matter of design), or they may be able to take avoiding action in such as the case of unsuitable ground conditions where it is not the contractor's responsibility. At least they need to know so that they may advise the employer should it seem likely that he may be called upon to meet extra cost.

The court or arbitrator has a discretion to override provisions which would exclude entitlement to compensation absolutely for failure to give notice within the time stipulated, but it is safer and certainly wiser for a contractor to assume that time limits ought to be observed. Conversely the A/E/QS should not assume that a claim which is notified outside the time limits can be ignored. He should still keep such records and make such investigations as can reasonably be made. Where a contractor fails to give notice because the matter has not become apparent earlier, then the conditions must be examined to establish whether or not he is entitled to claim. As indicated above, the general case is that he would be. On the other hand, if he failed to do so but it was perfectly obvious that he could have given notice much earlier and that because of this the A/E/QS were 'prevented from or substantially prejudiced by such failure in investigating the said claim' (ICE 52(4)(e)), then he should have no complaint if the claim were reduced to what could be established.

For claims not based on provisions within the contract, i.e. for damages in breach, there is no time limit on notification beyond that imposed by the Limitation Act 1980 (6 years for simple contracts and 12 years for contracts under seal). It is, however, clearly in everybody's interests that claims be dealt with sooner rather than later. With the passage of time facts become more difficult to establish — and their effect on work long completed more so. As a generalization it may be said that a contractor can legally recover only what he can prove.

Records and particulars	Where conditions of contract require notice of intention to claim, it is sufficient for the purpose of meeting the requirement if the notice indicates the intention to claim in general terms and identifies the events or circumstances giving rise to the claim. Most forms of contract go on, however, to require the keeping of records and/or the submission of particulars.

GC/Wks 1 Edition 2, in Condition 54(3)(c)(ii), requires the Contractor to have provided documents and information 'as soon as reasonably practicable after incurring the expense'. Edition 3 Condition 46 requires that 'the Contractor, as soon as reasonably practicable, and in any case within 56 days of incurring the expense, provides full details of all expenses incurred and evidence that the expenses directly result from the occurrence of one of the events described ...'. There is an obvious difficulty in interpretation where expense is incurred over a long period of time as a result of an event. The distinction between the two types of particulars required in the later edition is significant. Particulars of expense go to quantum. Particulars of causation go to the principle of liability or entitlement.

The ICE Conditions, in Clause 52(4), are primarily concerned with the keeping of contemporary records, although 'full and detailed particulars of the amount claimed' must also be submitted. FIDIC 4 Clause 53.2 requires contemporary records to be kept. Clause 53.3 requires an account giving particulars of both the amount claimed and the grounds upon which the claim is based to be sent to the Engineer 'within 28 days, or such other reasonable time as may be agreed by the Engineer, of giving notice'. JCT 80 Clause 26.1.2 requires the contractor to submit 'upon request of the Architect such information as should reasonably enable the Architect to form an opinion' as to entitlement. 26.1.3 similarly requires submission of details of loss and/or expense as are reasonably necessary for ascertainment.

The time limits stipulated for the submission of particulars of a claim are subject to the same comments as time limits on notification. There is an unfortunate tendency to regard the submission of particulars of claims as something to be left until after completion. This is highly undesirable, but any general improvement probably depends on a corresponding willingness to deal with claims as they arise.

The importance of contemporary records relevant to a claim cannot be over-emphasized. If possible they should be agreed between contractor and RE/CW at the time. An RE/CW who refuses to check and agree contemporary records is very unwise, even if he believes the claim to be unfounded. If such refusal is met, a contractor should still continue to submit records so that the opportunity for contemporary checking can be demonstrated.

PRESENTATION

As indicated earlier, a claim may arise in an informal way, be dealt with by discussion and be settled by inclusion in the next interim payment or in the final account. There are, however, occasions when this does not suffice and a letter is required setting out the matters at issue, stating the grounds on which it is considered entitlement is based, with reference to previous correspondence, other documents etc. as necessary, and showing the amount claimed and how it has been arrived at. For convenience, the letter might well be headed 'Claim' and, if there were several of them, it might be convenient to number them in series; business-like, comprehensive, concise, matter of fact, but not giving the appearance of anything untoward. There is a difference of opinion which it has not been possible to resolve and it seems necessary to submit the matter formally, partly that there shall be no doubt about the facts of the matter and what is being claimed and partly that it may be sent to higher authority (the architect or the engineer as distinct from the RE or C/W) if necessary for decision.

It may be that some claims will be settled and some will not. It may be that some may become complicated by later events and need restating, it may be that an individual claim may be so complex as to require something more than would normally be dealt with by a lengthy letter plus enclosures.

If at some stage during the job or even at the end it becomes necessary to deal with a single complicated claim or collect together a number of earlier claims which have become interconnected, then it may be necessary to construct a document in a form which seems to be becoming 'traditional' in the sense that it is bulky, not to say massive, and is labelled 'claim'. Even so, it is better to give the appearance of expecting settlement to be achievable rather than dress it up in the regalia one associates with litigation of X versus Y ... In the matter of ... Whereas ... etc.

There is no need to assume or convey that the matter is verging upon arbitration, but the principles of pleadings in arbitration or litigation, described above, may usefully be adopted. This will be of great help to those having to deal with a claim and thereby perhaps earn their blessing or goodwill rather than the reverse. The submission should set out concisely but comprehensively the gist of the whole matter so that in the compass of 10–15 pages at most, the architect, engineer or quantity surveyor can understand what is at issue. It is counter-productive to expect these people to be able to read through a document of between 100 and 1000 pages including documents and schedules and correspondence and calculations and so on so as to instruct their staff on the investigation they are required to make. It is not to be supposed that because such a mass of information is condensed into 10–15 pages it is worth any less in terms of money, though some may seem to think so. To one contractor making use of this helpful device the comment was made 'If that is all there is to it (ten pages or so), it cannot be worth very much.' This is perhaps why some contractors feel it necessary to spread themselves and type the main narrative in triple rather than double spacing! Claims should be valued on their intrinsic merit, not per page of claim.

Thus a summary of a few pages concisely but comprehensively setting out the essential point at issue will enable an A/E/QS receiving it to quickly understand the substance of the claim being made. It will enable him to direct the efforts of his staff towards corroborating or countering the points being made. Such a summary would of course be backed up by details and evidence, which should be as extensive as may be necessary to make the point — but still not unnecessarily verbose. Drawings, schedules, programmes, charts, etc., should be provided as appendices. Copies of relevant correspondence are also helpful, as letters may be distributed through a number of files and considerable time can be spent in locating them.

All the documents comprising the claim — the narrative itself and the several supporting documents (which are better dealt with as appendices to avoid breaking up the narrative unnecessarily) should be referenced and each carefully paginated so that in referring to them (whether in the body of the claim or discussion) a simple reference can ensure that whoever is being invited to look at a particular drawing, chart, schedule, calculation or whatever can look it up with a minimum of difficulty and delay and be sure that he is looking at the right thing. The same remarks apply to any rejoinder which the architect, engineer or quantity surveyor may make. It is also to be hoped that if these people find themselves unable to agree (as will frequently be the case), they will at least say why. A dogmatic, unexplained 'No' can quite significantly damage relationships and make further negotiations difficult and protracted — even at times to the extent of precipitating arbitration.

So far as the contractor is concerned, he is to be expected to present his case clearly and succinctly, emphasizing his point by all means, but avoiding unnecessary verbiage and particularly avoiding recrimination and innuendo, which are more likely to give offence and be counter-productive than invite cool, impartial consideration. If there is considered to be fault on the part of the employer or his professional advisers, then of course this must be said in plain, but polite terms. If there is a breach of some term or other of the contract then no amount of euphemism will provide an effective substitute to saying so. In a case some years ago a contractor was using every ploy he could think of to avoid using that awful word 'breach'. On the point being put to him he hotly denied that he could even think that the employer could be in breach. Whereupon it was indicated that if that were the case there was nothing further to discuss — there being no other grounds upon which he could claim. As a result he rapidly changed his mind, the matter was discussed in its proper context and agreement reached amicably.

Finally, a policy needs to be settled on the approach to quantification. At a practical level, a claim as submitted will only be cut down, it will not be increased by the A/E/QS, arbitrator or judge. Lawyers, whose arithmetical skills often lag behind their skills of linguistic analysis, have a habit of dividing claims, or differences between claims and evaluations, by simple factors such as two or three, to obtain settlement figures. Such an approach can lead in turn to claims being submitted with an exaggeration factor of two or three or more to compensate. The whole system degenerates into a lottery of meaningless numbers. Some leeway is needed for negotiation, but it must surely be the aim that submissions should contain reasonably reliable assessments, and that this should be respected in the evaluation by the A/E/QS. Mutual respect and trust are fundamental to the satisfactory conduct of professional dealings.

ESTABLISHMENT

It is for the contractor to state the reason why he considers himself entitled, and to how much. Some contractors seem to think that if they merely inform the architect, engineer or quantity surveyor that something is wrong, that they are losing money, or not being paid as much as they expected, then it is up to the architect or engineer or quantity surveyor to find reasons and make an evaluation. If they do not go that far, many feel that if they base their claim wrongly then it is up to the employer's professional advisers to correct it and perhaps to indicate the correct basis. Such ideas are totally fallacious. Should a dispute ever get to arbitration then there is no question but that the claimant must prepare his points of claim and state the amount he is seeking. There is no difference in initiating a claim, nor should there be, for the contractor is the only one who can know the effect of circumstances upon him and certainly no one else can know the financial consequences.

Although it is undoubtedly the case that it is for the contractor to state why he considers himself entitled, and to quote conditions of contract where appropriate in support of his contentions, it is not to be thought that Conditions of Contract contain a 'claims clause' as such which if quoted acts in some way as an 'open sesame'. Clause 52(4) of the ICE Conditions has sometimes been regarded as one such but this is purely a procedural clause and of itself gives no entitlement to payment.

Claims usually arise from events or circumstances where one party is alleged to have done something to the detriment of the other, or has failed to do something he has undertaken to do. The Conditions of Contract attempt to anticipate such events and circumstances in one or other of their clauses and it is one (or more) of these that needs to be quoted in support of any claim. Where no such provision covers the event or circumstances in question then one must seek some principle of common law which covers the matter.

Admittedly it may not always be possible in the first instance to cite a condition of contract with absolute certainty — it may be necessary to quote alternative grounds — but clearly if it is to be expected that serious consideration be given to a claim (not to mention some payment on account) then a decision must be made and the claim prepared accordingly. Occasionally, in the course of discussion it may become apparent that the ground chosen is incorrect. There would seem to be no reason why at that point the contractor should not restate his case on other (and this time) correct grounds. Obviously he should avoid such an occurrence if at all possible as it does not reflect well upon his efficiency or credibility to have to change ground. Sometimes, however, it is unavoidable and again, provided a contractor is not acting frivolously, he should not be penalized. He would in fact be able to take such a course upon referring the matter to arbitration (when, perhaps for the first time, he has the benefit of legal advice).

In establishing claims it is necessary as far as possible to identify each separate event or matter which is considered to give rise to an entitlement of payment, to state the reasons for so considering and to evaluate its effect. Claims, however, are often composite; work in connection with a variation order may involve not only dissimilarity of conditions but also extra time, which may need to be distinguished from delay as such. It may be necessary on occasion to dissect a claim, even on some arbitrary basis, where one aspect attracts profit and another, being in the nature of damages, does not. On the other hand, a number of matters may cause delay and disruption with the result that there is a cumulative effect such that it is not possible to separate the result financially of any one cause or event in isolation. In such a case, they may be taken together and assessed as a whole — provided profit is eliminated and there is no overlap.

EXAMINATION

The technique to be employed in examining claims corresponds to the technique involved in constructing them, and this matter is dealt with in more detail in Chapter 12. Suffice it to say here that it is necessary to be objective, to attempt to prove or disprove factually the assertions or allegations made. It is necessary to check facts, starting with the documents which constitute the contract. One is entitled to assume nothing. Check the facts. It is often possible to reach agreement between the two sides as to certain facts (weather, number of men, working or idle plant, hours worked, etc.) without necessarily reaching agreement at that stage as to their import. Such a step can save a great deal of time in checking these matters independently.

CONCLUSION

In the following chapters examples are given of claims which may be regarded as variations on the themes set out at the end of Chapter 1. They have necessarily been simplified in some respects to bring them within the compass of a book such as this, but endeavour has been made to keep the way in which they frequently arise and are (mis)handled as close to reality as possible.

All the cases are based on actual experience or decided cases but are all fictitious as to detailed facts. Where possible, reference is made to reported cases which provide authority for any propositions of law involved. In giving examples there is always the danger of illustrating a particular point which will never recur. Some attempt has therefore been made to select matters of general application, and at the end of each case to set out briefly the points of principle involved both so that they may be applicable beyond the so-called case being discussed, and also so that, on the dangers perhaps being recognized, some steps may be taken to prevent such claims recurring. Preventive medicine is usually more economical than surgical treatment.

In applying points illustrated here to other cases care must be taken to compare the basic factors such as the actual Conditions of Contract obtaining — not merely the same Form (JCT, ICE, GC/Wks 1 etc.) but the relevant edition and more particularly the existence of *ad hoc* conditions and other contract documentation which may drastically alter the situation.

Chapter 4
Claims concerning the existence of a contract

GENERALLY

Claims are mostly concerned with entitlements and liabilities arising under, or as a result of, a contract. It is, however, a prerequisite for such claims that the contract has come into existence and is legally valid. The existence of a valid contract may be disputed. Possible scenarios include:

(a) An employer issues a letter of intent, but subsequently denies that a binding contract exists, in order to avoid obligations either to employ the contractor to complete the work or to pay for work already done or reimburse costs incurred by the contractor.

(b) A contractor denies the existence of a contract (or asserts an implied substitute contract) so as to obtain 'reasonable payment' instead of the entitlements fixed by the contract, or to avoid obligations arising under or as a result of the contract.

(c) An employer denies the existence of a variation or supplementary contract to make additional payment.

(d) A contractor denies that a variation or supplementary contract is binding.

'Variation' is used in this context to mean the variation of an existing contract by means of a further contract. This is distinct from a variation 'under the contract' which leaves the original contract intact.

Examples

If a contract is held invalid, entitlements or rights dependent on the contract are lost but alternative entitlements may arise in quasi-contract or under an implied substitute contract. Where a variation is held invalid, the original contract will be revived. The possibilities are best illustrated by some reported cases, mostly concerning building and civil engineering works.

1. *Courtney & Fairbairn v Tolaini Bros*[1] — A building contractor entered into negotiations with a land-owner regarding a proposed development comprising a motel, hotel and filling station. The builder wrote offering to introduce the owner to various sources of finance, on the basis that if finance were forthcoming from those sources, he would be employed to carry out the construction work. The letter proposed that the owner should:

> 'be prepared to instruct your quantity surveyor to negotiate fair and reasonable contract sums in respect of each of the three projects as they arise. (These would incidentally be based upon agreed estimates of the net cost of work and general overheads with a margin for profit of 5 per cent) which, I am sure you will agree, is indeed reasonable . . .'

The owner replied agreeing to the terms specified in the letter but, after finance had been successfully introduced, negotiations as to the net cost of work and general overheads broke down. The owner employed another contractor to do the work, but still used the finance introduced by the plaintiffs. The plaintiffs claimed the loss of profits which they would have made if they had been employed as builders, but the Court of Appeal held that there was no binding contract. It was a mere agreement to agree and the plaintiff therefore had no remedy.

2. *Brogden v Metropolitan Railway Co*[2] — The defendant railway company had drawn up a contract for the supply of coal by the plaintiff. They sent it to the plaintiff, who filled in blanks in the document, but there was no formal execution of the contract. Both parties proceeded to act in accordance with its terms as regards performance and payment. A dispute arose and the defendants then denied there was a binding contract. The House of Lords held that there was a binding contract, which had been complete as soon as the first load of coals was supplied and invoiced, and the invoice was paid at that price.

3. *Peter Lind v Mersey Docks and Harbour Board*[3] — Lind had submitted two tenders for the construction of a container freight terminal, one at a fixed price, one with a variation

---

1. *Courtney & Fairbairn v Tolaini Bros* [1975] 1 WLR 297.
2. *Brogden v Metropolitan Railway Co* [1877] 2 App Cas 666.
3. *Peter Lind v Mersey Docks and Harbour Board* [1972] 2 Lloyd's Rep 234.

of price clause, both open for 6 months. After 5 months, Lind wrote asking to increase their fixed price tender, but the Board wrote back that they 'accepted your tender'. Lind began work but refused to sign a formal contract. After the 6 months tender validity period had expired, the Board wrote again, this time stating that they were arranging for a formal contract to be drawn up on the fixed price basis. Lind continued working but refused to sign. It was held that there was no binding contract and Lind were entitled to recover payment on a *quantum meruit* basis. The first acceptance did not conclude a contract as it did not specify which tender was accepted. Cooke J stated 'It seems to me that an acceptance, in order to be unequivocal, must be unequivocal to the business man as well as to the lawyer'. The second letter was not a valid acceptance as the fixed price offer had already expired. The starting of work did not constitute acceptance as discussions were still in progress on new rates.

4.   *British Steel Corporation v Cleveland Bridge*[4] — Cleveland Bridge were contractors for a building with a space-frame roof in Dammam. They contacted BSC to supply the special cast steel nodes required and issued a letter of intent. As the work was urgent, BSC started immediately and in fact completed and delivered all 137 nodes while negotiations on the terms of a contract were still continuing. Agreement on terms was never reached. BSC sued for approximately £200,000 as the value of the nodes supplied, but Cleveland Bridge counter-claimed for £800,000 for damages due to late delivery and delivery out of sequence. It was held that there was no contract. BSC were entitled to the £200,000 (which was the figure in the inchoate contract[5]) on the basis of quasi-contract; but the counter-claim for damages for late delivery and delivery out of sequence depended on the existence of a contract and therefore failed.

5.   *Trollope & Colls v Atomic Power Constructions*[6] — Work was started before the contract was agreed, but after several months agreement was reached and the parties entered into a formal contract. Subsequently, however, the contractor claimed that the work performed prior to execution of the contract should be valued on a *quantum meruit*. It was held that the claim failed: the contract as eventually agreed referred back to the start of the work.

6.   *Williams v Roffey Bros & Nicholls (Contractors) Ltd*[7] — The defendant main contractor, refurbishing a block of flats, had agreed to pay the plaintiff, a carpentry sub-contractor, an additional sum of £10,300 on top of the original sub-contract price of £20,000, to continue with and complete the original sub-contract work on the remaining flats. The sub-contractor continued with the work and completed most of the flats, but eventually stopped work in response to non-payment by the main contractor. He sued the main contractor, who denied the claim on the grounds that the later agreement was void for lack of consideration.

The judge in the County Court found that the original sub-contract price was too low and he concluded that in such a situation, where the parties subsequently agreed that additional monies should be paid to the sub-contractor, the agreement was in the interests of both parties and therefore did not fail for lack of consideration. The Court of Appeal recognized the general principle established in *Stilk v Myrick* that the performance of an existing contractual obligation does not constitute consideration for a fresh promise, but held that there was consideration in this case. Glidewell LJ said[8] the present state of the law was expressed in the following proposition:

'(i) if A has entered into a contract with B to do work for, or to supply goods or services to, B in return for payment by B and (ii) at some stage before A

---

4.   *British Steel Corporation v Cleveland Bridge Engineering* [1984] 1 All ER 504.
5.   An 'inchoate' contract is one where the process leading to agreement has been started but not completed. It is accordingly not binding in law.
6.   *Trollope & Colls v Atomic Power Constructions* [1963] 1 WLR 333.
7.   *Williams v Roffey Bros & Nicholls (Contractors) Ltd* [1991] 1 QB 1.
8.   Ibid at pp 15, 16.

has completely performed his obligations under the contract B has reason to doubt whether A will, or will be able to, complete his side of the bargain and (iii) B thereupon promises A an additional payment in return for A's promise to perform his contractual obligations on time and (iv) as a result of giving his promise B obtains in practice a benefit, or obviates a disbenefit, and (v) B's promise is not given as a result of economic duress or fraud on the part of A, then (vi) the benefit to B is capable of being consideration for B's promise, so that the promise will be legally binding.'

Purchas LJ said[9] that there was an advantage to the main contractor from a pragmatic point of view; it was apparent that the sub-contractor would otherwise not have completed the work, although failure to complete would have been a breach of the sub-contract. An agreement to pay extra induced by a threat not to complete would, however, have been voidable under the doctrine of economic duress.

7. *Atlas Express v Kafco*[10] — The plaintiff transport company had agreed to deliver cartons of basketware for the defendant to Woolworths stores at £1.10 per carton. On the first load it became apparent to the plaintiff that their depot manager had made a mistaken assessment of the number of cartons per load, and they refused to take any more loads unless the defendant agreed to pay a minimum £440 per load. The defendant was a small company, dependent on the Woolworths order. As it was for the Christmas trade, they would have been unable to find alternative carriers in time. Woolworths would have sued for non-performance if the defendant had failed to deliver. The defendant agreed to the new rate 'unwillingly and under compulsion', but later refused to pay the invoice in full. They paid £10,000 on account but made clear through their solicitor that they considered the contract as subject to duress. Held: the new rate agreed was void for economic duress.

Choice of position

In the case where the existence or validity or relevance of a contract is open to dispute, a party may have to choose between alternative positions. It cannot deny the existence or relevance of a contract and, at the same time, assert rights created by the disputed contract. In particular a contractor cannot insist on being employed to carry out future work on the basis of a *quantum meruit*. The entitlement to a *quantum meruit* depends on the contract being out the way or the work being outside the contract. The right to be employed depends on the existence of a contract covering the work. It must be open to the employer, if the contractor says there is no binding contract, to accept the contractor at his word and bring in someone else to carry out the work. In retrospect, however, it is open to a party to frame a claim on alternative grounds, so long as they are kept separate and internally consistent.

Recognition of a valid contract

The question whether a contract exists is effectively a question whether the court would recognize the transaction as a contract. The law is not concerned with the name given by the parties to their transaction: it might be called an agreement, a sub-contract, a guarantee, a collateral warranty, a supplementary agreement, a bill of sale, an insurance policy, and still be a contract. It might be called a contract, but be invalid.

Except in specific situations, the law does not require any formalities for a binding contract. Generally, there are just three essential requirements for a binding contract: intention to create legal relations, consideration and agreement. There are also various grounds, such as public policy or illegality, whereby a contract may be set aside.

The question whether a contract has come into existence is one issue which cannot be referred to an arbitrator under the contract arbitration clause, nor could it be decided by the A/E/QS. The jurisdiction of the arbitrator appointed under an arbitration clause depends on the existence of the contract. He is not allowed to pronounce on his own jurisdiction, therefore he cannot decide whether the contract exists.[11] The power of the A/E/QS likewise

9. *Williams v Roffey Bros & Nicholls (Contractors) Ltd* [1991] 1 QB 1, at pp 22, 23.
10. *Atlas Express v Kafco* [1989] 1 QB 833.
11. *Duke of Buccleuch v Metropolitan Board of Works* [1870] LR 5 Exch 211.

depends on the existence of the contract. An arbitrator may, however, have jurisdiction to decide whether the contract has subsequently been frustrated. The arbitration clause survives for the resolution of disputes.[12]

Illegality and public policy

At common law, a contract tainted with illegality or contrary to public policy is wholly or partially unenforceable. This is known as the 'ex turpi causa' defence, referring to the maxim 'ex turpi causa non oritur actio': there can be no right of action based on an intention to do wrong. In cases where an objectionable clause can be severed, the contract may be enforceable as to the rest, but it depends whether the whole of the contract is tainted and whether the courts are prepared to assist on the grounds of public policy. For example, a contract made with intent to defraud the Inland Revenue will not be treated as severable, it will be wholly unenforceable.[13]

Unenforceability of the contract does not, however, entail all other rights of action being unenforceable. For example, if there were a claim based on negligent misrepresentation which did not depend on the contract, that claim would be enforceable though associated with the same transaction. In *Strongman Ltd v Sincock*[14] it was held that a builder who had entered into a contract for building work for which he did not have a licence (which was a legal requirement at the time) could not recover payment under the contract; but he was able to recover damages from the architect on the basis of an assurance that he would obtain the necessary licence. The court held that the assurance gave rise to a collateral contract.

Unenforceability depends on either the contract being illegal or contrary to public policy at the time of contract, or the parties intending at the time of contract to perform the contract in an illegal way. The mere fact that one party does perform the contract in an illegal way does not make it unenforceable. Thus, a contract to transport goods on a lorry in excess of its permitted weight would be unenforceable;[15] but the mere fact that a lorry was used in excess of its permitted weight in the performance of a contract would not render the contract unenforceable unless it had been the intention of the parties at the time of contract to overload the lorry.[16]

Where one party alone has an illegal intention at the time of contract, the contract is still enforceable by the other party, unless he participates in the illegality.[17] The parties' knowledge, or lack of knowledge, of the law is irrelevant.

PARTIES

Privity of contract

A construction project will usually involve not just a single contract, but a whole network of contracts. Under conventional arrangements, most of the individual contracts depend largely on the terms and provisions of the main contract between the employer and main contractor (which is why the main contract is considered by commentators in much greater depth than the others), but this should not obscure the essential point stemming from the doctrine of privity of contract: that each individual contract only binds the immediate parties to it.[18]

The identities of the parties to a contract are fixed when the contract is formed. A party may assign the benefits of a contract, but it may not assign the burdens without the consent of the other party. The law of agency does, however, enable one person to enter into a contract on behalf of another under certain conditions.

---

12. *Heyman v Darwins* [1942] AC 356.
13. *Miller v Karlinski* [1945] 62 TLR 85.
14. *Strongman Ltd v Sincock* [1955] 2 QB 525.
15. *Ashmore, Benson, Pease & Co v A V Dawson Ltd* [1973] 1 WLR 828.
16. *Coral Leisure Group v Barnett* [1981] ICR 503.
17. *Mason v Clarke* [1955] AC 778.
18. *Dunlop v Selfridge* [1915] AC 847. There is a second rule that the consideration must move from the party entitled to sue upon the contract: *Tweddle v Atkinson* [1861] 1 B & S 393.

The identity of the other party to a contract can assume special importance. For example, a contractor might believe he has entered into a contract with a person of substance, but find that his contract is actually or only with some other person, who has become insolvent. The identity of the parties is also relevant to the validity of a contract; there are rules concerning the capacity of individuals and corporate bodies to enter into binding contracts.

Each party to a contract need not be a single legal person, it may comprise a group of persons, but the persons in the group must be jointly or jointly and severally liable,[19] as in a partnership or joint venture. An agreement with a number of separate persons would be treated as a number of separate contracts. A legal 'person' includes a corporation, such as a local authority or a limited company.[20]

Within a network of contracts, rights, obligations, liabilities and duties can only be pursued or passed on through the chains of contracts, but each contract in the chain is a separate link. The ability to pursue contractual rights therefore depends on the terms of the specific contract with the next party in the chain against whom the right must be pursued (in the absence of a collateral contract giving a direct right of action), and on the solvency of that person. For example, a sub-contractor cannot generally pursue the employer direct for payment, the employer cannot pursue the sub-contractor direct for defective work. An employer may be able to obtain an assignment of a right of action to pursue a sub-contractor if the main contractor becomes insolvent, but such an approach is unlikely to help a sub-contractor obtain payment. Similar considerations apply in relation to passing on liability.

Capacity

For a contract to be binding, the parties must each have the 'capacity' to contract. There are, for example, legal rules concerning the contracting capacity of drunks, lunatics and infants. More significantly in commercial transactions, the powers of public authorities and other statutory corporations to enter into contracts may be circumscribed by their statutes or standing orders. The common law rules on this have been severely cut back, however, by statute. At common law, a contract made by a statutory corporation in excess of its powers or disregarding prescribed formalities was *ultra vires* (beyond its powers) and such a contract was void.[21] Requirements for special formalities by corporations in making contracts were abolished by the Corporate Bodies' Contracts Act 1960.

Within the European Community, the position on corporate capacity has been significantly altered in relation to limited companies (which are statutory corporations) by a Community Directive, now enacted in the UK as s35 of the Companies Act 1985. This provides that a transaction, decided upon by the directors of a company in favour of a person dealing in good faith with the company, is deemed to be within the capacity of the company. This does not, however, apply to save a purported contract with a corporation which was not in existence at the time of contract.[22]

Agency

An exception to the doctrine of privity of contract is provided by the law of agency. An agent is a person with the power to change the legal position of another person known as his 'principal'. This power to bind the principal derives from 'authority', conferred by the principal on the agent. Where an agent has authority to enter into a contract on behalf of his principal and a contract is made by the agent acting within his authority, the principal is then bound by the contract and, except in certain situations, the agent drops out of the picture.

---

19. The distinction between joint and joint and several liability is mainly procedural. Where persons are only jointly liable, any action must be brought against all the persons. All persons still living must be named on the writ. Where parties are made jointly and severally liable, each person may be sued separately for the full amount outstanding; they need not all be named on a single writ. In both cases, the discharge of the obligation by one person discharges the obligations of the others, subject to rights of the one to claim contribution from the others.
20. A partnership is not a corporation. Formerly a partnership had to sue or be sued by naming all the partners, but it may now sue or be sued in the partnership name: RSC Order 81.
21. *Hazell v Hammersmith and Fulham LBC* [1991] 2 WLR 372 is an example where the *ultra vires* doctrine still applies — with devastating effects.
22. *Rover International v Cannon Film Sales (No 3)* [1989] 1 WLR 912.

Authority may be either 'actual' or 'apparent'. Actual authority is a matter of agreement between the principal and the agent. It may be stated in an express agreement, or it may be implied by conduct or the nature of the agent's appointment, for example, if he is appointed as the principal's solicitor. It does not depend on the other party's knowledge of its existence or scope, although an agent who did not disclose he was acting as agent might find himself bound.

Apparent authority, on the other hand, is conferred by the representation of the principal to the other party either by words or conduct. It cannot be conferred by the agent's own representations. The other party is entitled to assume that an agent has such authority as he appears to have or would normally have, whether or not the principal has in fact granted such authority. The apparent authority can be limited if the principal advises the other party of the extent of the agent's actual authority.

Apparent authority may also be conferred by statute. A partner has unlimited authority to act as agent for the partnership.[23] A director has unlimited authority to bind a limited company in favour of a party dealing in good faith.[24]

Actual authority and apparent authority will often coincide, but this is not essential. Actual authority may also be conferred retrospectively by 'ratification' by the principal. If the agent has, without prior authority, held himself out as entering into a contract on the principal's behalf, the principal may ratify the contract, in which case it is considered as valid from the start.

An agent will generally not be liable to the other party in connection with contracts entered into on behalf of his principal so long as he makes clear that he had done so on behalf of his principal and does not exceed his actual or apparent authority. If he fails to disclose that he is acting on behalf of a principal (the 'undisclosed principal' principle), and he exceeds his actual authority he may be liable to the other party in damages for any loss suffered, unless the principal ratifies the agreement. If an agent represents that he has greater authority than he actually or apparently possesses, he may be liable to the other party for breach of warranty of authority; this arises by virtue of an implied collateral contract between the agent and the other party. An agent will also owe duties to his principal under the contract of agency or, possibly, in tort.

It is thus of great importance that an engineer, architect or quantity surveyor inviting or accepting tenders or ordering work should state clearly that he does so as agent for the employer unless he intends to contract himself as principal. He should also confirm the extent of his authority with the employer. This is particularly so in the case of site investigation or aerial survey, where the contractor might reasonably assume the A/E was contracting directly, or letters of intent, where it may be unclear whether the employer has authorized work to be started.

An agent may also be appointed to act on behalf of a party during the performance of a contract, with authority to bind his principal by communications given or received. Thus, the agent appointed by the contractor under the standard forms of contract binds the contractor by his words and actions. The architect, engineer or quantity surveyor appointed under the contract between the employer and contractor acts as the agent of the employer in giving and receiving notices and certain other functions. The authority in this case is apparent rather than actual; since it derives from the representations made in the contract between employer and contractor, it does not depend on the Conditions of Engagement between the A/E/QS and the employer.

Other agency functions of the A/E/QS include ordering variations and agreeing (as distinct from fixing) new rates for varied work, but the position is confused in some standard forms

---

23. Partnership Act 1890 s5.
24. Companies Act 1985 s35.

of contract by arbitration provisions allowing the employer to dispute the decisions, instructions, directions, certificates or valuations of the A/E/QS; this is inconsistent with the concept of agency.

INTENTION TO CREATE LEGAL RELATIONS

The first essential requirement for a binding contract is 'intention to create legal relations'. For example, social arrangements are not legally enforceable. At a commercial level, the operation of this rule can be observed in an offer or acceptance made 'subject to contract'. It is established that the phrase 'subject to contract', contained in an otherwise valid offer or acceptance, deprives an agreement of legal effect by negating intention to create legal relations. Other phrases are used under the popular impression that they achieve the same result, but the impression is incorrect. Thus in *Edwards v Skyways*[25] it was held that the words '*ex gratia*' do not carry a necessary or even a probable legal implication that the agreement is to be without legal effect.

The heading 'Letter of Intent' may be sufficient to avoid complete acceptance of a tender, but it does not necessarily negate intent to create legal relations. The effect of a letter of intent depends on the wording of the letter rather than its heading.

Another recent creation is the 'Letter of comfort'. In *Kleinwort Benson v Malaysia Mining Corp*,[26] Hirst J held that a 'letter of comfort' provided by the Malaysia Mining Corp in respect of its trading subsidiary manifested an intention to create legal relations. The Court of Appeal agreed that there was a presumption of intention to create legal relations in commercial relationships, but reversed the decision on the facts.

CONSIDERATION

A promise is only binding in law if it is given in return for 'good consideration' or the contract is made under seal or executed as a deed.[27] Where the contract is under seal or executed as a deed, no consideration is necessary.

Consideration has been defined as 'an act or forbearance of one party; or the promise thereof'.[28] It commonly comprises a payment of money or a promise to pay money, but it can comprise some other benefit to the person giving the original promise or a detriment suffered by the person to whom the promise was given.

Extrinsic evidence (i.e. not expressed in the agreement itself) is admissible to prove consideration.[29]

The law is not concerned with the sufficiency of consideration. The rule cannot be used to escape from a contract merely because the bargain is commercially improvident — for example, the term 'a peppercorn rent' derives from the proposition that a peppercorn may be accepted as good consideration. The impact of the requirement of consideration is principally to be found in two further rules that:

1. Past consideration is no consideration.
2. Discharge of an existing contractual obligation to the promisor is no consideration for a fresh promise.

Past consideration

The meaning of the first rule is illustrated by *Roscorla v Thomas*,[30] which concerned the sale of a horse. After the sale had been concluded, the vendor gave a guarantee that the

---

25. *Edwards v Skyways Ltd* [1964] 1 WLR 349.
26. *Kleinwort Benson v Malaysia Mining Corp* [1988] 1 WLR 799; [1989] 1 WLR 379.
27. The use of the phrase 'under seal' is replaced by 'by deed' or 'executed as a deed' for contracts made after 1989, following the Law of Property (Miscellaneous Provisions) Act 1989 and the Companies Act 1985 s36A, inserted by the Companies Act 1989 s130.
28. Per Sir Frederick Pollock, adopted by the House of Lords in *Dunlop v Selfridge* [1915] AC 847.
29. *Pao On v Lau Yiu* [1980] AC 614.
30. *Roscorla v Thomas* [1842] 3 QB 234.

horse was 'free from vice'. The purchaser soon discovered that the horse was not free from vice, but he was unable to recover under the guarantee. The guarantee was a promise which did not form part of the original contract. It was not supported by the original consideration, i.e. the price paid, and there was no fresh consideration.

The second rule means that agreements to accept part payment,[31] or waive entitlement to interest on late payment are not binding,[32] nor are agreements to pay extra money binding[33] unless there is fresh consideration.

Recent cases indicate a greater willingness to infer fresh consideration from fairly minor acts, for example, the adjustment of a performance bond,[34] or forbearance from pressing for a variation order,[35] or even pragmatic commercial benefit as in *Williams v Roffey Bros & Nicholls*.[36]

Performance of an outstanding contractual duty to a third party is regarded as sufficient consideration for a promise by a new party.[37]

The rules do not affect agreements to settle unliquidated claims (i.e. where the amount is not fixed); such agreements are binding.[38] Also if work is carried out at the request of the eventual promisor with the expectation by both parties that it will be paid for, agreement on the amount of payment after the work is completed will be a valid promise.[39]

AGREEMENT

The final essential requirement for a valid contract is agreement. There must be agreement on all material points and the agreement must be sufficiently certain. As stated by Cheshire & Fifoot:[40] 'Agreement is not a mental state but an act and, as an act, is a matter of inference from conduct. The parties are to be judged, not by what is in their minds, but by what they have said or written or done'.

Where agreement is concluded after work is started, the contract refers back to the commencement of the work.[41]

Offer and acceptance

Agreement is normally analysed in terms of 'offer and acceptance', although it may equally emerge from a course of correspondence or negotiation. There are two classes of contract. The first class of contracts requires either acceptance of an offer to be communicated to the offeror or agreement to emerge in negotiation. In legal terminology, these are classified as 'bilateral' or 'synallagmatic' contracts. The second class does not require communication of acceptance. Such contracts are variously termed 'option', 'unilateral' or 'if' contracts, where the offer may be accepted merely by doing the act required.

The most famous example of an 'if' contract concerned an advertisement for the sale of 'carbolic smoke balls' guaranteed to prevent influenza. The advertisement promised £100 to anyone who contracted influenza after purchasing one of the balls and using it in accordance with the instructions. A lady purchased and used one of the balls but contracted influenza. She sued for the £100. The manufacturers said there was no contract, but it was held[42] that the offer constituted an offer capable of acceptance merely by following its terms. It did not require communication of the acceptance to the offeror.

---

31. *D & C Builders v Rees* [1966] 2 QB 617.
32. *Foakes v Beer* [1884] 9 App Cas 605.
33. *Stilk v Myrick* [1809] 2 Camp 317.
34. *North Ocean Shipping v Hyundai* [1979] QB 705.
35. *Comyn Ching v Oriental Tubes* [1979] 17 BLR 47.
36. *Williams v Roffey Bros & Nicholls (Contractors) Ltd* [1991] 1 QB 1.
37. *New Zealand Shipping Co v A M Satterthwaite* [1975] AC 154.
38. *Wilkinson v Byers* [1834] 1 A & E 106.
39. *re Casey's Patents, Stewart v Casey* [1892] 1 Ch 104.
40. Cheshire G C, Fifoot G H S & Furmston M P, *Law of Contract* 12th edn, p 28, Butterworth & Co., London.
41. *Trollope & Colls v Atomic Power Constructions* [1963] 1 WLR 333.
42. *Carlill v Carbolic Smoke Ball Co* [1893] 1 QB 256.

In construction, we try to establish synallagmatic contracts, with clear offer and acceptance, by the system of tenders, on the basis that a tender is an offer which is open to acceptance. Two recent cases illustrate, however, that caution should be exercised in inviting and dealing with tenders to avoid unintended obligations arising. In *Harvela Investments v Royal Trust Co of Canada*,[43] the House of Lords held that vendors, by inviting sealed offers for the purchase of shares without reservation, had assumed a binding obligation to enter into a binding contract with the tenderer submitting the highest fixed price tender. In *Blackpool & Fylde Aero Club v Blackpool BC*,[44] the local authority, inviting tenders for the operation of pleasure flights from Blackpool Airport, had included a clause in the invitation of tenders, 'The Council do not bind themselves to accept all or any part of any tender'. The council refused to consider the lowest tender in the mistaken belief that it had been submitted after the closing time for return of tenders. The Court of Appeal held that, notwithstanding the reservation, the invitation to tender gave rise to a binding obligation to give proper consideration to tenders which conformed with the conditions of tender, and the local authority was accordingly liable to the Aero Club in damages.

Offers

An offer, in order to be capable of acceptance, must indicate an intention to be bound. An offer must be distinguished from a mere 'invitation to treat', which cannot immediately be accepted. For example, most advertisements would be held to be mere invitations to treat, as would the prices marked on goods on display.[45] Even a statement of a price in reply to an enquiry does not necessarily constitute an offer.[46] In *Gibson v Manchester CC*[47] it was held that a letter from a local authority to tenants regarding the proposed sale of a council house was 'not an offer to sell but an invitation of a formal offer from the tenant'.

Covering letters

Not infrequently (particularly in engineering work) some point may be made in a covering letter to a tender concerning some basic matter about the method or other important consideration affecting the execution of the work or time on which the Tender (as submitted on a pro-forma Tender Form) has been based. Such letter will be of no effect unless it is referred to on the Tender Form, and if the tender were to be accepted without specific reference to it, then it would form no part of the contract — with possible dire results.

Revocation

An offer may generally be revoked by the offeror at any time before it is accepted. The rule applies even though the offeror has promised to keep the offer open for a certain time.[48] If, however, the promise to hold the offer open was supported by consideration or was made under seal, that promise would itself be binding as a contract, and the offeror would be liable in damages for withdrawal of the offer — normally, the extent of the liability would be the difference between the withdrawn offer and the next lowest tender. That approach is rarely used. Where it is considered important to ensure tenders are not withdrawn before the expiry of the tender validity period, promises to keep tenders open are usually required to be supported by 'bid-bonds'. Withdrawal of the offer then leads to forfeiture of the bond.

Revocation must generally be communicated to the offeree. Revocation is effective when it reaches the offeree not, as with an acceptance, when it is put in the post. An offer may also cease to exist by lapse of time, either by express stipulation or if it is a necessary inference to be drawn from particular facts.[49] It is not sufficient for the offeror just to act inconsistently with the offer (e.g. selling goods to another person) but the offer will lapse

43. *Harvela Investments Ltd v Royal Trust Co of Canada* [1986] AC 207.
44. *Blackpool & Fylde Aero Club v Blackpool Borough Council* [1990] 1 WLR 1195.
45. *Pharmaceutical Society v Boots Chemist* [1953] 1 QB 401.
46. *Harvey v Facey* [1893] AC 552.
47. *Gibson v Manchester CC* [1979] 1 WLR 294.
48. *Routledge v Grant* [1828] 4 Bing 653.
49. *Ramsgate Victoria Hotel Co v Montefiore* [1866] LR 1 Ex 109.

if the offeree has learnt of the inconsistent act through a third party before attempting to accept.[50]

Acceptance

For acceptance of an offer to lead to a binding contract, the offer must be open for acceptance and the offeree must unreservedly assent to the exact terms proposed by the offeror. If an offer contains alternative offers, the acceptance must state which offer is accepted; otherwise it is of no effect.[51] To be effective, acceptance must be communicated to the offeror, unless there is a waiver of acceptance as in the case of an 'if' contract. Acceptance can also be effected by conduct,[52] but not by mere silence and inaction.[53] Any stipulation as to method of communication must be observed.

Effective acceptance

There are special rules as to when and where acceptance is effective, according to the means of communication adopted. Acceptance by post is effective immediately the letter is put in the post in the normal course.[54] A telex acceptance takes effect when and where it appears on the offeror's machine, at least, if during normal office hours.[55] A telephone acceptance is effective when and where it is heard by the offeror.[56] These rules are of particular importance in two respects. Firstly, where an offer is revoked, the rules determine whether the acceptance took effect before or after the offer was revoked. For example, where acceptance of a tender was posted before revocation of the tender reached the offeree, there would be a binding contract. Secondly, a contract is considered to be made where acceptance takes effect: this can determine the 'proper law' of the contract, in the absence of any express stipulation. For example, if acceptance is effective in Vienna, the contract might[57] (according to English law) be subject to Austrian law and the English courts would apply Austrian law in dealing with any litigation arising out of the contract.

Counter-offers

Qualified acceptances, which introduce new terms or are not in the same terms as the tender or are otherwise qualified in any way, are not acceptances at all but are 'counter-offers'. A counter-offer kills off the original offer. A contract would arise should the tenderer accept this counter-offer, either in writing or by conduct, but as a counter-offer 'kills off' the original tender, the employer could not subsequently accept the original tender (should the contractor decline to accept the counter-offer) without the express agreement of the contractor.

Qualified acceptances are to be deprecated as unnecessary, serving no really useful purpose and potentially dangerous. The conduct of the parties may be taken to indicate that a contract exists, but what its terms are may not be easy to establish. It will be necessary to trace backwards each step in the negotiations to see just what offer or counter-offer or counter-counter-offer has been tacitly accepted by one party or the other by their subsequent conduct. But a mere request for further information is not a counter-offer.[58]

Acceptance subject to condition

An acceptance which is made 'subject' to anything does not give rise immediately to a contract, though this may eventuate when the matter to which it is subject occurs. It may not be open to either party to withdraw after the conditional acceptance. For example, if an acceptance is made 'subject to planning permission being received', then a contract would arise on the receipt of planning permission. Similarly with an acceptance subject to 'financial

---

50. *Dickinson v Dodds* [1876] 2 ChD 463.
51. *Peter Lind v Mersey Docks and Harbour Board* [1972] 2 Lloyd's Rep 234.
52. *Brogden v Metropolitan Railway Co* [1877] 2 App Cas 666.
53. *Felthouse v Bindley* [1862] 11 CB 869; *The 'Leonidas'* [1985] 1 WLR 925.
54. *Adams v Lindsell* [1818] 1 B & Ald 681.
55. *Brinkibon v Stalag Stahl* [1983] 2 AC 34.
56. *Gill & Duffus Landauer Ltd v London Export Corp* [1982] 2 Lloyd's Rep 627.
57. The place where the contract is made is only one factor in determining the proper law.
58. *Stevenson Jacques & Co v McLean* [1880] 5 QBD 346; *Gibson v Manchester CC* [1979] 1 WLR 294.

approval from the Ministry . . .'. This practice can give rise to problems, and possibly claims, and is therefore to be avoided.

CERTAINTY

The law also requires that agreement must be sufficiently certain. The courts will not make an agreement for the parties. On the other hand, the courts will try to give meaning to a contract if they find the parties intended to be bound. Thus, in *Hillas v Arcos*,[59] an agreement for the supply of softwood goods 'of fair specification' with prices fixed by reference to the seller's current schedule of prices was held sufficiently certain. But in *Scammell v Ouston*,[60] an order for a van with the price to be paid 'on hire purchase terms over a period of 2 years' was held to be so obscure and so incapable of any definite or precise meaning that the court was unable to attribute to the parties any particular intention; therefore the contract was invalid. In particular, a 'mere agreement to agree' is not binding. As stated by Maugham J in *Foley v Classique Coaches*:[61]

> 'It is indisputable that unless all the material terms of the contract are agreed, there is no binding obligation. An agreement to agree in the future is not a contract; nor is there a contract if a material term is neither settled nor implied by law and the document contains no machinery for ascertaining it.'

FORMALITIES

Except for certain types of contract where there are specific statutory requirements, it is not necessary for a contract to be in writing. An oral contract is generally valid, although difficulties may arise in proving its terms. Some relevant exceptions are:

1. Contracts for the sale or other disposition of land or any interest in land — the Law of Property Act 1925 s40 requires a memorandum or note in writing, signed by the party or a lawfully authorized representative. The section has been applied to contracts for extraction of gravel, and rights to materials arising from demolition of buildings.

2. Arbitration agreements — if it is to come within the Arbitration Acts, the agreement must be in writing.[62]

3. Contracts of guarantee or suretyship require a memorandum or note in writing signed by the party to be charged or a lawfully authorized representative.[63] The requirement does not apply to contracts of indemnity.

An invitation to tender or the Form of Contract may stipulate specific formalities, for example that the acceptance should be in writing or that the contract should depend on the execution of a formal Agreement. The effect of such a stipulation depends 'whether the execution of a further contract is a condition or a term of the bargain or whether it is a mere expression of the desire of the parties as to the manner in which the transaction already agreed to will in fact go through'.[64] The tendency is to construe such a stipulation as a mere expression of the desire of the parties, in which case the agreement is a binding contract and the reference to a more formal document may be ignored. On the other hand, in *Okura v Navara Shipping Corp*,[65] it was held that an agreement that the terms were 'to be incorporated in a memorandum of agreement in a mutually acceptable manner' meant that there was no concluded contract until this was done.

Such stipulations may be subject to the equitable doctrine of part performance, which is to the effect that where one party has been allowed by the other to act to his detriment

59. *Hillas v Arcos* [1932] 147 LT 503.
60. *Scammell v Ouston* [1941] AC 251.
61. *Foley v Classique Coaches* [1934] 2 KB 1 at p 13.
62. Arbitration Act 1950 s32.
63. Statute of Frauds 1677 s4.
64. *Von Hatzfeldt-Wildenburg v Alexander* [1912] 1 Ch 284.
65. *Okura & Co Ltd v Navara Shipping Corp SA* [1982] 2 Lloyd's Rep 573.

in reliance on the contract, the other party will not be allowed to set up the requirement of writing to deny the contract.

Simple contracts

A written contract may consist of an exchange of offer and acceptance in writing, or it may be a formal Agreement comprising a single document or collection of documents embodying the agreement of the parties and executed by all the parties. It is not uncommon for a contract to be established first by offer and acceptance, to be superseded later by a formal Agreement. For example the ICE Tender Form says 'Unless and until a formal Agreement is prepared and executed, this tender, together with your written acceptance thereof, shall constitute a binding contract between us'.

The Limitation Act 1980 distinguishes between 'simple contracts' and 'specialties'. A specialty is a contract under seal or executed as a deed. The effect of the contract being executed as a deed is that the limitation period is extended from the basic 6 years for a simple contract, to 12 years for a specialty.[66] A contract formed by exchange of offer and acceptance would be a simple contract. A formal contract or Agreement may be executed under hand, i.e. by the signatures of the parties or their authorized representatives, as a simple contract, or it may be executed under deed. The ICE Tender Form pro forma indicates the formal Agreement as being under seal or by deed, with the corollary that the limitation period of 12 years instead of 6 will apply.

Formal agreements

By the completion of a formal agreement, the original tender, any intervening correspondence and the eventual acceptance are superseded. The rule is that where the agreement of the parties has been reduced to a formal agreement and the document containing the agreement has been signed by one or both of them, the party signing will be bound by the terms of the formal agreement, whether or not he has read them and whether or not he is ignorant of their precise legal effect.[67]

It is therefore essential that all documents contained in the original simple contract are incorporated in the Agreement. This includes any correspondence forming part of the Tender and any correspondence passing between Tender and Acceptance. Paragraph 2 of the ICE Agreement pro forma does not make express provision for these, so they must be added if they occur. Alternatively, specific amendments to the original contract documents can be agreed to embody the outcome of the post-tender correspondence. This can produce a cleaner arrangement, less susceptible to dispute, and it is recommended.

The JCT Form provides only for a formal Agreement though not necessarily under seal or by deed. Nevertheless, should the employer 'accept' a tender by letter as a preliminary to executing a formal contract, then at that stage there will be a contract. An exception to this would be the case where the acceptance said 'subject to contract'. It is recommended that this course should not be adopted, particularly if there is any suggestion of 'requesting' or 'allowing' the contractor to start work. Should the contractor make a start and access to the site is not denied him then it may well be that despite the proviso a contract may have come into being by the conduct of the parties. It is much better that all matters should be cleared, including queries about the tender, finance (by the employer) and availability of the site before attempting to accept, and then to accept in clean and simple terms, following up with a formal contract if required. The remarks in connection with the ICE Form concerning correspondence apply here also.

GC/Wks 1 is intended to be used as a simple contract, no provision being made for completing an Agreement.

LETTERS OF INTENT

A 'letter of intent' per se is not necessarily an acceptance. It can become dangerous if taken in any way beyond indicating an intention.

66. Limitation Act 1980 s5, s8(1).
67. *L'Estrange v Graucob* [1934] 2 KB 394.

Any 'suggestion' or 'request' to start work or place orders etc. should be viewed with suspicion; even an 'instruction' to do some such should not be acted upon unless accompanied by some undertaking as to payment. This would thus set up a 'mini-contract' which would be absorbed into the main contract if and when it comes into existence, or stand on its own feet if not.

The use of qualified acceptances and of letters of intent can lead to problems of whether or not there is a binding contract, particularly when these are considered in the light of the subsequent conduct of the parties — placing orders, arranging sub-contracts, providing plant, starting work on site by the contractor or permitting access to or possession of site, supplying drawings or other information or making payment by the employer.

Entitlement to payment

Needless to say, the wisdom or prudence of clarifying the contractual position before work is started or materials are ordered will often be disregarded, sometimes deliberately. Where a full contract does not come into existence and the work is aborted, the question of entitlement to payment or compensation arises. The recent tendency of the courts has been to hold that the contractor in such circumstances is entitled to payment for work clearly instructed or required. This would not extend, however, to steps undertaken by the contractor of his own initiative merely in anticipation of the full contract.

Entitlement to payment has been based variously on quasi-contract[68] and implied contracts.[69] Since the enactment of the Supply of Goods & Services Act 1982, the implied contract solution is to be preferred. Section 15 of the Act provides that where the consideration for a service is not determined by the contract, there is an implied term that the party contracting with the supplier will pay a reasonable charge. The same result would be reached so far as entitlement to payment is concerned through quasi-contract, but the Supply of Goods & Services Act also provides other implied terms, including a term that the supplier will carry out the service with reasonable care and skill. Quasi-contract does not deal with those other aspects.

CASE 4.1 CLAIM ARISING OUT OF LETTER OF INTENT

Pertinent particulars of contract

Tender dated 12 June 1978 totalling £2,496,181 for a new oiling jetty at . . . .
. . . . Conditions of Contract ICE 5 (though this is not material to the matter of the claim).

Correspondence had passed between the engineer and the tenderer following receipt of the tender, from which it had become apparent that the steel piles would require at least 9 months for delivery. All other matters had been resolved but the employer was not in a position to accept pending negotiation of terms with the prospective users. The engineer was therefore instructed to send a letter of intent in the following terms:

Letter of intent

Engineer to Contractor   *7 August 1978*

My clients have instructed me to inform you that as all matters concerning your tender have been satisfactorily resolved, it is their intention to accept your tender dated 12 June 1978 for work as set out in the contract documents together with the subsequent correspondence listed in the Appendix to this letter.

As you are aware, completion is required in $2\frac{1}{2}$ years but as indicated in

---

68. *British Steel Corporation v Cleveland Bridge Engineering* [1984] 1 All ER 504.
69. In *Turriff Construction v Regalia Knitting Mills* [1971] 9 BLR 20, a letter of intent was held to be a collateral contract to pay for preliminary work. See also *OTM Ltd v Hydranautics* [1981] 2 Lloyd's Rep 211; *William Smithett & Cape (Sugar) Ltd v Bangladesh Sugar & Food Industries Corp* [1986] 1 Lloyd's Rep 375; *Craven-Ellis v Cannons Ltd* [1936] 2 KB 403; *William Lacey (Hounslow) Ltd v Davis* [1957] 1 WLR 932, discussed by Richard Winward in 'Options, letters of intent and agreements to agree: current developments'. In *Legal Obligations in Construction*. Centre of Construction Law and Management, King's College, London, 1992.

your letter dated 22 June 1978 delivery of the steel piles will require at least 9 months. As it may well be another 6–8 weeks from now before a formal contract can be signed it is suggested that you might wish to place an order for the steel piles so as to be able to take advantage of the summer season of 1979. A list of the pile lengths is enclosed.

Should you wish to set up any part of your site organization such as levelling and preparing working area, erecting offices, stores etc, the site can be made available to you at any time.

Contractor to Engineer   11 August 1978

Thank you for your letter of 7 August 1978. We are very pleased to hear that your clients intend to accept our tender.

We understand that the supply position of the piles is further deteriorating and we have therefore taken immediate steps to place an order for them.

We have some hutting just coming free from another job which we intend to use in this contract, so we shall be glad to take advantage of your suggestion that we might start some preliminary work in the working area.

Two weeks later   An exchange of letters between contractor and supplier set up a firm contract for the supply and delivery of piles.

Three weeks later still   The contractor dispatches by sea hutting sections and materials for foundations and other preparatory work, some light excavating plant and a small gang of men to undertake erection.

Twelve weeks after letter of intent

Engineer to Contractor   10 November 1978

The delay in dealing with this matter of a contract for the construction of a jetty at . . . . is very much regretted. I am, however, now instructed by my clients to inform you that they have been unable to complete satisfactory negotiations with the prospective users of this jetty. They have therefore reluctantly come to the conclusion that they cannot proceed with this project.

It is understood that you have some temporary huts on site. I should be glad if you would arrange to remove these as soon as possible and restore the site to its original condition.

Contractor to Engineer   13 November 1978

We have received your letter of 10 November 1978 and regret to hear that this project is not to proceed.

We will arrange for the removal of the huts and the restoring of the site as you request. We will also take steps to cancel the order for the steel piles.

As soon as we know the cancellation charges for the steel piles and have completed work at site we will send you our account for this abortive work.

Engineer to Contractor   22 November 1978

I am in receipt of your letter of 13 November 1978 and have referred the

> *matter to my clients. They note with considerable concern your proposal to render an account for abortive work and for cancellation charges in connection with the piles and instruct me to point out that my letter to you of 7 August 1978 was a letter of intent only and not a firm acceptance.*
>
> *They are therefore under no contractual obligation to you in this matter. They also request that you expedite removal of your huts from the site as the land is to be sold.*

If the contractor did not know before, he knows now that a letter of intent is perhaps better than a letter of no intent, but no more than that. It is not clear from this correspondence whether the engineer has so advised his clients or whether he himself is not clear as to the situation. Certainly he has carefully phrased all his letters as being instructions from his client, but he should have advised them in quite strong terms that this sort of action is to be deprecated.

The contractor evidently decides he has nothing to lose in making a further attempt.

Contractor to Engineer   *25 November 1978*

> *We note the contents of your letter of 22 November 1978 with concern and astonishment. Your letter of intent instructed us to place an order for the piles and actually gave a list of lengths for ordering. You also gave permission for setting up huts and levelling and preparing a working area.*
>
> *We have been in touch with the pile suppliers and they inform us that they would be prepared to cancel our contract with them on payment of a cancellation charge of £7,295. Our costs in putting huts on site and the preparatory work there up to 22 November amounted to £4,286 plus hire charges for the huts of £1,200 from our subsidiary company, to which we must add our overheads and profit at 30 per cent. We estimate the cost of dismantling and removing our huts and restoring the site will cost another £2,500.*
>
> *We should be glad to hear from you as soon as possible that your clients will accept these costs.*

There is little that one can criticize about the contractor's claim except perhaps part of his charge for the huts and the 30 per cent overheads on this item. They were coming free from another job and would probably have been put into store anyway until this job materialized.

Engineer to Contractor   *8 December 1978*

> *I am in receipt of your letter of 25 November 1978 and again have referred the matter to my principals. They wish me to point out that the placing of an order for steel piles was only a suggestion and not, as you state, an instruction. The temporary use of the site was permissive only and you were not formally given possession. They are not prepared to accept any part of the costs claimed by you.*

Points of principle involved

What can the contractor do? Ideally, where a contractor is required to do some work or to enter into some liability prior to the principal contract being settled, the letter of intent ought to contain a clearly defined offer, which it would be open to the contractor to accept, by either words or conduct. This would set up a mini-contract, which would be absorbed into the principal contract if and when it eventuated.[70] Should the principal contract not

---

70. *Trollope & Colls v Atomic Power Constructions* [1963] 1 WLR 333.

proceed, then the mini-contract would remain in its own right and any rights and obligations would be settled accordingly.

Where the letter of intent is unclear, the courts may still find some entitlement to compensation for work actually carried out following a request or instruction in a letter of intent. This may be either on the basis of an implied contract or quasi-contract. In this case, the letters from the Engineer have been worded to avoid any use of the words 'instruction' or 'request', but talk only of 'suggestion'. Nevertheless, the courts would tend to look at the substance of the transaction, in particular whether the steps suggested were for the benefit of the employer or the contractor, and how specific the suggestion was. The basis of quasi-contractual entitlement is to prevent unjust enrichment; it amounts to reasonable payment where work is done by one party at the request of another, in the absence of a contract but with the common understanding that it would be paid for. There must be a request; work done by a prospective contractor on his own initiative would not create a legal obligation.

CASE 4.2 CLAIM BASED ON DEFECT IN FORMAL AGREEMENT

Pertinent particulars of contract

Contract for the construction of an oiling jetty in Singapore. The documents comprised:

Tender dated 3 June 1980 (note that the wording of the *pro forma* at page 26 of FIDIC had been amended to read '. . . at the rates and prices quoted in the Bill of Quantities' instead of 'for the sum of';

Conditions of Contract: International (FIDIC) third edition;

Bill of Quantities, which included an item in the Preamble reading as follows:
'Steel reinforcement to be supplied by the employer.
The prices for fixing steel reinforcement supplied by the employer shall include for taking delivery from store, cleaning, cutting, bending and fixing.'

Background to claim

There were three items in Bill No 5 reading as follows:

Item 37	Fixing steel reinforcement 16 mm diam supplied by the Employer	42.8 tonnes
Item 38	Ditto 20 mm diam and ditto	27.5 tonnes
Item 39	Ditto 25 mm and ditto	36.3 tonnes

The material was available when the Bill was prepared but there was a substantial delay before tenders were invited. In fact it was not until tenders were received that it was found that a large part of this steel reinforcement had been used on other works and was no longer available. The following correspondence took place:

Engineer to Tenderer   *11 June 1980*

   With reference to your tender dated 13 June 1980, I regret to inform you that the steel reinforcement for Items 37, 38 and 39 of Bill No. 5 is no longer available. Will you therefore please quote your prices for supplying this material, the item coverage being similar to that for other items in the Bill where you are supplying reinforcement.

Tenderer to Engineer   *19 June 1980*

   With reference to your letter of 11 June, we confirm that we are able to supply the necessary reinforcement and our prices in substitution for those quoted in Bill No 5 are as follows:

Item 37 16 mm   per tonne $. . . . .
Item 38 20 mm   per tonne $. . . . .
Item 39 25 mm   per tonne $. . . . .

This will increase our tender by the sum of $. . . . .

Whether or not such a letter was (or should have been) sent to other tenderers as well is a separate issue and does not affect the problem here. In view of the wording of the tender form, the tenderer was ill-advised to refer to 'an increase in his tender'. Nothing should be introduced which is likely to give rise to ambiguity as to whether the contract is to be for a lump sum or is for measure and value.

The tender was otherwise satisfactory and was recommended to the employer for acceptance, which he did in the following terms:

Employer to Contractor   *30 June 1980*

I have to inform you that your tender dated 13 June 1980 in conjunction with the engineer's letter of 11 June and your letter of 19 June is accepted.

In accordance with Clause 9 of the Conditions you are required to execute a formal contract. This will be forwarded to you in a few days.

Clause 9 reads:

'The contractor shall when called upon to do so enter into and execute a Contract Agreement to be prepared and completed at the cost of the Employer, in the form annexed with such modification as may be necessary'.

There is no doubt that at this point there is a valid contract under which the contractor has undertaken to supply the reinforcement. Para 5 of the Tender says 'Unless and until a formal Agreement is prepared and executed, this Tender, together with your written acceptance thereof, shall constitute a binding contract between us.' In preparing the formal Agreement, however, reference to the letter of acceptance was omitted and there was no separate reference to the correspondence covering the matter, nor was the B/Q formally amended. The contractor did not notice the omission and executed the Agreement under seal.

The administration of the contract was handed over to other staff of the employer, and the contractor's agent was new to the firm. About three months after the work had started the agent wrote to the resident engineer:

Agent to Resident Engineer   *20 October 1980*

With reference to items 37, 38 and 39 of Bill No 5, will you please let us know when and where we can collect the steel reinforcement? We understand from your store staff that no such steel is available.

Resident Engineer to Agent   *23 October 1980*

With reference to your letter of 20 October, your attention is drawn to the engineer's letter of 11 June and your firm's reply of 19 June, in which you undertook to supply the steel in question.

Agent to Resident Engineer   *27 October 1980*

In reply to your letter of 23 October, I have no copies of the letters you quote and they were not included in the contract documents. As they were not referred to in the Agreement I had no reason to know of their existence.

I have, however, checked with my Head Office and they have sent me copies of the letters you refer to but they point out that as they were not included in the Agreement, they assumed that your people had reverted to the original position and were after all supplying the steel.

As the letters had been referred to in the acceptance and the formal Agreement followed a few days later without any further correspondence about this steel, it is a little difficult to believe that the contractor really thought the employer had changed his mind; at the very least he should have queried it. Obviously the matter has slipped on both sides but the question now is what is the true contractual position? Here we have a contract under seal, which supersedes the previous documentation and discussions.[71] Possibly there is a 'mistake' which could be rectified by the courts or arbitration,[72] but the matter could involve considerable argument (and therefore expense) in this situation, and success would not be reliable. The lapse of time does not of itself bar rectification, but where one of the parties has acted upon the erroneous document in good faith and cannot be restored to its former position, rectification would not be granted without adjustment. If agreement can be reached on the matter, recourse to court or arbitrator will be avoided. Financially it makes no difference because if the contractor supplies the steel he gets paid for doing so. But what about the delay arising from the steel having not yet been ordered?

Resident Engineer to Agent   *31 October 1980*

With reference to your letter of 27 October, I am advised that the correspondence referred to in my letter of 23 October was incorporated in the acceptance and the responsibility for supplying the steel is thus yours.

The fact is that we have no steel to supply, so that there is no alternative but for you to arrange supply.

The responsibility for the defect in the Agreement is being 'dodged' here. Clearly the matter is getting rather involved to be dealt with at Agent/RE level and it would seem that they both passed it to 'higher authority', as the next letter we find is from the contractor's Head Office.

Contractor to Engineer   *8 November 1980*

We refer to correspondence between our agent and your RE between 20 and 31 October (copies attached). We agree the matter is clear up to the date of acceptance but the fact that the letters of 11 and 19 June were not included in the formal Agreement and that the letter of acceptance was not referred to creates an entirely different situation.

We note that there is in fact no steel available to be supplied to us so, in accordance with our telephone discussion, we confirm we have now placed orders for supply.

The best time for delivery we can get is two months, plus a further month for shipment and delivery to Singapore. To obtain this we have had to pay an extra $100.00 per tonne in excess of the prices on which our quotation of 19 June was based (a total of $10,660 on the quantities in question). We are, however, more concerned about the delay which will

---

71. *L'Estrange v Graucob* [1934] 2 KB 394; *Jacobs v Batavia & General Plantations Trust* [1924] 1 Ch 287.
72. An arbitrator may have jurisdiction to rectify the contract depending on the words of the arbitration clause: *Ashville Investments Ltd v Elmer Contractors* [1989] QB 488.

inevitably occur. We can do a certain amount of re-organization but there will be at least six weeks' delay and probably some disruption and loss of productivity which altogether will involve about $60,000.

We will let you know in due course what our actual costs are, but in the meantime we must formally notify you of our intention to reclaim such costs.

Of course it should not have happened, but it did. The dates are different and the venue is changed, but the facts are essentially as given here. There is no doubt that both sides are to blame. Both sides will no doubt endeavour to minimize their own responsibility. On the evidence here, however, it seems fairly evenly divided. This is one case where it is probably justified to split the costs 50/50 — a course more often thought to be taken in settling claims than is in fact the case.

Point of principle involved

The tender and its acceptance must reflect the agreement reached between the parties, including any correspondence which has intervened (as was in fact done in this case). The Agreement, if completed, must similarly reflect the complete agreement reached. Neither FIDIC nor ICE give any indication in their Forms of Agreement either that such correspondence may occur or that, if it does, it must be incorporated. Reference to it in the letter of acceptance and the inclusion of that in the Agreement gets it in indirectly. It is better if such matters are dealt with more positively. Alternatively, the effect of such correspondence must be reflected by way of actual amendment of the documents affected (in this case the B/Q).

The employees on each side (RE, QS, agent etc.) must each check the documents to ensure that they have the correct information. It may be arguable that reference to the acceptance is not necessary in the Agreement, if the remaining documents fully cover the obligations of both sides. Be that as it may, if there has been pertinent correspondence it must be included one way or another and inclusion of the acceptance (provided this in fact refers to it) is one way of so doing.

CASE 4.3 CLAIM BASED ON QUALIFIED ACCEPTANCE (COUNTER-OFFER) AND TACIT ACCEPTANCE OF COUNTER-COUNTER-OFFER

Pertinent particulars of contract

Invitation to tender for a building project dated November 1977 required completion within 21 months for a lump-sum on a firm price basis.

Tender dated 11 November 1977 offered to carry out the work for £104,000 but in a time of 24 months and required the inclusion of price fluctuation provisions.

Conditions of Contract: As at invitation — JCT 63/77 Clauses 31A–F deleted; GC/Wks 1 Conditions 11A–F not included.

Tender dated 11 November required these clauses included.

Acceptance

23 November 1977

I have to inform you that your tender dated 11 November 1977 is accepted in the sum of £104,000 less £2,214 in respect of arithmetical errors in extensions and costs in the Bill of Quantities. It is agreed that the time for completion is to be 24 months but your request for price fluctuation provisions to be included is not agreed as there is general agreement in the industry that such clauses should apply only to contracts in excess of two years.

94

> *Further I must point out that some of your Preliminary Items are grossly overpriced. These must be reduced and the excess distributed over the remaining B/Q items.*

> *Possession of the site is hereby given you with effect from 14 days after the date of this letter.*

Whoever wrote this letter is very unwise in attempting to deal with errors in the B/Q in this cavalier fashion. The contract is to be on a lump-sum and in such case *prima facie* the lump-sum of the tender overrides the bill total. Errors in the B/Q should be dealt with by correspondence before acceptance and the contractor offered the choice of adhering to, amending or withdrawing his tender.

Although there was a general agreement in the industry that contracts expected to last two years (later reduced to one year) could be on a firm price basis, this was merely advisory and in no way binding in any individual case. Again, such a matter should be dealt with by correspondence before attempting to 'accept'.

It is not clear whether this 'acceptance' has been written by the architect or a non-professional department of the employer — perhaps the latter as the next letter is addressed to the employer.

Contractor to Employer   *26 November 1977*

> *Thank you for your letter dated 23 November 1977. We regret, however, that we are unable to agree to this contract being on a firm price basis at the price quoted. If the inclusion of price fluctuation clauses cannot be agreed to, we would need to increase our price by £20,000.*

Short and to the point *but* it would have been better to be quite clear as to whether this amounted to a fresh offer.

Architect to Contractor   *3 December 1977*

> *With reference to your letter dated 26 November I have been instructed to inform you that your request to increase your tender by £20,000 is not acceptable. It is therefore intended to revert to your original tender including price fluctuation provisions. I am instructed to inform you that that tender is hereby accepted in the sum of £104,000 less £2,214 in respect of arithmetical errors in the B/Q and subject to a redistribution of the excessive prices for preliminaries referred to in para 2 of my letter dated 23 November 1977 which letter is now cancelled.*

The original acceptance was no acceptance at all but a counter-offer because it introduced terms not in the original tender. This proposition is generally well understood but what may not be so well understood is that a counter-offer 'kills off' the original offer, which is accordingly no longer open for acceptance. This second 'acceptance' is a further counter-offer for the same reason.

As the original 'acceptance' is now cancelled, the position as to possession of site is somewhat equivocal.

Contractor to Architect   *8 December 1977*

> *Thank you for your letter dated 3 December 1977. It is regretted that we cannot agree to proceed with this contract on the basis of your letter. We note the 'errors' in pricing the Bill of Quantities but would point out that*

other items are underpriced which more than offset this reduction. Further, to redistribute the Preliminary Items as you require would involve us in additional costs of finance.

We are, however, prepared to stand by the offer contained in our letter dated 26 November 1977 to execute the work for the sum of £124,000 on a firm price basis.

Had the architect taken up the matter of the errors in the B/Q before his first attempt to accept, the contractor might well have agreed the correction. As to the redistribution of overpriced preliminaries, the architect is right to bring the matter up because leaving things as they are would involve making payments on account with insufficient collateral by way of value received. He is wrong, however, in not taking this to a conclusion and getting agreement on how they are to be redistributed, again before attempting to accept. The contractor is right in saying it will cost him more for additional finance but he makes no effort to meet the architect's point. At least he now makes a fresh definitive offer.

Architect to Contractor   *14 December 1977*

I am instructed to inform you that my client considers there is a binding contract with you and you are accordingly requested to proceed without further delay.

The client may consider there is a binding contract, but there is no indication of how the architect advised him. In any case this latest letter completely begs the question of what contract, 'on what basis?' — at the point of the second 'acceptance' or following the contractor's last letter? Does this latest letter amount to acceptance of that?

After about 3 weeks from the last letter the contractor starts work on the site, variations are issued, interim payments made and the work eventually completed. Both sides seem to have forgotten that the letter giving possession of site was cancelled, raising the query 'From what date does the contract period run?' This might have been important had the employer attempted to recover liquidated damages. In the event, the quantity surveyor produced a final account which may be summarized as follows:

	£	£	£
Contract sum	104,000		
Less errors in B/Q	2,214	101,786	
Add variation of price		14,241	
Variations add	15,078		
omit	12,146	2,932	
PC sums add	41,222		
omit	38,000	3,222	122,181

The contractor disputed this and claimed:

	£	£	£
Contract sum as tender	104,000		
Add as letter dated			
8 December 1977	20,000	124,000	
Variations as valued by QS		2,932	
PC sums ditto		3,222	130,154
		Amount of claim	7,973

Points of principle involved

In situations such as this where there is offer, counter-offer and counter-counter-offer etc., there can easily be doubt as to the point at which a contract comes into being, and hence as to its terms. If there is clear disagreement on terms[73] or a purported acceptance does not specify which of alternative offers is accepted,[74] it may even be found there is no contract and that, instead, the contractor is entitled to a *quantum meruit* for work actually performed. That might well have been a correct solution in this case, but a court would only reach such a solution if it were pleaded. Where both parties choose to put their cases solely on the basis that work has been carried out under a valid contract, a contract will be found. A party might well choose not to deny the existence of a contract, as it could not then rely on any terms of the contract. In any event, a finding of no contract has a number of drawbacks, and the courts usually seek to extract a contract and identify its terms where work has been carried out and it appears that the parties intended to be bound.

On the facts of this case, both the first and second 'acceptance' were in fact counter-offers. By the first the original offer was 'killed off' so it was not open for subsequent acceptance. The contractor's revised offer (if offer it were) was likewise killed off by the second 'acceptance' but was effectively reiterated in the contractor's letter of 8 December. The letter of 14 December from the architect, acting as agent for the employer, gave a request to proceed on the basis of a 'binding contract'. The conduct of the contractor in proceeding with the works would be a tacit acceptance of that position,[75] but the only binding contract that could exist would relate to the offer open for acceptance, i.e. that reiterated in the contractor's letter of 8 December, so the architect's letter of 14 December can only be construed as an acceptance of that offer. On that basis the contractor would be entitled to the amount claimed. Probably the same financial outcome would be reached on a quasi-contractual approach.[76]

The position under the ICE Conditions would be similar except that the 'errors in extension and cast' would become irrelevant upon remeasurement because under those conditions (especially the 5th edition) the contract would be on a measure and value basis and not for a lump sum. Had there been errors in the rates which had been challenged the position might well be different.

Such situations can be avoided by resolving all matters of errors in B/Q, redistribution of money in Preliminary Items, or indeed any other matters requiring to be resolved before a tender is accepted, and then accepting it (original tender as amended or modified by correspondence) in simple terms without introducing any new matter.

It may seem that such situations are so obvious that they cannot have happened in any well regulated office. The fact is that they have and they do, particularly in those organizations where contracts are handled by non-professional people. In some cases they even occur with Local Authorities where a legal department (perhaps more experienced in conveyancing and local bye-laws, etc.) requires that tenders be accepted 'subject to contract' but seeks to avoid the delay so caused (it may take 2 or 3 months before a formal contract is produced for signing or sealing) by including in the acceptance 'permission' to start work or giving possession of site. In such circumstances if the contractor does in fact enter upon the site and start work, and is allowed to do so, then it is probable that despite the proviso in the acceptance there is a 'valid' contract which the Authority could not avoid if it attempted to rely upon that proviso.

---

73. *British Steel Corporation v Cleveland Bridge Engineering* [1984] 1 All ER 504.
74. *Peter Lind v Mersey Docks & Harbour Board* [1972] 2 Lloyd's Rep 234.
75. *Brogden v Metropolitan Railway Co* [1877] 2 App Cas 666; *Butler Machine Tool Co v Ex-cell-O Corp (England) Ltd* [1979] 1 WLR 401.
76. In *British Steel Corporation v Cleveland Bridge Engineering* [1984] 1 All ER 504, the supplier's entitlement was assessed by reference to the quotation submitted. cf *Rover International v Cannon Film Sales (No 3)* [1989] 1 WLR 912 where it was said that the contract did not apply, therefore it could not limit the amount of payment due.

Chapter 5
Claims arising from documentation

GENERALLY

In preparing and examining claims (and in preparing and reviewing contract documents) it is essential to bear in mind that one is concerned with the documents which are incorporated in the contract, what the documents say and what they provide for, not which documents one thinks should have been incorporated, what the documents should have said, or what they should have provided for. This may appear very obvious but it is surprisingly easy to assume that certain documents would or would not be incorporated in the contract, to read into a document what one expects to see or instinctively feels should be.

Documentation should be structured, so far as possible, to make clear, rather than conceal, the requirements and expectations of the employer, the obligations and risks to be undertaken by each party, and the corresponding entitlements to payment or compensation. Generally drawings should be regarded as stating what is required, the specification stating the quality of workmanship and materials, the conditions of contract setting out the obligations of the parties and the allocation of risks between them, and the Bills of Quantities determining the amount to be paid for work performed.

Contract/policy

Care needs to be taken to distinguish between matters of contract and matters of policy. It may be an employer's policy to provide for price fluctuation in contracts lasting more than one year but if in fact the requisite clause is not incorporated, then clearly it will not be operative.

An employer may shun qualified tenders and tenderers should certainly make every effort to avoid qualifications by exploring matters with the A/E in the tender period or making the qualification by way of an alternative tender. Clearly, commercial considerations indicate that action should be taken to get the tendering period extended in order to resolve the problem before submitting a tender but this is not always possible. There may be occasions when a qualification is unavoidable (receipt of vital information from a supplier or sub-contractor only hours before tenders are due). There may be so much money involved that any public authority which dismissed or ignored such a tender (provided it were genuine and bona fide) could be open to criticism of misuse of public funds.

In this and other connections care must be taken not to confuse policy and contract. A contract must be construed solely upon the terms it contains; an employer's policy cannot of itself amend such terms or introduce additional terms.

Intentions of the parties

The concept of a contract is considered to be a *consensus ad idem*, a meeting of minds on the same thing. It is, however, a matter of apparent, rather than actual, intentions. The nature of the agreement is to be found in what the parties actually said or wrote; what they may later claim to have been their intentions is immaterial if this differs from or is not directly reflected in the documents. An A/E/QS should be wary of claims based on allegations of intention and confine his consideration to what the documents express. Thus in *Reardon Smith Line v Yngvar Hansen-Tangen*,[1] Lord Wilberforce stated:

'When one speaks of the intention of the parties to the contract, one is speaking objectively — the parties cannot themselves give direct evidence of what their intention was — and what must be ascertained is what is to be taken as the intention which reasonable people would have had if placed in the situation of the parties'.

Similarly, in *Eyre v Measday*[2] (a medical case involving an ineffective sterilization operation) Slade LJ stated:

'In order to ascertain what was the nature and what were the terms of the contract, this court has to apply an objective rather than a subjective test. The test thus does not depend on what either the plaintiff or the defendant *thought* were the terms of the contract in her or his own mind. It depends on what the court objectively considers that the words used by the respective parties must be reasonably taken to have meant. It would therefore be of no assistance to the defendant to say that he did not intend to enter into a contract which absolutely

---

1. *Reardon-Smith Line v Yngvar Hansen-Tangen* [1976] 1 WLR 989 at p 996.
2. *Eyre v Measday* [1986] 1 All ER 488 at pp 492, 493.

guaranteed the plaintiff's future sterility. It would likewise be of no assistance to the plaintiff to say that she firmly believed that she was being offered a contract of this nature.'

THE VARIOUS DOCUMENTS

Formal agreements

Where the parties have entered into a formal agreement following a course of negotiation, that agreement will generally supersede anything that was written or said in the course of negotiations.[3]

In a few instances, the courts have been willing to infer a collateral contract where a significant aspect of the negotiations has been omitted from the formal agreement,[4] but such an inference will rarely be made where both parties are commercial organizations.

Documents surviving negotiation

Where there has been a course of negotiation and the contract has not been reduced to a formal agreement it is necessary, in order properly to consider a claim, to establish the precise terms which survive and which have been overridden or superseded. Particular problems arise where both parties have sought to establish the contract on their own terms (sometimes referred to as the 'battle of forms') or where a tender was qualified and the qualification was not addressed fully in the acceptance. The basic rule is that a counter-offer kills off an offer. If a counter-offer is accepted, the counter-offer and acceptance form the contract. Any part of the offer overridden by the counter-offer does not apply. Mere reference in the eventual acceptance to the original offer will not revive that offer as part of the contract.[5]

***Ad hoc* conditions**

Conditions of contract are usually one of the 'standard' Forms (JCT, ICE or GC/Wks 1) or possibly derivatives of the first two named. In some cases *ad hoc* conditions are added or substituted or clauses are deleted, to 'tailor' pattern-drafted documents to the particular requirements of a given job. Great care is needed in drafting *ad hoc* amendments to ensure that they are contractually sound in themselves, that they do not conflict with standard clauses and that they do not alter by implication clauses which are not intended to be altered. It is essential to remember that *ad hoc* clauses must not be read in isolation, but with the conditions as a whole. This can have a drastic effect on the provisions of standard forms.

Documents incorporated by reference

It is not essential that a document is bound into a formal agreement for it to form part of the contract. Documents may also be incorporated by reference. Doubt exists, however, as to the precise status of certain documents to which reference is made in standard forms of contract and specifications, for example, standard methods of measurement,[6] British Standards or Codes of Practice.

Post-contract documents

In general, only documents in existence at the time of formation of the contract can be incorporated in the contract. Documents issued afterwards cannot be deemed to be included, unless there is specific machinery for subsequent incorporation. In that situation, the document becomes part of the contract only to the extent stipulated. For example, Clause 5.3 of JCT 80 postulates a possible (though not mandatory) use of descriptive schedules. As these are provided after acceptance they cannot override the requirements on which the contractor has tendered. Sub-clause 5.3.2 adds that 'Nothing contained in the descriptive documents . . . shall impose any obligation beyond those imposed by the Contract Documents'. This puts a heavy onus on the Bills of Quantities to supply the deficiency by describing the quality of workmanship and materials.

Many forms of contract provide for programmes to be submitted by the contractor after the commencement of the contract. Such programmes do not become a full part of the

---

3. *L'Estrange v Graucob* [1934] 2 KB 394.
4. *De Lassalle v Guildford* [1901] 2 KB 215; *Esso Petroleum v Mardon* (1976) QB 801.
5. *Butler Machine Tool Co v Ex-cell-O Corp (England) Ltd* [1979] 1 WLR 401.
6. *Farr v Ministry of Transport* [1965] 5 BLR 94.

contract; they do not, for example, impose an automatic obligation on the contractor to comply with the order or timing shown. On the other hand, a programme may be given a specific place in the contract to impose binding obligations. For example, Clause 42 in ICE5 and ICE6 imposes an obligation on the Employer 'to give to the Contractor possession of so much of the site as may be required to enable the Contractor to commence and proceed with the Works in accordance with the programme referred to in Clause 14 . . .'. GC/Works 1 Edition 3 provides in Condition 33 for post-contract submission of a 'Programme' covering not only timing but also details of method of work, labour and plant. Condition 31(1) then requires that the Contractor 'shall execute the Works . . . in accordance with the Programme'. This introduces a very broad obligation.

There are other examples of exceptions to the general rule. For example, reference to a future published price list has been held binding;[7] published lists of construction price indices form part of many contracts; and reference to arbitration statutes will be interpreted as those current at the date of the reference.[8]

RECTIFICATION

Where a formal agreement has been completed but it does not reflect what was actually agreed in negotiations, it is open to the parties to correct the agreement. Such an agreement could be framed as consent to rectification, or as a variation.[9]

Where there is a dispute as to what was originally agreed or one party declines to correct the formal agreement, a party may apply to the courts for rectification of the contract, to correct it in accordance with the intended agreement. Rectification is an equitable remedy. It is not, however, subject to the doctrine of *laches*.[10]

An arbitrator with jurisdiction to deal with matters 'arising under a contract' has the power to grant rectification of the contract.[11] The Engineer under ICE5 or ICE6 also has the power to grant rectification acting under Clause 66 since, acting under that clause, his powers are co-extensive with those of an arbitrator. The JCT Arbitration Rules, incorporated by reference into JCT 80 by Amendment 6 (1988), expressly empower the arbitrator to grant rectification.

DISCREPANCIES

Having established which documents form the contract, there remains the possibility of discrepancies within or between the various documents. It is possible that a discrepancy of sufficient significance could even render a contract void for uncertainty or mistake.[12] But most discrepancies or ambiguities would be dealt with, in the absence of express provisions, by application of the common law rules for construing contracts, described below.[13]

At a practical level, interpreting contractual requirements according to the common law rules might not lead to the appropriate or intended result (for example, where the drawings show Concrete Grade 30, the specification says Grade 40 and the Bills of Quantities refer to Grade 25). Reliance on the common law rules also has the drawback in relation to performance of work that legal interpretations are open to dispute and may be referred to a judge or arbitrator. There is no implied power for either party to issue an order to resolve a discrepancy. Most standard forms therefore contain express provisions empowering the architect, engineer or quantity surveyor to issue orders to correct any discrepancies or

---

7. *Hillas v Arcos* [1932] 147 LT 503.
8. *Food Corporation of India v Marastro* [1987] 1 WLR 134.
9. A variation must be supported by consideration or be under seal or by deed to be binding. Consent to rectification would provide consideration as compromise of a right of action. Alternatively, in some cases, the discharge of an existing contract and substitution of a new contract would of itself provide sufficient consideration.
10. See page 36.
11. *Ashville Investments Ltd v Elmer Contractors Ltd* [1989] QB 488.
12. For example, *Raffles v Wichelhaus* [1864] 2 H & C 906.
13. See pages 114, 115.

ambiguities and make any appropriate adjustments to entitlements. Such powers are, however, limited in scope. The provisions generally only confer a discretion on the A/E/QS to explain and adjust discrepancies or ambiguities relating to what is required to be performed and the quality of workmanship and materials (e.g. deciding the grade of concrete required in the example quoted above). Discrepancies and ambiguities in provisions concerning allocation of risk or entitlements to time or money are still to be resolved according to the common law rules.

Precedence of documents

It is not uncommon to try and overcome ambiguities or discrepancies by stipulating an order of precedence between the contract documents. For example, Clause 2.2.1 of JCT 80 reads:

> 'Nothing contained in the Contract Bills shall override or modify the application or interpretation of that which is contained in the Articles of Agreement, the Conditions or the Appendix.'

This corresponds to the last part of Clause 12(1) of the 1963/77 edition which has caused so much trouble and which has been heavily criticized in the courts.[14] Where some specific new provision or modification of an existing one is required in the conditions of contract, it should be made by way of a supplementary condition and not included in the Bill of Quantities. If it is so included even to the extent of departures from the Standard Method of Measurement (which one would expect to find in a B/Q), there may be some difficulty in sustaining it in face of the provisions of Clause 2.2.2.2 of JCT 80 — even if the departure is necessary and intended.

Generally, orders of precedence of documents are a source of confusion and a trap for the unwary. They serve as an encouragement to careless drafting.

CONTRACT TERMS

A construction contract typically comprises a number of documents containing words, numbers, charts and drawings. The conventional legal analysis of a contract talks of 'terms of the contract'. The meaning of the word 'terms' in this context is explained by Cheshire & Fifoot[15] that 'If a statement is a term of a contract, it creates a legal obligation for whose breach an appropriate action lies at common law'.

The meaning of the word may be clarified by an example of its use as part of a typical Statement of Claim in a court action. The contract is between an employer, R Dunbye Ltd, and a builder, Collapsible Constructors Ltd. A dispute has arisen over a reinforced concrete beam which has failed.

Between

R Dunbye Ltd	*Plaintiff*
and	
Collapsible Constructors Ltd	*Defendant*

STATEMENT OF CLAIM

1. *By a contract in writing dated 7 January 1990, the Defendant undertook to construct for the Plaintiff a four-storey office block comprising a reinforced concrete frame with brick infill panels and concrete slab floors.*

2. *The general arrangement of the reinforced concrete frame, including Beam Mark A, was shown on Drawing No 456/73.*

3. *The reinforcement details for the reinforced concrete frame, including Beam Mark A, were shown on Drawing No 456/75C.*

---

14. *English Industrial Estates v George Wimpey* [1972] 7 BLR 94.
15. Cheshire G C, Fifoot C H S, Furmston M P, *The Law of Contract*, 12th edn., p 127.

4. *It was a term of the contract that the Defendant would construct the said Beam Mark A in accordance with the Drawings No 456/73 and 456/75C; in particular that the beam would be reinforced with 4 No 12 mm diameter high tensile bars Grade 460 to BS 4449: 1988 in the bottom face.*

5. *In breach of the said term, the Defendant constructed the said beam Mark A reinforced with only 2 No 10 mm diameter Mild steel bars, Grade 250, in the bottom face.*

6. *By reason of the said breach, the beam Mark A was of inadequate strength and failed under normal loading, causing loss and damage.*

7. *By reason of the matters aforesaid, the Plaintiff claims damages.*

The Statement of Claim would then continue by particularizing the heads of damage and the amount claimed under each head.

The basic principles applied by lawyers in drafting Statements of Claim are equally applicable in dealing with compensation-type claims under a standard form construction contract. The first step is to identify the relevant terms in the contract which give rise to entitlement to adjustment of time and/or money, then determine whether the facts come within the relevant terms and whether the consequences and heads of loss and damage flow from the alleged cause. The heads of loss and damage must then be quantified.

Classification of terms   At common law, contract terms are classified as 'conditions' or 'warranties'. Conditions are the more significant terms: they are regarded as of such significance that breach entitles the other party to reject the goods or work, and/or repudiate the contract and cease to perform any further obligations under the contract. Where the breach of condition is limited in scope, the injured party may reject specific goods or work without terminating the contract as a whole.

A warranty is a lesser term. Breach of warranty entitles the aggrieved party merely to recover damages, that is, financial compensation; it does not excuse the injured party from further performance of his own obligations; nor does it entitle the injured party to reject goods or work.

The law also recognizes a class of 'innominate terms'[16] (that is, terms without a name) which may be regarded as either conditions or warranties according to the seriousness of the breach and the specific consequences. There is a tendency in the courts now to regard all contractual terms in this way, unless they are explicitly stated by statute or in the contract to be conditions.

As an example, failure to make due payment on time is regarded only as a breach of warranty unless it is stipulated to be a condition. A contractor who stops work for non-payment without the protection of such a stipulation could therefore be liable himself to damages for non-completion or late completion. On the other hand, if a party withheld payment to the extent of manifesting or evincing an intention not to be bound by the contract, that could amount to a fundamental breach, entitling the other party to repudiate the contract.

In some cases, a fundamental breach or breach of condition by one party will inevitably prevent the other party from continuing with his own performance. Where performance is not prevented, the injured party must elect whether or not to treat the breach as bringing the contract to an end.[17] If the injured party chooses to carry on with the contract after a breach of condition, he is still entitled to claim damages as for breach of warranty.

---

16. *Hong Kong Fir Shipping Co v Kawasaki Kisen Kaisha* [1962] 2 QB 26.
17. *Hochster v De La Tour* [1853] 2 E & B 678. See also *Morrison Knudsen v British Columbia Hydro & Power Authority* [1978] 85 DLR (3d) 186.

Adjustment provisions   The common law classification of terms is of limited relevance to construction contracts, which contain internal means to deal with breaches of most obligations, particularly those of the employer, through adjustment of entitlements. This may have the effect of making the breach of an obligation not actionable at common law. For example, if it were a term of the contract that the employer would provide possession of part of the site on a stipulated day, failure to provide possession as stipulated would constitute a breach of contract entitling the contractor to sue for damages at common law; but provisions for compensation to be assessed and paid under the contract override the common law right.[18] On the other hand, analogies can sometimes be drawn between the internal adjustment provisions and the common law rules on warranties and conditions, to provide useful guidance.

Express terms   Terms derived from statements written in the contract or from express oral agreements are called 'express terms'. In some instances, a term will be stated directly, as an obligation or requirement, or an imposition of risk. For example:

> 'The contractor shall construct the works in accordance with the drawings and specification . . .'
> 'The employer shall give possession of sufficient of the Site to enable the Contractor to proceed . . .'
> 'All timber shall be treated with creosote . . .'
> 'The employer shall pay to the contractor within 14 days . . .'
> 'The contractor shall indemnify the employer against all third party claims . . .'

In other instances, parts of a contract must be taken together to derive the relevant term. For example, the lines on a drawing are neutral until taken in conjunction with an obligation to construct the works in accordance with the drawings, or to provide possession of the Site described by lines on the drawings.

What about the effect of words and statements which supply reference data or information, for example, indicating the presence or location of services, or the level of an Ordnance Survey benchmark, the position of an existing building or the nature of its foundations? The frequency of such information in construction contracts is acknowledged by the ICE New Engineering Contract which has made a distinction between 'Site Information' and 'Works Information' — Site Information is information about the Site and its surroundings, Works Information defines the performance obligations. The inclusion in contract documentation of information about the Site and its surroundings will probably be construed, in the absence of a disclaimer, as a warranty that the information is accurate. It might even be construed, particularly if some interpretation is included, as a warranty that the information is complete or representative. It is not uncommon, however, for such warranties to be excluded or restricted in effect (so far as the law will allow) by a disclaimer or exemption clause, or by stipulation that the information does not form part of the contract.

The possibility of liability in respect of information about the site which proves to be incorrect or unrepresentative gives rise to an unfortunate dilemma, since engineering considerations lead to the view that all relevant information should be made available at time of tender. The dilemma is being overtaken, however, by a tendency in legislation and the courts to encourage the disclosure of information on an equitable basis. Most standard forms of contract, particularly those relating to civil engineering, have adopted policies along those lines.

Similar problems can arise where a contractor's method statement or programme is bound into the contract.[19]

The effect of express terms is found by the process of 'construing' the words of the contract. This comprises two stages: interpretation, which is attributing meaning to the individual

---

18.   This view is not universally accepted, but the current tendency in the courts is to hold parties to their contractually agreed arrangements.
19.   *Yorkshire Water Authority v Sir Alfred McAlpine (Northern) Ltd* [1985] 32 BLR 114.

words; and construction, which is putting a meaning to the contract where there is more than one literal interpretation possible.

In interpreting the express terms of a contract the basic rule is that the words are to be understood in their plain, ordinary and popular sense, unless they have a special sense in the particular trade;[20] or, unless from the context of the document and the intention of the parties to be collected from it, they appear to be used in a different sense; or, unless in their strict sense, they are incapable of being carried into effect.[21] In practice, there is often scope for argument as to the meaning of the words, and the process of construction comes into play.

Implied terms

Additional terms may be implied by law, either as standard terms, to be implied unless the implication would be contrary to the express words of the agreement, or as specific terms relating to a particular transaction.

Standard terms

Standard terms are implied by common law, statute, custom and practice, or from established course of dealing. The most common standard implied terms are those now codified in the Sale of Goods Act 1979[22] and the Supply of Goods and Services Act 1982. These include implied terms as to price, quality and fitness of the goods or service, and time for performance.

Under both Acts, where the price of goods or services is not determined by the parties, the buyer must pay a reasonable price.[23] What is a reasonable price is a question of fact dependent on the circumstances in each case.[24] (No such term can be implied, however, unless there is a contract: if there is clear disagreement on price, there can be no contract.[25] The implied term cannot be used to overcome the disagreement.)

In a contract for the sale of goods, unless a different intention appears from the contract, stipulations as to time of payment are not of the essence.[26] 'Of the essence' is another legal way of saying that a term is a condition. Making time 'not of the essence' makes the term merely a warranty. Accordingly, in the absence of express provision or unless it amounts to a fundamental breach, late payment does not entitle the other party to cease performance and repudiate the contract.

In a contract for services, the Supply of Goods and Services Act 1982 provides that where the supplier acts in the course of a business, there is an implied term that the supplier shall carry out the service with reasonable care and skill,[27] and that he shall carry out the service within a reasonable time.[28] What is a reasonable time is a question of fact.[29]

In a contract for the supply of goods (whether by sale or hire) there are several implied terms related to quality. Where the supply is by description, the goods shall correspond with the description.[30] Where the supply is by sample, the goods shall correspond with the sample.[31] Where the seller supplies goods in the course of a business, it is an implied term that the goods shall be of merchantable quality, subject to defects drawn to the buyer's attention or evident on pre-contract inspection.[32] 'Merchantable quality' is defined as 'fit

---

20. *Robertson v French* [1803] 4 East 130.
21. *Mallan v May* [1844] 13 M & W 511.
22. The law on Sales of Goods was first codified in the Sale of Goods Act 1893. Many of the cases refer to the old Act.
23. SGA s8, SGSA s15(1).
24. SGA s8(3), SGSA s15(2).
25. *British Steel Corporation v Cleveland Bridge Engineering* [1984] 1 All ER 504.
26. SGA s10(1). The Supply of Goods and Services Act 1982 is silent on this question.
27. SGSA s13.
28. SGSA s14(1).
29. SGSA s14(2).
30. SGA s13(1); SGSA s8.
31. SGA s15; SGSA s8 (3).
32. SGA s14(2) and s15(2); SGSA s9(2) and s10(2).

for the purpose or purposes for which goods of that kind are commonly bought as it is reasonable to expect having regard to any description applied to them, the price (if relevant) and all other relevant circumstances'.[33] Where goods are supplied with instructions, merchantable quality means that the goods will be fit for the purpose for which they were supplied if used in accordance with the instructions.[34] Where the buyer makes known the particular purpose for which the goods are being bought and the buyer reasonably relies on the seller, there is an implied term that the goods will be fit for that purpose.[35] These implied terms are independent and may apply cumulatively.

It will be seen from the statutory definition of 'merchantable quality' that it is effectively a grade on a scale of fitness for purpose. Other grades on this scale depend on the detail with which the purpose has been specified. This is illustrated by *Aswan Engineering Establishment Co v Lupidine*[36] where pails were supplied as 'heavy duty shipping containers'. The sales literature stated that the pails could be stacked six high and referred to tests carried out at 20°C. The pails were purchased to contain a waterproofing compound, and the full pails were stacked six high for shipping in standard 20 ft containers. Some of the containers were shipped to Kuwait where they stood on the quayside for several days. The temperatures in the containers were estimated to have reached 60°C. The pails failed and the black and sticky waterproofing compound was released. It was held that 'A reasonable customer would not expect (the pails) to be capable of being stacked six high in all climatic conditions and all temperatures'. The buyer did not disclose the destination of the pails beforehand so they could not show reliance on the sellers as to fitness for the particular purpose. Accordingly, the claim for damages failed.

There have been a number of cases suggesting that a similar term will be implied by common law, by analogy with the Sale of Goods Act, in the case of works supplied under a design and construct contract, to the effect that the works will be fit for the intended purpose.[37] The legal position is still evolving,[38] so it is preferable to deal with the matter in any design and construct contract by express terms, stating the agreed intention of the parties. It is equally important to do so in any sub-contract involving design services. Such express terms may, however, be incompatible with the cover provided by standard professional indemnity insurance policies. Such cover is normally based on liability imposed by common law rather than assumed by contract, so it is important to ensure that appropriate design liability insurance is effected.[39]

Certain statutory implied terms are stated to be conditions,[40] entitling the buyer to reject the goods and rescind the contract. The buyer may waive the condition, or may elect to treat the breach of the condition as a breach of warranty and not as a ground for treating the contract as repudiated.[41] It is further provided, however, that the right to rescind is lost after a reasonable opportunity for inspection and/or a reasonable time. The buyer is then deemed to have accepted the goods and his remedy is limited to damages for breach of warranty.[42] A similar scheme may be observed in most forms of construction contract where the employer reserves the right for his agent, the architect or engineer, during the construction period to reject work which does not comply with the specification; after substantial completion, the right is reduced to the power to order rectification of defective

---

33. SGA s14(6); SGSA s9(9) is similar.
34. *Wormell v RHM Agriculture East Ltd* [1986] 1 WLR 336; [1986] 1 All ER 769; [1987] 1 WLR 1091; [1987] 3 All ER 75.
35. SGA s14(3); SGSA ss14(4) and (5).
36. *Aswan Engineering Establishment Co v Lupidine* [1987] 1 WLR 1.
37. *Greaves v Baynham Meikle & Partners* [1975] 1 WLR 1095; *IBA v EMI* [1980] 14 BLR 1; *Newham LBC v Taylor Woodrow Anglian Ltd* [1981] 19 BLR 99; *Viking Grain Storage v T H White Installations* [1985] 33 BLR 103.
38. See Humphrey Lloyd QC, Fitness of the Product. In *Construction Contract Policy, Improved Procedures and Practice*. Centre of Construction Law and Management, King's College, London, 1989 p. 36.
39. There is the added problem that PI policies are written on a claims-made basis — a policy only applies to a claim brought in the years that the policy is in force.
40. SGA ss12, 13, 14, 15; SGSA ss2, 3, 4, 5, 7, 8, 9, 10.
41. SGA s11(3); SGSA is silent on this point.
42. SGA ss34, 35; SGSA is silent on this point. See also *Bernstein v Pamson Motors (Golders Green)* [1987] 2 All ER 220.

work. The analogy is illuminating because under the Sale of Goods Act, so long as the right to reject endures, it does not require any demonstration of actual loss or damage suffered as a result of the non-compliance. This indicates that the right to reject under the contractual provisions similarly depends simply on whether or not the work complies strictly with the specification. Such an approach has the merit of simplicity, but it may not make engineering common sense.

Certain statutory duties are also imposed by the Defective Premises Act 1972 on every person who takes on work for or in connection with a dwelling. These duties cannot be excluded or restricted by any term of an agreement. They are, however, independent of contract; they do not create implied terms in a contract.

Standard terms may also be implied by custom or trade usage providing there is no inconsistency between the usage and the terms of the contract. To be binding, the usage must be notorious, certain and reasonable, and not contrary to law.

Finally, standard terms may be implied on the basis of a previous course of dealing. Where two parties have consistently dealt on the basis of particular terms on earlier and similar occasions, those terms may be implied providing they are not incompatible with the express terms of the present contract.

It is of equal importance to know that certain terms will not be implied as standard. For example, there is a standard implied term that a building owner will allow his building contractor sufficient possession of the site to carry out the work, but *not* that he warrants freedom from interference by third parties to prevent access,[43] nor does he impliedly warrant the fitness of the site.[44] It is an implied term of a contract for professional services that the professional will exercise due skill, care and diligence in the performance of his duties, but he does not impliedly warrant that the product of his services will be fit for purpose.

Standard implied terms may be overridden by express terms, subject to some statutory limitations;[45] equally, the refusal by the courts to imply a term does not prevent the parties incorporating an express term to the same effect.

Specific transactions

The second category of implied terms comprises terms implied into specific transactions. These are more problematic and are governed by different principles. The aim of the law in this context is to fill in gaps in contracts on the basis of the presumed intention of the parties. As stated by Bowen L J in '*The Moorcock*':[46]

> 'Now an implied warranty, or, as it is called, a covenant in law, as distinguished from an express contract or express warranty, really is in all cases founded on the presumed intention of the parties, and upon reason. The implication which the law draws from what must obviously have been the intention of the parties, the law draws with the object of giving efficacy to the transaction and preventing such a failure of consideration as cannot have been within the contemplation of either side. . . . In business transactions such as this, what the law desires to effect by the implication is to give such business efficacy to the transaction as must have been intended at all events by both parties who are businessmen; not to impose on one side all the perils of the transaction, or to emancipate one side from all the chances of failure, but to make each party promise in law as

---

43. *Porter v Tottenham UDC* [1915] 1 KB 776.
44. *Appleby v Myers* [1867] LR 2 CP 651.
45. Certain terms under the Sale of Goods Act may not be excluded. See SGA s55 and UCTA s6 as amended by SGA Schedule 2.
46. '*The Moorcock*' [1889] 14 PD 64.

much, as at all events, as it must have been in the contemplation of both parties that he should be responsible for in respect of those perils or chances.'

This statement was supplemented by the 'officious bystander' test,[47] as a means of determining the presumed intention of the parties. The test supposes an officious bystander intervening at the time of contract with a question to the parties 'What will happen in such and such a case' or alternatively suggesting an express provision to deal with the case. Whether a term is to be implied and the nature of such a term are both to be determined on the basis of the parties' presumed response: 'Of course so and so will happen; it is too clear'.

Unfortunately, parties often leave matters unsaid because they are reluctant to commit themselves; they would not willingly respond 'of course'. Lord Denning attempted to meet this problem by means of a test of reasonableness,[48] but in *Liverpool CC v Irwin*,[49] the House of Lords rejected reasonableness in favour of necessity. A term will be implied where it is obvious that a term has been left unstated. The obligation then to be read into the contract is such as the contract implicitly required, no more, no less; a test in other words of necessity. The test of necessity will usually result in setting a balance between the parties based on criteria of reasonableness. Thus Lord Wilberforce concluded in that case (which concerned a tenancy agreement drawn up by the local authority landlord, without any statement of the landlord's own obligations towards maintenance of the common parts):[50]

'An obligation to take reasonable care to keep in reasonable repair and usability fits the requirements of the case. Such a definition involves — and I think rightly — recognition that the tenants themselves have their responsibilities. What is reasonable to expect of a landlord has a clear relation to what a reasonable set of tenants should do for themselves.'

The impact of *Liverpool CC v Irwin* has already been significant. In *Finchbourne v Rodrigues*,[51] the Court of Appeal held that a term would be implied into a lease agreement that maintenance charges to be fixed by the landlord (who had misleadingly set himself up as the managing surveyor) would be 'fair and reasonable'. In *Merton LBC v Leach*,[52] Vinelott J held there to be an implied term in the JCT Form that the Employer 'undertook to ensure that there would at all times be a person who would carry out the duties to be performed by the architect and that he would perform those duties with reasonable diligence, skill and care and that where the contract required the architect to exercise his discretion he would act fairly'.

Nevertheless, there is still a presumption against implied terms.[53] It is preferable to deal with matters, so far as possible, on the basis of construction of the express terms rather than introducing implied terms.[54] In many instances the supposed implied term can be seen to be merely a means of expressing the effect of an express term.

The possibility of implied terms may not be used to overturn clear express terms:[55]

'If the express terms are perfectly clear and free from ambiguity, there is no choice to be made between different possible meanings: the clear terms must be applied even if the court thinks some other terms would have been more suitable. An unexpressed term can be implied if and only if the court finds that

47. *Reigate v Union Manufacturing (Ramsbottom) Ltd* [1918] 1 KB 592; *Shirlaw v Southern Foundries* [1939] 2 KB 206.
48. *Liverpool CC v Irwin* [1975] 3 All ER 658 (CA); see also *Shell v Lostock Garages Ltd* [1977] 1 WLR 1187.
49. *Liverpool CC v Irwin* [1977] AC 239 (HL).
50. *Liverpool CC v Irwin* [1977] AC 239 at p 256.
51. *Finchbourne v Rodrigues* [1976] 3 All ER 581.
52. *Merton LBC v Stanley Hugh Leach* [1985] 32 BLR 51.
53. *Luxor (Eastbourne) Ltd v Cooper* [1941] AC 108 per Lord Wright at p 137.
54. *Mona Oil Equipment v Rhodesia Railways* [1949] 2 All ER 1014 at p 1017.
55. *Trollope & Colls v NW Hospital Board* [1973] 1 WLR 601 per Lord Pearson at p 609.

the parties must have intended that term to form part of their contract: it is not enough for the court to find that such a term would have been adopted by the parties as reasonable men if it had been suggested to them.'

An A/E/QS should accordingly be very wary in dealing with an assertion that 'such and such a term must be implied'. The guidelines laid down by the courts should be followed closely. Unless the term is a standard implied term, it is better and safer to approach matters on the basis of construction of express terms.

Co-operation/non-prevention

It has been said that a term will readily be implied into a contract that the parties shall co-operate to ensure the performance of their bargain.[56] Analysis of the cases reveals, however, that the legal concept of co-operation is restricted to an obligation firstly to perform those duties which must be performed to enable the other party to perform his own obligations under the contract and secondly not to prevent the other party from performance. The implied obligation does not extend to active co-operation. The point was made in *Mona Oil Equipment v Rhodesia Railways*:[57]

'It is, no doubt, true that every business contract depends for its smooth working on co-operation, but in the ordinary business contract, and apart, of course, from express terms, the law can enforce co-operation only in a limited degree — to the extent that is necessary to make the contract workable. For any higher degree of co-operation, the parties must rely on the desire that both of them usually have that the business should get done.'

In practice the extent to which express terms can be employed to impose co-operation is limited due, firstly, to the restriction that, in law, a bare agreement to agree is not binding and, secondly and more significantly, the impotence of the law to do any more than award compensation retrospectively. Nevertheless, it has been held that where a contract provided for performance 'at a time to be agreed', both parties were bound to make a reasonable effort to find a mutually satisfactory time.[58]

There is a familiar example in the construction industry where a term will be implied that one party shall not prevent the other from performance. It concerns stipulations as to time for completion and liquidated damages. In the absence of provisions for the adjustment of the time for completion, a party will lose the benefit of the stipulation if it prevents or obstructs performance, for example, by not providing possession of the site or by instructing additional work.[59]

The broader principle in regard to co-operation is founded on two passages. The first is in *Stirling v Maitland and Boyd*,[60] where Cockburn C J said:

'I look on the law to be that, if a party enters into an arrangement which can only take effect by the continuance of a certain existing state of circumstances, there is an implied engagement on his part that he shall do nothing of his own motion to put an end to that state of circumstances under which alone the arrangement can be operative.'

The second is in *Mackay v Dick* where Lord Blackburn said:[61]

'I think I may safely say, as a general rule, that where in a written contract

---

56. Chitty on Contracts, para 849, 26th edn Sweet & Maxwell, London.
57. *Mona Oil Equipment v Rhodesia Railways* [1949] 2 All ER 1014 per Devlin J at p 1018.
58. *Terry v Moss's Empires Ltd* [1915] 32 TLR 92; c.f. *Walford v Miles* [1992] 1 All ER 453.
59. *Holme v Guppy* [1838] 3 M & W 387.
60. *Stirling v Maitland and Boyd* [1864] 5 B & S 840 at p 852 per Cockburn CJ (Mellor and Shee JJ concurring).
61. *Mackay v Dick* [1881] 6 App Cas 251 at p 263.

it appears that both parties have agreed that something shall be done, which cannot effectually be done unless both concur in doing it, the construction of the contract is that each agrees to do all that is necessary to be done on his part for the carrying out of that thing, though there may be no express words to that effect.'

A good example of this principle was given by Lord Romer in *Luxor (Eastbourne) v Cooper*:[62]

'If I employ a man for reward to build a house on my land I subject myself to an implied condition that I will do nothing to prevent him carrying out the work.'

On the other hand, in the same case, it was held that a building owner was not bound to enter into a contract with a willing purchaser introduced by an estate agent so as to enable the agent to earn his commission. No obligation of non-prevention would be implied to protect a merely contingent right to earn commission.[63] Other cases to the same effect have concerned share options:[64] companies have been held entitled to sell off subsidiary companies or terminate an individual's employment, notwithstanding that this resulted in the loss of share option rights.

Where the contract contains explicit provisions which cater for the situation of non-cooperation, no additional term will be implied. This point arose in *Rosehaugh Stanhope v Redpath Dorman Long* where Bingham L J said:[65]

'It is very well known that the courts will readily imply a *Mackay v Dick* term, but I am not for my part persuaded that it would be appropriate to do so here. A term will only be implied where it is necessary to give business efficacy to the contract, so that no term will be implied if the contract is effective without it. . . . It seems to me that on a reasonably commercial construction of clause 21(1), and particularly sub-clause (1)(b), any lack of co-operation by the plaintiffs would entitle the defendants to reimbursement under the clause. If that is so, then there is no necessity to imply a term for breach of which damages would lie.'

In *Alghussein Establishment v Eton College*,[66] the House of Lords put the point as a matter of construction rather than an implied term. It is a rule of construction that a man cannot be permitted to take advantage of his own wrong. What constitutes a 'wrong' in this context was clarified by Lord Jauncey as follows:[67]

'It is well established by a long line of authority that a contracting party will not in normal circumstances be entitled to take advantage of his own breach as against the other party.'

Lord Jauncey quoted with approval from *Cheall v APEX*:[68]

'Except in the unlikely case that the contract contains clear provisions to the contrary, it is to be presumed that it was not the intention of the parties that either party should be entitled to rely on his own breaches of his primary obligations as bringing the contract to an end, i.e. as terminating any further primary obligations on his part then remaining unperformed.'

---

62. *Luxor (Eastbourne) Ltd v Cooper* [1941] AC 108 at p 154.
63. *Luxor (Eastbourne) Ltd v Cooper* [1941] AC 108.
64. *Thompson v ASDA-MFI Group* [1988] Ch 241; *Micklefield v SAC Technology Ltd* [1991] 1 All ER 275.
65. *Rosehaugh Stanhope v Redpath Dorman Long Ltd* [1990] 50 BLR 69.
66. *Alghussein Establishment v Eton College* [1988] 1 WLR 587.
67. *Alghussein Establishment v Eton College* [1988] 1 WLR 587 per Lord Jauncey at p 591.
68. Ibid at p 593; *Cheall v APEX* [1983] 2 AC 180 at pp 188–189.

He continued:[69]

> 'There was nothing in (the cases) to suggest that the foregoing proposition was limited to cases where the parties in breach were seeking to avoid the contract and I can see no reason for so limiting it. A party who seeks to obtain a benefit under a continuing contract on account of his breach is just as much taking advantage of his own wrong as is a party who relies on his breach to avoid a contract and thereby escape his obligations.'

EXPRESS TERMS OVERRIDDEN

The law also intervenes in contracts by wholly or partially disregarding certain types of express terms, interpreting such terms more strongly against one party, or limiting their effect. The common law has long applied rules based on public policy or judicial hostility to unfair contract terms. In recent years, the need for judicial ingenuity has been relieved by legislation, particularly the Misrepresentation Act 1967 and the Unfair Contract Terms Act 1977.

The law operates in various ways to overcome or limit express terms. There is no overall scheme of rules, just a collection of rules.

Penalty clauses

A penalty clause is an agreement to pay a sum of money set by or calculated in accordance with the contract, in the event of a breach of contract, where the amount set or so calculated is unrelated to the loss or damage which might be suffered in the event of such breach. Relief against penalty clauses was historically provided by equity. The legal position is that a penalty clause remains in the contract and can be sued on, but it will not be enforced by the court beyond the sum which represents, in the events which have happened, the actual loss of the party seeking payment.[70]

The rule against penalty clauses cannot be applied to provide relief from other types of onerous contractual provisions.

Exclusion clauses

At common law, exclusion clauses are construed strictly *contra proferentem*, that is, more strongly against the party seeking to rely on the clause. (This is distinct from the *contra proferentem* rule in the construction of contracts generally, where it is applied only as a last resort and only against the party which prepared the contract document.) Thus, a clause which purports to exclude liability but does not refer specifically to negligence, will be construed by a court as not excluding liability for negligence.[71]

In *Peak Construction (Liverpool) Ltd v McKinney Foundations*[72] Salmon LJ (as he then was) stated that liquidated damages and extension of time clauses in printed forms of contract must be construed strictly *contra proferentem*. It has been pointed out[73] that no authority was given for that proposition of law, nor does it accord with earlier decisions. In that case the form of contract was a non-standard form of contract prepared by the employer; it is submitted that application of the *contra proferentem* rule was justified on that basis alone, and that it ought not to be applied generally to forms of contract which are drafted by representatives of all interested parties, and which provide entitlement to payment as well as extensions of time for delays caused by the employer or his agents.

At one time, the common law also developed a doctrine of 'fundamental breach', whereby a breach of contract might be regarded as so fundamental that the protection of an exclusion clause could not be relied upon. Following the Unfair Contract Terms Act, 1977 ('UCTA'),

---

69. *Alghussein Establishment v Eton College* [1988] 1 WLR 587 at p 594.
70. *Jobson v Johnson* [1989] 1 WLR 1026.
71. *Alderslade v Hendon Laundry Ltd* [1945] KB 189.
72. *Peak Construction (Liverpool) v McKinney Foundations* [1970] 1 BLR 114.
73. Terence Burke 1985 'The Liability of the Contractor for Late Completion' in *The Liability of Contractors* 71 at p 80. Centre for Commercial Studies, Queen Mary College and Longman Group UK Ltd.

however, the doctrine was repudiated by the House of Lords.[74] (The term 'fundamental breach' is still used to describe a breach which is such as to entitle the innocent party to elect to put an end to all primary obligations of both parties remaining unperformed.)

Exclusion clauses are also limited by statute. UCTA restricts the exclusion of the statutory implied terms, in the Sale of Goods Act 1979 and the Supply of Goods and Services Act 1982 either absolutely or by reference to criteria of reasonableness. The Defective Premises Act 1972 states in relation to duties under the Act 'Any term of an agreement which purports to exclude or restrict, or has the effect of excluding or restricting, the operation of any of the provisions of this Act, or any liability arising by virtue of any such provision, shall be void'.

One of the most significant restrictions on exclusion clauses is that contained in the Misrepresentation Act 1967 s3 (as substituted by UCTA s8). This provides:

> 'If a contract contains a term which would exclude or restrict —
> (a) any liability to which a party to a contract may be subject by reason of any misrepresentation made by him before the contact was made; or
> (b) any remedy available to another party to the contract by reason of such a misrepresentation,
> that term shall be of no effect except in so far as it satisfies the requirement of reasonableness as stated in Section 11(1) of the Unfair Contract Terms Act 1977; and it is for those claiming that the term satisfies that requirement to show that it does.'

The significance for construction contracts concerns liability in respect of site information, particularly site investigation data which is provided outside of the contract documents. The section is notable because it puts the onus on the party seeking the protection of a disclaimer clause to show that the disclaimer satisfies the requirement of 'reasonableness'.

Terms excluding or restricting a party's liability for negligence are also dealt with by UCTA. Liability for death or personal injury resulting from negligence cannot be excluded or restricted. In other cases, a person cannot exclude his liability for negligence 'except in so far as the term or notice satisfies the requirement of reasonableness'.[75]

There is also a more general requirement in UCTA of reasonableness in exemption clauses, but it is limited to two situations: where one party deals as a consumer (which is rarely the case in construction contracts) or where one party deals 'on the other's written standard terms of business'.

In those situations, s3(2) applies. This provides:

> 'As against that party, the other cannot by reference to any contract term —
> (a) when himself in breach of contract, exclude or restrict any liability of his in respect of the breach; or
> (b) claim to be entitled —
> (i) to render a contractual performance substantially different from that which was reasonably expected of him, or
> (ii) in respect of the whole or any part of his contractual obligation, to render no performance at all,
> except in so far as (in any of the cases mentioned above in this subsection) the contract term satisfies the requirement of reasonableness.'

A standard form of contract agreed between representative bodies could not be considered as the employer's 'written standard terms of business', but any *ad hoc* amendments probably

---

74. *Photo Productions Ltd v Securicor* [1980] AC 827.
75. Unfair Contract Terms Act 1977 s2.

would, particularly if qualifications of tenders were restricted. Forms drafted unilaterally, such as GC/Works 1, should probably be considered as the employer's written standard terms of business.[76]

s13 of UCTA refers to varieties of exemption clause (that is, clauses which either exclude or restrict liability) and makes clear that exemption clauses come in many guises. For example, requirements as to notice or time for submission of claims could, if they purported to exclude or restrict liability in the event of non-compliance, be considered as exemption clauses.

The 'reasonableness' test is set out in s11 of UCTA, with reference to a Schedule of guidelines.[77] The basic test is that:

> 'the term shall have been a fair and reasonable one to be included having regard
> to the circumstances which were, or ought reasonably to have been, known to
> or in the contemplation of the parties when the contract was made.'

The guidelines indicate that the test should take into account the strength of the bargaining positions of the parties relative to each other.

Clauses limiting liability are subject to slightly different considerations from those which exclude liability. Limitation clauses will be accepted more readily as satisfying the criterion of reasonableness.[78]

RULES OF CONSTRUCTION

The object of construction of the terms of a written agreement is to obtain from it the intention of the parties to the agreement. A number of rules have been laid down relating to the process of construing a contract. The principal rules relevant to building and civil engineering contracts are as follows:

1. Every contract is to be construed or interpreted with reference to its object and the whole of its terms.[79]

2. A contract is to be construed or interpreted against the background of the surrounding circumstances or matrix of facts known to the parties at or before the agreement in so far as those throw light on what was the commercial or business object of the transaction objectively ascertained.[80]

3. The conduct of the parties after the contract was concluded is not to be regarded as an aid to interpretation.[81]

4. In the case of commercial contracts, business common sense should be the principal criterion, both as to whether ambiguity or uncertainty exists or should be recognized, and as to the meaning intended by the parties. Business common sense implies that the parties are presumed, so far as possible, to have acted as experienced, responsible and prudent persons in settling the terms of the contract.[82]

5. General words to be applied by an independent professional are to be interpreted by him following objective standards prevailing in the profession.[83]

---

76. In Hong Kong, the Control of Exemption Clauses Ordinance (Cap 471) contains similar provisions to UCTA and is probably applicable to the unilaterally drafted Government contracts.
77. Unfair Contract Terms Act 1977 Schedule 2.
78. *Ailsa Craig v Malvern Fishing* [1983] 1 WLR 964.
79. *Allen v Cameron* [1833] 1 C & M 832; *NE Railway v Hastings* [1900] AC 260.
80. *Prenn v Simmonds* [1971] 1 WLR 1381; *Reardon Smith Line v Yngvar Hansen-Tangen* [1976] 1 WLR 989.
81. *James Miller & Partners v Whitworth Street Estates* [1970] AC 583.
82. *Antaios Cia Naviera v Salen Rederierna, The 'Antaios'* [1985] AC 191; *Mitsui Construction Co v A-G for Hong Kong* [1986] 33 BLR 1; *Reardon-Smith Line v Yngvar Hansen-Tangen* [1976] 1 WLR 989.
83. *Sudbrook v Eggleton* [1983] 1 AC 444; see also *Finchbourne v Rodrigues* (1976) 3 All ER 581.

6. What is fair and reasonable is to be ascertained by reference to the background of practices prevailing.[84]

7. If one item is mentioned specifically, its inclusion may be taken to indicate that another item not mentioned has been omitted deliberately: '*inclusio unius est exclusio alterius*'.

8. In a list of two or more items followed by general words (e.g. 'bench marks, sight rails pegs and other things used in setting out the Works') the general words are to be interpreted as referring to the same class of items as those specifically listed: the '*ejusdem generis*' rule.

9. Extrinsic evidence may be admitted to explain a latent ambiguity.[85]

10. If other rules of interpretation fail to resolve an ambiguity or uncertainty, the document is to be applied '*contra proferentem*', that is, more strongly against the party which prepared the document.[86]

These rules should be followed when applying the contract in preparing or considering claims.

A further rule is that specific amendments will be given more weight than printed words in standard forms. Manuscript or typed wording overrides the printed word if there is inconsistency, on the basis that the intention is to ascertain the true intention of the parties.[87] Thus special conditions of contract will override general conditions, particular specifications will override general specifications. The courts are generally reluctant, however, to disregard any words in a contract if the inconsistencies can be reconciled and they would probably not indulge in speculation as to whether, for example, drawings were more or less specific than specifications. Particular regard should be given to whether the attention of the party has been drawn to the overriding provision. Thus in *A Davies v William Old Ltd*,[88] it was held:

> 'For the doctrine that selected *ad hoc* words prevail over general pro forma printed words to apply the *ad hoc* words must be selected to express a mutual intent of the parties. Each case depends on its own facts and the primary question of fact in each case is whether the sub-contractor's attention has been properly drawn to the particular conditions.'

Drafting conventions   There are also certain drafting conventions for legal documents. For example, in an agreement, any 'recitals' — the statements at the beginning, starting with the word 'Whereas' and stating the purpose or object of the agreement — do not form part of the operative terms of the agreement; they may not be used to introduce an ambiguity, but they may be referred to in order to resolve an ambiguity or to explain the matrix of facts known to the parties at the time of contract.

Different words used in a document are presumed to be intended to have different meanings even if they have potentially the same literal meaning. The effect of this rule is to turn on its head the guidance given to students of non-legal English composition, that they should avoid repetition of words. In contractual documents, it is essential to use the same word to mean the same thing.

Words used with capital initial letters (other than proper nouns) refer to words defined in the document — definition is conventionally achieved either by a list of definitions or by the use of brackets and quotation marks, e.g. (the 'Specification').

These drafting conventions should be followed in preparing contract documents, with

---

84. *Reardon Smith Line v Yngvar Hansen-Tangen* [1976] 1 WLR 989.
85. *Raffles v Wichelhaus* [1864] 2 H & C 906.
86. *Borradaile v Hunter* [1843] 5 M & G 639; *Lindus v Melrose* [1858[3 H & N 177.
87. *Robertson v French* [1803] 4 East 130.
88. *A Davies v William Old Ltd* [1969] 113 Sol Jo 262, The Digest (1979 Reissue) para 2566. See also *Interfoto Picture Library v Stiletto Visual Programmes Ltd* (1989) QB 433.

a view to ensuring that the intentions of the parties are carried into effect. They are also important in applying the contract in preparing or considering claims.

Conventional estoppel   An estoppel is originally a legal bar which binds a party in legal proceedings from relying on or denying the existence of certain facts. In contract law, the doctrine of 'equitable estoppel' was developed by Lord Denning MR,[89] by which an agreement, without consideration, not to insist on a contractual right will be held binding, notwithstanding the lack of consideration. In general, such an agreement may be rescinded by reasonable notice with prospective effect, but not so as to change what has gone before.

The concept of estoppel was further applied by Lord Denning MR to circumvent the rule of construction that the conduct of the parties after the contract was concluded is not to be regarded as an aid to interpretation. He expounded a doctrine of 'conventional estoppel', in *Amalgamated Investment v Texas Commerce*,[90] as follows:

> 'If parties to a contract, by their course of dealing, put a particular interpretation on the terms of it, on the faith of which each of them to the knowledge of the other acts and conducts their mutual affairs, they are bound by that interpretation just as much as if they had written it down as being a variation of the contract.
> ... They are bound by the "conventional basis" on which they conducted their affairs. The reason is because it would be altogether unjust to allow either party to insist on the strict interpretation of the original terms of the contract when it would be inequitable to do so, having regard to dealings which have taken place between the parties ...'

He concluded that there was:

> '... one general principle (of estoppel) shorn of limitations. When the parties to a transaction proceed on the basis of an underlying assumption (either of fact or of law, and whether due to misrepresentation or mistake, makes no difference), on which they have conducted the dealing between them, neither of them will be allowed to go back on that assumption when it would be unfair or unjust to allow him to do so.'

Lord Denning's conclusion was stated without disagreement by Lord Templeman delivering the opinion of the Privy Council in *A-G of Hong Kong v Humphreys Estate Ltd*,[91] but Lord Templeman added that to found an estoppel, the plaintiff had to show not only that they had acted to their detriment and to the knowledge of the defendant in the hope that the defendant would not withdraw from the agreement in principle, the plaintiff had also to show firstly, that the defendant had created or encouraged the belief on the part of the plaintiff and secondly, that the plaintiff had relied on that belief or expectation.

CASE 5.1   CLAIM BASED ON PROVISION CONTAINED IN COVERING LETTER TO TENDER

Pertinent particulars of contract   Tender dated 1 April 1980 (not referring to covering letter).

Covering letter of same date saying that tender was based on using steel ex UK at £.......... per tonne.

Other contract documents: Drawings; Specification; Bill of Quantities; Conditions of Contract
— any of the three main Forms may be assumed in this case as follows:
JCT 63/77 with Clauses 31A to F (JCT 80 Clauses 39 and 40) deleted
ICE 4 or ICE 5 — Price Fluctuations not included
GC/Wks 1 Edn 1 or Edn 2 — Conditions 11A to 11F not applicable.

---

89. *Central London Property Trust v High Trees House* [1947] KB 130.
90. *Amalgamated Investment v Texas Commerce* [1982] 1 QB 84 at p 112.
91. *A-G of Hong Kong v Humphreys Estate Ltd* [1987] AC 114.

Contractor to Architect/Engineer   *1 September 1980*

Contract No ..... for .... at ....

> *With reference to Certificate No 4 we included in our statement an item for 250 tonnes of steel reinforcement supplied and fixed in the Works at an extra cost of £10.20 per tonne. This item, however, was deleted. In subsequent discussion the quantity surveyors contended that this was not payable as the contract is on a fixed price basis and contains no Price Fluctuation Clause.*
>
> *We would, however, draw your attention to the covering letter to our tender in which we said that our tender was based on using steel ex UK and that if in view of the steel position then obtaining we had to get it elsewhere we would expect to be reimbursed the extra cost.*
>
> *We therefore contend we are entitled to payment of the sum of £3,060 and would be glad if you would include this in the next certificate.*

As a letter notifying a claim this is reasonably straightforward. The contractor has evidently included this extra cost in his interim statement as a matter of course and only when it is deleted does the need to enter a 'claim' arise. It recites the facts of the matter but does not show how the sum of £3,060 is arrived at (it is something more than 250 t at £10.20).

Architect/Engineer to Contractor   *9 September 1980*

> *With reference to your letter dated 1 September 1980, clearly the contract contains no provision for price fluctuation.*
>
> *I would also point out that the covering letter to your tender was in effect a qualification, contrary to the requirements of the Invitation to Tender, which indicated that qualifications would not be permitted.*
>
> *In any case you give no supporting evidence as to how the £3,060 is arrived at nor do you state why it was necessary to obtain steel from elsewhere.*

The first paragraph is only restating the obvious and the second is confusing policy with contract. Many authorities adopt a policy of discouraging or prohibiting qualifications but should a contractor find it necessary to qualify his tender, the matter cannot simply be ignored. Whether the policy must be followed in each and every case regardless of the public interest is very much open to question. The third paragraph is, however, quite unnecessary and suggests that after all perhaps the writer is not so sure of himself as he would wish to appear.

Contractor to Architect/Engineer   *11 September 1980*

> *In reply to your letter of 9 September, we are aware that it is your Department's policy to discourage qualified tenders but there are occasions when a qualification is unavoidable. In this case we could get no firm promise of delivery from BSC and considered that if we were to meet your requirements as to date for completion, we might well have to import steel. This position did not become apparent until 48 hours before tenders were due. As we did not wish to load our tender against a risk which might not eventuate we decided we had no alternative but to qualify our tender.*
>
> *In fact, BSC were unable to meet our requirements and we were obliged to import from West Germany — as we informed your Site Representative at the time. We enclose copies of invoices for the materials delivered and*

*the quotations from BSC on which we based our tender. From these you
will see that the nett difference is £10.20 per tonne to which we have
added 20 per cent for overheads and profit — which we are sure you will
agree is very reasonable.*

Again a fairly straightforward letter — but now revealing that 20 per cent has been added for overheads and profit — though the letter in question talks of 'extra cost' without defining what is meant.

Architect/Engineer to Contractor   *2 October 1980*

    *I reply to your letter of the 11 September and have to inform you that
your claim is rejected.*

Oh dear! Could the man not at least say why? Perhaps he does not know that his decision is in fact correct. Obviously, if he knew the reason why this is so he should tell the contractor. As it is, there is a risk that the contractor will feel sore, will be wondering whether it is worth taking the matter to arbitration or whether there is anything else he can do (e.g. look for some weakness in the contract documents to exploit).

The use of an unexplained 'No' can be quite a big factor in escalating a matter which should be relatively routine into a 'claim' in the more formal sense. It tends to suggest that the A/E/QS does not have any solid reason or at best is not sure of his ground and so the contractor is inclined to persist. The giving of an explanation may either convince the contractor into acceptance or provide some specific point on which further evidence or perhaps case law can be quoted and help towards resolution.

**Points of principle
involved**

The point here upon which the contractor's claim fails is that the covering letter forms no part of the contract. It was not referred to in the tender itself, it was not referred to in the acceptance and the contractor failed to pick up the latter point before commencing work.[92] Architects, engineers and quantity surveyors confronted with such a situation when examining tenders must check whether such a covering letter is intended to form part of the contract and, if so, at least ensure that it is specifically referred to in the acceptance.

On the matter of policy regarding qualified tenders, if the lowest tender were, say, £50,000 or even £20,000 below the next and the extra cost of steel likely to be involved were, say, £5,000, to pass over the lowest tender would be to oblige the employer to incur an additional expenditure of £45,000 (or £15,000 as the case may be) because of a general policy. Whilst such a policy may be thought to be justified on the grounds of discouraging irregular tenders, a positive waste of money (particularly if it is public money) cannot be justified where the tender in question is not irregular. To adhere to a so-called matter of principle because one is unable to distinguish a genuine from an irregular tender and to have no better means of dealing with the latter if and when it arises is a confession of weakness and insufficient justification.

CASE 5.2   CLAIMS IN RESPECT OF ERRORS IN BILLS OF QUANTITIES (Building Forms and Method of Measurement)

**Pertinent particulars
of contract**

Contract for the erection of warehouses at .... The documents comprised Drawings (no Specification), Conditions of Contract JCT 63/67 including Clause 31F (Price adjustment by formula), Bills of Quantities based on Standard Method of Measurement Edition 6 (1979).

Tender dated 1 May 1979 in the sum of £452,500. (NB: total of B/Q £452,876.) Time for completion 21 months.

---

92. See *Davis Contractors Ltd v Fareham UDC* [1956] AC 696.

Acceptance dated 7 June. Formal contract executed 14 June 1979.

During 1979/1980 in the course of preparing statements for interim payments, measuring and agreeing prices for variations and preparing the final account, the contractor drew attention to a number of (what he considered) errors in the Bills of Quantities. These were raised first orally in the ordinary course of events, but where the matter was at all complex or some written evidence was asked for, there was an exchange of letters. All these matters were eventually resolved and agreed without having been formally classified as 'claims', yet in each case there was for a while a lack of agreement and hence, technically, a claim.

Attention is drawn to the following clauses of the Conditions of Contract which are relevant:

Clause 1 — The contractor shall . . . carry out . . . the Works shewn upon the Contract Drawings and described by or referred to in the Contract Bills . . .

Clause 12(1) — The quality and quantity of the work included in the Contract Sum shall be deemed to be that which is set out in the Contract Bills which Bills unless otherwise expressly stated in respect of any specified item shall be deemed to have been prepared in accordance with the Standard Method of Measurement 6th Edition . . . but save as aforesaid nothing contained in the Contract Bills shall override, modify, or affect in any way whatsoever the application or interpretation of that which is contained in these Conditions.

(2) — Any error in description or in quantity in or omission from the Contract Bills . . . shall be corrected and deemed a variation required by the architect.

Development of claims
(a) Discrepancy as to quality of concrete

The first matter at issue was the relatively simple one of a discrepancy between the drawings and the B/Q. The former indicated the quality of certain reinforced concrete floors and beams as 'Ref C25P as BS 5328/76' but the Bills gave the mix as 'C20P as BS 5328/76'.

The matter was raised first at a site meeting when the contractor's agent asked which quality of concrete he was to use, to which he got the reply 'As shewn on the drawings'.

The agent was not incorrect in putting the question this way because of the wording of Clause 1(1) of the Conditions which requires the contractor to 'carry out the Works . . . described by or referred to in the Contract Bills'. Normally one should be able to say that work is to be carried out in accordance with the drawings and specification but, in the absence of the latter, Bills have tended to act as specification also. Clause 12 of the Conditions refers to the 'quality and quantity of work included in the Contract Sum'.

The matter of an increased rate was raised by the contractor's QS with the site QS, who pointed out that before he could deal with the matter the contractor needed to give notice to the architect, under Clause 1(2).

Admittedly the matter had been raised (and probably minuted) at the site meeting but this is not a notice. In this case the matter is unlikely to be disputed, but as a general principle if the Conditions say '. . . the Contractor . . . shall give notice . . .' then he is under obligation to do so, and in some situations could find himself in difficulties if he does not comply.

Contractor to Architect   *8 August 1979*

At the site meeting on 3 August we pointed out the discrepancy between the drawings and B/Q in respect of the quality of concrete to be used in the suspended floors to the Warehouse Block. You instructed us to use concrete grade C25P. As this is a discrepancy within the meaning of Clause 1(2) of the Conditions, we should be glad if you would accept this letter as our written notice concerning this matter and confirm your instructions.

119

Architect to Contractor   *10 August 1979*
Copy to QS

> *With reference to your letter dated 8 August, I confirm that you are required to use concrete quality C25P for the warehouse floors as shewn on the drawings.*
>
> *The quantity surveyor will deal with the matter of the rate.*

The matter was then taken up between site QS and contractor QS. The B/Q read as follows:

Item: Concrete Grade C20P as BS 5328/76 in: (*inter alia*)

24 B: Suspended slab 250 mm thick, upper surface finished to receive screed.   1,250 m³   £25.60

24 F: Deep reinforced beams of cross-sectional area exceeding 0.25 m².   250 m³   £24.80

The contractor was claiming £1.69 per m³ for the additional cost of the stronger mix: 1,500 m³ at £1.69 = £2,535.

The site QS asked the contractor QS for an analysis of the £1.69 rate and was given the following:

Contractor to QS   *24 August 1979*

> *With reference to our claim for additional cost using C25P grade concrete for the warehouse floors and beams, the additional price of £1.69 has been arrived at as follows: Material quantities derived from BS*

		Cement		*Fine Agg*		*Coarse Agg*	
C25P	*kg*	*350*		*650*		*1,180*	
C20P	*kg*	*300*		*700*		*1,170*	
Difference		*+50*		*−50*		*+10*	
Conversion to m³				*× 1.59*		*× 1.35*	
Prices		*£30 t*		*£6.60 m³*		*£5.70 m³*	
Differences		$\frac{50}{1000} \times 30 = 1.50$		$\frac{50}{1590} \times 6.60 = -0.21$		$\frac{10}{1350} \times 5.70 = 0.04$	
Add for waste	*5%*		*0.08*	*10%*	*0.02*	*10%*	*0.00*
			1.58		*−0.23*		*0.04*
					1.39		
Add for site oncosts 14.45%					*0.20*	*1.59*	
Add for HO oncosts and profit 6%						*0.10*	*£1.69*

The site QS asked for some substantiation of the addition of 14.45 per cent and 6 per cent. At first the contractor was disinclined to produce this but, upon being reassured that the information would be treated confidentially, the site QS was shown the build-up of the tender prices, which included these percentages. The rate was then agreed.

(b)   Error in quantity of excavation for foundations

In checking through the quantities for their own internal purposes, the contractor found that the quantity of excavation in foundations as given in the B/Q (145 m³) was seriously deficient. Reference to the taking off confirmed that there was an error and the quantity should in fact be 1,450 m³. This was clearly an error within the meaning of Clause 12(2)

120

and there would have been no problem had the contractor not priced this item at a very low rate (£0.83 instead of £2.83 per m³). This rate had been queried before acceptance but the contractor had elected not to correct the rate (he had rounded-off his tender anyway, presumably to make sure of getting the job and so felt he should not risk increasing his tender).

The contractor would have been wiser to correct the rate but adhere to his lump-sum offer.

Further, in the course of the work the ground turned out to be much more difficult than expected. The contractor said he was prepared to stand by the B/Q price up to the amount of the B/Q quantity but he sought payment of the additional quantity of 1,305 m³ at the 'correct' rate of £2.83. He also sought an increase in the rate for the whole quantity on the grounds that the subsoil was more difficult than he could have expected.

This obviously involved matters outside the day-to-day negotiation of prices and the contractor was advised to put his claim in writing.

Contractor to Quantity Surveyor   *4 September 1979*

We would draw your attention to item 12F of the B/Q which is for 145 m³ of excavation for foundations at £0.83. The quantity is in error and your site QS has agreed that it should be 1,450 m³. The rate of £0.83 is also in error and should have been £2.83. This was queried before acceptance, when we agreed to adhere to the rate but of course at that time we were not aware that the quantity was in error.

We are prepared to stand by our price for the B/Q quantity but claim a corrected rate of £2.83 for the additional quantity, i.e. 1,305 m³ at £2 =   *£2,610.*

We would also point out that the ground was much more difficult than we could possibly have expected, being largely in building debris with lengths of old steel bar and angle. The boreholes showed no indication of this and we claim an additional £2 per m³.

                                       £2,900
                                       £5,510

Quantity Surveyor to Architect   *7 September 1979*

The contractor has entered a claim totalling £5,510 in connection with the excavation for foundations in terms of the attached letter.

The quantity for Item 12F should have been 1,450 m³, but was incorrectly typed as 145. The contractor is therefore entitled to the extra 1,305 m³ at £0.83 = £1,083.15.

Regarding the 'correction' of the rate, as they say, this was queried before acceptance but they chose to adhere to it. They could have corrected it then but still adhered to their tender price had they chosen to do so. It is unfortunate, but in our opinion this matter comes within the provisions of Clause 13 of the Conditions under which such errors cannot be corrected. We therefore propose to reject this part of the claim.

Regarding the difficulty of excavation, we understand from the Clerk of Works that the contractor's statement is correct as to fact. He had, however, not quoted any provision of the contract under which he is claiming entitlement. In our view there is no such provision; no variation or provisional sum is involved so that Clause 11(6) does not apply. The

Method of Measurement requires 'rock' to be measured separately — but clearly the material is not rock — it is not even concrete or brickwork in the mass, but is rubble and debris. We recommend this part of the claim also be rejected.

Architect to Quantity Surveyor   *20 September 1979*

From the advice contained in your letter dated 7 September 1979 I agree I would be unable to certify any payment beyond £1,083.15.

Quantity Surveyor to Contractor   *24 September 1979*

With reference to your claim in respect of the foundation excavation I have to inform you that the quantity of item 12F will be corrected to add 1,305 m³ at £0.83 = £1,083.15. In view of the terms of Clause 13 of the Conditions, the rate of £0.83 cannot now be corrected.

Regarding the difficulty of excavation, it is regretted that no extra payment can be allowed. The material is not rock within the meaning of Clause D13.1 of the Standard Method of Measurement. Further, the Site Plan shows that the corner where these foundations occur was formerly a public tip. This was therefore a matter for which you should have made allowance in your price.

The contractor accepted this decision.

The matter of an incorrect rate or an underpriced item sometimes arises in connection with variations. The contract, however, makes provisions for variations and stipulates that in the case of work of similar character executed under similar conditions the bill rate shall apply. Even if the character or conditions are not similar the B/Q rates are to be the basis of the prices paid for varied work. It must of course be assumed that the variation is required in any case and has not been issued merely to take advantage of a low rate. Subject to that it is probable that an incorrect price would apply to any variation within the ambit of Clause 11(2).

(c) Measurement of formwork

The third claim arising in the course of preparing the final account concerned the measurement of formwork 'to edges and faces of foundations'.

The B/Q item for foundation concrete read:

Item 7C Concrete grade C10P in foundations exceeding 300 mm
thick in trench including formwork to vertical faces adjacent
to excavated face and removal   331 m³

The contractor's QS claimed that the Standard Method of Measurement stipulated that such formwork should be measured separately and that it was not possible with concrete measured in cube to ascertain what formwork was required.

The site QS replied that the word 'included' in the description of item 7C was quite clear and he could not disregard it.

The contractor accordingly entered a claim as follows:

Contractor to Quantity Surveyor   *1 November 1979*

Item 7C of the B/Q is for concrete foundations and is measured in cubic metres. The description says 'including formwork' but we contend that it is not feasible to include such a surface item in a cube measurement. In any case Clause F14 of the Standard Method of Measurement requires formwork to edges and faces of foundations to be measured separately. We therefore claim

Rough formwork 610 mm high and removing	1,084 m	£1.20	£1,300.80

Quantity Surveyor to Contractor   8 November 1979

With reference to your claim for formwork to foundations, I regret I am unable to accept your contention. It is agreed that formwork of this kind is usually measured separately (as required by the SMM), but in this case it was not. The drawings showing these foundations were available at time of tender and you could have ascertained the extent of the requirement. The fact that the SMM was not complied with is unfortunate but immaterial.

It is to be assumed that this method of dealing with the formwork was due to its being added at the last moment, and an 'easy way out' of a problem was adopted. The method is not advocated but an important point of principle is involved.

Contractor to Quantity Surveyor   23 November 1979

We cannot agree that non-compliance with the SMM is immaterial. Clause 12(1) of the Conditions states that 'the bills shall be deemed to have been prepared in accordance with the principles of the SMM — unless otherwise expressly stated in respect of any specified item . . .' There is no statement in the Bill that this or any other item does not comply with the SMM and we consider it unfair to hide such a matter in the description.

Quantity Surveyor to Contractor   6 December 1979

The requirement to include formwork in the item is quite clearly stated in the item. Surely there can be no doubt that 'including formwork' must mean 'including formwork'; it cannot be said to be hidden nor is there any possible ambiguity. Your claim is accordingly not accepted.

Claims on the basis that the Method of Measurement has not been followed precisely are not uncommon and there is a tendency on the part of some quantity surveyors to feel that anything short of literal compliance must be an error and consequently the contractor is entitled to payment. The Method of Measurement should of course be followed unless there are really cogent reasons for not doing so but departure is not a contractual crime, provided the item descriptions are clear and unambiguous. In *Farr v Ministry of Transport*[93] Lord Guest explained that the Method of Measurement is probably not even to be considered as a contract document. Its significance, he said, is that the B/Q is to be read in the light of the Standard Method. The House of Lords also held that prices in Bills of Quantities are, in the absence of some contrary indication, inclusive of all work contingently and manifestly necessary.

There is, however, the problem that Clause 12(1) of the JCT Form quoted above says that the bills shall be deemed to have been prepared in accordance with the principles of the Standard Method 'unless otherwise expressly stated'. 'Stated' suggests something external to the bill description, and whilst in general this is sensible enough, it is difficult to see

---

93. *Farr v Ministry of Transport* [1965] 5 BLR 94.

how the obvious and unequivocal meaning of the words of a bill description can be ignored in the absence of such a statement.

Contractor to Quantity Surveyor   *20 December 1979*

We reluctantly accept the decision contained in your letter of 6 December. We must, however, point out that formwork necessarily requires working space. There is no reference to that in the item and it has not been measured separately. We accordingly claim payment for this item as follows:

Additional excavation in working space and filling with suitable material and compacting $678 \ m^3$ *at £4.33 = £2,935.74*

Our rate is made up of the 'correct' rate for excavation (£2.83) plus £1.50 for refilling and compacting.

Having made the point that the words in an item mean what they say, it is a little difficult to refute the claim now being made. In some circumstances it might be argued that working space is contingently and indispensably necessary to placing formwork, but formwork itself can be said to be similarly necessary and both formwork and working space are measurable under the SMM.

Quantity Surveyor to Architect   *4 January 1980*

The contractor has accepted the decision in respect of his claim for formwork to the foundations but has now claimed to be paid for working space for fixing it. It must be admitted that working space is measurable under the standard method. He has claimed an excavation rate of £2.83, i.e. the 'correct' rate in question in claim (a). The work is, however, of similar character and executed under similar conditions to that priced in the bill and I therefore consider the bill rate applicable, plus of course payment for the refilling.

I therefore consider he should be paid:

$$678 \ m^3 \ at \ £2.33 \ (0.83 + 1.50) = £1,579.74$$

instead of the £2,935.74 claimed.

You will remember that the matter of requiring formwork to the foundations arose only two days before the bill was printed and to avoid delay it was dealt with by amending item 7C, with the result that the requirement for working space was overlooked. This is regretted but the contractor is losing in that there is another $678 \ m^3$ being paid for at £0.83, while the employer is paying no more than he would have done had the item been included in the bill.

Architect to Quantity Surveyor   *10 January 1980*

I agree we shall have to accept this.

Quantity Surveyor to Contractor   *14 January 1980*

With reference to your claim for working space, your claim is accepted in principle but I must point out that the work involved (so far as excavation is concerned) is exactly similar — indeed merely an extension of

*what was required originally. It is regretted therefore that this part of the
item will have to be paid at £0.83 instead of £2.83 plus £1.50 for refilling
and compacting. This will reduce your claim from £2,935.74 to £1,579.74.*

Clause 12(1) has been relocated in the 1980 Edition. Clause 2.2.1 now deals with the overriding status of the Conditions and 2.2.2.1 with the preparation of bills in accordance with the SMM; this is now not 'deemed' but says '... are to have been prepared ...'. Clause 2.2.2.2 now attempts to treat any departure from the SMM as a matter requiring correction, without any 'unless otherwise expressly stated ...'. It is of course to be recommended that a standard method of measurement be followed unless there is good reason for not doing so, but to attempt to enforce it by such Draconian terms against an established legal principle (not to say common sense) is unwise, indeed possibly dangerous. Clause 12(1) has already been heavily criticized by the Court of Appeal[94] in connection with the overriding status of the Conditions ('... nothing contained in the Contract Bills shall override or modify or affect in any way whatsoever the application or interpretation of that which is contained in these provisions ...). This has given rise to considerable difficulty in the courts, which have suggested it should be amended. Any attempt to make documents of general application override particular documents is fraught with difficulty.

GC/Wks 1 is similar to JCT in that Condition 4(1) says, 'In the case of discrepancy between these Conditions and the Specification and/or the Bills of Quantities, the provisions of these Conditions shall prevail.' It does not preclude amendments to the Conditions being made in the B/Q so long as they can be read together and there is no discrepancy, nor does it attempt to prohibit 'departure' from the SMM, though Condition 5(1) says, 'The Bills of Quantities shall be deemed to have been prepared in accordance with the principles of the method of measurement expressed therein except where otherwise stated.' This too seems to call for a 'statement' rather than allow a clear, unambiguous description to suffice by itself. On the whole, however, it is rather less restrictive than JCT.

The contractor in this case still feels aggrieved, however, and has another shot in his locker. He now writes direct to the architect as required under Clause 11(6).

Contractor to Architect   *24 January 1980*

> *I refer to my claim dated 4 January 1980 in respect of the excavation for working space required to fix formwork for the foundation concrete. It has been admitted that omission of this item from the bill was an error. Clause 12(2) of the Conditions says 'any error in ... or omission from the Contract bills ... shall be corrected and deemed to be a variation ...'*
>
> *Clause 11(6) says 'If ... the architect is of the opinion that a variation ... has involved the contractor in direct loss and/or expense for which he would not be reimbursed in respect of a valuation made in accordance with the rules contained in sub-clause (4) of this Condition ... then the architect shall either himself ascertain or shall instruct the Quantity Surveyor to ascertain the amount of such loss or expense.'*
>
> *We formally claim that the additional cost and expense in this connection was £2,935.74, as stated in our letter of 20 December 1979.*

This part of the claim differs from that concerning the formwork in that here an error is involved; with the formwork there was no error within the meaning of Clause 11(6).

The architect discusses the matter further with the QS, who has to agree that the contractor's claim is logical and within the terms of the clauses quoted. He does, however, point out that the contractor was given the opportunity to correct the rate before acceptance (which

---

94. *English Industrial Estates v George Wimpey* [1972] 7 BLR 122.

need not have involved any increase in the tender price). On balance it is agreed that the claim should be accepted. There is, however, the question as to what constitutes 'direct loss and/or expense' and the architect requests the quantity surveyor to look into this aspect.

Discussion with the contractor reveals that he is unable to isolate the cost of this particular work. Excavation costs are shown as a whole but not distributed over the various bill items. The following figures are produced:

	£	
Direct costs of labour (including labour oncosts)	14,347.10	
Plant, fuel etc	2,073.15	16,420.25
Add site oncosts as in tender rates 14.45%		
Add overheads and profit 6% (do)		985.22
		17,405.47
Value of excavation items in final a/c		12,481.35
Overall 'loss'		£ 4,924.12

Known causes of loss		
(a) In respect of error in rate (1,450 m^3 at £2)	2,900.00	
(b) In respect of more difficult material (as claim)	2,900.00	
(c) In respect of working space (£2,935.74 − 1,579.74 as claim)	1,356.00	
		£ 7,156.00

As the contractor has no unit-costing system and so cannot demonstrate what the various items comprising the excavation have in fact cost, it could be argued that he cannot show the loss or expense involved in connection with this excavation for working space. It would, however, be not unreasonable to allocate the overall loss between the known factors causing it, which would give him:

$$\frac{1,356}{7,156} \times 4,924.12 = £933.06$$

plus of course the £1,579.74 originally offered, making a total of £2,512.80.

This amount was offered him in settlement and eventually accepted.

<table>
<tr><td>Points of principle involved</td><td>

Discrepancy — quality of concrete

Errors such as a simple discrepancy between B/Q and specification/drawings are unlikely to cause problems. The standard forms make provision for correction. Problems can arise where the price put against the (incorrect) B/Q item is either in error or is 'loaded'. The method of correction illustrated in claim (a) above would leave the original rate (with its error or loading etc.) intact, and is generally to be preferred to constructing a new rate.

Errors in quantity

Regarding errors in quantity there is usually no problem so long as the unit price is correct.

The case discussed here is based on JCT 63/77, Clause 12 of which says, 'Any error ... in quantity ... shall be corrected ... and deemed to be a variation ...' JCT 80 Clause 2.2.2.2 is similar.

In case of civil engineering contracts based on ICE5 or ICE6, the matter would be dealt with under Clause 56(2) as for any other change in quantity.

In both cases the objective is similar, to give to the contractor and require the employer to pay the rate which would have been payable had the correct quantity been stated in the

</td></tr>
</table>

first place. That means that all factors including labour, materials, plant, on and off site overheads and profit fall to be adjusted so far as they have been affected by the increase or decrease in quantity *per se*. If the price has been 'loaded' then the question whether this loading falls to be adjusted (e.g. consequent upon a reduction in quantity) or not (e.g. where the reasons for loading have been satisfied without regard to an increase in quantity) should be determined by reference to fact or reason rather than intuititve attempts to avoid payment just because the rate seems high or attempting to enforce a rate just because it seems advantageous.

If there is an error in the rate, it is probably generally correct to say that the B/Q price (high or low) should be the basis of the price applicable to the corrected quantity. This at least has the benefit of certainty and provides incentive for avoiding error. It follows that some care is needed when examining tenders to try to detect errors (as distinct from merely high or low prices).

A high or low price may be due to a number of reasons. If the quantity is small, the rate tendered may be low because the tenderer has considered the item to be insignificant. Conversely it may be high because the small quantity will have little effect on the tender. It may be low because the contractor has detected an over-measurement and is attempting to minimise the effect of correction, or high in the case of under-measurement to maximise the effect of correction. Again this needs to be watched when examining tenders and challenged then if thought necessary (or even then to take the opportunity of correcting the quantity and resolving the effect on the rate. There is a greater willingness at that stage to negotiate than after the contact is let).

It seems right that the contractor should be stuck with his price in this situation, unless he has been misled, but equally the employer should not expect to gain by attempting to enforce a reduction of an over-remunerative rate.

Departures from Method of Measurement

In the case of departures from the Method of Measurement, the rule should be that provided the B/Q item description is clear and unambiguous this is effective and operative whatever an M of M prescribes (on the legal axiom that the particular overrides the general). With the ICE Conditions there is no problem as all the documents are construed together, but with JCT and GC/Wks 1 the Conditions of Contract provide that the conditions cannot be amended by provisions in the B/Q. JCT 80 goes further and appears to make any departure 'correctable'. Where departures are preceded by a statement to the effect that such and such items are not measured in accordance with an M of M there will probably be no problem but it can always happen that such a statement is inadvertently omitted, yet the scope and requirement of the B/Q item may be perfectly clear. In such an event it would be less than sensible to say that the M of M must prevail, yet that is what JCT 80 attempts to do. It is likely to lead to as much trouble and criticism from the courts as Clause 12 of the previous edition.

Omission to measure

Omission to measure something required by the M of M can also cause difficulty, yet the problem must be judged on the same basis. Bill items must mean what they say, yet no description can be exhaustively complete, so what may be properly and safely implied? Only, it is submitted, matters which are contingently and indispensably necessary to the work described, and then on a narrow construction. Even so this must be construed in the light of the fact the Conditions of Contract provide that bills are based on Method of Measurement so that where, say, a type of temporary work (e.g. formwork) is generally required to be measured separately then it would require clear words in the description to include it there and it would not be correct to attempt to argue that formwork, being contingently and indispensably necessary to the use of concrete, could properly and safely be read into a bill of description.

CASE 5.3 CLAIM IN RESPECT OF ERRORS IN BILL OF QUANTITIES (Civil Engineering Forms and Method of Measurement)

Pertinent particulars of contract

Contract for the construction of a road.

The documents comprised Drawings, Specification, Conditions of Contract ICE 5 and B/Q based on Civil Engineering Standard Method of Measurement.

Tender dated 1 May 1979. Tender total £1,728,148. Time for completion 21 months.

Development of claim

(a) In the course of measuring completed work in the ordinary course of events, the contractor claimed there was an error in the B/Q in that separate items had not been provided in the Bill for rock excavation. 'Rock' was defined in geological terms in the Specification for fill and embankment purposes.

The main B/Q item in question read:

28c Excavate in any material in cuttings for re-use   380,000 m^3 at £

The matter was raised by the contractor's QS with the site QS, who asked the RE whether 'rock' had been encountered and if so whether any record had been made of the extent.

The RE replied that rock in terms of the Specification had been encountered and had been used as prescribed in forming the lower part of certain embankments. The latter had been recorded on drawings but the former not, as the RE had taken the view that 'any material' meant 'any material'.

In view of this the contractor decided that he must enter a claim.

> *Contractor to Engineer's Representative*   *8 August 1979*
>
> *We draw your attention to the fact that rock (as defined in Specification Clause ...) has been encountered, and in fact used as fill in embankment. Excavation of rock has not, however, been measured and we claim payment for this at £1.48 per m^3, in respect of 28,715 m^3.*

> *Engineer's Representative to Contractor*   *10 August 1979*
>
> *Your attention is drawn to the wording of all the excavation items in the B/Q, of which 28c is the largest. These are all in terms of 'Excavate in any material'. Surely this is quite clear and can mean nothing less than 'any material' and so must include rock. In any case no records have been kept of this excavation, no notice having been given that you intended to claim.*

> *Contractor to Engineer's Representative*   *17 August 1979*
>
> *We agree that in the ordinary way 'any material' would seem to be clear enough but we submit that this has to be read as an item in a Bill of Quantities which, according to Clause 57 of the Conditions 'shall be deemed to have been prepared ... according to the procedure set forth in the CESMM'. The CESMM requires rock to be measured separately.*
>
> *Clause 57 does contain a provision for not following this procedure but it does stipulate 'except where any statement or general or detailed description ... expressly shows to the contrary'. In our opinion the use of*

the words 'any material' are not sufficiently clear as to amount to an express departure and are ambiguous.

We regret you were not notified about this matter earlier so that you could have checked our records at the time. They are, however, available for your inspection at any time.

Engineer's Representative to Quantity Surveyor   *22 August 1979*

I enclose correspondence with the contractor in which he claims payment for the excavation of rock. I think this is self-explanatory and I would appreciate your opinion.

Quantity Surveyor to Engineer's Representative   *29 August 1979*

I agree that in the normal usage 'any material' is wide enough to include rock. The addition of the words 'for re-use' would, however, probably be sufficient to exclude unsuitable soft material — but this is to admit that the words 'any material' cannot in this contract be taken literally. Further I consider that the use of this term 'any material' has to be construed in the context that the Bill is deemed to have been prepared in accordance with the CESMM and as a general rule this requirement is followed. In my opinion this means that if in any given case something else is required (and this is quite permissible if not always advisable), care must be taken to ensure that against that background, against the usual expectations, this departure is expressly shown.

In this case, because, as I have indicated, it cannot be taken literally, there is ambiguity. It would have been a simple matter to put beyond all doubt by saying 'any material, including rock'. I consider the contractor's claim must be accepted in principle, as an error or omission from the B/Q in accordance with Clause 55.

Regarding the quantity, it is a pity that the contractor did not give notice earlier. I suggest you arrange for your inspectors to examine the records and see how far they can substantiate or correct the contractor's record drawings.

Finally, it seems to me that the rate claimed is somewhat high. If you agree the claim in principle I will ask my man on site to look into the rate.

This was evidently done as the next letter was:

Engineer's Representative to Contractor   *14 September 1979*

As discussed, I am prepared to accept your claim for extra payment for rock excavation in principle, but as you know I have had my inspectors examining your record drawings. Whilst there is a large measure of agreement, our records of rock levels between chainage 2100 and 2350 do not agree at all with yours. I have looked at such evidence as is still available and am of the opinion that no more than the quantities indicated by our records can be substantiated. I am therefore prepared to agree a volume of only 22,482 m^3.

Regarding the price, I understand that details of your build-up have been examined by the QS and you have agreed that a certain amount was in fact got out by ripper. I further understand that a revised rate of £1.16 has been provisionally agreed. I am prepared to approve this rate.

The contractor was inclined to cavil at the reduced quantity but the engineer wrote:

Engineer's Representative to Contractor   *21 September 1979*

I am sorry you consider the volume of 22,482 m³ to be understated, but I must point out that you failed to notify me of your intentions to claim before excavation commenced. I must draw your attention to Clause 52(4) which says:

'*(b) If the contractor intends to claim any additional payment pursuant to any Clause of these conditions other than Sub-clauses (1) and (2) of this clause he shall give notice in writing ... as soon as reasonably possible ... Upon the happening of such events the contractor shall keep such contemporary records as may be reasonably necessary to support any claim ... ', and*

'*(e) If the contractor fails to comply with any of the provisions of this clause ... then the contractor shall be entitled to payment in respect thereof only to the extent that the engineer has not been prevented from or substantially prejudiced by such failure in investigating the said claim.'*

The ICE Conditions are much better than either JCT or GC/Wks 1 in this connection in not necessarily requiring a 'statement' external to the item, but there must be no compromise about expressly showing the departure and making the item description clear and unambiguous. The normal construction of a B/Q must be in the light of the Method of Measurement[95] so that any changes or departures can be seen to be positive. This is not difficult; usually an extra two or three words (as in the case here illustrated) will put the matter beyond doubt.

The giving notice is an important requirement. The question has been asked as to what is 'reasonably possible'. This must depend on circumstances, but in the present case it would seem that notice could have been given earlier than in fact it was. If the contractor neglects to give notice he can hardly complain if the engineer is unable to establish or corroborate the facts later. This method is at least better than a sharp cut-off date beyond which claims will not be accepted at all. First it is doubtful if such terms can be enforced legally but in any case they do not overcome the practical problem of corroboration.

(b) Another matter raised by the contractor was the measurement of working space to the back of an abutment which was required to be shuttered.

Contractor to Engineer's Representative   *1 November 1979*

We would draw your attention to Item 37F in Bill Part 4 for the excavation to the abutment to Bridge ... According to the Specification Clause ... the back face of this wall is required to be shuttered, but the projection of the foundation (to which excavation would normally be measured) is only 150 mm and so is insufficient to provide working space.

We have discussed this matter with your site QS, who has refused to measure this additional excavation (which we had to do) on the grounds that CESMM Class E Note 8 says that 'additional excavation necessary to provide working space shall not be measured'. We are of course aware of this Note but in the terms of B/Q items we are unable to distinguish between those where working space is required and those where it is not.

---

95. See *A E Farr Ltd v Ministry of Transport* [1965] 5 BLR 94.

Figure 5.3.1

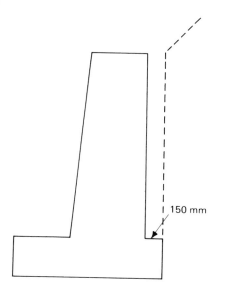

150 mm

Figure 5.3.2

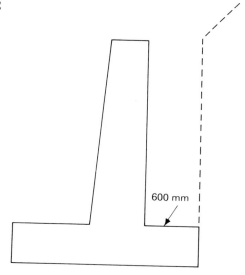

600 mm

We draw your attention to Item 22B in Bill Part 6 in connection with the retaining wall adjacent to this bridge. The wording is in exactly similar terms and the requirement for back shuttering is the same, but in this case the projection of the foundations (600 mm) is sufficient to provide working space to fix and remove the formwork.

We therefore claim the measurement of the additional excavation and back-filling:

61 m³	*Excavate for working space*	£3.55	£216.55
46 m³	*Backfilling with suitable material and compacting*	£2.40	£110.40	£326.95

Figures 5.3.1 and 5.3.2 illustrate the problem.

The B/Q items referred to read as follows:

37F	Excavate in material other than top-soil, rock or artificial hard material for abutment	306 m³	£3.55	£1,086.30

22B　Excavate in material other than top-soil, rock or
　　　artificial hard material for retaining wall

　　　　　　　　　　　　　　　1,414 m³　£3.55　£5,019.70

On the footing that each of these items appeared in separate Bill Parts which were referable to specific structures and could thus be identified on drawings the need for working space in the one case but not the other should have been apparent (see CESMM para 5.11). On this basis it would seem that this claim should be rejected.

Engineer's Representative to Contractor　　　　　　　　　　*8 November 1979*

　　It is pointed out that the requirements in each case are clearly shewn on drawings and the CESMM is quite unequivocal about working space not being measured. I must accordingly reject your claim.

Contractor to Engineer's Representative　　　　　　　　　　*23 November 1979*

　　We regret we are unable to accept your decision in connection with our claim for working space. We appreciate that Note E8 says working space shall not be measured, but it must follow that cases where it is required must be distinguished from those where it is not. When tendering we did in fact examine the drawings for the retaining wall (which appeared first) but did not check those for the abutment on the assumption that with the wording of the two items being identical, the requirements must be the same.

　　We consider we have been misled and that additional description should have been given, as required by CESMM para 3.2.

　　We still contend that this constitutes an error or omission within the meaning of Clause 55 of the Conditions and we should be glad if you would reconsider your decision.

Points of principle involved

The CESMM makes a point of brevity (paras 1.7, 2.5 and 3.3), but it also makes the point in 2.4 that the object of a B/Q is 'to provide such information . . . as to enable tenders to be prepared efficiently and accurately' and in 2.5 that ' . . . work should be itemised . . . in sufficient detail for it to be possible to distinguish between different classes of work and work of the same nature carried out in different locations, or in any other circumstances which may give rise to different considerations of cost'. Again in 5.10 ' . . . additional description may be provided if the nature, location . . . or other special characteristics . . . is thought likely to give rise to . . . considerations of cost'.

　　In this case, although Note E8 and para 5.11 suggest that the contractor is not entitled, it is considered that the principles of the CESMM as set out in the paragraphs quoted have not been complied with, that there is ambiguity between the two items because they are in the same words for different circumstances and to a certain extent constitute a trap for the contractor. It is probable that in the event of arbitration the *contra proferentem* rule would be applied and the Bill construed against the party putting it forward, i.e. the employer.

　　There are many instances of this kind in the CESMM where it says 'separate items are not required for this or that', or, as in this case, something 'shall not be measured'. In all such cases it is necessary to ensure that Bill descriptions set out clearly what is required and that if separate items are not required (for disposal, compaction, working space etc) then these are covered expressly in the description of the parent item. It is both pointless and dangerous to do otherwise. The case of *A E Farr Ltd v Ministry of Transport*[96] went from arbitration to the House of Lords (via the High Court and Court of Appeal) on the

---

96.　*A E Farr Ltd v Ministry of Transport* [1965] 5 BLR 94.

question of measuring working space. The contract in question was on ICE 4 and the 1953 Method of Measurement of Civil Engineering Quantities, but it illustrated the problems of loosely prepared Bills and the status of the Method of Measurement.

Had the MMRB been used in Case 5.3(b) the outcome might have been little different. In this case the items would (presumably) have read:

37F   Excavate in suitable material except rock for structural foundations

and 22B would have been in precisely similar terms.

In both cases the item coverage of para 6.13 would have applied, which included *inter alia*:

(n)   additional excavation the contractor may require for working space ... and its subsequent backfilling.

The requirement would have been operative in the case of Item 37F but not 22B, but no provision is made in MMRB or its Notes for Guidance to omit any part of item coverage which is not operative. So again the only way for the contractor to distinguish between the items is to look at the drawings. Whether it is feasible for him to do so for every item in the Bill in the short time available to him for tendering is questionable and whether a court would consider it possible is also doubtful.

There is of course the possibility that in order to comply with the item coverage the contractor might allow for working space in both cases. Neither example can be decided with certainty but the contractor is more likely to succeed in this case with CESMM than with MMRB.

See also the comment following Case 5.2 above.

Chapter 6
Claims arising in connection with execution of the work

GENERALLY

As has been said, contract documents are prepared in the light of events in prospect. Claims arising in connection with the execution of the work concern the occurrence of actual events, both physical and non-physical, including the discovery that an assumption as to existing fact at the time of contract was incorrect. Standard forms of contract effectively allocate the risks of events occurring between the parties by providing for additional payment and/or extension of time in certain circumstances. It is a matter of construction, in the light of the matrix of facts known to the parties at the time of contract, whether particular circumstances come within the ambit of the provisions.

For the purposes of contractual analysis, such events may be divided into five categories:

1. Where existing facts are found to be different from those anticipated or stated at the time of contract.

2. Where events outside the control of either party occurring after the time of contract are such as to render performance of the contract either impossible or more difficult than anticipated at the time of tender.

3. Where the conduct, statements or instructions of one party or its agents change or affect the obligations of the other party.

4. Where the contract is affected by the acts or omissions of third parties.

5. Where performance by one or other party turns out to be defective.

CATEGORIES OF EVENTS

Discovery of existing facts

The eventual burden of contractual obligations depends in part on facts which already exist at the moment when the contract comes into being but are not discovered until the work is under way. For example, the nature and topography of the ground in which the works are to be constructed, the existence and location of underground services on the site, the range of astronomical tides, and the condition of existing structures affected by the works are already facts at the time of contract. Claims in this category concern the extent to which these facts were or should have been known to the contractor or the extent to which, whether he knew or not, he nevertheless bears the risk.

In practice a tenderer needs to have certain information or make assumptions as to existing facts to provide a basis for his estimates, but there is no general principle of law that a contracting party is entitled to relief if his tender assumptions turn out to be wrong or he encounters unusually difficult or costly situations,[1] nor is there a general duty of disclosure. The general rule is that the terms of a contract are to be construed in the light of the matrix of facts known to the parties at the time of contract, whether or not they actually considered their relevance,[2] but that does not of itself provide relief if facts are unknown. Common law or statutory remedies may be available against a party if he or his agent has made pre-contract misrepresentations of fact or has expressly or impliedly warranted the accuracy of statements of fact which turn out to be incorrect, but generally any relief must be found in explicit provisions within the contract. Such provisions must be stipulated at the time of contract: there is no equitable jurisdiction to rewrite an improvident contract.[3]

Explicit provisions, such as ICE or FIDIC Clause 12, which depend on foreseeability as a criterion for additional payment or extensions of time for completion, necessarily require the basis of such foresight to be contractually defined. Foreseeability is well understood as a legal concept in relation to recoverability of damages,[4] but it does not follow automatically that the same definition of foreseeability applies or will be adopted in relation to performance obligations. The criterion can be framed by the contract in terms of what the contractor actually foresaw when he made his estimates, or what he ought to have foreseen if he had carried out investigations, or what some mythical experienced contractor could have foreseen on the basis of practicable (or impracticable) investigations. It may be stipulated

---

1. *British Movietonews v London & District Cinemas* [1952] AC 166 at 185.
2. *Reardon Smith Line v Yngvar Hansen-Tangen* [1976] 1 WLR 989.
3. *Clea Shipping v Bulk Oil (No 2)* [1984] 1 All ER 129.
4. *Victoria Laundry (Windsor) v Newman Industries* [1949] 2 KB 528, see pages 31, 32 *supra*.

that pre-contract information provided by or on behalf of the employer is to be taken into account, or not. Of necessity the reference date will normally be the date of tender rather than the date of contract.

Contractor deemed to have satisfied himself

ICE5 Clause 11 provides that the contractor is:

> 'deemed to have inspected and examined the Site and its surroundings and to have satisfied himself before submitting his tender as to the nature of the ground and subsoil (so far as is practicable and having taken into account any information in connection therewith which may have been provided by or on behalf of the Employer) the form and nature of the Site the extent and nature of the work ... the means of communication with and access to the Site ... and in general to have obtained for himself all necessary information (subject as above-mentioned) as to risks contingencies and all other circumstances ...'

GC/Wks 1 Edition 2 Condition 2(1) is apparently in much the same vein:

> 'The Contractor shall be deemed to have satisfied himself ... and generally to have obtained his own information on all matters affecting the execution of the Works and the prices tendered therefor except information given or referred to in the Bills of Quantities which is required to be given in accordance with the method of measurement expressed in the Bills of Quantities.'

Despite the apparent similarity, the impact and intent of the two provisions is radically different. There is no equivalent of ICE Clause 12 in the unamended GC/Wks 1 Edition 2; instead, Condition 2(2) stipulates:

> 'No claim by the Contractor for additional payment will be allowed on the ground of any misunderstanding or misinterpretation in respect of any such matter nor shall the Contractor be released from any risks or obligations imposed on or undertaken by him under the Contract on any such ground or on the ground that he did not or could not foresee any matter which might affect or have affected the execution of the Works.'

In the ICE Conditions, the objective of Clauses 11 and 12 is to allocate risks of physical conditions by reference to an objective standard of foreseeability, recognizing the reliance that will naturally be placed by tenderers on information supplied by or on behalf of the Employer at the time of tender. GC/Wks 1 Edition 2 Condition 2, on the other hand, is intended as an exclusion clause, to exclude liability in respect of any misrepresentation by the employer. As with any contractual provision excluding liability for misrepresentation, it will be subject (at least on domestic UK contracts) to the reasonableness test imposed by the Misrepresentation Act 1967 s3.[5]

An amendment to GC/Wks 1 Edition 2 was issued in 1987 which introduced entitlement to relief in the event of unforeseeable ground conditions. GC/Works 1 Edition 3 has moved much closer to ICE5; Condition 7 provides relief in the event of 'Unforeseeable Ground Conditions', defined as ground conditions which the Contractor

> 'did not know of, and which he could not reasonably have foreseen having regard to any information which he had or ought reasonably to have ascertained ...'

Disclosure by Employer

Under FIDIC4, Clause 12.2 provides relief similar to ICE Clause 12, but FIDIC4 Clause 11 goes further and imposes a positive duty of disclosure on the employer, as follows:

---

5. As amended by the Unfair Contract Terms Act 1977 s8. The UK legislation has been followed in some other common law countries; for example, the Misrepresentation Ordinance (Cap 284) in Hong Kong.

'The Employer shall have made available to the Contractor, before the submission by the Contractor of the Tender, such data on hydrological and sub-surface conditions as have been obtained by or on behalf of the Employer from investigations undertaken relevant to the Works but the Contractor shall be responsible for his own interpretation thereof.'

The clause continues:

'The Contractor shall be deemed to have inspected and examined the Site and its surroundings and information available in connection therewith and to have satisfied himself (so far as is practicable, having regard to considerations of cost and time) before submitting his Tender ...'

It concludes:

'The Contractor shall be deemed to have based his Tender on the data made available by the Employer and on his own inspection and examination, all as aforementioned.'

It may appear at first sight that FIDIC4 shifts more risk onto the Employer than ICE5 or GC/Works 1 Edition 3, but by introducing a positive duty of disclosure of defined scope on the Employer and placing responsibility for the interpretation of the data clearly on the Contractor, the clause may well promote better pre-contract preparation and sound tendering, and reduce the likelihood of disputes.

'Deeming' is a contractual device to fix a state of affairs as a fact for the purposes of a specific contract. The law is not, however, concerned with the truth of the fact — the law often employs fiction as a device. Accordingly, neither Clause 11 of ICE5 or FIDIC4, nor Conditon 2(1) of GC/Wks 1 Edition 2, nor Condition 7(1) of GC/Wks 1 Edition 3, imposes any actual duty on the Contractor. Rather the deemed inspection and examination is a legal fiction, to be accepted in relation to any matter or claim under the contract whether it is true or not. Subject to any legal or contractual requirement of reasonableness or practicability, the deemed act is to be accepted as fact, irrespective of the practical feasibility of having done what was deemed to be done.

This approach reflects a legal problem, that the contract (that is, the legally binding agreement as distinct from the documents proposed to form the written agreement) does not yet exist at the time of tender. The contract can therefore only deal with actions prior to the agreement in retrospect, either by deeming the performance of the action to be fact or by promising that the action has been performed. FIDIC4 Clause 11 deals with pre-contract provision of data by the Employer as a promise — 'The Employer shall have made available'. In ICE6, the same objective has been approached by a deeming provision. ICE6 Clause 11(1) provides:

'The Employer shall be deemed to have made available to the Contractor before the submission of the Tender all information on the nature of the ground and subsoil including hydrological conditions obtained by or on behalf of the Employer from investigations undertaken relevant to the Works.

The Contractor shall be responsible for the interpretation of all such information for the purposes of constructing the Works and for any design which is the Contractor's responsibility under the Contract.'

ICE6 Clause 11(3) then says:

'The Contractor shall be deemed to have based his Tender on the information made available by the Employer and on his own inspection and examination all as aforesaid ...'

138

The effect of the deeming provision in Clause 11(1) is not entirely clear, since it does not amount to a promise. It means that the employer cannot suddenly produce new data after the time of Tender and say it ought to have been taken into account by the Contractor. On the other hand, unlike FIDIC4, it does not create a clear duty of disclosure, nor does it provide any direct remedy to a Contractor if data has been withheld. What would be the position if, for example, information had been withheld which would have disclosed the existence of pockets of fine sand susceptible to piping, but the same information was available to the contractor from other published sources?

Interpretation of data

A warranty is probably to be implied that such information about boreholes etc as may have been proffered by the employer is accurate so far as it goes, but that does not amount to a warranty that the whole of the ground will be identical to the borehole logs or test results. Bores and trial pits give only a sample of the total site. How far they are representative of the whole site is a matter for expert interpretation within a wider geological and geotechnical context.

Problems can arise where site investigation reports provided by the employer include interpretation as well as data. The newer editions, ICE6 and FIDIC4, have both made clear that the contractor is only entitled to rely on the data. The interpretation of the data is the responsibility of the contractor and the contractor may not rely on the interpretation in the Site Investigation Reports.

Data on boreholes etc. will mean different things to a contractor than the designer; indeed, it is a source of many problems that the scope of pre-contract site investigations is sometimes fixed only with the purpose of providing information for the permanent works design, with inadequate regard to the needs of temporary works design and construction method selection.

Non-physical facts

Equally significant may be non-physical facts such as restrictions on working, requirements for permits, and fees and dues payable; these matters are usually dealt with in separate provisions.[6]

Subsequent events This category is concerned with what might be called true events — things happening or changing, rather than the mere discovery of existing but unknown facts. It is concerned with events which are beyond the control of either party. Examples include storms, subsequent legislation, strikes, fire, theft or accidents to persons or property.

Some events occurring after the time of contract may be so drastic as to prevent further performance of the works as originally contemplated by the contract. The contractual provisions relating to such events are considered later in Chapter 9.

Other events, which are beyond the control of either party, may increase the difficulty or cost of performance without preventing it. Some events in this category, such as inclement weather or subsequent legislation, are left as risks to be borne by the contractor, subject to any explicit relief under the contract. If events are not such as to prevent performance, there is little chance of extra-contractual relief for the contractor, so any relief must be provided by explicit provisions. Where the burden of risk is unclear, for example, the risk of damage to the works, the contract should allocate the risk explicitly, specifying any exceptions and provisions for transfer of the risk.

Insurable events

Some events outside the control of the parties can be covered by insurance and the contract may include a requirement for the contractor or employer to effect insurance corresponding

---

6. For example, Clause 6 of JCT 80, Clause 26 of ICE5.

to the allocation of risk. The contract will normally only stipulate insurance obligations so far as necessary to protect the employer's interests. The contractual stipulations do not prevent the contractor from effecting further insurance for his own interests.

Damage to the Works

One of the more frequent insurable events is damage to the Works. Under JCT 80, Clause 22 sets out alternative provisions for insurance of the Works. Under ICE5 and ICE6, Clause 20 defines the contractor's risk and responsibility, while Clause 21 provides for insurance of the risk. Condition 26 of GC/Wks 1 Edition 2 stipulates that the Works shall stand at the risk of the Contractor, but does not require the Contractor to insure the risk. In GC/Wks 1 Edition 3, Condition 19 defines the Contractor's risks, while Condition 8 now requires insurance of those risks. A prudent contractor would normally choose to insure against the risk, even where it is not a contractual obligation to do so. The difference is that, under ICE5, ICE6, JCT 80 and GC/Wks 1 Edition 3, the employer is empowered to effect an insurance policy in the name of the contractor and contra-charge him with the premiums, if he fails to comply with the insurance requirements. JCT 80 also contains alternative provisions whereby the employer may elect to assume responsibility for effecting the original policy.

The object of insurance requirements is not directly to transfer the risks to another party (the Insurance Company). The nature of the insurance cover is generally an 'indemnity policy'. The Insurance Company is to indemnify the party bearing the risk and thereby ensure, indirectly, that there shall be a fund of money available to make good damage which does occur, even to the extent of total loss. Both the risk and the obligation to complete the work remain with the contractor, subject to his right to an indemnity by the Insurers against the risk insured. Generally a risk is only covered by the insurance if the person insured bears the primary legal risk. It is therefore essential to effective insurance and the avoidance of duplicate premiums that risks are clearly defined and allocated. Just how far insurable risk rests with or is transferred to a contractor depends on the terms of the contract; for example, in *Farr v Admiralty*[7] it was held that the contractor and his insurers were liable for damage to the jetty under construction caused by the negligent navigation of one of the employer's vessels.

Under the ICE Conditions, the scope of the risk insured is subject to the same exclusions as the Contractor's risk under ICE5 Clause 20(3) or ICE6 Clause 20(2), in addition to any special exclusions added by insurers. When the Contractor's responsibility for the Works ceases in accordance with Clause 20(1), insurance cover ceases. Under ICE5 (but not ICE6), the Contractor's responsibility continues for 14 days after the issue of a Certificate of Completion. This is to allow the Employer time to effect his own insurance. It is important under all forms of contract that the Architect or Engineer should give notice to the Employer of the impending issue of completion certificates to enable the Employer to effect his own insurance cover.

Payment of a premium does not, of itself, ensure cover of loss or damage suffered. Apart from questions as to whether the party insured was bearing the risk at the relevant time, further exclusions and conditions may be imposed by the policy, usually including a requirement of prompt notification. Common law rules applicable to contracts of insurance also apply, including a strict requirement of full disclosure of all material facts at the time of effecting the policy and afterwards,[8] and the insurer's right of 'subrogation' — to defend the claim in the name of the insured without hindrance by the insured.

Under the JCT form, the position is different in that the insurance requirement is a Joint Names Policy which indemnifies both the Contractor and the Employer against their potential loss, within the terms of the policy. This permits, for example, Clause 23.3.2 whereby

---

7. *Farr v Admiralty* [1953] 1 WLR 965; see also *Pearce v Hereford Corp* [1968] 66 LGR 647.
8. Under the doctrine of *uberrimae fides*.

the Insurance policy may be extended to cover parts of the Works after the employer has taken possession.

Insurance provisions may be included in the contract in relation to contractor's plant, as in ICE5 Clause 21; the primary objective of this is to safeguard the employer's security in the contractor's plant provided by the vesting provisions of Clause 53. In ICE6, Clause 53 has been amended to recognize the limited use of plant directly owned by the contractor, and Clause 21 has consequently been amended to omit the requirement to insure contractor's plant other than plant for incorporation in the Works.

Third party liability

Forms of contract commonly provide for insurance against liability to third parties, again on an indemnity basis. The cover provided by policies is subject to the same exclusions of risk as the contractor's liability. Such a policy should not include the employer as a joint insured if it is intended to cover damage to the employer's property, since the employer is then not a third party.

Acts of the parties or their agents

Performance of the contract may also be affected by the acts or omissions of the parties, or delays in acting. Such acts are not necessarily deliberate but, in civil law,[9] it is generally the acts or words themselves, rather than the intention, that counts. Words are to be interpreted as they would be understood by a reasonable person rather than the meaning intended by the speaker or writer. Intent may be relevant, however, where the good faith or impartiality of the A/E/QS is in question.

Each party is responsible for the acts of its agents, acting within their actual or apparent authority.[10] Such acts are considered to be equivalent to the acts of the party itself. The apparent authority of the A/E/QS and the Contractor's Agent or Responsible Person are both to be found in the contract itself, but not all powers conferred on the A/E/QS by the contract are to be treated as powers of agency, nor is the A/E/QS considered automatically to have acted as the employer's agent prior to the contract.

Written instructions

In law, there is no essential distinction between the written and spoken word, except that proof of the spoken word poses problems of evidence. To avoid this problem, conditions of contract often impose requirements of formality, for example, that instructions must be given or confirmed in writing within a specified period in order to be recognized, and that notices must be given in certain forms and within specified time limits. Nevertheless, such formalities are not always observed precisely and this is often a source of disputed claims.

For example, an instruction may be given by a Clerk of Works or Site Inspector which, so far as he is concerned, is intended to be no more than a reminder of some requirement in the Specification or the remedy of some shortcoming. As understood by the recipient (who is not always the Agent) it is an instruction to be followed and then reported to the Site Engineer or Agent. The latter, getting it second or third hand, is quite likely to understand something different from the originator's intention and to him it may appear to be a variation order and thus a matter of additional payment — i.e. a claim. A system such as site notes in a duplicate book should be used to minimize the scope for misunderstandings. It is also important that the contents of such notes should be communicated promptly upwards to the Agent and A/E/QS, and that confirmations (or retractions) should be issued at the authorized level. What may have been thought to be a routine comment on what or how something was to be done could very well seem to be a variation order entitling the contractor to claim payment.

The question may arise whether an instruction by the Architect or Engineer constitutes

---

9. As distinct from the criminal law where intent is commonly a necessary ingredient.
10. See pages 80–82 *supra*.

a variation. In *Brodie v Cardiff Corporation*,[11] it was held that refusal by the Engineer to issue the written variation order required by the contract was not conclusive that an instruction was not a variation. Under ICE5 and ICE6 Clause 13 provides for payment for instructions beyond what could have been foreseen by an experienced contractor at the time of Tender. Under ICE5 the instruction need not be in writing, but ICE6 Clause 2(6) requires all instructions to be in writing or be confirmed by the contractor in writing.

GC/Wks 1 Edition 2 Condition 9 does not distinguish between instructions and variations, but Condition 9(2) provides for payment of any expense properly and directly incurred in complying with the SO's instructions, beyond that otherwise provided for in or reasonably contemplated by the Contract. Entitlement is subject to certain conditions being satisfied, including that the SO's instructions shall have been given or confirmed in writing. The instructions can apparently only be confirmed by the SO rather than the contractor, as Condition 2(2) provides for confirmation to be given by the SO of oral instructions 'upon a reasonable request by the Contractor made within fourteen days of the issue of such instructions'.

Under GC/Wks 1 Edition 3, Condition 40 provides for PM's Instructions, which are to be in writing except for specific classes of instruction which may be given orally provided they are confirmed in writing within 7 days. These are to be valued, as appropriate, either as 'Variation Instructions' under Condition 42 or 'other Instructions' under Condition 43.

Under JCT 80, Clause 13.2 provides 'The Architect/Supervising Officer may issue instructions requiring a Variation . . .', which rather begs the question. Clause 4.3 requires all instructions to be in writing, but Clause 4.3.2 provides a procedure for the contractor to confirm in writing to the Architect/Supervising Officer an oral instruction within 7 days of its issue, subject to dissent by the Architect/Supervising Office within a further 7 days.

Issue of further drawings and instructions

The architect/engineer is usually empowered to issue further drawings and instructions 'from time to time' during the course of the work. It was held in *Neodox v Swinton & Pendlebury*[12] that this means the contractor cannot expect all the information on Day 1. It was further held that such details or instructions should be given within a time reasonable in all the circumstances — including the convenience of the engineer. The opinion has been expressed that this will have application to ICE5 Clause 7 or JCT 80 Clause 5.4, but it must be pointed out that the contract in that case was unusual in giving the engineer authority to determine the programme. Also, as the judge pointed out, what is reasonable will depend upon many things.

It has since been held[13] that an architect or engineer is not automatically bound to provide information in accordance with a programme submitted by the contractor which shows early completion; but an architect/engineer who delays issuing further drawings and instructions is putting his employer (and himself) at risk.

Sub-contractors

The contractor is fully responsible in contract (though not in tort) for the acts of his sub-contractors, whether nominated or domestic. They are regarded as extensions of the contractor. On the other hand, only the contractor's Agent has authority under the contract to receive instructions from the A/E/QS. The A/E/QS should have no direct contact with sub-contractors without either an authorized representative of the contractor being present or the contractor's express consent to direct contact. This is an area where it is important to follow the correct contractual procedure. Otherwise, claims can not only be triggered but multiply with cumulative effect. An instruction direct to a sub-contractor can affect not

---

11. *Brodie v Cardiff Corporation* [1919] AC 337.
12. *Neodox v Swinton & Pendlebury BC* [1958] 5 BLR 34.
13. *Glenlion Construction v Guinness Trust* [1987] 39 BLR 89, relating to the JCT Form of Contract.

only the sub-contract itself but also the main contract (e.g. programme) and possibly other interlocked sub-contractors.

Nominated sub-contracts pose very considerable problems; the machinery for their operation in both JCT and ICE is cumbersome (though necessary) and the provisions are very onerous on the employer. Careful consideration should be given to whether there is not a better alternative. The best course is to specify the requirement and include it in the B/Q in the ordinary way and leave the contractor to fulfil the obligation, and this can be done in very many cases. The alternative of separate direct contracts may overcome some problems but introduce others (difficulty of co-ordination and control, and the effect of delay).

Intermeddling by third parties

The execution of the Works can be made more difficult by the acts or interventions of third parties, who are outside the contractual chain. These may include statutory authorities (e.g. building inspectors, factory inspectors, police), statutory undertakers, or other contractors employed by the employer. The general rule is that no warranty will be implied into a contract on the part of the employer that the contractor will not suffer hindrance by a third party. Thus in the leading case, *Porter v Tottenham UDC*,[14] a builder sought damages for breach of implied warranty when access to the site was prevented by an adjoining land owner; it was held that no such warranty would be implied.

Where the employer has some control over the third party, such as another contractor, the situation is different.[15] The work of statutory undertakers causes particularly severe problems, for example where diversions are required. The lack of contractual relationship by either party with statutory undertakers makes for open-ended delay and disruption. In the absence of explicit contractual provisions, claims for certain delays caused by statutory undertakers have been entertained in some countries,[16] based on denial of possession. Explicit provisions are included in some forms of contract, to allocate clearly the risks involved; for example, providing entitlement to relief subject to the contractor having made due efforts to liaise with the statutory undertakers.

Approvals and rejections

An important function of the employer's appointees — Engineer and Engineer's Representative, or Architect and Clerk of Works, or Supervising Officer and Resident Engineer or Clerk of Works — is to supervise the Works. Their primary function is to ensure, on behalf of the employer, that defective work is replaced or rectified before acceptance. Replacement or rectification of defective work is usually more difficult, time consuming and costly if it is picked up later rather than earlier. Conditions of contract therefore stipulate that the employer's appointed supervisors should have the right of access to inspect the works during construction and that work should not proceed beyond certain stages until earlier work has been inspected and approved. Extensive powers are provided for the supervisor to reject work and require its replacement or rectification. These powers (which are similar to the common law rights of a party to reject goods for breach of condition) extend up to substantial completion, often with the stipulation that previous approval should not prevent subsequent rejection. Failure to comply promptly with orders is stipulated as grounds for forfeiture.[17] Separate powers are conferred during the period of maintenance, usually limited to rectification rather than removal and replacement of defective work. (This corresponds more closely to common law rights in relation to defective goods where the goods have not been rejected within a reasonable time.) Issue of a final certificate and release of final retention are made dependent on completion of all rectification work required by the supervisor. Secondary enforcement powers are also provided in some forms of contract,[18] expressly empowering the employer to bring in another contractor to carry out

14. *Porter v Tottenham UDC* [1915] 1 KB 776.
15. Under the Hong Kong PWD Conditions (1977 Edition), the word 'Government' was used rather than 'employer', but this led to claims where other Government departments or Government legislation caused delays or extra cost; the 1985 edition changed to the word 'Employer'.
16. See Duncan Wallace I N QC 1986 *Construction Contracts Principles and Policies*, Para 4.14. Sweet & Maxwell, London.
17. ICE5 and FIDIC4 Clause 63(1) item (c); ICE6 Clause 63(1)(b)(iii); JCT 80 Clause 27.1.3; GC/Wks 1 Ed 2 Condition 45 item (a); GC/Wks 1 Ed 3 Condition 56.
18. ICE5, ICE6 and FIDIC4 Clause 49(4); GC/Wks 1 Ed 2 Condition 8; GC/Wks 1 Ed 3 Condition 53. JCT80 has no express provision without forfeiture.

the rectification work if the original contractor fails to do so, and to deduct the cost from monies due to the contractor. Note that the second contractor is brought in and employed by the employer, not the architect or engineer.

Defective performance

These powers give rise to disputes in various situations. The first is where the rejection of work by the supervisor is challenged on the grounds that the work complies with the specification. The contractor has little alternative in that situation but to complain and comply, since non-compliance risks forfeiture, but an unjustified rejection may subsequently be treated as an instruction giving rise to entitlement to relief. Alternatively, common law relief may be available if the unjustified rejection by the supervisor constitutes a breach of contract by the employer. Such a situation might arise, for example, where the A/E insists on an unjustified interpretation of the specification,[19] or where the A/E carries out the sampling or testing leading to the rejection and the sampling or testing itself does not conform with the specification.

The second situation where claims may arise is where the rejection is late, so that replacement or rectification is more costly then it need have been. The general rule is that a contractor is not entitled to rely on the employer's supervisor to point out defective work.[20] Situations might arise, however, where defective work has been identified promptly and instructions have been given. If the contractor complies with those instructions, what happens if the supervisor then issues further instructions?

The third case is where defective work comes to light after the maintenance certificate has been issued. Again the general rule is that the contractor cannot rely on the supervisor's failure to notice or point out defects. Under certain forms of contract, however, the maintenance or final certificate may be treated as conclusive that the contractor has discharged his contractual obligations.[21] There is no general rule as to whether a requirement for work to be to satisfaction of the supervisor is to be treated as the sole or over-riding criterion, or whether the approval is to be considered as for the super-added protection of the employer.[22] Generally the A/E/QS has no continuing powers under the contract once the final certificate has been issued, he is said to be *functus officio*.

CASE 6.1   CLAIM THAT SUBSOIL CONDITIONS WERE WORSE THAN EXPECTED (GC/Wks 1 Edition 2 — also generally applicable to JCT)

Pertinent particulars of contract

The contract was for the construction of a number of buildings on a rural site. The documents comprised: Conditions of Contract GC/Wks 1 Edn 2, Drawings, Specification, Bill of Quantities.

Tender dated 20 April 1979, acceptance dated 10 May 1979.

Contract Sum £2,584,797. Time for completion $2\frac{1}{2}$ years.

There was included as an Appendix to the Specification a copy of a Report on Site Investigations (boreholes and trial pits) by a specialist contractor and samples from the boreholes were available for inspection.

The contract comprised bulk excavation for some twenty buildings distributed over some 250 hectares, together with access roads to them (involving excavation in cuttings and forming embankments) in hilly terrain. Material from the excavations was to be used in filling under certain buildings and in embankments, the surplus being deposited in tipping areas within the boundaries of the site.

The B/Q was prepared in accordance with SMM 6 but included the following Preamble:

19. *Brodie v Cardiff Corporation* [1919] AC 337.
20. *East Ham v Bernard Sunley & Sons* [1966] AC 406 at 449.
21. *Southern Water Authority v Carey* [1985] 2 All ER 1077.
22. *NCB v William Neill* [1985] QB 300.

'Excavation, Filling and Disposal
Filling to buildings and to form road embankments has been measured in accordance with para D34 of the SMM and the volume required deducted from the volume of excavation measured in accordance with para D10. The difference, without any allowance for bulking or compaction, has been billed as disposed on site within any of the three tipping areas shown on the drawings.'

The B/Q contained a number of sections each including some excavation but the following may be taken as representative so far as this claim is concerned:

Excavate in any material except topsoil of rock, maximum depth not exceeding 4.0 m to reduce levels in forming sites for buildings	62,181 m^3	0.82	50,988.42
Ditto but in rock ditto	14,400 m^3	1.16	16,704.00
Excavate in any material except topsoil or rock in forming cuttings for roadways, maximum depth not exceeding 4.0 m	282,422 m^3	0.82	231,586.04
Ditto but in rock ditto	63,000 m^3	1.16	73,080.00
Filling with material (including rock) selected from excavated material to make up levels under buildings	18,775 m^3	0.53	9,950.75
Ditto in embankments to roads	226,413 m^3	0.64	144,904.32
Disposal of surplus material in filling areas on site	176,815 m^3	0.36	63,653.40

Events giving rise to claim

The first intimation of trouble was given at a periodic progress meeting on site on 18 July 1979 when the Clerk of Works complained of lack of progress. The contractor then alleged that the material being met with in excavation was very different from what he could have expected. It was very wet and he doubted whether much of it would be satisfactory for use as fill. He was, however, mainly concerned at that stage with the fact that no rock was being found in the area of the Lorry Park although an 'assumed rock line' was shewn on the relevant drawing. He needed that rock to form the embankment for road A–A, which was the only practical access across the valley to the main part of the site where the buildings and access roads were located. He asked for instructions.

The Clerk of Works said that this was a matter for the contractor but asked if any tests had been made as to the water content, drawing attention to Clause E 104 of the Specification (which stipulated limits for fill). He also asked the contractor which drawing showed rock in the Lorry Park area. This was later stated to be 2016.14/78.

The Clerk of Works' reaction savoured rather of the conventional 'No' and lacked conviction. He would have been better advised to ask for the contractor's reasons for seeking instructions, pointing out that under the Conditons 2(1) 'The contractor shall be deemed to have satisfied himself as regards . . . the nature of the materials . . . to be excavated . . .'

Conditions did not improve and two months later (19 September 1979) the embankment on road A–A was still not completed. The contractor had managed to get some plant across the valley on mats and was endeavouring to get material from nearby building sites and cuttings. He was finding, however, that the rock where exposed would not carry his lorry traffic as he had expected and he said it would be necessary to import appropriate 'blanket' material. For this he requested a variation. The Clerk of Works refused this, contending that it was in the nature of temporary work which was the contractor's responsibility. He also urged the contractor to speed up the work as even at this relatively early stage progress was about $2\frac{1}{2}$ months behind expectation. The contractor said he was aware of this but

145

would be asking for an extension of time. In the meantime he considered the best way out of the difficulty would be to import material for the embankment and for this he asked for a variation. The Clerk of Works said he would refer the matter to the Superintending Officer.

Again the Clerk of Works lost the opportunity to persuade or convince the contractor that (in his opinion at least) it really was the contractor's problem and that being so he would not be entitled to an extension of time. More particularly his indecision regarding liability for the import of material makes it seem that he is not sure of where responsibility lies. This is something he should have followed up domestically (with the SO or QS) so that he could be sure of what line to take with the contractor. However, he does warn the SO formally of the situation and asks him to write to the contractor.

Superintending Office to Contractor   *17 October 1979*

> *Your attention is drawn to the persistent lack of progress on this job and I must point out that unless there is some substantial improvement quickly, work will be further hindered if not brought to a standstill over the winter months.*

> *Your attention is drawn to Condition 29 concerning your liability for liquidated damages.*

The SO would have been better advised to ask for the contractor's proposals to ensure completion on time rather than threaten liquidated damages at this stage. It is wise to bear liquidated damages in mind to ensure that they are not jeopardised by failing to give extension of time when due or by issuing variation orders or failing to issue drawings or instructions when required and so compounding delay. In situations such as this it is better first to get the position clarified: (a) as to whether the contractor cannot or is unlikely to finish on time, and (b) that he is not entitled to an extension of time. The contractor here seems to think he is entitled, and the Clerk of Works has not disillusioned him. The contractor somewhat tardily replies:

Contractor to Superintending Officer   *7 November 1979*

> *We are in receipt of your letter of 17 October and are more than a little surprised at its contents. You must be aware from reports of the progress meetings of the difficulties we are meeting with on site. Not only is the material more difficult to excavate than we had any reason to expect but our proposals to resolve the situation by importing material for the embankment on Road A–A and for the use of blanket material to protect the rock formation to take our traffic have not been accepted and our requests for variation orders have not been met. We have asked for instructions as to what you require to be done with this wet material but so far we have received none.*

> *In spite of the fact that we are sustaining heavy losses on this job, we have in fact brought in some all-in ballast as blanket material and this is proving successful. We again ask for a variation order to cover this matter.*

> *We are aware that the job is running late and have asked the Clerk of Works for an extension of time, but to date have received no reply. Pending this we take strong exception to your threat to inflict liquidated damages, a course we would strongly resist.*

> *Further, we reserve our right to claim for the additional cost of excavation and for delay and disruption caused by the misleading information on which we were asked to tender.*

Does the contractor think that the best method of defence is to attack? Or does he perhaps think that the Clerk of Works and SO are not sure of their ground? Or is his letter simply a reaction to the threat of liquidated damages? His letter is somewhat garbled and he does nothing constructive to make such case as he may think he has. Had he done so he might have made a better impression on the SO or alternatively he may have discovered that his case was not in fact as good as he may have thought.

Superintending Officer to Contractor   *21 November 1979*

> *I have to acknowledge receipt of your letter of 7 November and to point out:*
>
> (a) *That the difficulty in handling this material is a matter for yourselves and you were informed of this at the progress meeting on 18 July.*
>
> (b) *That your request for a variation to cover the importation of blanket material to cover rock formation was refused at the meeting on 19 September.*
>
> (c) *That you have made no formal application for an extension of time as required by the Conditions of Contract.*
>
> *I do not consider you have any grounds for claim and would like to know what is the misleading information to which you refer.*

Point (c) of para 1 is perhaps the only constructive one made. It would have been better to organize a formal meeting at which these matters could be discussed, the contractor being asked to state why he considered himself entitled to the variations requested, what ground he thought he had both for an extension of time and for a delay and disruption claim, and being told why his contentions were thought not to be valid. If he could not be persuaded otherwise, he could then be advised to put his case in writing which could be properly considered and not dismissed (as in para 2) before it was even formulated. The second part of that paragraph suggests an uneasy conscience. In connection with claims there has been speculation that one of the problems is difficulty of communication, but getting together is not necessarily confrontation.

The line being taken by each side in this case so far is frequently met with, and the matter often bumbles along until the end of the contract and beyond when positions become entrenched and both sides find it difficult to retract.

In this case, work ceases at Christmas and does not start up again until early March. In the meantime the SO gives a further warning about delay and the contractor gets down to formulating a claim, which he submits in the following terms:

Contractor to Superintending Officer   *4 January 1980*

> *As we informed you, we have had to close down the work as the weather is making earthworks quite impossible. We intend to resume as soon as conditions permit. In the meantime we must request an extension of time in accordance with Condition 28 because:*
>
> (a) *ground conditions are much worse than we had any reason to expect;*
>
> (b) *absence of rock in the area of the lorry park has caused serious delay in gaining access to the main construction area in spite of our efforts to get plant across by means of mats etc;*
>
> (c) *the rock being encountered is quite hard* in situ *but once exposed to the weather it tends to disintegrate under lorry traffic;*

(d) *there was delay in the issue of revised details for the culvert on road A—A;*

(e) *the weather throughout the summer has been worse than average and during October/November has been exceptionally bad.*

We consider we have been delayed by these causes for about four months to date and we expect it will be another two months before we can restart work.

We are submitting in a separate letter a claim for the additional cost involved.

Contractor to Superintending Officer   *5 January 1980*

Claim in connection with earthworks

1. *We have frequently notified you at site meetings and in correspondence of the difficulties we are encountering in the earthworks. In the six months since we began work on site we have been able to do less than 25% of the total earthworks compared with the 75% we expected to complete by the end of 1979.*

2. *The general material to be excavated has proved much more difficult and was much wetter than could have been expected from the bores and trial pits.*

3. *The rock, whilst quite hard* in situ, *once exposed to the weather tends to disintegrate under lorry traffic and we have had to import materials to form a blanket over the rock surface. We consider this to be a variation but no order has been issued in spite of repeated requests.*

4. *Contrary to what was shewn on the drawings, no rock was encountered in the area of the lorry park. We were relying on this to provide fill for the embankment on road A—A, which is virtually the only practical access to the sites of the buildings and their access roads where other fill material is available. We managed to get some plant and lorries across by means of temporary mats but this has involved a complete re-organization of our strategy for the job and has substantially increased the length of haul needed both to put excavated material into embankment and the removal of surplus to tip.*

5. *All these matters have caused delay for which we have claimed extension of time. Delay so far amounts to about four months and we estimate that provided we can restart on 1 March, the total delay by that time will be twenty-four weeks.*

6. *We attach details of our claim and we should be glad if you would include £100,000 in the next certificate in respect of the work carried out to date.*

CLAIM

(a) *Additional cost of excavation*	*62,181*	
Excavation in material other		
than rock and topsoil	*282,422*	
	344,603 m³ at 0.50	*177,301.50*
(b) *Import of material to form access*		
roads for lorry traffic on site	*28,500 m³ at 1.46*	*41,610.00*
		c/f £218,911.50

148

b/f £218,911.50

(c) Increased haul for disposal of
material in embankment and tips
18,775
226,413

176,815   *422,003 m³ at 0.20*   *84,400.60*

(d) Disruption and dislocation
consequent on foregoing
involving 24 weeks' delay   *@ £2,800 per week*   *67,200.00*

£370,512.10

Superintending Officer to Contractor   *8 January 1980*

I have to acknowledge receipt of your letters of 4 and 5 January 1980 which are receiving attention.

'Notification' at site meetings is not sufficient for formal notices required by the Conditions of Contract. The boreholes and trial pits had been put down in the dry summer of 1977 and this was made clear. In acknowledging claims avoid saying they will be 'given consideration' lest in the context this be capable of being misconstrued into an undertaking to pay.

Superintending Officer to Contractor   *5 February 1980*

We have now had opportunity to examine your application for extension of time and your claims.

2. *Regarding subsoil conditions, your attention is drawn to Condition 2 of the General Conditions of Contract which says 'The contractor shall be deemed to have satisfied himself as regards ... the nature of the materials ... to be excavated ...' Further, you were supplied with data derived from the boreholes sunk and trial pits dug on site. Sub-clause (2) of this Condition says 'No claim by the contractor will be allowed on the ground of any misunderstanding or misinterpretation of such matter ...'*

3. *Regarding the rock and the fact that it has been found to disintegrate under lorry traffic, the same considerations apply. No variation of the Works is involved so far as the Authority is concerned.*

4. *Regarding the non-availability of rock in the area of the lorry park, this is indeed unfortunate but, as you will see from the drawings, no borehole was put down in this area and the 'assumed rock line' shewn on Drawing 2016.14/78 was shewn only to enable a quantity to be included in the B/Q. It is considered that Condition 2 applies in this case also and your claim for increased haul and your request for a variation for the importation of embankment material cannot be agreed. In any case you do not indicate how the haul programme has been affected or what additional haul you consider to be involved.*

5. *Regarding disruption and dislocation, it is considered that this arises from the foregoing matters, none of which is the responsibility of the Authority for the reasons stated.*

6. *For the same reasons I am unable to grant an extension of time.*

This letter is reasonably satisfactory except that the last sentence of para 4 is unnecessary and undermines the effect of the preceding argument. As a general rule, the SO or A/E/QS ought to keep records and establish all primary facts relevant to a notified claim, even if he rejects the claim or considers it unjustified, as the matter may be referred later to arbitration. Identification of the relevant primary facts, and therefore what records ought to be kept, depends on analysis of the relevant contractual provisions which should be identified by the contractor in the notification. The SO or A/E/QS and the contractor ought, at all times, to keep general records of weather, number and distribution of men, types and distribution of plant, and factual notes of progress. When a claim situation arises, they should identify the specific issues involved and the additional specific records required. For example in this case, the additional specific records needed would include the origins, destinations and numbers of trucks, the nature of materials excavated, what materials were placed as fill or disposed to tip, the times and dates, and the conditions prevailing or encountered.

The effect on the haul programme could only have been signalled by the contractor's records initially. Early steps should have been taken to enable the SO to keep records to verify the facts and satisfy himself that the contractor was keeping suitable and adequate records. Assessment of the effect on the haul programme involves, however, not only facts from records, but also comparison of those facts with the programme that would otherwise have been achieved. Establishing that base programme does not involve records of actual progress during the execution of the works. It would therefore be both unnecessary and inappropriate for the SO to enquire as to the base programme if he is rejecting the claim. Also, no reference is made to inclement weather nor to the alleged delay in issuing details of the culvert.

Contractor to Superintending Officer   *13 February 1980*

Thank you for your letter of 5 February with which we are unable to agree. We based our tender on information you supplied and we cannot be expected to undertake risks which are unforeseeable. Other Conditions of Contract recognize this principle and we consider it should apply in this case also. We reserve the right to raise the matter again later and are considering taking it to arbitration.

Nor can we accept your decision regarding extension of time. On grounds of inclement weather alone we consider we are entitled to three months' extension and then there was the further month waiting for details of this culvert (applied for in July and not supplied until 8 August).

The SO was wrong in not dealing with these matters with the rest. If delay can be attributed to exceptionally inclement weather then extension of time should be given. The contractor will not, however, be entitled to any compensation in respect of it unless some action of the Authority has pushed him into bad weather he would not otherwise have met. That does not seem to be the case here. Regarding the culvert, the fact was that the work was already delayed and, on the evidence, was not delayed any further by the absence of these details.

In cases such as this costs (and losses) can rapidly escalate and it is most important to arrive at the real cause of the trouble and at where responsibility for it lies. In the case in question responsibility lies clearly with the contractor and it would have been cheaper for him to import, say, 10,000 m^3 of suitable material at his own expense to form the vital embankment if a reasoned case had been put up in, say, August 1979 and authoritative answer given by even the end of that month.

The 'assumed rock line' shown on the drawing was indeed unfortunate. It is dangerous to put such information on a drawing upon mere conjecture. In *Pearson & Son v Dublin Corporation*,[23] for example, tender drawings prepared by the employer's engineer represented 'rashly and without enquiry' a wall which did not in fact exist. That was held

---

23. *Pearson & Son v Dublin Corporation* [1907] AC 351, see Keating *Building Contracts* 4th Ed p 92.

to amount to fraud which vitiated a disclaimer clause. In this case, an 'assumed rock line' does not represent that the rock line is as shown, but it comes close to representing that there is sufficient information known to justify the line drawn. Entitlement to damages for misrepresentation does not now depend on the existence of fraud. Following the Misrepresentation Act 1967, negligent or even innocent misrepresentation may suffice as grounds for recovery of damages.

The contractor's reference to what other Conditions of Contract provide is quite pointless. There is no general principle that a contractor should not be expected to undertake risks which are unforeseeable;[24] the existence of provisions for relief in other Conditions of Contract is, in this instance,[25] not so much recognition of the principle, as recognition that the general principle does not exist.

Points of principle involved

Under JCT 80, the position would have been different to the extent that there is no equivalent of GC/Wks 1 Ed 2 Cond 2. In that situation, the requirement in SMM6 Paragraph D3 — to either give particulars of soils data or state a description of the ground and strata which is to be assumed — may have a different effect. It may be interpreted as implying that a change from the data given or description stated constitutes an alteration to the quality of the Works as described by or referred to in the Contract Bills and, therefore, is deemed to be a variation under JCT 80 Clause 13.1.1. This interpretation has been more explicitly adopted in Amendment 7:1988 to JCT 80, which accompanied the issue of the new SMM7. Clause 2.2.2.2, as amended, introduces the word 'information', reflecting the requirement of SMM7 Rule 10.3 that certain information be provided. Section D Rule P1 then states that the information to be provided includes a description of ground conditions, either by reference to site investigation data, or by a statement of what is to be assumed. Clause 2.2.2.2, as amended, stipulates that any error in or omission of such information is to be 'corrected', and Clause 13.5, as amended, provides for work to be treated as a variation where 'the instruction for that work differs from the description given for such work in the Contract Bills.'.

More generally, in deciding whether to supply information on soils or services at time of tender, the employer is on the horns of a dilemma. Should he supply information in order to obtain a realistic tender, but with the possibility that the information might be used against him by the contractor? Or should he volunteer no information and rely on a form of contract fixing the contractor with all the risk? The further question is whether he should just disclose raw data, or interpret the data as 'rock lines' or similar.

The problem is addressed in some contracts or methods of measurement by including separate items in the Bills of Quantities for excavation and other work in different types of material, or for obstructions encountered, so that the issue becomes one of measurement rather than foreseeability. In practice, however, the arguments are not reduced by this approach.

The ICE and FIDIC Conditions go further by providing relief on account of physical conditions and artificial obstructions which could not reasonably have been foreseen by an experienced contractor at time of tender, and expressly allowing to be taken into account any information provided by or on behalf of the employer in connection with the nature of the ground and subsoil.

In the latest editions, FIDIC4 and ICE6, there has been introduced an obligation or expectation that the employer will disclose all available data on ground conditions, but, at the same time, stipulating that the contractor is responsible for the interpretation of the

---

24. *Davis Contractors v Fareham UDC* [1956] AC 696; *British Movietonews v London & District Cinemas* [1952] AC 166.
25. The contrary argument, sometimes advanced, that there is no general principle because some form of contract makes explicit provision, is equally invalid as a guiding rule. Forms of contract frequently include codified versions of common law rules, to allow the matter to be dealt with under the contract and to avoid difficulties on overseas contracts.

data. Such moves towards disclosure and limited permitted reliance are not driven by charitable thoughts, but inexorably by developments in the law as well as sound engineering. The old common law allowed liability for information supplied to be excluded, except if the disclaimer clause were vitiated by fraud.[26] Recent developments in statute[27] and common law have tended to be less supportive of harsh contracts. In *Mitsui v A−G for Hong Kong*[28] the Privy Council stated a presumption, to be applied in construing commercial contracts, that the parties' intentions at the time of contract were consistent with business common sense. In particular Lord Bridge stated that responsible public authorities and contractors were to be presumed not to have intended to embark on a 'gamble' involving hundreds of thousands of pounds.

In *Mitsui*, the bill of quantities for the construction of a tunnel provided a number of items for different types of lining, but only a single rate for excavation. The type of lining was to be instructed by the engineer, but it could reasonably be inferred that each type of lining corresponded to a type of ground condition. The cost of excavation and the rate of progress would also be related to the type of ground and, as has been commented,[29] the contractor could have avoided the eventual problems by adopting a pricing structure which put the time-related costs against the lining items. In the event, the quantities of lining changed considerably from those billed, and the contractor took approximately double the time and incurred double the cost to complete the works. It was held that the contract should be construed as if it were intended to provide relief.[30]

There is separate authority that a person who supplies information leading to a contract ought to have regard to 'the gravity of the inquiry or the importance and influence attached to the answer'.[31] In the new climate it might be argued that the 'assumed rock line' in the example above was intended by the parties to be the basis of the contract, though it is fair to say that nobody but the contractor (knowing the methods he proposed to adopt) could have appreciated the importance of this few thousand cubic yards of rock which represented only a small proportion of the total.

CASE 6.2   CLAIM THAT PHYSICAL CONDITIONS ENCOUNTERED WERE WORSE THAN COULD HAVE BEEN EXPECTED BY AN EXPERIENCED CONTRACTOR

Pertinent particulars of contract

The contract was for the construction of an underpass on the outskirts of a city on a road adjacent to a river. The contract documents comprised:

Drawings, Specification, Bills of Quantities (total of B/Q £1,424,778).
Conditions of Contract: ICE 5.

Tender dated 8 January 1980. Time for completion $2\frac{1}{2}$ years.
Acceptance dated 11 February 1980.

There was available for the inspection of tenderers a Report on Site Investigations (bore holes and probings) by a specialist contractor and samples from the bore holes were also available for inspection on request.

There was a disclaimer in the Specification concerning this information, as follows (Clause 62):

'Site investigations consisting of bores and probes have been carried out by Messrs

---

26. *Boyd & Forrest v Glasgow & SW Railway* [1915] SC (HL) 20.
27. Misrepresentation Act 1967; Unfair Contract Terms Act 1977.
28. *Mitsui Construction v A-G for Hong Kong* [1986] 33 BLR 1.
29. Duncan Wallace I N 1987 *How Much Measurement?* 3 Const LJ 3 at p 12.
30. Neither the extent of the relief, nor the basis of its calculation was discussed in the law reports.
31. *Hedley Byrne & Co v Heller & Partners* [1964] AC 465 at 539; approved in *Howard Marine & Dredging v Ogden (Excavations) Ltd* [1978] 1 QB 574 by Lord Denning MR at p 591 and by Shaw LJ at p 601.

> ... and a copy of their Report together with samples taken from the bore holes may be inspected at the Engineer's office at ...
>
> Such information is given without guarantee and the Employer shall not be held responsible for any inaccuracy in the same. The contractor shall not be entitled to additional payment on the ground of any misunderstanding or misinterpretation in any respect.'

Such disclaimers are not uncommon in civil engineering contracts, but their benefit is inclined to be much overrated, possibly inducing an unjustified and counter-productive impression of invulnerability in those responsible for pre-contract site investigations. In the case of ICE5, ICE6 and FIDIC4, the effect of disclaimers is limited by the wording of Clauses 11 and 12, as the experienced contractor of Clause 12 is considered subject to the provisions of Clause 11; he is not entitled to rely on the information supplied as the sole basis of foresight, but if information is provided by or on behalf of the Employer, then it may be taken into account, whether or not it is guaranteed. As the criterion of foreseeability is that of the experienced contractor, the actual Contractor's own interpretation (or misinterpretation) is not conclusive.[32] 'Taking into account' necessarily involves objective analysis and interpretation of the information provided.

In this case the material to be excavated proved to be much more difficult than the contractor had expected and he entered a claim under Clause 12.

Events giving rise to claim

Contractor to Engineer   *13 June 1980*

As has been discussed at length at several progress meetings on site, the excavation for this underpass is proving very much more difficult than we expected. It is much more expensive to excavate, requires steel sheet piling to retain the ground in the centre section and continuous pumping.

We therefore formally claim to be paid the extra cost involved and request a variation order to be issued under Clause 12(2)(d).

Engineer to Contractor   *18 June 1980*

In reply to your letter of 13 June, I cannot accept that the ground conditions being encountered are any worse than should have been anticipated by an experienced contractor. When tendering you had the opportunity to inspect the Report on Site Investigations and also the bore samples.

I regret I am unable to agree to issue any variation order.

Contractor to Engineer   *26 June 1980*

We were surprised at the contents of your letter of 18 June, particularly at the implication that we are not experienced contractors. We have had many years' experience in civil engineering work more complicated than the present project.

We fully appreciate that the Report on Site Investigations was available for inspection but it is a pity it was not supplied with the tender documents as there really was not time to study it fully in the tender period, which was only six weeks. We would also point out that in all there were only four bores put down, which is clearly insufficient for a job of this size and location.

We should be glad if you would reconsider the matter in the light of this letter.

---

32. The contractor's own expectations are evidence of what an experienced contractor could foresee.

The generation of heat in these situations, usually accompanied by deteriorating relationships all round, is not uncommon. It is sometimes caused by unfortunate wording of letters or oral comments. The present case may be more a matter of 'if the cap fits' because all the engineer has done is to make reference to the criterion (set out in Clause 12) by which such matters have to be judged. In this situation whether the contractor underestimated the difficulty or misjudged the quality of the ground is not in issue. Clause 12 requires that these physical conditions '. . . could not reasonably have been foreseen by an experienced contractor . . .' The practice of not supplying copies of Site Investigation reports to tenderers for study is unfortunate, but making reports available for inspection is still regarded as providing the information. A 6-week tender period does not preclude inspection of the SI Report, although it may limit the amount of analysis or additional investigation that could reasonably be carried out pre-tender. The experienced contractor is to be considered as having been subject to the same conditions as the actual contractor. If there were special circumstances which, in the view of the contractor, necessitated extra time for study of the reports or further site investigation, he should have made a request during the tender period. The employer may have refused but, in the absence of a pre-contract request, the contractor's subsequent complaint will carry little weight.

The relevance of the information provided by or on behalf of the employer varies. If it is argued for the employer that the information did disclose the difficult physical conditions, that is a matter for expert evidence as to the reasonable interpretation of the results. On the other hand, if it is accepted on behalf of the employer that the data alone did not disclose the physical conditions encountered, the question of foreseeability depends on what other information was reasonably available. Clause 11 does not entitle the Contractor to rely solely on the information supplied by the Employer, it is for the experienced contractor also to have made his own enquiries, consulted the Geological Survey, made a site visit, taken advice from soils experts etc., if needed. That there were only four bores in this case must have been apparent to the contractor when tendering and an experienced contractor would have judged accordingly the reliance that he might reasonably place on the data as a guide to the whole site.

Engineer to Contractor   *2 July 1980*

With reference to your letter of 26 June, you have misconstrued my intentions in making reference to 'an experienced contractor'. All I was intending to do was to draw your attention to the terms of Clause 12 of the Conditions.

I cannot agree that there were insufficient bores put down. In any case your attention is drawn to Clause 62 of the Specification.

The second paragraph of this reply is somewhat pointless, since the correctness of the information has not been called in question. The engineer missed the point that the contractor nevertheless chose to tender; he should also have drawn attention to Clause 11 of the Conditions under which 'The Contractor shall be deemed . . . to have satisfied himself . . . as to the nature of the ground and subsoil (so far as is practicable and having taken into account any information . . . which may have been provided by . . . the Employer)'. Note that this last is only one of the things which the contractor has to take into account.

This issue seems to have lapsed (at least temporarily), for the next letter raises a different matter.

Contractor to Engineer   *8 July 1980*

We have to draw your attention to the fact that the drawings showing the location of services are incorrect. Some water mains are about a metre from where they are shewn to be and in the case of some electric cables even more.

> *We are keeping records of the additional costs involved for which we intend to submit a claim later.*

The contractor is no doubt disappointed that his Clause 12 claim has not made the headway he hoped and expected. He is here tactically trying to put the engineer in the wrong by saying the drawings are incorrect. Technically that may be so but it is very well known in the industry that Statutory Undertakers do not have accurate records of their equipment and further there are instruments available to locate precisely the location of services before excavation is commenced.

> *Engineer to Contractor*   *10 July 1980*
>
> With reference to your letter of 8 July, as you must know from previous experience Statutory Undertakers cannot give the precise location of their services. In any case it is perfectly possible to locate these before commencing excavation.
>
> You were warned in the tender documents that services existed. It is this fact rather than their precise location which is of importance.
>
> It is therefore not seen that you are entitled to any extra payment. You do not in any case indicate the clause under which you intend to claim.

Is the reference to previous experience a gentle nudge over the previous claim? Again there is a hiatus in the correspondence on this subject and the next letter on the file concerns yet another problem met with in excavation.

> *Engineer to Contractor*   *14 July 1980*
>
> I have to confirm oral instructions given on site this morning to cease work with the excavator in the central section and continue with hand excavation around the timbers of the ship which has been discovered. Arrangements are being made for an archaeologist to inspect these timbers as soon as possible.
>
> Your attention is drawn to Clause 32 of the Conditions.

Evidently the inspection took place, but it was found that the timbers in question, whilst old, were of no archaeological interest.

> *Engineer to Contractor*   *21 July 1980*
>
> I have to inform you that the ship's timbers encountered are of no archaeological interest and normal working may be resumed.

> *Contractor to Engineer*   *23 July 1980*
>
> Thank you for your letter of 21 July. We enclose herewith daywork sheets totalling £1,487.20 for the hand excavation around the ship's timbers. The facts have been agreed and the sheet signed by your inspector.
>
> We are also preparing a claim for the delay of one week involving loss of productivity of workmen and plant and additional site and general overheads.
>
> We also wish to give notice of a claim under Clause 12 in respect of artificial obstructions (namely derelict ship's timbers) which could not possibly have been foreseen, even by an experienced contractor.

155

At last the contractor is on firmer ground, he has an order from the engineer on the one hand and a clear case under Clause 12 on the other. Or has he? The engineer is either feeling a little over-confident in view of the two previous claims, or he feels embarrassed about the '. . . remains . . . of archaeological interest . . .' for the next letter we find is as follows:

Engineer to Contractor   *25 July 1980*

> *Your daywork account in respect of hand excavation around the old ship's timbers is grossly excessive and unacceptable. My instructions were for hand excavation and the need for the crane and lorries is not understood. These last would have been required in any case to remove the material.*
>
> *As to your proposed claim for delay, as the remains turned out not to be archaeological, their occurrence can only be regarded as a contractual risk. For the same reason no claim under Clause 12 can be entertained.*

The engineer must have been away on his travels or on holiday and some over-enthusiastic assistant must have taken it upon himself to 'see the contractor off'. The engineer cannot have been too pleased to return to find the following reply.

Contractor to Engineer   *28 July 1980*

> *We were astonished to receive your letter of 25 July. The labour and plant times were all agreed with your inspector. It is agreed that the excavated material had to be removed but you must admit that the crane and the lorries were being used grossly under capacity. To show our goodwill, however, we are prepared to allow a credit of £45, as the estimated cost of removal of this excavated material which would have been included in Bill rates.*
>
> *Regarding the delay, this arose directly out of your instruction for hand excavation and we must insist on being reimbursed the cost.*
>
> *Similarly we must maintain that we have a legitimate claim under Clause 12 for the extra cost, delay and disruption arising out of the encountering of this totally unforeseeable physical obstruction.*

An ill-conceived letter can do substantial damage to the organization on whose behalf it is written. In the present case, the engineer was correct in his treatment of the original Clause 12 claim and the matter of the services and it is a pity that the situation should be put in jeopardy. There is (uncharacteristically) no reply to the contractor's letter of 28 July. One can only assume that he had some discussion with the contractor to get the matter back on a proper footing, for the next thing one sees is a sum of £1,442.20 (£1,487.20 less £45) included in the next certificate. Following shortly after is a claim for the week's delay comprising:

> *Pile frame and piling gang — totally idle for one week.*
> *Excavating gang (other than those on daywork) — transferred to other work but only partly productive (say 40% loss of output).*
> *Compressor, hammers, air lines etc, and 22 RB idle, claimed at daywork rates.*
> *Site overheads, totalling £1,644.*
> *General overheads and profit at $12\frac{1}{2}\%$ on the foregoing.*

The engineer put the claim to the quantity surveyor for investigation and report which when analysed into its essentials amounted to the following:

Pile frame, compressor and equipment, 22 RB excavator: claim at daywork rates not admissible. The work in question (hand excavation) was contractually a variation order under Clause 51. The work involved fell to be paid for at full cost including overheads and profit. The consequential delay was, however, in the nature of the damage. Daywork rates for this plant are inappropriate as the plant was not working. The proper rate to be paid for idle plant was therefore 'depreciation' rate, which would be about 2/3 long-term hire rate.

Labour idle: should be paid for at cost, including of course all the extras that are payable to or in respect of the men (insurances, HWP, guaranteed time etc, etc), but not profit.

Loss of productivity: it is to be hoped that some records were kept of what these men were able to do from which the proper labour content could be assessed. It is almost impossible to calculate or check a loss of productivity for the few men affected over such a short time. The 40% claimed appears excessive but in the circumstances is probably not far wrong. If the loss of productivity were more extensive or more prolonged more information would be required. The contractor would be entitled to be paid the excess cost (= loss of productivity), but not profit.

Site overheads: enquiry elicited the statement that '15% had been included in the tender for these i.e. £213,717/130 = £1,644 per week plus general overheads and profit $12\frac{1}{2}\%$ (£178,098).

Investigation showed that the percentages claimed had in fact been included but they had been wrongly applied in this case (each being taken as a percentage of the tender total). The correct figures were:

Nett amount of tender total (labour, plant, materials and sub-contracts) was	£1,101,278	
Of which 15% represents	165,191	÷ 130 = £1,271 p w
	£1,266,469	
$12\frac{1}{2}\%$ for general overheads and profit consisted of $7\frac{1}{2}\%$ overheads and 5% profit. As we are concerned only with overheads this is	94,986	
5% profit on the same figure is	63,323	£1,424,778

Site overheads for one week should therefore be £1,271, instead of £1,644.

Regarding general overheads, there are two schools of thought. The Standing Joint Committee for the ICE Conditions ('CCSJC') has given guidance in regard to one query that 'costs' as defined in ICE5 include only those 'on' or 'off site' *variable* overhead costs which are affected by activities on site; that as a general rule they would not include fixed head office costs but that in the event that the contractor is able to make out a special case, acceptable to the Engineer, that these costs were in fact incurred, then he would be entitled to payment. The CCSJC warn, however, that their comments do not purport to be a legal definition.

The real sticking point is not the definition of 'cost', which is stated in ICE5 Clause 1(5) as including overheads whether on or off the site, but the wording of the entitlement provisions which refers to 'cost incurred'. Are non-specific general overheads to be presumed to be incurred? By analogy with the rule on 'general profit' in the *Victoria Laundry* case,[33] the use of a conjectural approach to such general overheads appears legally acceptable in

---

33. *Victoria Laundry (Windsor) v Newman Industries* [1949] 2 KB 528 see pages 31, 32 *supra*.

appropriate situations; on the other hand, the rule on general profit is linked with the doctrine of mitigation, which may not apply to claims under contractual provisions. The courts have not been consistent in their attitude towards claims for overheads, but recent decisions, both in England and the United States, support the payment of general overheads for delay, calculated by reference to the tender assumptions.[34] Such an approach does not appear to be justified in all cases, and it is not uncommon for tender assumptions on overheads[35] to be exaggerated in claim submissions. Profit is a separate issue from overheads. It does not form part of 'cost' and is not payable on compensation-type claims, unless it is expressly so provided in the contract, as under part of ICE5 Clause 12.

Points of principle involved

Clause 12 of the ICE Conditions is sometimes referred to as 'the contractor's lifeboat'. To the extent that it is intended to rescue contractors from disaster in extreme conditions, that is a valid description, but it is not intended and should not operate as a rescue service for those who have set out in unseaworthy boats with inadequate preparation or incompetent crew. Clause 11 does not reduce the basis of tendering or claim evaluation solely to analysis of the information provided by or on behalf of the employer at time of tender. There remains a heavy onus on the contractor to satisfy himself, when pricing the works, as to physical conditions and artificial obstructions which can be foreseen.

Clause 12 reflects a policy decision not to require contractors to bear risks which they cannot realistically price. It provides that the contractor should be reimbursed to the extent that conditions encountered could not reasonably have been foreseen by an experienced contractor. Having included such a provision, issues should not be 'fudged' by woolly disclaimers, nor should the policy be undermined by unwillingness to implement the clause if the circumstances warrant its application.

A further point arises as to the position of a contractor who has special knowledge of the physical conditions, beyond that of the 'experienced contractor'. Perhaps he has worked in the area before, or he has undertaken a detailed investigation. The problem rarely arises, because if such a contractor has allowed for the special difficulties which his knowledge or investigations revealed, he would not need to claim. Alternatively, his tender would have been higher than those where less investigation had been undertaken, and his tender would then be unsuccessful. Notwithstanding the objective criterion of Clause 12 it would be dangerous for a contractor to submit a tender disregarding his actual knowledge.

Probably the best course of action for a tenderer with special knowledge of difficulties is to draw any such conditions to the attention of the employer and, if possible, all other tenderers, in order to force the successful tender sum up to a level which allows for the special difficulty. As a tender strategy, contractors should keep good news to themselves, but share the bad news with all their competitors. For employers there is no advantage in a successful tender sum which is low but which will be inflated by claims. Far better to discover the problems beforehand by adequate site investigation, and fix the tenderers with knowledge of any special difficulties to be priced.

CLAIM 6.3   CLAIM IN RESPECT OF DAMAGE TO WORKS AND TO EXISTING SEWER

Pertinent particulars of contract

The contract was for the laying of a sewer in a semi-urban area, at one point crossing a main road which was on an embankment. In the main road was an old brick sewer but its line and level were not known with any precision. The new sewer was designed to pass under the old. It was stipulated that the section below the embankment had to be done in heading.

---

34.   *Finnegan v Sheffield CC* [1988] 43 BLR 124; see also Duncan Wallace I N, QC 1986 *Construction Contracts Principles and Policies*, paras 8—27 — 8—36, Sweet & Maxwell, London.
35.   The ICE New Engineering Contract as issued for consultation has adopted a radical approach of calculating entitlement to general overheads as a fixed percentage of cost; but there is no separate entitlement to overheads for prolongation and the percentage proposed in the supporting guidelines is a modest 5 per cent.

The documents comprised: Drawings, Specification, Conditions of Contract (ICE 4), Bill of Quantities totalling £728,447.

Tender dated 14 January 1973. Acceptance dated 19 February 1973. Time for completion 17 months.

Events giving rise to the claim

In the course of driving the heading under the embankment there was a collapse in the roof and it soon became apparent that the old sewer was relatively close above the heading and had fractured. The heading was flooded. The RE was informed and went immediately to the site.

The contractor had got some pumps to work but it was clear that water was entering the heading as fast as it was being pumped out. The contractor's agent asked the RE for instructions. Fortunately there was a manhole on the upstream side of the fracture and the RE instructed the contractor to stop off the outlet and temporarily pipe the effluent into a manhole on the new sewer about 100 metres away and pump the effluent into it. The old sewer could then be approached from below and repaired.

This the contractor proceeded to do but no variation order or any other instruction or confirmation was issued in writing, nor did the agent confirm to the RE the instructions received orally or indicate any intention of making a claim.

The repair was completed and work on the new sewer proceeded. Some time later the contractor notified his insurance company and claimed the cost of the work involved consisting of:

Temporary work in the relief drain and pumping the sewage	2,000	
Pumping and clearing the heading	500	
Breaking out the fractured sewer and repairing	4,800	
Reinstating embankment to prevent any subsidence of either sewer or road	1,650	
Delay to the works (some 6 weeks)	5,000	£13,950

The insurance company denied liability on the grounds that they had not been informed at the time, that the damage had been caused by faulty design (in that the new sewer was too close to the old and the work could not be done without damaging the old) and/or failure by the employer/engineer to locate the sewer properly and/or the work was done as a result of an instruction from the RE. The contractor then presented the above claim to the engineer.

Contractor to Engineer   *14 August 1973*

With reference to the damage to the existing sewer below the embankment, we enclose herewith our claim for the work done and costs incurred in connection therewith. You will remember that when damage occurred we immediately informed the RE, who visited the site and gave us instructions as to what he required us to do. We followed those instructions and completed the work to his satisfaction so far as we are aware.

We now claim reimbursement of the costs and expenses involved on the grounds that the damage was caused by the new sewer being designed to pass too close to the old and damage to the latter was therefore inevitable. We would further point out that at the time of tender there was no information on the drawings as to the location of this sewer and we contend that it was not practicable for us to obtain any more information regarding this in the time allowed us to tender.

There are three matters of principle involved in this letter:

(a) that the contractor was instructed by the RE as to what to do, and that he followed these instructions to satisfactory completion;

(b) that the cause of the damage was due to design;

(c) that the contractor had satisfied himself 'so far as practicable' when tendering as to what was required.

Regarding (a) the contractor omits to say under what clause he considers the instructions to have been given and why they were not confirmed by him at the time if he thought there was a variation. It is quite possible for an RE or inspector to give instructions believing in all good faith that the matter in question is the contractor's responsibility and for the contractor to believe that a variation is intended. Confirmation by the contractor immediately following the event will bring the matter to a head whilst it is still fresh.

Clause 51(2) says 'No such variation shall be made by the contractor without an order in writing of the engineer.' (ICE 5 makes specific provision for confirmation of oral instructions.) Clause 13 does not expressly require instructions and directions to be given in writing and Clause 68 deals with notices. Clause 12 does expressly require notice to be in writing, and further provides that the cost of any work done prior to such notice shall not be reimbursable (note that ICE 5 has been amended). Clause 52(4) requires an account for claims for additional expense to be submitted monthly, with a proviso regarding relief if the contractor has given such notice at the earliest practical opportunity. (Note that ICE5 differs significantly.)

Regarding (b), this can only refer to Clause 20(2), 'excepted risks'. There are two points involved: first, whether the damage can possibly have been due 'to a cause *solely* due to the engineer's design of the Works (note that ICE 5 has been amended so that it is no longer necessary to show that design was the sole cause); second, whether the damage is the inevitable result of the design.

Regarding (c), he is fairly certainly referring to Clause 11, which says 'The contractor shall inspect and examine the site and its surroundings and shall satisfy himself before submitting his tender as to the nature of the ground and subsoil (so far as practicable), the form and nature of the site, the quantities and nature of the work . . .' Technically speaking, the firm when tendering is not 'the Contractor' of the contract, which is why ICE 5 now uses the formula of 'deeming'. Practicability in this clause refers only to the ground and subsoil and does not really touch on a tenderer satisfying himself as to the location of the sewer and the possible difficulty in working in close (?how close) proximity. The fact that the location of the old sewer was not precisely known was declared to tenderers who chose to make an offer in face of such lack of knowledge and held themselves out to be able to execute the work.

The reply to the letter needs to be carefully worded.

Engineer to Contractor   *24 August 1973*

Your letter dated 14 August forwarding a claim in connection with the damage to the existing sewer is acknowledged.

It is agreed that the RE visited the site to inspect the damage and discuss with your agent what needed to be done but the 'instructions' to which you refer were more a matter of summarising the agreement reached. Clearly the RE would not have approved proposals had they been unacceptable to the Local Authority but he could not nor would have wished to require measures that were unnecessarily elaborate or more expensive than necessary to meet the case. Had you thought otherwise, it was open to you to state at the time that you considered this arrangement constituted some instruction under the Conditions of Contract, and to state which. This was not done.

The contention that the damage was due to design is not accepted. It is clear there was never any possibility of the new sewer striking the old as when the latter was opened up it was found to be some two metres above the new, ample space for you to put in timbering to your heading adequate to support the ground above without disturbing its support to the sewer. I consider the timbering provided to have been inadequate and that rather more care should have been taken in executing the work.

You tendered for the work in the knowledge that the location of the old sewer was not precisely known. Such information as existed was made available to all tenderers. You had opportunity to consider whether this was sufficient or involved an unacceptable risk to you.

It is regretted that in the circumstances no part of your claim can be admitted.

The engineer has done the best he can. There is a certain amount of prevarication as the RE should first have asked the contractor for his proposals and the contractor should have made contact with the Local Authority. It is in circumstances such as this, however, that the obvious urgency to do something outweighs considerations of paperwork. This should nevertheless have been followed up so that there was no doubt in anyone's mind as to where responsibility lay.

The contractor was unable to accept the decision, probably because of pressure from the insurance company. These companies have experts who are well aware of the Conditions of Contract and who are reluctant to settle claims if they see any possibility of recovery elsewhere.

For the purpose of this example it is to be assumed that the matter was taken to arbitration. The contractor's case failed. The damage was mainly to third party property. It was not caused by faulty design. The 'instructions' given, if in fact they amounted to instructions, were no more nor any different from what the contractor was obligated to do in any case. The contractor failed to give notice at the time.

The general outline (though not the detail) is based on the case of *Pearce C J Ltd v Hereford Corporation*[36] in which it was held that design was not the cause of the collapse. That being so, the work in question was not a variation nor were the instructions given pursuant to Clause 13.

Points of principle involved

As with Case 6.1 the contractor is deemed to have satisfied himself as to what he is offering to do. He knew that the precise location of the drain was not known but chose to tender. Having done so he cannot plead that the work was more difficult or more costly than he expected. Note that circumstances where he might be able to plead that he had tendered within the limitations of what an experienced contractor might reasonably expect must be expressly set out in the contract (e.g. ICE 5 Clauses 12(4), 13(3) and 14(6)), but even with this it is considered that Pearce would not have succeeded in the Hereford case.

The old sewer turned out to be some two metres from the old. If it had been in closer proximity the work might have been more difficult, but as it was not literally in the line and did not actually touch, the work would have been possible.

Absence of notice can be fatal to a claim which may be otherwise sound. Under ICE 4 Clause 12, the cost of all work done prior to the giving of notice 'shall be deemed to

---

36. *Pearce C J Ltd v Hereford Corporation* [1968] 66 LGR 647.

have been covered in the rates and prices', and care should be taken to watch out for *ad hoc* clauses which might be inserted in contracts reviving this or similar stipulation. ICE 5 requires a notice 'as soon as reasonably possible after the happening of the events giving rise to the claim' (52(4)(b)). Use of the word 'reasonable' has been criticized as being too indefinite but whilst it is difficult to say in advance what this may mean, it is not usually so difficult to decide in given circumstances what is reasonable.

In the Hereford case the claim failed anyway, so failure to give notice was irrelevant, but contractors must be careful to give notice whenever the Conditions of Contract require it or they consider they need to seek additional payment. Engineers should recognize this necessity (they need to know from the employer's point of view anyway) and should not immediately or automatically condemn a contractor as being 'claims conscious'.

Under ICE4, the contractor would only have been entitled to an indemnity from the employer if it was 'damage to property resulting from any act or neglect by the Employer his agents...' This would include any act or neglect by the engineer.[37] Under ICE5 and ICE6, there is an additional express right to indemnity in respect of 'damage which is the unavoidable result of the construction of the Works in accordance with the Contract'. The outcome in this case would, however, probably be unchanged.

CASE 6.4 CLAIM IN RESPECT OF WORK OMITTED FROM CONTRACT AND GIVEN TO ANOTHER CONTRACTOR TO EXECUTE

Pertinent particulars of contract

The contract was for the construction of a number of buildings on an extensive site and included landscaping with provision of topsoil, turfing, seeding and planting of trees. This landscaping was included in the B/Q partly as measured work (topsoil, turfing, seeding etc) and partly as a Provisional Sum (covering unspecified work) and a PC sum for trees.

The documents comprised: Drawings, Bill of Quantities (no Specification), Conditions of Contract JCT 63/77.

Contract Sum £453,021. Contract period 21 months.

Total of landscaping bill £41,884, including a Provisional Sum of £5,000 (the latter followed by an item for general attendance priced at £300 and another for profit 5%). The Bill also included a Preamble stating:

> 'The topsoil generally is to be obtained from material excavated on site and dumped in temporary spoil heaps. Should the quantity available be insufficient to meet requirements the architect may direct the contractor in writing to obtain topsoil from elsewhere. Payment shall be made for such additional topsoil at the rate set down against Item L 10 F hereunder' [which was priced at £3 per m^3].

Events giving rise to claim

Work on site had been subject to a number of delays due to a relatively large number of variations, a spell of exceptionally inclement weather in the autumn and winter of 1978, delay in execution of work by Statutory Undertakers and prolonged labour troubles in 1979. Instead of being completed in February 1979, work was not even substantially completed until October 1979, too late to do turfing and seeding and too early for shrub and tree planting. Even then there were minor items to be done. The architect issued a variation order omitting the whole of the landscaping from the contract and let a separate contract to a 'specialist' firm for the work to be carried out in the following year.

Architect to Contractor   *21 September 1979*

VARIATION NO 143
You are hereby requested to omit the whole of the landscaping work as

---

37. *Brighton v Cleghorn* [1967] see Abrahamson *Engineering Law and the ICE Conditions* 4th edn, p 106.

Bill L and also the associated earthworks in Bill B and drainage in Bill D as indicated on the attached key drawing.

Contractor to Architect   *11 March 1980*

We refer to Variation No 143 dated 21 September 1979 in which you ordered the omission of the whole of the landscaping as well as some earthworks and drainage. We notice that another contractor has appeared on site and has commenced erecting hut etc. Whilst we have little work remaining to be done we are still technically in possession of the site and we must protest at another firm being given access without any reference to us.

We must reserve our rights regarding any damage which may occur to the work carried out under our contract.

We understand that this firm is to undertake the landscaping work omitted from our contract. We therefore reserve the right to claim compensation in respect of lost overheads and profit on this work.

Architect to Contractor   *14 March 1980*

Your attention is drawn to Clause 29 of the Conditions of Contract under which you are required to permit the execution of work 'by artists, tradesmen or others engaged by the Employer'. Work on your contract should have been completed some months ago and you should have been off the site before now.

Regarding your right to claim compensation, your attention is drawn to Clause 11(2) of the Conditions which says 'The term variation ... means ... and includes the ... omission ... of any work' and Sub-clause 4(d) says 'The prices in the Contract Bills shall determine the valuation of items omitted.'

A reply so prompt and out of keeping with the tardy issue of instructions earlier in the job might seem to suggest that the contractor's reaction was not altogether unexpected.

Contractor to Architect   *18 March 1980*

We cannot accept your view of Clause 29 of the Conditions. There was in the Contract a list of other contractors being or to be employed direct by the employer. This landscaping work was not amongst them. There was a Provisional Sum for unspecified work which we expected to do ourselves; there was a PC Sum for the supply of trees and shrubs but their planting was measured and there were earthworks and drainage which were obviously for us to do.

We cannot accept your view regarding your powers under Clause 11. It is true that work may be omitted, but only if it is in fact not required at all. Work cannot be omitted from our contract and given to others to carry out.

When you say we should have been off the site, we would draw your attention to Variation No 154 issued on 10 March 1980. We formally request an extension of time up to 24 March to cover the work involved.

Architect to Contractor   *21 March 1980*

I refer to para 3 of your letter of 18 March. Variation No 154 refers to

*a trivial amount of work and would have been issued much earlier had it
not been for delay for which you are responsible.*

The architect makes no reference to paras 1 and 2 of the letter of 18 March. Perhaps, rather belatedly, he has sought advice. The contractor is quite correct regarding the architect's powers to omit work and is entitled to loss of overheads and profit in so far as the omission of this work prevented him from recovering overheads incurred and profit he would have earned.

Assuming the B/Q included the following items:

Earthworks in Bill B			1,418
Drainage in Bill D			793
Landscaping Provisional Sum		5,000	
PC Sum	5,000		
Attendance	300		
Profit	250	5,550	
Remainder		31,334	41,884
Total value of work omitted			£44,095

then the contractor would be entitled to overheads (demonstrated by reference to the tender build-up to be 22%) and profit (similarly at 5%) as follows:

Measured work	1,418		
	793		
	31,334	33,545	of which $\dfrac{27}{127}$ = 7,131.61

He could have expected 5% profit out of the Provisional Sum but probably not overheads as he should have recouped actual overheads in measured work except for the loss of turnover to carry them which gave rise to the foregoing item

$$\frac{100}{105} \times 5\% \times 5,000 \qquad\qquad 238.09$$

Profit on PC Sum	250.00
	£7,619.70

In fact the loss of measured work on which to recoup overheads could be complicated by the out-turn of other variations, the time required for the varied work, c.f. the original time and contract value, but looking at the original contract sum only, the contractor could well have lost that sort of money because of the thoughtless omission of work he was expecting to do.

Regarding the extension of time, the work involved may be relatively trivial but the contractor is entitled to an extension of time beyond the date of the order sufficient to enable him to do the work. It matters not that some or even all of the previous delay may have been attributable to the contractor. The onus of proof that such a variation would have been issued earlier but for the contractor's delay is on the architect. If the nature of the variation is such that its need would have become apparent only after the work had reached a certain stage, the architect may be able to escape, but it is for him to prove. It is only too easy to negative the employer's rights in liquidated damages by the ill-considered issue of a late variation order.[38]

---

38. For a review of recent Australian decisions on this point, see Terence M Burke *Prevention by Variation of the Works after Date for Completion* (1984) 2 ICLR 8. See also p 276 *infra*.

Points of principle involved

Provisions as to the architect's/engineer's powers to order variations under the contract are, in all the Standard Forms, apparently very wide as discussed below in relation to Case 6.6.[39] On the other hand, the contractor is entitled to perform all the work included in his contract.[40] On basic principles of agency, if the contractor wishes to allege that the architect or engineer is acting outside the apparent authority conferred on him by the contract, the contractor must complain directly to the employer so that he may confirm or overrule the order. The employer will not be liable for the actions of an agent outside his apparent authority.[41]

Regarding time for completion, it is sometimes argued that the contractor is entitled in such case to an extension of time sufficient to enable him to do the work involved but running only from when he should otherwise have completed the work. Such a contention is quite unreliable.

CASE 6.5 CLAIM IN CONNECTION WITH ISSUE OF FURTHER DRAWINGS AND ENGINEER'S INSTRUCTIONS AS TO METHODS OF WORKING

Note: The case from which this example is drawn was based on Conditions prepared by a particular Authority for its own use. Even so, it has been suggested that some of the findings may be applicable not only to the ICE Conditions (ICE 4 more than ICE 5) and to FIDIC (International Conditions), but also to the Standard Building Forms (JCT 63/77 and possibly JCT 80).

The extent to which this may be possible is discussed in the commentary on this example for which purpose ICE 4 has been taken as the basis, with *ad hoc* conditions to reflect the particular conditions applicable to the case in question.

Pertinent particulars of contract

The contract was for the construction of a sewage works and the laying of some 1500 m of sewers on the outskirts of a city. The documents comprised:

Drawings (which were outline only and qualified in Clause 2 of the Specification).

Specification (of which the following clauses are relevant):

2. The sewers, manholes and sewage treatment works are shewn in outline on the Drawings but the precise positions, lines, depths and directions of these works are not indicated and the Contractor shall construct the works at the rates and prices in the Bill of Quantities in such portions, lines, depths and directions *as will be determined by the Engineer* as the contract proceeds and after trial holes have been made as provided hereinafter. The contractor shall set out the works *under the general directions of the Engineer* and shall provide all necessary instruments etc. He shall be responsible for the corrections of the position, levels and dimensions of the several works according to the Drawings and *written instructions of the engineer.*

7. The contractor shall excavate and afterwards refill trial holes ahead of the works *whenever and wherever required by the engineer.* The precise distance between the new sewers and any existing sewers, pipes, gullies, services, cables, etc shall be *determined by the engineer on the site* as the work of the sewer-laying proceeds and after trial holes have been dug.

(Note: italics used here to draw attention to the special requirements.)

---

39. See page 173.
40. *Gallagher v Hirsch* [1899] NY 45 App Div 467; *Carr v Berriman Pty Ltd* [1953] 27 ALJ 273; *Commissioner for Main Roads v Reed and Stuart* [1974] 12 BLR 56.
41. *Sharpe v San Paulo Rly* [1873] LR 8 Ch App 597.

14.   All excavations shall be securely timbered with suitable timber or alternative form of sheeting as may be and where necessary to the satisfaction of the engineer.

Bill of Quantities: based on the SMM for CEQ and including the following Preamble:

'The price for laying sewers shall be inclusive of all excavation and refilling in all types of strata, timbering of excavations trenches and headings and special timbering such as close sheeting if running sand is met with or the nature of the soil demands it; subsoil drains, sumps and pumping, laying and jointing pipes.'

Conditions of Contract amended as follows:

Clause 5 — add Sub-clause (2): 'The engineer's drawings and specification shall be considered binding as regards the general scheme and arrangement of works. In cases where the engineer gives his approval in writing to any particular appliance as reasonably complying with the intention of the specification, the said plans shall be considered binding only so far as they indicate the relation of that appliance to the general scheme of the works and before the work is put in hand detailed drawings shall be submitted to the engineer for his written approval.'

Clause 13 — delete and substitute: 'The contractor shall execute complete and maintain the works under the direction of and to the satisfaction of the engineer and shall comply with and adhere strictly to the engineer's instructions and directions on any matter. The contractor shall take instructions and directions only from the engineer or engineer's representative.'

Clause 51 — delete second sentence and substitute: 'No addition shall be made to the Contract Price in respect of any variation of or addition to the said works unless the same shall have been given by the engineer in writing or unless such instructions shall state that the matter thereof is to be the subject of an extra charge.'

Clause 66 — delete second sentence and substitute: 'Such decision in respect of the true intent and meaning of the Drawings, the quality of the materials and workmanship shall be final and conclusive. In respect of all other matters such decision shall be final and binding upon the employer and contractor until completion of the work and shall be forthwith given effect to by the contractor.'

The contract was sealed on 18 March 1973.

Development of the situation

At a meeting called by the engineer on 6 April 1973 preparatory to commencing work a number of matters were discussed, in the course of which the contractor stated that he had tendered on the basis that 50 per cent of the trenches for sewers and pipe lines would not be timbered at all. This the engineer considered to be reasonable.

Engineer to Contractor   *7 April 1973*

In accordance with Clause 41 of the Conditions of Contract you are hereby instructed to commence work within 14 days of the date of this letter.

The section of sewer from chainage 428 to 717 is to be put in hand first, for which you already have drawings. Trial holes are to be opened at points to be indicated by the RE between chainages 820 and 950.

Contractor to Engineer   *16 April 1973*

With reference to your letter of 7 April we had intended to start work on the sewage works concurrently with the first sewer line and we should be glad if you would confirm that we may take possession of the site of that work.

We had also expected to start work on the sewers from the bottom end and to work progressively away from the sewage works. The section you have instructed us to commence is just below the middle, and from the location of the trial pits requested the next section is not likely to be contiguous. This would be most uneconomical for us and we would ask you to reconsider.

Engineer to Contractor   *21 April 1973*

The site of the sewage works will not be available for another six weeks.

Regarding the sequence in which the work is to be carried out, this is a matter to be determined by myself — see Clause 2 of the Specification.

This contract does not seem to be getting off to a good start and one wonders what was discussed at the preliminary meeting. No doubt the RE and Agent respectively were introduced but one might have expected this vital matter of starting and sequence to have been discussed.

Contractor to Engineer   *26 April 1973*

With reference to your letter of 21 April, we must inform you that we do not accept your interpretation of the Specification. We are of course prepared to do everything reasonably possible in carrying out this work and fully accept that the work has to be to your satisfaction. We cannot, however, accept that you can control the sequence of working without regard to our requirements and we reserve the right to claim extra costs involved in adopting methods of working and following sequences we did not allow for in our tender.

This letter seems to have been ignored for the next one on the file is:

Engineer to Contractor   *4 May 1973*

You are requested to proceed with the sewer from chainage 820 to chainage 950, for which drawings are forwarded herewith.

There seems to be a wide difference of opinion between the contractor and the engineer as to how the job shall be run and who controls the sequence of work. The engineer seems to be reading Clauses 2 and 7 of the Specification as giving him the power to have the work done as he thinks fit (for what may appear to him good reasons), whilst the contractor regards these clauses as only a small extension of the general requirement of any contract, i.e. that the work be carried out in accordance with the contract to the satisfaction of the engineer. The same basic considerations apply to building contracts under the JCT Form.

From the next letters it would seem that two new matters crop up.

Contractor to Engineer   *7 May 1973*

At site progress meetings we have repeatedly asked for details of the pump house and filter beds, particularly of the reinforcement (including bending schedules). We need to get this material ordered immediately if we are to have any hope of completing by the due date.

We also need details of certain manholes (as list attached) and catch pits. These should have been issued much earlier and the delay is involving us in additional costs and expenses for which we reserve the right to enter a claim in due course.

167

Resident Engineer to Contractor   *11 May 1973*

It is noted that you have brought excavating plant to the site for the length Ch 820–950. The section must be done in normal trench and close sheeted. Battering back the sides of the trench will not be permitted.

Contractor to Engineer   *14 May 1973*

We have been notified by the RE that we are not allowed to batter back the sides of the trench in the section Ch 820–950. We would remind you that we stated at the very first meeting you called on this contract that we had allowed in our tender for 50 per cent of the trenches not being timbered, which you agreed at the time was reasonable.

You are stipulating the sections of work to be undertaken and the sequences they are to follow without any regard to our problems or considerations of economic working. We are being delayed through lack of drawings and instructions and now our methods of working are being altered.

We must request an early meeting at which these matters can be discussed.

Engineer to Contractor   *19 May 1973*

According to the terms of the contract, the methods by which the work is carried out are to be to my direction and satisfaction. Accordingly I insist that the section Ch 820–950 be excavated vertically and close sheeted.

The engineer might have been well advised to accede to the meeting suggested by the contractor. He obviously has very strong views as to his powers under the contract and it would have been better to try to persuade the contractor to his view rather than act in this cavalier fashion.

It might be opportune to look back at the contract documents and consider them in the light of events; in the context of circumstances encountered they often look very different from how they appeared in prospect:

1. *Who controls the work?* The engineer obviously considers that the phrases in italics in Specification Clauses 2 and 7 give him complete power. Looked at in retrospect, this may indeed be so but it is only fair to add that if anything so very different from the normal course of events was required then it should have been said in plain words. Clearly the terms of ICE (4 or 5) Clause 13 cannot be construed as conferring such power upon the engineer, much less so Clause 1 of JCT 63/77 (or 2.1 of JCT 80). GC/Wks 1 is in much the same terms as ICE.

2. *Who controls the method?* Here the engineer is on rather stronger ground in that Clause 14 of the Specification says 'All excavations shall be securely timbered . . .' In his letter of 19 May he would have been better advised to quote this rather than give the woolly generalization he did use. Perhaps he was trying to avoid the recrimination that he made no such comment at the preliminary meeting when he agreed that the contractor's assumption of timbering only 50 per cent of the trenches was reasonable.

3. *When could the contractor expect the further drawings?* In this case, given that the engineer had power to control the sequence and method of execution, clearly he would have corresponding jurisdiction over the issue of drawings. The Conditions of Contract say that further drawings shall be issued 'from time to time' (ICE 4 Clause 8, ICE 5 Clause 7, JCT 63/77 Clause 3(4), JCT 80 Clause 5.4, GC/Wks 1 Condition 7), so clearly they cannot

be expected to be supplied all on 'Day 1' — nor is the contractor in this case so arguing. But he is saying that regard should be had to his economic considerations.

In *Neodox v Swinton and Pendlebury*[42] Diplock J held that details and instructions necessary for the execution of the works must be given 'in a reasonable time', failing which the employer would be liable in damages for breach of contract. He went on to say that what is a reasonable time does not depend solely upon the convenience and financial interests of the contractor; the engineer should have time to provide them, reasonable from his point of view and that of the employer. Further, factors which must be borne in mind are:

(a) The order in which the engineer has determined the works shall be carried out (as he is entitled to do under Clause 2 of the Specification). (NB: This factor does not apply in contracts generally but only in cases where express provisions give the engineer such powers.)

(b) Whether the contractor has requested particular details and instructions. Clearly the contractor should ask if he is or should have been aware of the deficiency, but this does not relieve the engineer of the onus of supplying details he knows will be required.

(c) The time, including any extension of time, within which the contractor is bound to complete the works.

Diplock J emphasized in mentioning these matters that 'they are not intended to be exhaustive or anything like it.' It is important not to lose sight of this reservation, as in most contracts there are other matters normally or frequently obtaining which would affect this issue. For example:

(i) The provisions of such as ICE (4 and 5) Clause 43, to complete 'within the time stated', or JCT 63/77 Clause 21(1) to complete 'on or before the Date for Completion' (JCT 80 Clause 23.1), or GC/Wks 1 Condition 28(1) to complete 'on or before the date for completion'. It would seem that unless these clauses are amended by some *ad hoc* provision, the contractor is entitled to take less than the full contract period. How much less is perhaps open to question. In the normal way he will make some allowance for circumstances likely to cause delay and for which he will get no extension of time (shortage of labour, late delivery of material, difficulty in obtaining plant, etc). If a contractor were to plan to complete in less than, say, 85 per cent of the contract period he would be wise to enter some stipulation with his tender as to the supply of information.

(ii) The provision of a programme (ICE (4 and 5) Clause 14, JCT 80 Clause 5.3). Although these are post-contract documents clearly they serve a purpose to indicate to the engineer or architect when certain operations or phases of work will be taken in hand, and likewise to put them on notice that outstanding information concerning such operations or phases needs to be supplied. The contractor would be wise to indicate these requirements (including the letting of Nominated Sub-contracts) on the programme.

(iii) The need to comply with dates for completion of sections of the Works.

(iv) The need to comply with requirements such as dates for railway possessions, etc.

(v) Needs dictated by tidal or climatic conditions.

There may well be others applicable to individual cases.

In the present case the contractor did not take such a look or perhaps seek advice until the end of the job, when he put in a claim in the following terms:

---

42. *Neodox v Swinton & Pendlebury BC* [1958] 5 BLR 34.

We herewith formally submit our claims in respect of the several matters arising under this contract which have been at issue between us virtually throughout the contract.

1. *Delay in supply of details in connection both with the sewers and the sewage works, which we contend have caused us delay to the extent of 48 weeks at £1,425 per week*   £68,400

2. *Additional costs over and above those allowed for in tendering caused by the engineer's requirements in requiring the whole of the sewer trenches to be excavated vertically and heavily timbered instead of being excavated by machine with battered sides allowed for in tendering*   £28,980

3. *Additional costs for working to a sequence required by the engineer instead of to a simple and logical sequence we had assumed when tendering and on which we based our prices*   £38,760

The contractor backed up this summary of claims with detailed calculations but the engineer rejected these completely on the grounds he had maintained throughout the contract, namely that under the contract he was entitled to order the work to be done in the manner and sequence he directed.

The dispute was referred to arbitration and the decision of the arbitrator was, in turn, referred to the High Court under the now defunct[43] Case Stated procedure. The judgment of Diplock J, in so far as it concerned the matters discussed in this example, has been summarized above.

Points of principle involved

1. Issue of further drawings and instructions

This shall be from 'time to time' as stipulated in the contract, but unless the engineer/architect is taking complete control of the job the contractor may well be able to sustain a case for when he requires these to be issued. The *Neodox* case is important in this connection but the reservations of Diplock J must not be overlooked.

2. Control of works and methods

Responsibility for and control of the mode of construction and methods of working, including the timing of operations, generally rest with the contractor, except in so far as express powers are conferred on the architect or engineer.[44] Under ICE5 the mode and manner of construction are subject to the approval of the Engineer, by Clause 13(2); methods of construction and programme are subject to his approval under Clause 14. Apart from the power of disapproval, the Engineer also has powers under both clauses to issue instructions, but provision is made for entitlement to extension of time and additional payment if the Engineer's requirements are more onerous than could reasonably have been foreseen by an experienced contractor at time of tender. Such an arrangement is not to be implied into other forms of contract; the arrangements must be set out explicitly in the contract.

3. Implied terms re performance by engineer

Some aspects of the *Neodox* decision require careful reconsideration in the light of subsequent developments in the law. In particular, Diplock J declined to imply terms as to the engineer's competence or skill, or the reasonableness of his decisions. He said:[45]

43. The Case Stated procedure was abolished in England and Wales by the Arbitration Act 1979.
44. For a review of this topic, see Barber J N 1989 Risks in the method of construction. In *Construction Contract Policy, Improved Procedures and Practice*, p 57. Centre of Construction Law & Management, King's College, London.
45. *Neodox v Swinton & Pendlebury BC* [1958] 5 BLR 34 at 47.

'(The engineer's) decision as to whether one method or another is satisfactory to him must, of course, be an honest one, but it does not seem to me that the Corporation warrant his competency or skill; or warrant that his decision shall be reasonable ... It seems to me to be no more than what the contract itself calls for, provided only that the engineer is fair and impartial in making his decision to give such decision.'

Following the House of Lords decision in *Liverpool CC v Irwin*,[46] the position has changed. In *Merton LBC v Stanley Leach Ltd*[47] Vinelott J held, in relation to a contract under the JCT Form (relying on *Liverpool CC v Irwin*), that there was an implied term that the employer 'undertook to ensure that there would at all times be a person who would carry out the duties to be performed by the architect and that he would perform those duties with reasonable diligence, skill and care and that where the contract required the architect to exercise his discretion he would act fairly.'

This means that the employer does impliedly warrant the exercise of competence and skill by the engineer, and does impliedly warrant that the engineer's decisions will be reached by the engineer exercising his discretion fairly.

CASE 6.6   CLAIM CONCERNING THE VALIDITY OF A VARIATION ORDER

Pertinent particulars of contract

The contract was for the erection of an office block and the documents comprised:

Drawings, Conditions of Contract JCT 80;
Bill of Quantities based on SMM 6,
Tender in the sum of £422,187 dated 6 February 1980;
Acceptance dated 11 March 1980;
Possession of site 25 March. Time for completion 18 months.

Background to problem

Work on site commenced soon after possession of site was given and proceeded much as many jobs proceed, i.e. with a number of variations issued under Clause 13. The variations took extra time and there was delay on account of exceptionally adverse weather and also a strike for which extensions of time totalling four and a half months were given. Altogether work proceeded reasonably well but the contractor found that his tender was rather too keen and he was losing money.

About fifteen months after commencement, the architect issued a variation for an annexe, a separate building connected to the main building by a covered way at first floor level. The form of construction was not quite the same as that for the main building and the estimated cost was £20,000.

The contractor's agent was concerned about accepting this extra work and sought instructions from his Head Office. One of the directors telephoned the architect and arranged a meeting to discuss the matter but the outcome was not very satisfactory, the architect maintaining that this work was within the scope of Clause 13, the contractor disputing this and saying they were unwilling to accept it and refusing to be persuaded.

The following correspondence ensued:

Contractor to Architect   *25 June 1981*

We refer to your Variation No 74 dated 10 June for the annexe now required to the main building. Normally we would be only too willing to undertake this work but in this case we regret we cannot do so. We

---

46. *Liverpool CC v Irwin* [1977] AC 239 see page 109 *supra*.
47. *Merton LBC v Stanley Leach Ltd* [1985] 32 BLR 51.

consider it to be outside the scope of Clause 13; it is relatively late in the contract period and we regret we are unable to do this work at rates and prices for corresponding items in the B/Q.

We would, however, be quite prepared to undertake the work on the basis of a separate contract for which we would be willing to negotiate a price.

Architect to Contractor   *30 June 1981*

Thank you for your letter of 25 March, but I must inform you that I do not agree that the work is outwith the scope of Clause 13. The relevant Sub-clause reads: '13.1.1.1 the addition omission or substitution of any work'. No limit is placed upon the amount of such additional work, which in the present case is estimated to cost no more than about 5% of the contract sum, which is by no means excessive.

The Employer is urgently needing the additional accommodation and I shall be glad to hear that you are prepared to withdraw your objection and make an early start.

Contractor to Architect   *3 July 1981*

We regret we must refuse to accept your order to execute the work as a variation under the contract. Admittedly the amount involved is a small proportion of the contract sum but we must draw your attention to the fact that the estimated out-turn of Variations 1−73 is an addition of some 10% to the contract sum. From the employer's point of view some 75% of this will be offset by the Contingency Sums in the contract, but for us the effect is that the whole £40,000 worth of work has had to be done at unremunerative prices as we are losing money on this contract to a significant extent. We make no complaint about this as so far the variations, although numerous, are all within the scope of Clause 13.

We are, however, advised that this additional work is not within its scope. It is not necessary for the achievement of the original concept of the contract and was not the sort of additional work which was within the contemplation of the parties at the outset.

As stated in our letter of 25 June we are quite willing to do the work at a negotiated price. If the matter is as urgent as you indicate we would be willing to make a start as soon as agreement in principle is reached and in advance of negotiations as to price. We would point out that we are probably in a better position than anyone else to do the work quickly and economically. We have our organization on site and are prepared to take full account of that fact in negotiating.

This letter is very reasonable even if it does end with a bit of sales promotion. This matter of how far clauses permitting variations can be taken is a difficult one. In most Forms they are widely drawn but clearly there must be some limit. In the present case the words 'we are advised' probably mean they have taken legal advice (or that they wish to give that impression). Either way the architect should pause and consider (or take legal advice also). It was not part of the original scheme. The original contract can be completed without it (though the employer's requirement remains unsatisfied). It is relatively rather late in the day, which does not help.

A rough and ready test might be to say, 'If the contractor refuses, can he be sued for breach?' If he could, the work can be safely ordered as a variation; if not, it probably could not.

Points of principle involved

The provisions as to the architect's/engineer's powers to order variations under the contract are widely drawn in all the Standard Forms, but they have their 'elastic limits'. These limits depend partly on the wording of the particular clause, partly on the valuation provisions (a contract is to be construed as a whole), and partly on the reaction of the contractor at the time of the instruction.

In *Sir Lindsay Parkinson v Commissioner of Works*,[48] the question arose after the parties had entered into a supplementary agreement for acceleration, which set limits (both maximum and minimum) on the profits to be earned by the contractor. Together with the acceleration measures, the total cost of the work contemplated at the time of the supplementary agreement amounted to approximately £5 million. The architect subsequently ordered considerable extra work under the broadly worded power in the original contract, taking the cost to some £6.7 million. The Court of Appeal held that the supplementary agreement, with its limit on profit, did not apply to work beyond that contemplated by the parties at the time of the supplementary agreement; the contractor was entitled to be paid a *quantum meruit* on the excess.

Under FIDIC4, ICE5 and ICE6, the powers are in two halves: a power combined with a duty to order variations necessary for the completion of the Works, and a wider but qualified power to order other variations. Thus ICE5 Clause 51(1) states: 'The Engineer shall order any variation to any part of the Works that may in his opinion be necessary for the completion of the Works and shall have power to order any variation that for any other reason shall in his opinion be desirable for the satisfactory completion and functioning of the Works.' ICE6 is identical except that it refers to 'improved functioning'. FIDIC4 Clause 51(1) is not so qualified in relation to the wider power. The powers conferred by GC/Wks 1 Ed 2 Condition 7 (Ed 3 Condition 40) and JCT 80 Clause 13.1 do not distinguish the different situations and are virtually unqualified.

In GC/Wks 1 Editions 2 and 3, JCT80 and FIDIC4, however, where the variation might be considered outside the contemplation of the contract, there are effectively provisions for valuation on a *quantum meruit* or reasonable price, not by reference to the contract Bills of Quantities. GC/Wks 1 Ed 2 Condition 9(1) requires the QS to value work at 'fair rates and prices' rather than by reference to the Bills of Quantities where 'the instruction therefor was issued at such a time or was of such content as to make it unreasonable for the alteration or addition to be so valued'. Ed 3 Condition 42(9) is similar. FIDIC4 Clause 52(3) makes special provision where the total additions to or deductions from the Contract Price taken together are in excess of 15 per cent of the Effective Contract Price, while Clause 13.5.6 of JCT80 provides for a fair valuation 'to the extent that the valuation of any work or liabilities directly associated with a variation cannot reasonably be effected in the valuation by the application of Clauses 13.5.1 to 5'.

It will not generally be open to a contractor to claim that an order was outside the powers of the architect or engineer unless he protested at the time. In *Ranger v Great Western Railway*,[49] the contractor had accepted an instruction to carry out additional work under a variation power, but subsequently claimed to be paid on a *quantum meruit*. The Lord Chancellor held[50] it was not open to the contractor, having done the works on an agreement, to reject its terms and claim remuneration on a *quantum meruit*, as if there were no such express agreement.

If the contractor wishes to protest he must register his protest before proceeding and since his claim involves challenging the authority of the architect or engineer as agent of the employer, he should also communicate his protest to the employer.[51] A contractor cannot,

---

48. *Sir Lindsay Parkinson v Commissioner of Public Buildings and Works* [1949] 2 KB 632.
49. *Ranger v Great Western Railway* [1854] 5 HLC 72.
50. *Ibid* at p 101.
51. As to whether the employer himself has power to order the work, see Myers J J, *When might a contractor refuse to perform work ordered in writing by an employer* (1987) 4 ICLR 155.

173

however, insist both that he carry out the work and that he be paid at rates not referred to in the contract; either the work is within the contract or it is not.

CASE 6.7 CLAIM IN CONNECTION WITH THE NOMINATION OF A SUB-CONTRACTOR TO WHOM THE CONTRACTOR OBJECTS

Pertinent particulars of contract

The contract was for the construction of an extension to a hospital. The documents comprised:

Drawings, Bill of Quantities (no Specification), Conditions of Contract JCT 63/77.
Tender dated 27 January 1978. Acceptance dated 28 February 1978.
Contract Sum £1,481,288. Time for completion $2\frac{1}{2}$ years.

The B/Q included a large proportion of PC Sums, one of which was for piling and for which tenders had been invited prior to acceptance of the main contract.

Events giving rise to the claim

The date for possession of site was stated in the Appendix to be 1 April 1978 so that the date for completion was 30 September 1980. Instructions concerning the piling were promptly issued.

Architect to Contractor   *7 March 1978*

> *I enclose herewith quotations from Patent Piling Ltd in the sum of £148,217, together with setting out drawings, details of the piles and Bill of Quantities. Please accept this as soon as possible and arrange with the firm for an early start on site.*

The contractor, apparently more anxious to please the architect than to concern himself with contractual considerations, does as he is told on 10 March using his standard order form with printed conditions of his own on the back. His order is acknowledged:

Patent Piling Ltd to Contractor   *16 March 1978*

> *Thank you for your valued order of 10 March. We regret, however, that we cannot accept the printed conditions on the reverse of your order form as there is conflict with those printed on the back of our tender.*
>
> *Your conditions stipulate that we receive payment only after you yourselves have been paid, whereas we require payment within 14 days of date of invoice. Also, you make provision for liquidated damages (though no amount has been stated). We suggest the inclusion of a rate of £1 per week for this. Finally, your order is in terms of a lump sum, whereas of course the piling actually installed would be measured and paid for.*

The contractor reacts as might be expected, by asking the architect for instructions. The architect is busy getting out details for pile caps and foundation beams and puts this letter to the QS to deal with. The QS realizes that there are several matters, apart from those raised, which should have been dealt with before 'instructions' were given to accept. Clearly it is important to get this sub-contract let quickly, so he calls a meeting between the contractor, sub-contractor and himself at which the matter can be thrashed out. With the intervention of Easter this could not be until 3 April. The QS realizes that by the inclusion of further conditions the contractor's 'acceptance' is in fact a counter-offer. Not only is there not a contract but by the counter-offer the original tender has been 'killed off'. The sub-contractor, however, thinks the job is virtually his and thus he may be able to exert some pressure in the negotiations. The meeting on 3 April 1978 is opened by the QS.

> *QS to Patent Piling Ltd:*
> *First of all may I assume your quotation dated 30 January is still open for acceptance?*

This surprises Patent Piling Ltd a little who believed (?hoped) that it had in fact been accepted on their terms, they not having been rejected. However, the quotation was subject to price fluctuation, so he agreed that it was.

> *QS to Patent Piling Ltd:*
> *That being so, may we next turn to the time for completion, none is stated in the tender. What does the contractor require?*

> *Contractor:*
> *There is virtually nothing we can do until this piling is completed. We had hoped for a start to be made this week and we had programmed for completion in four months.*

> *Patent Piling Ltd:*
> *Unfortunately that is just not possible. We have certain other contracts in hand where our plant is tied up. We cannot start until the end of April and would require six months to complete.*

Is this to be interpreted as signs of pressure or does he mean it? Has he really got no spare rig or can he not get one elsewhere? Who was the second lowest tenderer and is his tender still open for acceptance? In any case it would probably do no harm to canvass the possibility of alternatives being open.

> *QS to Patent Piling Ltd:*
> *That is unfortunate because I can confirm the urgency to get this piling done. If you really cannot manage it perhaps we had better look elsewhere.*

> *Patent Piling Ltd:*
> *But our tender has been accepted as instructed by the architect, you cannot go elsewhere.*

> *QS to Patent Piling Ltd:*
> *The contractor's acceptance was a qualified one and so (if he does not mind my saying so) no acceptance at all but a counter-offer. That offer you were not prepared to accept but made another offer of your own, which led to this meeting. As your original quotation was killed off by the contractor's counter-offer, I had to establish first that you were prepared to revive your original offer, which you confirmed this morning. Now, what can you do?*

> *Patent Piling Ltd:*
> *In all the circumstances, the best we can offer is to start in three weeks' time, i.e. on 24 April, and we will try to complete in four months.*

This is better, now perhaps some positive progress can be made.

> *Contractor:*
> *We shall have lost about two months at least. What about liquidated damages? We are liable to £1,500 per week, we could not agree to the £1 suggested by Patent Piling Ltd.*

Patent Piling Ltd were wise to put in this £1 per week rather than leave it open as the contractor had done in his order. Left like that there would be doubt as to whether liquidated damages were applicable at zero pounds per week (which would preclude recovery of actual damages), or whether unliquidated damages were to apply. In the present case it would seem that the piling is on the critical path and that a month's delay here (the contractor was exaggerating when he said two months) would result in a month's delay to the main contract. This month cannot be held against the sub-contractor so the contractor must, separately, seek an extension of time on grounds of late instructions.

After further debate, Patent Piling Ltd, who have realized they have not yet got the job in their pocket, make an offer.

Patent Piling Ltd:
We would be prepared to accept liquidated damages of £1,000 per week but, whilst we would make every effort to complete in four months, we could not accept a contract period of less than five months.

Contractor:
We would be prepared, though reluctantly, to agree to that, provided we were given an extension of time now of, say, $2\frac{1}{2}$ months to cover the delay on this piling. We shall also have to claim additional costs.

QS to Contractor:
You will need to put your claim for extension of time formally to the architect, but I must point out that if Patent Piling Ltd do start work on 24 April and do manage to complete in four months, the delay to you will be only three weeks. You should therefore give preliminary notice and claim the actual delay when the extent is known. As to extra costs, these must be minimal, as you admitted earlier that there was nothing you could do until the piling was complete. I will put your point to the architect in the meantime.

Now, what about payment? The main contract provides for monthly payment and a retention of 5 per cent. Under Clause 27 of the Conditions the architect informs the contractor and sub-contractor of the amount included in any certificate in respect of the sub-contract and requires the contractor to pay that within fourteen days of receiving the certificate.

Patent Piling Ltd:
That would be acceptable to us.

QS:
Next, what about the defects liability period? That in the main contract is six months, which would mean that the contractor will be liable for the piling for two and a half years.

Patent Piling Ltd:
It sounds a long time but we would be prepared to accept that, provided we were paid our retention under Clause 27(e) of the main contract.

QS:
I will put that to the architect but I am sure he will agree. Finally, a matter which in a sense should have come first but I think this only a formality — the basis of the sub-contract. The contractor accepted your quote in terms of a lump sum, but in your reply you said the actual amount installed would be subject to measurement. Your tender did in fact quote a total sum, though I accept that the whole bill is stated to be provisional. Could we get this tidied up?

Patent Piling Ltd:
The quantities are all provisional. The actual amount installed would need

to be measured. So our tender is really at the unit prices quoted in the B/Q.

QS:
That is understood. I think, however, it would be simplest and safest if you were to submit a revised quotation embodying all the matters we have discussed and agreed here. Would that be acceptable to you both?

Contractor and Patent Piling Ltd:
Yes.

The QS put the result of this meeting to the architect, who agreed with what had been arranged. He cancelled his original instructions and told the contractor to accept Patent Piling Ltd's revised quotation.

Patent Piling Ltd started work when promised but in fact encountered difficulties. They were due to have completed by 23 September 1978 (five months from 24 April) but in fact did not complete until 19 October (three and a half weeks late).

Contractor to Architect   *1 November 1978*

Patent Piling Ltd completed piling work on 19 October, some $3\frac{1}{2}$ weeks after the due date for completion of their work. Enclosed is a copy of a letter in which they claim that delay was due (a) to exceptionally inclement weather in May and (b) to the Electricity Authority in the removal of a cable which crossed the site and fouled three pile positions.

We confirm the facts they state and would add that we too wrote to the Electricity Authority urging them to remove this cable, but to no effect.

We also claim extension of time in our own behalf totalling $12\frac{1}{2}$ weeks. Some 5 weeks were lost in accepting the piling tender, their contract period was 1 month longer than we planned for and they were $3\frac{1}{2}$ weeks late in completing.

We hereby claim to be reimbursed for the additional overheads incurred over this period, i.e. $12\frac{1}{2}$ weeks at £1,700 per week = £21,250.

The architect asks the QS to take this up with the contractor. The QS argues that some of the initial delay was due to the contractor himself not handling the original acceptance properly. He points out that he could not expect Patent Piling Ltd to start until he himself had been given possession of the site and that they did in fact start on 24 April. This three weeks plus the longer contract period (four weeks) plus delay in completing totalled ten and a half weeks which the contractor agreed and the QS agreed to put to the architect.

Regarding the claim for reimbursement, the QS pointed out that the contractor himself had made the point that there was little he could do until piling was complete so that additional overheads at £1,700 per week (based on 15 per cent of the contract value over 130 weeks) could not be sustained.

The contractor had put up certain offices, stores, mess huts and workshops, the capital value of which he put at £50,000. The QS suggested a depreciation rate of 15 per cent but the contractor stated that the life of buildings of that type was no more than five years and that repairs and maintenance would add another 5 per cent (say £240 per week).

Some staff had been engaged but were unable to do any effective work (it had been possible to accommodate two or three elsewhere). Salaries of the staff in question totalled £280 per week. Increased costs of labour and materials would be reimbursed under the Price

Fluctuation Clause, so the delay would have no effect on this. There was nothing identifiable by any of Head Office overheads which could be attributed to this delay.

The contractor agreed to settlement on this basis.

The QS therefore recommended to the architect that the contractor should be given an extension of time of ten and a half weeks and that the claim be settled in the sum of £5,460, i.e. $10\frac{1}{2}$ weeks at £240 + £280 under Clause 24 of the Conditions of Contract.

The architect said that this amount would be certified for payment but that under his terms of appointment he would need to report the matter to the employer. (Note that the architect does not first seek approval from the employer as under Clause 24 he has authority to certify.)

Points of principle involved

There are several matters concerning nominated sub-contracts which are really the concern of the contractor/sub-contractor and which the architect/QS cannot settle for him. These include the conditions of sub-contract (if any), time for completion, timing, liquidated or unliquidated damages, payment, retention and defects liability period. Imposition of sub-contract terms on the main contractor may lead to the employer being deprived of the benefit of warranties under the main contract.[52] If the contractor's requirement cannot be obtained beforehand and included in the tender documents then the selected tender must be sent to the contractor to get these matters settled before any request (much less instruction) is issued to accept. By the same token, regardless of the terms of the architect's instructions, the contractor would be foolish to accept a quotation without getting these matters settled. He might find himself in contract with a sub-contractor and quite unable to get such deficiencies remedied.

Such a situation cannot happen with JCT 80 if the procedures using Tender NSC/1, Agreement NSC/2, Nomination NSC/3 and Sub-contract Form NSC/4 are followed. Even so, Sub-clause 35.7.2 of JCT 80 provides for the settlement of any particular conditions remaining to be agreed. If the alternative forms using NSC/2a and NSC/4a or indeed any *ad hoc* or informal methods are adopted, the same basic points must be agreed before a workable sub-contract can come into being.

CASE 6.8 CLAIM IN RESPECT OF DEFAULT OF A NOMINATED SUB-CONTRACTOR

Pertinent particulars of contract

All as for Case 6.7

This case concerns the nomination of a heating sub-contractor to provide a hot water supply and a steam installation for sterilizers. The PC Sum was for £150,000 but the lowest tender received amounted to £238,146.

Learning from his experience with the piling sub-contract, the architect put the tender to the contractor, pointing out the matters yet to be settled and requesting him to negotiate with the sub-contractor and report back when agreement had been reached. It was something of a shock some three weeks later to get the following letter:

Development of claim

Contractor to Architect   *7 August 1979*

As requested, we have been in negotiation with Heating Systems Ltd but have been unable to reach agreement with them:

(a) The time for completion required is 18 months. The firm states that delivery time for the heating boilers is 14 months and for the steam boiler 15 months. We shall have about one month's work to do after they are off the site. The due date for completion (taking account of

---

52. *Gloucestershire CC v Richardson* [1969] 1 AC 480.

178

*the last extension of time) is 10 October 1980. On dates given by
Heating Systems Ltd work would not be complete until December
1980.*

*(b) Heating Systems Ltd refuse to indemnify us under Clause 27(a)(iii)
and (iv) of the main contract and we are therefore unwilling to
accept them as nominated sub-contractors.*

*(c) Should it be possible to overcome point (b) we would still be
unwilling to employ them because from enquiries made it would
seem that their financial position is not altogether satisfactory. To
counter this we asked them to provide a bond for due performance
in the sum of £50,000 (which is what we believe might be involved
if they were to default). This they have refused to provide and we
have reasons to believe that they are unable to provide it.*

Your instructions are requested.

An urgent conference was called on 11 August between the architect and QS. The former
pointed out that this tender was already substantially in excess of the PC and that to go
elsewhere would inevitably involve greater cost and take time. The QS agreed but pointed
out that the next lowest tender received was some £30,000 higher and he thought Heating
Systems Ltd might have made a mistake or were unduly cutting the tender in order to get
the job. When examining tenders he had called for a schedule of prices but this did not
show anything wrong. This was a design and install job — was the architect satisfied with
the installation proposed? The architect replied that he had had it checked in his drawing
office (though he had no qualified heating engineer) but nothing had been found wrong.

This meeting was followed on 12 August by one with the contractor. From discussion
it appeared that the indemnities referred to under (b) of the contractor's letter of 7 August
were Royalties and Patent Rights under Clause 7, Injury to Persons and Property under
Clause 18 and Liquidated Damages. The architect considered the first of no importance
and the second was a matter for which the sub-contractor would be liable under statute or
in common law. Regarding the third he asked the QS the position if there were no liquidated
damages, to which the QS replied that in the event of delay for which he was not entitled
to an extension of time, the sub-contractor would be liable to the contractor for such actual
damages as could be proved. The contractor said that this was not altogether satisfactory
but he would not refuse to accept nomination on this ground alone.

This brought them to the question of the sub-contractor's financial position. The QS said
he also had made enquiries but without much success. The bank reference was in the usual
vague terms and quite unhelpful. He was inclined to agree with the contractor that if Heating
Systems Ltd were unable (as distinct from unwilling) to provide a bond there was probably
some cause for concern.

The architect took the point but considered the evidence insufficient to justify passing
over this tender in favour of another some £30,000 higher (even supposing it to be still
open for acceptance). Further there was already a potential delay of 3 months or so and
he was being strongly pressed by the Hospital Authority to get on with the work. He had
indicated to them the trouble with this sub-contract (though, it is suspected, in less than
unequivocal terms) and they seemed anxious to proceed. He must therefore formally instruct
the contractor to accept the tender.

The contractor agreed with considerable reluctance, but nevertheless sought to cover
himself in the following terms:

Contractor to Architect   *14 August 1979*

*As instructed at the meeting held in your office on 12 August we have
today accepted the tender from Heating Systems Ltd.*

179

We hereby apply for an extension of time to 31 December 1980 in respect of the delay which will inevitably result from this sub-contract.

We must also point that we take no responsibility for any breach of Clauses 7 and 18 of the Conditions caused by any act or default of Heating Systems Ltd. We also reserve the right to claim any loss or expense we may incur in the event of this sub-contractor's default.

Oh dear, oh dear! Just what sort of a pickle has this turned out to be?

(a) We have the architect virtually dismissing the employer's rights to indemnity. He might even be right that there is little risk of infringement of patent rights but he has no authority to waive these rights himself. He should at least have obtained more information.

(b) The position outlined by the QS as to damages for delay was not incorrect, but he really should have warned the architect and contractor of the difficulties of proving unliquidated damages. As it is the contractor seems to have been lulled into a feeling of almost false security. He should of course know better — but many do not.

(c) The architect seems so concerned about incurring additional cost and losing further time by looking elsewhere that one might be forgiven for feeling that he had something of a guilty conscience. Perhaps his total estimate was escalating rather badly and there might be some difficulty in explaining the lost time. There are often good and unavoidable reasons for both but it is not always easy or pleasant to explain them, particularly if the employer himself has been the cause and the architect has perhaps been somewhat less than blunt in giving warning of the consequences of alterations, indecisions etc. By the same token the QS, who is looked to as being the business adviser of the team, really should have warned the architect of the risks he was running and made a positive recommendation that the matter be reported to the Hospital Authority as a matter of urgency, recommending that this tender be rejected and another sought.

(d) The architect had no authority to *instruct* the contractor to accept in face of what was apparently a valid objection under Clause 27(a).

(e) Last in the line, the contractor agreed to accept when he could and should have refused. He can hardly say he was coerced into accepting, but if he considered that objection was well founded he should have taken the matter to the other party to the contract — the Hospital Authority. His bleat of 14 August is understandable and will probably get him his extension of time but is unlikely to do him any more good than that except to enable him to say 'I told you so' if Heating Systems Ltd default.

Which is just what they did. In March 1980 they started work on site on internal pipework, to enable the contractor to get his finishings on the way. In June 1980 the architect had included in that month's certificate £12,500 in respect of work done by Heating Systems Ltd. This sum remained unpaid and the architect notified the employer, drawing attention to Clause 27(c). In July the employer paid the sub-contractor direct. The contractor protested on the grounds that he had contra-accounts against Heating Systems Ltd for huts and other facilities provided. In August 1980 the job closed down for the summer holiday and when it was reopened the sub-contractors did not return. Search of the site revealed that their plant and equipment and all unfixed materials had been removed, including that of some sub-sub-contractors. The huts (which had been provided at rental by the contractor) were empty. Enquiry revealed that a liquidator had been appointed.

So, where does everybody stand now? The architect is of course obliged to report the matter to the employer, at this stage probably only the bare facts that the sub-contractor was in liquidation, that it would be necessary to let another contract for completion and that there would be additional cost and delay.

The architect was inclined to feel that the contractor should arrange for the work to be completed but the contractor drew attention to the outcome of the case of *Bickerton v NW Metropolitan Hospital Board*[53] in which case the contractor (who completed the work) was held to be entitled to be paid the extra cost.

A contract for completing the work was arranged with another heating specialist (who refused to accept responsibility for the original design and insisted on making certain amendments). An assignment was agreed upon between the liquidator, the contractor, the employer and the boiler suppliers in respect of the contract for the supply of the boilers.

Of course this all took some time to arrange and the second sub-contract for completing the work was not let until the end of October 1980. It was due to be completed by 27 March 1981 but was not in fact completed until 16 April 1981 — a total delay of twenty-eight weeks beyond 10 October 1980 up to which date the contractor had been given an extension of time.

The contractor then presented a claim both in respect of his own costs and expenses and those of certain sub-contractors whose work had been affected by the default of Heating Systems Ltd. It was set out under the following heads:

Claim by plastering and tiling sub-contractor in respect of delay and disruption	7,797	
Claim by terrazzo sub-contractor in respect of delay and return visit to site	1,249	
Claim by plumbing sub-contractor for delay and disruption	5,621	14,667
Claim by main contractor		
(a) for disruption to uncompleted work on site — say 10% on labour content (50% of say £400,000 of work)		20,000
		34,667
(b) additional overheads for period of 28 weeks delay by heating sub-contract 15%		5,200
		£39,867

Each sub-contract had to be dealt with as a self-standing contract and each in accordance with its own terms.

Plastering sub-contractor: Enquiry shewed that the claim had been based on a loss of productivity in respect of ten men for two periods totalling ten weeks. The claim was for 50 per cent of the wages paid plus 15 per cent for overheads. The men were in fact being paid a bonus on output and records shewed that output had in fact reduced by 35 per cent compared with other periods. Taking labour costs including all the direct oncosts (National Insurance, HWP, etc, etc) at £3.50 per hour:

8 weeks × 10 men × 50 hours × 3.50 =	£14,000	
£14,000 × 35%	4,900	
Oncosts in tender were at 12½% of direct costs	613	£5,513

---

53. *Bickerton v NW Metropolitan Hospital Board* [1970] 1 All ER 1039.

Terrazzo sub-contractor: There proved to be no real basis to the claim as put and it was established that the men had been withdrawn from site and found other work. There was therefore only the extra cost of return visit to site to be paid. Records shewed this to be:

	£648.00	
Add overheads at 15%	97.20	£745.20

Plumbing sub-contractor: This claim proved more difficult to establish than that of the plasterer. Again the contractor was claiming a loss of output of something like 50 per cent for a period when admittedly work was hampered. The degree of disruption, however, was much less than in the case of the plasterer. Fortunately the Clerk of Works had daily returns of the numbers and distribution of men on site and was able from his own diary to piece together some indication of the work in hand in the period in question. The total labour costs for the period were £12,400 but by reference to the work done and the B/Q prices, there could not have been a loss of output of more than 20 per cent.

3,100 hours at £4 = 12,400 × 20% =	2,480	
Add overheads at 15%	372	£2,852

Main contractor: The work mainly affected here was joinery and the biggest effect of the delay was in the joinery works (the contractor's own). This was rather difficult to establish but records shewed that in monetary value output from the shops dropped in the same two periods that had affected the plasterers. All the machines were hourly rated and with the help of the firm's accountant it was established reasonably well that the unproductive costs of the joinery shop labour and machinery plus hired storage amounted to:

	5,100.00	
There were two joiners on site whom the Clerk of Works could agree were virtually supernumerary for a period of eight weeks. 8 × 2 × 50 × 3.39 =	2,712.00	£7,812.00

Regarding the additional overheads, it was found that extra work ordered had (by way of additional Preliminaries and overheads included in the B/Q prices) accounted for about twenty of the twenty-eight weeks of extra time at the rate of turnover of the original contract value to original time. This left eight weeks to be paid for.

The original Contract Sum could be analysed for this purpose as follows:

Contract Sum	1,481,288			
Profit 5%	70,537	1,410,751		
HO overheads $8\frac{1}{2}$%		110,520	1,300,231	
Site overheads $12\frac{1}{2}$%			144,470	£1,155,761

These last were virtually all time related, so 144,470 ÷ 130 = £1,111.3 per week.

Thus for eight weeks	£8,890.40

Regarding Head Office overheads the delay on this job had no demonstrable effect on turnover generally and the contractor could point to very little direct cost and expense he had suffered. There were additional visits of QS and Contract Manager to site over the period, but again this should be related to the eight weeks referred to above. The QS agreed to a figure of   £500.00

The claim was thus settled as follows:

Plastering sub-contractor	5,513.00	
Terrazzo sub-contractor	745.20	
Plumbing sub-contractor	2,852.00	9,110.20
Main contractor, loss of productivity in joinery shop and by site joiners		7,812.00
Additional site overheads		8,890.40
Additional HO overheads		500.00
		£26,312.60

Points of principle involved

The *Bickerton* case arose out of the refusal of the architect to make a new nomination to replace a defaulting sub-contractor. Although the architect wanted the facility of nomination in the first place (with its design content) he sought to rely on the contractual chain and make the contractor responsible for the consequence of the nominee's default.

This situation could not arise now under JCT 80 provided the recommended procedure is followed. What the effect of 'listing' sub-contractors in the main contract (as a permitted alternative) will be remains to be seen.

The situation could not arise under ICE as all the consequences of nomination and renomination in case of default are spelt out, but again the procedure stipulated must be closely followed. In the case of GC/Wks 1 Ed 2, Condition 38(5) leaves the liability for extra cost on the shoulders of the main contractor.

Architects, engineers and quantity surveyors must be careful to take note of legitimate objections by contractors to nominations. If they act negligently by misapplying the provisions of the contract (how well did the architect in this case do?) then they may be personally liable to the extent that the employer is unable to recover from the contractor (see *Sutcliffe v Thackrah*).[54]

In brief, nominated sub-contracts are to be avoided if at all possible. In most cases (even with electrical and mechanical services and equipment, machinery, etc.) it is possible to specify what is required, stipulate that qualified labour is to be used for installation, include it in the contract (specification and Bill) as part of the works and leave it to the contractor to organize.

---

54. *Sutcliffe v Thackrah* [1974] AC 727.

Chapter 7
Claims concerning payment for work

GENERALLY

There is a distinction at common law between payment for performance of a contract, payment as compensation for breach of the contract, and payment for work done outside the contract. As explained in Chapter 2, different rules apply to determine the amount payable in each case. The distinction is mirrored in the payment provisions of construction contracts — some provisions relate to payment for work performed under the contract; others relate to payment for loss and expense occasioned by the act or omission of either party or their agents. Analogies may be drawn between common law rules and corresponding contractual provisions.

It is axiomatic that the contractual payment provisions cannot relate to work done outside the contract, but construction contracts commonly provide for work to be varied from that originally specified, as part of the contract. Payment provisions differentiate between work which formed part of the contract initially and work added or modified after the contract is in being. Payment for the varied work may reflect, though not necessarily coincide with, common law rules relating to work outside the contract. This chapter is concerned with payment for work performed under the contract, both as originally specified and as varied.

If life were simple the work to be performed under a contract would be precisely defined at the time of contract, with the corresponding entitlement to payment also fixed. In a less than ideal world there will almost always be changes required, both for deliberate modifications and to deal with unintentional shortcomings (incomplete designs, approximations, errors, omissions and ambiguities). In the absence of special provisions to accommodate changes within the contract, they can still be dealt with so long as both the parties are willing. The parties may agree to vary the original contract, or a substitute contract will be implied where changes have already been performed following instructions without express agreement on price. Reliance on willingness is, however, dangerous. If there is no right for the employer to *order* the required changes within a binding contract, it would be open to the contractor to refuse an instruction involving the changes[1] or to hold out for an exorbitant price. Similarly, if the contractor does not have the right to carry out all the work, it would be open to the employer to bring in other contractors.

To enable changes to the works to be ordered within a binding contract, the contract must incorporate 'machinery' to fix corresponding changes in the price, which satisfies the legal requirement of certainty at time of contract. Remeasurement at fixed rates is an obvious example of such machinery, but the output it provides may not always be considered acceptable or appropriate. For situations where such a simple mechanism is inadequate, judgment must be applied as part of the machinery to provide the output. The question is, whose judgment? There are various possibilities which meet the legal requirement of certainty at time of contract. The contract may stipulate that:

1. A 'fair' or 'reasonable' price shall be paid. If the parties then cannot agree what is a fair or reasonable price, they can apply to the courts who will decide the matter with the assistance of expert or other evidence.
2. The price shall be fixed by an independent third party.
3. The price shall be agreed between the parties or, failing such agreement, it shall be fixed by an independent third party.

The contract may additionally stipulate factors to be taken into account as criteria or guidance in fixing prices. The crucial point is that an agreement to agree in the future is, by itself, not regarded in law as sufficiently certain to create a binding contract.[2] That does not preclude contractual provisions *allowing* for the price of variations to be agreed, but, if the possibility of agreement is mentioned, there must also be machinery to fix the price in default of agreement. An arbitrator jointly appointed by the parties would constitute an independent third party. As a matter of law, the engineer, architect, quantity surveyor or supervising officer (possibly subject to review by an independent arbitrator[3]) is also deemed to be capable of acting as an independent third party, although employed by one of the parties.

It also appears permissible for a contract to stipulate that one of the parties alone should have the power to fix the price, but the cases indicate that such a provision will be heavily circumscribed by implied terms that the party should act reasonably and not capriciously.[4]

VALUATION OF CONTRACT WORK

Some Forms of Contract are essentially for lump sum contracts subject to variations. The Bills of Quantities, where provided, are intended only to define the work and to provide a basis for valuing variations. For example, JCT80 (with Quantities) provides in Clause

---

1. See Case 6.6, page 171.
2. *Foley v Classique Coaches* [1934] 2 KB 1; *Walford v Miles* [1992] 1 All ER 453.
3. *Northern Regional Health Authority v Derek Crouch Construction Ltd* [1984] QB 644 at p 670; Cf *Hickman v Roberts* [1913] AC 229 at p 234 where Lord Alverstone considered that the professional integrity of engineers and architects could, by itself, be relied upon as sufficient.
4. In *May & Butcher v R* [1934] 2 KB 17 at p 21, Viscount Dunedin said '... with regard to price it is a perfectly good contract to say that the price is to be settled by the buyer.' He quoted no authority for the proposition and his remark was *obiter*, but it was approved by the Court of Appeal in *Lombard Tricity Finance v Paton* [1989] 1 All ER 918 in relation to finance rates. The Court of Appeal stressed, however, the unlikelihood that a finance company could adjust its finance rates capriciously. In *Finchbourne v Rodrigues* [1976] 3 All ER 581, the Court of Appeal held that a term would be implied that costs to be fixed by a landlord (who had misleadingly set himself up in a lease agreement as the managing surveyor) would be fair and reasonable.

14.1 'The quality and quantity of the work included in the Contract Sum shall be that which is set out in the Contract Bills.' Deficiencies in, or failure to comply strictly with, Methods of Measurement can lead to claims that the Contract Bills were incomplete, but that is a separate matter dealt with in Chapter 5.

ICE5, ICE6 and FIDIC4, on the other hand, are 'measure and value' contracts. The quantities in the B/Q issued at tender stage do not purport to be accurate measurements, but serve as a basis for establishing rates. Thus in ICE5 and ICE6, Clause 55(1) states:

'The quantities set out in the Bill of Quantities are the estimated quantities of the work but they are not to be taken as the actual and correct quantities of the Works to be executed by the Contractor in fulfilment of his obligations under the Contract.'

FIDIC4 Clause 55.1 is similar.

GC/Wks 1 Edition 2 can be either lump sum or measure and value; it allows for 'Provisional Bills of Quantities' or 'Bills of Approximate Quantities' as an option by incorporation of relevant clauses. GC/Wks 1 Edition 3 has been published initially as 'Lump sum with quantities'. A separate 'measure and value' version is understood to be planned.

The principle of measure and value contracts is that valuations of the works originally comprised in the contract are to be based on actual measurements and the rates in the Bills. The main problem encountered usually centres on variations in the quantities as such. There is a school of thought which considers that the rates in the B/Q apply to whatever the quantity in the event. The alternative view is that the contractor is entitled to take into account, in assessing his price, the quantity stated in the B/Q. If that is the case then it follows that should the actual quantity differ, some adjustment of the rate (up or down) should follow to the extent that the quantities of themselves affect the price. The basis for the latter view as a matter of general principle, independent of explicit provisions, must be based either on the concept of misrepresentation — that the billed quantities are represented as reasonable estimates of the quantities required, or an implied term that the quantities are reasonable estimates. In truth, rates may well be dependent on the quantity, particularly where a lump sum expense (e.g. setting up a piling rig) has to be spread across a measured quantity. There may also be arguments whether work constitutes a variation or is part of the original works.

The need to test the general principle is avoided with ICE5 and ICE6 by the adoption of explicit provisions and by the Standard Method of Measurement. Clause 56(2) provides for rates to be adjusted if an increase or decrease in quantities renders rates or prices inapplicable and warrants an adjustment. The clause contains no threshold below which it does not apply, though with small differences it will be more difficult, if not impossible, to justify a consequential difference of price. It should also be noted that adjustment may be up or down, which should be sufficient to deter a contractor from putting forward frivolous claims. The Standard Method of Measurement has evolved to provide combinations of lump sum and measured items for work to avoid problems with spreading lump sum costs.

FIDIC4 adopts a completely different approach, providing for adjustment in Clause 52.3 if the net additions and deductions on completion exceed 15 per cent of the Effective Contract Price. GC/Wks 1 Edition 2 is silent on the point. GC/Wks 1 Edition 3 Condition 42(9) allows for measurement at fair rates and prices of alterations in or additions to the Works, where the relevant Variation Instruction was of such a content as to make valuation at billed rates or based on billed rates unreasonable.

The practice has been encountered of labelling quantities as 'provisional' to warn that an item is subject to particular uncertainty. Such a warning may have some practical effect but, in the absence of any reference in the Conditions of Contract, the contractual effect ought not to exceed the practical. If the label is relied upon as an exclusion clause, the rules on excluding liability for misrepresentation may apply.

VALUATION OF VARIED WORK

At common law, in the absence of explicit contractual provisions or subsequent express agreement, a substitute contract would be implied to pay on a *quantum meruit* for work instructed and carried out.[5] Earlier editions of Forms of Contract adopted formulations for the valuation of variations which bore a close resemblance to a *quantum meruit*. For example, the first four editions of the ICE Conditions provided for 'fair and reasonable' payment for variations. The intention behind the formulation appears, however, to have been that the price to be fixed for a variation should be based so far as possible on how the contractor would have priced the work if invited to do so at the time of tender. Edward Rimmer, in his paper and discussion which led to the ICE Conditions,[6] expounded a more detailed philosophy of the proper approach to pricing variations, as follows:

> 'The safeguard to which the Employer is properly entitled is that a Contractor shall not, in the event of variation, obtain for either the varied work or any additional work prices which are in excess of the level of the prices upon which he accepted the tender. This safeguard is one which the conditions should give, and in the Author's opinion it should be possible to give it without the necessity of precluding the Engineer from giving full consideration to the changed conditions brought about by variations, whether as part of the rate to be applied to the varied work or as a revision of any other rate.'

The widespread acceptance in the civil engineering profession that the contractual provisions should be interpreted as intended by Rimmer was confirmed in the discussion of a paper by Charles Haswell, entitled 'Rate fixing in civil engineering contracts',[7] in which he set out the following proposition:

> 'A satisfactory interpretation of his responsibility is for the Engineer to determine, for new or substituted items, the rate which the contractor would have inserted against that item had it been included at the time of tender. To implement this it is obviously necessary for the Engineer to be familiar with the usual practice adopted by contractors in preparing their tenders.'

In the discussion of Haswell's paper,[8] the proposition received almost unanimous support. Such acceptance by the profession of a method of valuation is significant. In *Sudbrook v Eggleton*,[9] a contractual agreement for a valuer to fix a fair and reasonable price was held to mean that 'a fair and reasonable price would be assessed by applying objective standards used by valuers in the exercise of their professional task'. If the construction professions are unanimous on how variations should be valued under a particular form of contract, and on the meaning to be attributed to words such as 'fair and reasonable' in that context it appears that the unanimity will be respected by the courts.

The tender prices are also *prima facie* a satisfactory basis for assessing a *quantum meruit* in that they are evidence of the market price for work under the same conditions.[10] Nevertheless a true extra-contractual *quantum meruit* is not in principle limited by the prices in an existing contract.[11] There were those who contended that a 'fair and reasonable' price in ICE4 should be interpreted without reference to the original contract prices. Later editions of most Forms of Contract have seen fit to resolve the matter by expressing the formulation in greater detail.

---

5. See Chapter 2 (page 34).
6. Rimmer, E. 1939 'The conditions of engineering contracts'. *ICE Journal* **11**:18.
7. Haswell, C. 1963 'Rate fixing in civil engineering contracts'. Proc. Instn. Civ. Engrs. Vol 24, February 1963, p 223 at p 224.
8. Discussion on 'Rate fixing in civil engineering contracts'. Proc. Instn. Civ. Engrs. Vol 25, February 1964, pp 192−231.
9. *Sudbrook Trading Estate v Eggleton* [1983] 1 AC 444 at p 479.
10. As in *British Steel Corp v Cleveland Bridge* [1984] 1 All ER 504; *Way v Latilla* [1937] 3 All ER 759.
11. *Rover International v Cannon Film Sales (No 3)* [1989] 1 WLR 912.

Thus JCT80 provides in Clause 13.5:

> '.1 To the extent that the Valuation relates to the execution of additional or substituted work which can properly be valued by measurement such work shall be measured and shall be valued in accordance with the following rules:
>
> .1.1 where the work is of similar character to, is executed under similar conditions as, and does not significantly change the quantity of, work set out in the Contract Bills, the rates and prices for the work so set out shall determine the Valuation;
>
> .1.2 where the work is of similar character to work set out in the Contract Bills but is not executed under similar conditions thereto and/or significantly changes the quantity thereof, the rates and prices for the work so set out shall be the basis for determining the valuation and the valuation shall include a fair allowance for such difference in conditions and/or quantity;
>
> .1.3 where the work is not of similar character to work set out in the Contract Bills the work shall be valued at fair rates and prices.'

ICE5 Clause 52(1) provides:

> 'The value of all variations ... shall be ascertained ... in accordance with the following principles. Where work is of similar character and executed under similar conditions to work priced in the Bill of Quantities it shall be valued at such rates and prices contained therein as may be applicable. Where work is not of a similar character or is not executed under similar conditions the rates and prices in the Bill of Quantities shall be used as the basis for valuation so far as may be reasonable failing which a fair valuation shall be made ...'

ICE6 is similar except that it specifically excepts work 'ordered during the Defects Correction Period'.

GC/Wks 1 Edition 2 Condition 9(1) provides:

> 'The value of alterations in, additions to and omissions from the Works ... shall be ascertained ... as follows:
> (a) by measurement and valuation at the rates and prices for similar work in the Bills of Quantities or Schedules of Rates in so far as such rates and prices apply;
> (b) if such rates and prices do not apply, by measurement and valuation at rates and prices deduced therefrom in so far as it is practicable to do so;
> (c) if such rates and prices do not apply and it is not practicable to deduce rates and prices therefrom, by measurement and valuation at fair rates and prices ...'

There is also a proviso to Condition 9(1) allowing the adoption of fair rates and prices in place of the rules in sub-paragraph (a) or (b) where in the opinion of the QS it would be unreasonable by virtue of the timing or content of the instruction to apply those sub-paragraphs.

GC/Wks 1 Edition 3 Condition 42 is similar except that it allows as an alternative for valuation by 'acceptance by the PM of a lump sum quotation prepared by the Contractor and submitted to the QS'.

All the forms of contract refer to 'similarity' but differ in the extent to which they explain the word. ICE5 and ICE6 draw out the requirement for similarity of both character and conditions. JCT80 emphasizes that similarity in the clauses means similarity in all respects, and mentions changes of quantity. GC/Wks 1 in both Editions 2 and 3 maintains a discreet shroud of obscurity.

189

In principle these provisions can only mean that dissimilarity must include not only physical characteristics (quality of concrete, type of timber etc and the obvious conditions of execution) but also matters of timing and sequence — how the work can be executed in relation to what is going on concurrently and what this may entail in terms of output and other costs.

One of the factors of dissimilarity is the time taken to do the varied work compared with the time originally required to do a similar amount (general value) of contract work. Consider a situation where an architect or engineer issues variation orders involving a nett additional amount of work, which requires a disproportionate time for execution. Take the case of a contract valued at £100,000 to be completed in ten months. Variations of nett additional value of £20,000 require an additional four months. What, if anything, is the contractor entitled to over and above the B/Q prices? Assuming that static or identifiable items of overheads are included in Preliminaries and that these have been appropriately adjusted, there remain other more general overhead costs which can only have been reflected in prices for measured work. Put another way they may be said to be a function of turnover. To simplify the matter for the purposes of illustration, it may be argued that the original contract was based on a turnover of £100,000 ÷ 10 = £10,000 per month. The varied work should therefore carry overheads for £20,000 ÷ 10,000 = 2 months, leaving two months of time-related overheads not being recouped.

Such assumptions as to how overheads and profit are distributed through the contract rates and prices should be treated cautiously in that there is generally no requirement that overheads and profit should be distributed in any particular manner. Probably there is a presumption that overheads and profits are distributed evenly through the rates and that prices for Preliminaries items correspond to the item coverage as defined, but it is still open to either side to argue and demonstrate that some other distribution had been adopted. In that case the actual distribution ought reasonably to be taken into account in any adjustment.

This raises a conceptual difficulty in that the actual distribution can only be reliably demonstrated by reference to the actual tender make-up, which is not part of the contract. Contractual provisions stipulate that new rates are to be based on or deduced from the rates and prices in the Bills of Quantities. It is submitted that reference to the tender make-up is not precluded as part of the process of deduction and is to be preferred to conjectural retrospective analysis, but there can be significant problems in dealing with errors or non-standard practices in tender make-ups. (It goes without saying that such reference to the tender build-up must be treated as strictly confidential both as regards the contract in question and any future contracts. It should not be considered as creating a precedent or reference for application on future contracts.)

Another of the factors of dissimilarity lies in the effect of conditions and circumstances on the components of the cost or price. To the extent that these costs are labour, plant or materials, the matter is obvious. What is not so obvious is the effect on those costs often accounted for indirectly (by way of percentages, etc) but which are nevertheless real costs, i.e. overheads. Whether these be incurred on site or at head office makes no difference; if they have been affected as compared with the basis of the B/Q prices, then they fall to be adjusted.

It may be a matter of debate whether such costs are recoverable as part of the cost of the variation or under separate provisions such as contained in JCT 63/77 Clause 11(6), which says:

> '. . . if a variation . . . has involved the contractor in direct loss and/or expense for which he would not be reimbursed . . . in accordance with Sub-clause (4) . . . the architect . . . or . . . quantity surveyor shall . . . ascertain such loss or expense.'

In JCT80, the corresponding Clause 13 amends this to read:

'13.5.5 If compliance with ... a Variation ... substantially changes the conditions under which any other work is executed, then such other work shall be treated as if it had been the subject of ... a Variation ...

13.5.6 To the extent that the Valuation does not relate to the execution of additional or substituted work or the omission of work or to the extent that the valuation of any work or liabilities directly associated with a Variation cannot reasonably be effected in the Valuation by the application of clauses 13.5.1 to .5 a fair valuation thereof shall be made.'

In the case of ICE5 and ICE6 such matters must really be picked up under Clause 52(1) because Clause 52(2) deals with the consequential effect on the prices for other items rather than the components of the items which are themselves varied and there is no 'fall back' clause. In ICE5 and ICE6 Clause 52(2) says:

'... if the nature or amount of any variation relative to the nature or amount of the whole of the contract work or to any part thereof shall be such that ... any rate or price ... for any item of work is by reason of such variation rendered unreasonable or inapplicable ... the Engineer shall fix such rate or price as in the circumstances he shall think reasonable and proper.'

GC/Wks 1 Edition 3 Condition 42(5) also allows some relief:

'If in the opinion of the QS the VI has a disruptive effect on work not within the direct scope of the VI then the QS shall make any adjustment to the rates for such work that he considers appropriate.'

EXTRA TIME FOR VARIED WORK

Another contractual consequence of variations or changes in quantities is that the contractor may become entitled to an extension of time for completion of the works. All the Standard Forms provide for such entitlement[12] and it is a common feature that the basis for assessing entitlement is expressed in terms of what is 'fair' or 'fair and reasonable', with little further guidance. A second common feature is that provision is made for entitlement to be assessed in respect of both past and future delays.

Whereas the delaying effect of a 3-week strike or a 2-day storm is generally obvious, a matter of history to be established by records, the delaying effect of a variation is dependent not only on the nature and amount of the varied work and the timing of the instruction, but also on the steps taken to perform and/or expedite the additional or changed work. Is it to be assumed that no additional resources are to be deployed? Are the rates of progress in the pre- or post-contract programme to be regarded as inviolate? If steps are taken to expedite the work, is the contractor entitled to recover any additional costs incurred? If no steps are taken to expedite the work, is the contractor entitled to extension of time and to recover the cost of prolongation for the extended period? Is it incumbent on the contractor to minimize the delay? Or to minimize the total extra cost? Is it open to the contractor to adopt steps to expedite the work and then seek recompense?

It would be nice to be able to give clear answers to these questions, but honesty demands that one admits a degree of confusion exists both in principle and in practice. The situation whereby contractual disputes are all to be referred to arbitration rather than the courts, with the arbitration award then treated as a secret, means that such confusion can persist. Furthermore, courts and arbitrators tend, by their nature, only to be concerned with retrospective assessments of entitlement, by which stage it is too late to implement any measures to expedite the work. For reasons explained in Chapter 8, the attitude of the courts in the UK to extension of time provisions has discouraged a constructive approach to their interpretation.

---

12. ICE5, ICE6 and FIDIC4 Clause 44; JCT 80 Clause 25; GC/Wks 1 Ed 2 Condition 28; GC/Wks 1 Ed 3 Condition 36.

The problem has arisen partly because steps to expedite variations have been termed 'acceleration'. This is an accurate description, but it has led to confusion with acceleration in the sense of advancing a date for completion already set — a move which has commonly been outside the powers of the A/E/QS under the contract, either to order or to certify payment. Thus expediting the work comprised in variations has also come to be seen as outside the powers of the A/E/QS. On the other hand, A/E/QSs have been quite happy, much to the chagrin of employers, not only to grant extensions of time based on unexpedited working, but also to certify payment of associated prolongation costs.

The problems can be avoided, though not totally solved, if the confusion is cleared up. The A/E/QS does not have the power, in the absence of explicit provisions, to advance the date for completion once set by the contract or by the grant of extension of time. Explicit provision is now made for such acceleration of the works in ICE6 Clause 46(3) and GC/Wks 1 Edition 3 Condition 38, where the contractor agrees to a request to complete the Works within a time shorter than the time otherwise fixed under the Contract.

On the other hand, the A/E/QS does have the power within all the existing Forms of Contract to take into account the costs of expediting work when fixing rates for variations or revised rates due to increased quantities. So long as the A/E/QS makes clear in advance that the rates will include for expediting the varied work, and assuming it is reasonably practicable so to expedite the work, the extension of time and the rates for the variation can and should be assessed accordingly. It will be appreciated that such an arrangement can only be introduced prospectively. If the A/E/QS does not take the initiative, it is quite open for the contractor to do so (he should have a better idea of the labour, plant and organizational aspects involved). If the A/E/QS does not initiate an arrangement or if the contractor's proposals are rejected, it is open to the contractor, having first given notice of potential delay requiring extension of time (and consequential prolongation costs), to force the issue. He can do this by giving notice that he regards the extension of time as granted (or not granted, as the case may be) in respect of varied work as an implied requirement to expedite or accelerate that, and related, work. If, on the other hand, no steps have been taken by either side to raise or deal with the matter at the appropriate time, it cannot be raised later.

On contracts under ICE6 or GC/Wks 1 Edition 3, it is possible to deal with such situations under the new acceleration provisions, but it is not necessary to do so and avoidance of the word 'acceleration' in this context is strongly recommended — it invariably attracts criticism. The better approach is to consider what is done as 'expediting' the works. Nearly all the standard Forms of Contract stipulate an obligation for the contractor to proceed with the works with 'diligence' and/or 'expedition'.[13] This obligation is separate from, and concurrent with, the obligation to complete the works within a specified time. There is a tendency, particularly when dealing retrospectively with claims, to consider only the obligation to complete the works, but expediting the works is, and should be, a fundamental objective, as well as an obligation, in any construction contract.

INTERIM PAYMENTS

Under all three domestic Forms of Contract and under FIDIC4, the contractor is entitled to interim payment in connection with variations and delays. FIDIC4 is particularly clear on this point; Sub-clauses 52.1 and 52.2 both say that 'until such time as rates and prices are agreed or fixed, the Engineer shall determine provisional rates or prices to enable on-account payments to be included in certificates ...'

Should the A/E fail to include monies in respect of variations and delays in interim certificates without valid reason, he would be in danger of putting his employer in breach of the relevant clause (JCT80 Clause 30.6.1; ICE5 and ICE6 Clause 60(1)d); GC/Wks 1

---

13. ICE5 Clause 41; ICE6 Clause 41(2); FIDIC4 Clause 41.1; JCT80 Clause 23.1; GC/Wks 1 Ed 2 Condition 6; GC/Wks 1 Ed 3 Condition 34(1).

Edition 2 Condition 40(5); GC/Wks 1 Edition 3 Condition 48(2)(c); FIDIC4 Clause 52.1 or 52.2). In the case of ICE5 or ICE6 this might amount to a failure by the Engineer to certify, giving entitlement to interest under Clause 60(6) or 60(7) respectively. Similarly under GC/Wks 1 Edition 3 Condition 47, it might amount to a failure by the PM or QS to comply with a time limit specified in the Contract. This aspect is considered in more detail in Chapter 11.

Interim and final payments are also subject to rights of set-off, whereby amounts may be deducted under explicit provisions of the contract by the A/E/QS when certifying, or as an equitable set-off by the employer when paying on the certificate. The latter possibility is considered above in Chapter 2.

Materials not incorporated in the Works

All the Standard Forms make provision for payment for materials on site. The JCT and ICE Forms also make provision for payment for off-site materials.

It is as well to take some care to establish that the contractor has good title in any materials not yet incorporated in the works for which payment is to be made, so that property passes to the employer. It is possible for contracts of sale between suppliers and the contractor to contain special terms reserving ownership to the seller until some specified condition has been fulfilled and/or reserving certain rights in respect of further disposal of the goods by the buyer. These are known as 'Romalpa' clauses. Such a clause must establish a specific charge over identifiable material or goods; it must make it clear that although possession passes to the buyer on delivery, legal ownership is retained by the seller; it must make it clear that if the buyer resells the goods he does so as trustee or agent until the seller has been fully paid; it cannot be capable of interpretation as covering other goods or assets and so becoming a floating charge (which is not valid unless registered).[14]

Care should also be taken to check the insurance on off-site materials before payment as this is the subject of separate contractual provisions[15] from the insurance of the Works.

There is no provision for payment for off-site materials in GC/Wks 1 Editions 2 or 3 and there is a risk that if the supplier goes into liquidation, the liquidator may claim payment for goods already paid for. Absence of a provision in the contract may enable the provisions of the Bankruptcy or Insolvency Acts to prevail. The use of *ad hoc* provisions or procedures introduced post contract is apt to be unreliable. It is fairly common practice in Scotland (where the law is slightly different from that in England) for the employer formally to purchase such materials from the contractor. This certainly solves the problem of title but at the risk of introducing a different problem. If, when the time comes for these materials to be used (the employer 'supplying' them to the contractor), the employer could be responsible for any shortcomings or defects — which could prove embarrassing and possibly expensive.

There is similarly no provision in FIDIC4 for payment for off-site materials. Any *ad hoc* provisions relating to contracts or supply contracts involving a foreign element should take account of the local or applicable law which may be different from English law.

CASE 7.1 CLAIM FOR ADJUSTMENT IN RESPECT OF INCREASED QUANTITIES

Pertinent particulars of contract

The contract was for the construction of a length of road improvement consisting of cut and fill with a surplus of excavated material for disposal.

The documents comprised: Drawings, Specification, Conditions of Contract ICE5, Bill of Quantities.

---

14. *Aluminium Industrie Vaasen BV v Romalpa Ltd* [1976] 1 WLR 676; *Borden (UK) Ltd v Scottish Timber Products Ltd* [1980] Ch 228. See generally Chitty on Contracts, 25th edn, paras 4206–4208. Sweet & Maxwell, London.
15. ICE5 and ICE6 Clause 54(3)(b); JCT 80 Clause 30.3.9.

Tender dated 13 February 1976. Tender total £1,244,767.
Acceptance dated 23 April 1976. Time for completion 2 years.
Price fluctuation based on NEDO formula included.

The B/Q, which was based on CESMM, included the following:

Preamble
The volume of fill and compaction in embankments has been measured to the profiles shewn on the Drawings. The excavation for this requirement has been shewn in terms of the same quantity without any allowance for bulking upon excavation or recompaction in fill. The remaining quantity has been shewn for disposal.

The price for excavation and fill shall allow for the contractor's own assessment of bulking and recompaction.

Bill Items

Excavate top-soil, maximum depth not exceeding 0.25 m and set aside for re-use	10,400 m^3
Excavate material other than top-soil and rock in cuttings for re-use	254,800 m^3
Excavate material other than top-soil and rock in cuttings and disposal in tip provided by the contractor	101,200 m^3
Filling and compaction of selected excavated material other than top-soil or rock to form embankments	254,800 m^3

Events leading to claim

There was a little more excavation in the cuttings than originally estimated (though there was no variation affecting the excavation, the volume of the embankments remaining the same).

About three weeks before completion of excavation the contractor's agent wrote to the RE:

Contractor's agent to RE   *20 September 1977*

The excavation for this road is now almost complete and we estimate that there are roughly 15,000 m^3 of excavation remaining. It is clear, however, that our existing tip is almost full and will not take the whole quantity. We shall therefore have to locate another tip but our present enquiries indicate that nothing is available within a distance of 7–8 miles (our present tip is about 1 mile away).

Should this prove to be the case, we shall have to claim the additional cost of haulage.

RE to Agent   *23 September 1977*

Your problem concerning disposal of excavated material is noted but this is a matter entirely for yourselves as no variation is involved requiring additional excavation. The bill item is quite clear that disposal of surplus excavated material is to a tip to be provided by the contractor.

No claim for additional cost can be entertained.

The RE's reaction to the contractor's preliminary warning is a little overdone. Disposal is of course a matter for the contractor but the RE should have asked the contractor for his reasons for thinking he might be entitled to extra payment. To dismiss the claim before it is formulated is premature and to brush it off as 'your problem' will not help relationships.

About two months later, in the course of preparing (jointly with the engineer's QS) a statement for an interim payment the contractor's QS takes up the matter:

Contractor's QS (CQS):
I now have the final excavation figures: the part we measured about two weeks ago. The total of 'Excavate for disposal' is 106,146 — an increase of 4,946 m³ on the B/Q quantity. Have you got your figures and can you agree this item?

Engineer's QS (EQS):
Yes, that tallies precisely with mine, so we shall be able to include that in this month's interim.

CQS:
Good! but at what price? We wrote to the RE on 20 September saying we would have to look for a new tip because of the extra quantity of excavation in cuttings. We eventually found one but it was nearly ten miles away compared with the one mile to our original tip. So, we shall be looking for an increased rate.

EQS:
But why? As the RE said in his reply, there has been no variation, why should you expect us to pay for the additional haul?

CQS:
We consider we are entitled under Clause 56(2).

EQS:
Yes, I see that covers the point in principle but surely you cannot expect it to apply to such a marginal increase; why, it is under 5 per cent. It is difficult to accept that allowances for bulking and compaction on a total of some 350,000 m³ could be estimated within such fine limits.

CQS:
I take your point but you will agree that there is no lower 'threshold' stated in the clause.

EQS:
No, but I have always thought there ought to be. I do not see how adjustment of rate can be justified for such small margins.

CQS:
Is that not our problem? We have to persuade you, we have to produce the evidence, and in this case I think we can. I am quite prepared to show you all our figures, including those we used when tendering.

You will remember that we had the contract for the previous stretch of this road, so we had had some experience of what bulking and compaction in this stuff would be. Also, we can show you from our records that we were tipping in the original tip until the day we completed the embankments and that from the next day we had to go to the new tip.

EQS:
Well, I remain to be convinced but let us have a look at your figures.

CQS:
When we negotiated for the original tip (which was an old quarry) we were given precise profiles we would have to work to. We reckoned this had a

volume of 137,000 m³. We used the figures for bulking we had had for the previous contract, 20 per cent on excavation with 90 per cent recompaction of the stuff in the loose when put in embankments. In the tip we did not have to compact to your road specification and we considered we should allow only 5 per cent, i.e. 95 per cent of the loose volume when tipped. Here are our original tender figures:

Quantities in B/Q	Excavate and fill	Excavate and dispose
	254,800	101,200
Allow for bulking 20%	50,960	20,240
Total quantity 'in the loose' to be transported	305,760	121,440
Assuming recompaction to be 90%, 305,760 becomes	275,184	
Less total required in embankments	254,800	
Surplus ('compacted')	20,384	
Which, in the loose, would be × 10/9 =		22,649
Total volume to be transported to tip		144,089
Allowing 5% compaction in tip this would become		136,885

As you see, this fitted in almost precisely. Certainly, in view of our previous experience with this material, we saw no reason at that stage to pay a deposit or retaining fee on an additional tip, just in case. There could equally well have been a small reduction.

So we consider we are entitled to rely on the quantity given in the B/Q, together with Clause 56(2) taking up the effect of a change.

EQS:
I agree that your allowances for bulking and compaction seem reasonable but with such a small difference I still contend that an underestimation of bulking of even $2\frac{1}{2}$ per cent would have led to the same situation. That would have given you about 145,000 m³ to dispose of instead of 137,000 m³.

CQS:
Maybe so, but had that been the case, had there been no increase in the B/Q quantity, the extra haulage would have been to our account. As it is, the situation arises solely out of the additional quantity we had to dig. If you look at the record drawings of the earthworks, the embankment had reached Chainage 2158. If you work out the quantity required to complete you will see it is about 5,000 m³. Also, if you look at our driver's log sheets, you can see they started at the new tip the day after we reached Chainage 2158.

EQS:
Right, I will accept that and recommend it to the engineer provided we can agree a reasonable rate for the additional haul.

CQS:
Again, here are our tender figures. If you look at the various quantities of cut and fill and their locations, you will see on this drawing where we intended to place them, including those being taken to tip. These figures shew an average haul of just under one mile. In fact we worked on the basis of one mile in our price.

Now, if you look at Spence Geddes, you will see that he gives an average difference of 0.07 hours per kilometre, which I have translated into 0.113 hours per mile. The mileage to the new tip was 9.7, which you can check if you wish. We were using 6-ton lorries and on the basis that these will carry 3.42 m³ of material in the solid, the additional cost will be:

$$\left[\left(\frac{0.98 \times £4.33}{3.42} \right) + 25\% \right] + 6\% = £1.64 \ per \ m^3.$$

The 0.98 hours is the extra time required (round trip) for a distance of 8.7 miles.

The £4.33 is the running rate per hour for a 6-ton truck. You will see from our tender figures that we allowed 25 per cent for site overheads and 6 per cent for HO overheads. For 4,946 m³ we therefore claim £8,111.44.

The engineer's QS agreed that the basis of the figures was reasonable and asked the contractor's QS to send in a letter setting out the main points discussed and the amount claimed. He then reported the substance of the foregoing discussion to the RE and engineer, confirming his agreement with the contractor's view of his entitlement under Clause 56(2) and indicating that he had examined the figures and was satisfied that the additional rate of £1.64 per m³ for the additional quantity was reasonable.

The claim was accepted and payment made in the next certificate.

Points of principle involved

Under ICE5 the quantities in the B/Q are stated by Clause 55(1) to be estimated quantities, not to be taken as the actual and correct quantities of the Works to be executed by the Contractor in fulfilment of his obligations under the Contract: he is obliged to execute whatever turns out to be involved in the Works. Nevertheless, Clause 56(2) provides for the rates or prices in the B/Q to be adjusted if the quantities turn out to be different. In construing these clauses, each must be read in the light of the other. The contractor is entitled to base his prices on the quantities in the B/Q, but any adjustment to rates or prices is to be determined on the basis that the contractor was obliged to take appropriate steps on his own initiative as soon as the difference in quantity became apparent. He is also required to give notice to the Engineer under Clause 52(4)(a) if he intends to claim a higher rate or price.

There is no 'threshold' stated in Clause 56(2). the policy of the clause apparently being that it is the difference that is fundamental, not the size of it. Of course it will always be much more difficult to make a case for an increase or decrease of price where only a small difference of quantity is involved and it will be necessary to seek and provide any necessary corroboration reasonably required.

The requirement for the operation of Clause 56(2) is not only that adjustment to the price should be warranted by the increase or decrease of the quantity 'of itself', but also that the rate or price should have been rendered 'unreasonable or inapplicable'.

Clause 56(2) does not, however, provide for a contractor to be denied an increase (nor an employer to be entitled to a decrease) in a price on the grounds that the total original price was high, nor does it entitle a contractor to make up deficiencies in his original price.

CASE 7.2 CLAIM IN RESPECT OF VARIED WORK AND CONSEQUENTIAL EFFECT ON PRICES FOR CONTRACT WORK

Pertinent particulars of contract

The contract was for the construction of a new runway and ancillary works. The subsoil consisted of peat and sand. The former had to be removed to tip and the latter used to fill low areas along the runway, the surplus to be spread and levelled at the north end.

Figure 7.2.1

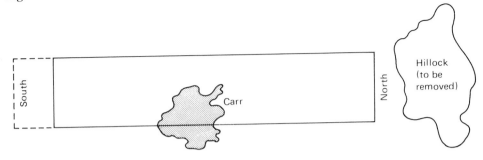

There was a peat 'carr' about midlength which was to have been dealt with by removing the overlying peat and some of the softer material below it, leaving some 5 m of the relatively soft material and tipping into and over it.

The documents comprised: Drawings, Specification, Conditions of Contract (ICE5).
Tender dated 5 April 1979. Tender total £3,427,486.
Acceptance dated 8 May 1979. Time for completion 2 years.
The Bill of Quantities (based on CESMM) contained the following items:

		£
Preliminaries		
Insurance against damage to the Works	Item	3,450
Insurance for constructional plant	Item	Included
Insurance against damage to third party	Item	14,500
Workmen's compensation insurance	Item	Included
Establishment and removal of accommodation for Engineer's staff	Item	25,400
Servicing Engineer's accommodation	104 weeks at £100	10,400
Provision of access to site	Item	2,100
Maintenance of access to site	104 weeks at £50	5,200
Establishment and removal of accommodation for Contractor	Item	42,500
Servicing accommodation for Contractor	104 weeks at £200	20,800
Establishment of all plant and equipment on site	Item	17,850
Maintenance of all plant and equipment	104 weeks	Included
		£142,200

The main items for excavation with which the claim was concerned consisted of:

Excavate peat and dispose in tipping area about 2 miles from south end of runway	310,000 m³	1.14	353,400
Excavate in gravelly sand to reduce levels and deposit to make up levels under and adjacent to runway	727,000 m³	0.49	356,230

There was a hillock of gravelly sand at the north end of the runway which had to be removed and so was available for fill, any surplus being spread and levelled in the vicinity.

Events giving rise to claim

On 9 November 1979 a variation order was issued to extend the runway at its southern end by some 500 m. The area was relatively low and required fill (about 35,000 m³).

On 3 March 1980 another variation order was issued to empty the carr completely and fill with gravelly sand from excavations (about 28,000 m³).

Figure 7.2.2

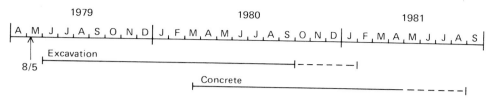

The contractor claimed that his haulage plan was completely upset, that the average of haul substantially increased and that there was delay involved of some four months.

The contractor made no demur about the variation for the extension although it was outside the original site limits, but when it came to preparing the next interim certificate he claimed an increased rate for the excavation/fill for this area on the grounds of additional haul. This was not accepted on the argument that fill was available from the original runway area but the contractor contended he had had to bring some material from the hillock at the north end.

Whilst this debate was developing, it was decided it was not possible to leave soft material in the bottom of the carr, hence the second variation referred to.

Following this, the contractor claimed that the whole of his scheme for cut/fill had been altered and asked for a revised rate for the whole of the remaining excavation. Further, he contended that part of the excavation would be extended into a second winter. He said he would require an extension of time of 4 months.

The RE continued to contend that the work involved in the two variations was precisely the same as the original contract work and that sufficient material was available in the runway area plus the hillock at the northern end to meet the requirements and consequently it was only a matter of minor adjustment to the locations of cut and fill. The quantities involved amounted to little more than one month's excavation and he was therefore unable to accept that excavation would need to continue over a second winter.

It was clear that the time had come for the matter to be dealt with rather more formally and the contractor submitted the following claim:

Contractor to Engineer (copy to RE)   *11 June 1980*

We refer to Variation Order No 10 for the extension to the runway and Variation Order No 17 for the clearing of the carr. The requirement for the additional excavation and fill for these two areas, coming when they did, completely disrupted our original haulage scheme. The rate for excavating peat is not affected as this is taken to tip in any case and the area we are using will accommodate the additional quantity.

In the case of the gravelly sand, however, the incidence of 35,000 m³ of fill in the extension (November 1979) and 28,000 m³ in the carr (March 1980) has caused the average haul to be increased significantly and we claim we are entitled to be paid an increased price in accordance with Clause 52 of the Conditions.

We had originally planned to move material from either end towards the middle, any deficiency coming from the hillock at the north end of the runway. When we received the variation order for the extension we had already moved material from the south end of the runway northwards and so we had to start this work by using fill from the hillock until we could reorganise our haulage scheme. In the meantime we had taken some 10,000 m³ a distance of 3,500 m compared with an average haul of 386 m calculated for our tender.

199

Then in March 1980 we received the variation order to excavate the carr completely and refill with gravelly sand. This too had to come from the northern end as there was no longer any fill available southwards. Further, the excavation in the carr proved much more difficult than that originally involved. It was almost liquid and we attempted to use pumps but the peat detritus tended to jam them. We installed mascerators to deal with this but the sand content caused excessive wear in these and the pumps and we had to abandon the attempt.

All this involved us in delay which we currently assess at four months and we formally request that the time for completion be extended accordingly.

We attach particulars of our claim and, as you will see, we have shewn the progressive effect on the haul distance caused by these two variations.

CLAIM

1. Progress of excavation and fill in gravelly sand

Total quantity originally required	727,000		
Volume dealt with by 9/11/79	240,000	487,000	
Add quantity in extension to runway		35,000	522,000
Volume dealt with between 9/11/79 and 3/3/80			120,000
			402,000
Additional quantity in carr			28,000
			430,000

2. Effect on average haul

Average haul now required to suit revised scheme of working	488 m
Average haul allowed for in tender	386 m
Increase	102 m

Note: the increased average haul is in excess of that considered to be the economic limit for D8 tractors.

3. Revised items and rates required

(a) Additional cost of excavating material from hillock with face shovel, loading into lorries and transporting approx 3.5 km (cf scraper) to runway extension	10,000 m³	1.10	11,000
(b) Extra over peat excavation for excavating in lower part of carr and removing semi-liquid material to top	28,000 m³	0.90	25,200
(c) Additional cost for average haul of 488 m, cf 386 m (reduced output/increased haul for D8 scrapers)	790,000 m³	0.09	71,100
(d) Site overheads and oncosts for period of 4 months at £25,706 per month			102,824
			£210,124

The claim is reasonably well stated but lacks detail. This is often the case when those immediately concerned know the layout of the work and much of what has happened as the work has proceeded. The claim should be addressed towards the engineer rather than the RE and it should be assumed that he knows little or nothing of the detail.

The contractor makes no point of whether the extension to the runway is properly a variation under Clause 51 or whether it was in effect a separate contract. It could have been argued that it had nothing to do with the original concept of the contract and was outside the original site. However, it was accepted as a variation at the time and the contractor has probably lost the opportunity to claim otherwise even if he wished to do so. Nothing need turn on the point, provided the contractor gets paid a satisfactory price but if the engineer is inclined to stick rigidly to B/Q prices he might find it disconcerting to have it suggested that the variation was outwith the scope of the contract. There are indeed advantages from the contractor's point of view in dealing with it as a variation because of its repercussions on the original work, and so allowing the provisions of Clause 52 to apply fully.

The RE asked the QS to examine and report on the claim, as a result of which the following letter was written:

RE to Contractor (copy to Engineer)   *25 June 1980*

Your claim for additional payment in respect of Variation Orders 10 and 17 has been examined and the following additional information is required:

(a) Particulars of how the average haul distances of 488 and 386 m have been arrived at; it is difficult to accept that these could have been calculated so precisely. In any case, no reason is seen for claiming additional cost on the 240,000 m³ which had been dealt with before Variation Order No 10 was issued.

(b) The reason for starting work on the extension using material from the far end of the runway when taking it from nearer-by on the runway itself would have involved a shorter haul.

(c) Particulars of how the rate for excavating in the carr has been arrived at and why any revised rate is required anyway, observing that it was basically 'excavation in peat' and exactly similar to the immediately overlying materials.

(d) What rate has been included in the B/Q prices for overheads (site and Head Office), observing that some part of this has been included in Preliminary Items and in the measured items for extra work. In any case I could not accept that a period of four months' delay has occurred until it becomes clearer when you may expect to complete the excavation.

Following receipt of this information it is proposed that a meeting be arranged to discuss the matter.

There had obviously been consultation between the RE and engineer, and provided the latter is satisfied as to the principles involved he may well leave the next stage to the RE and QS.

Contractor to RE   *5 July 1980*

The further information you require is as follows:

(a) Average haul. Attached are two prints shewing how the distances in question have been arrived at. As you will see the whole area has been gridded in 10 m squares, and the quantities of excavation and/or fill in each have been shewn. The destination of each 'parcel' of excavation is shewn and the distances indicated. Schedules of the quantities and distances are attached, shewing the computation of the average.

(b) It was necessary to start on the extension as quickly as possible because although you had set no time limits, our programme required

starting concreting of the slab from the south end. It would have been impractical to start at the original point and come back to concrete the extension. Further, by November 1979 the material for fill available at the southern end of the runway had been moved northwards.

(c) *Regarding excavation in the carr, we allowed in our tender for a certain amount of wet material, but the lower part of the carr was semi-liquid and was by far the worst we have encountered. Also, the original carr material was included in the price for the 'ordinary' peat, which price was therefore an average. We could have absorbed these extra costs into the total for peat excavation and obtained a new average (which would of course have been relatively small but applied to a large quantity), but we considered it simpler and easier to substantiate if it were dealt with separately. As to the cost, we kept daily records of the plant and labour employed, which your inspector verified and signed as to fact.*

(d) *Site overheads were included in the tender price at 15 per cent and spread over a working period of twenty months. Head Office overheads were included at 8 per cent.*

There followed a meeting at which these matters were discussed. To avoid confusion it is better to retain the sequence of the original parts of the claim if possible rather than follow that of the engineer's questions which are put out of sequence.

(a) Excavation in the northern hillock for the runway extension

The reasons for having to use this fill for this purpose were accepted. There was nothing quite comparable in the original contract but the build-up of the rate for excavation of peat and remove to tip was examined to give an indication of the basis of excavating plant rates, lorry rates and running time which could be applied to the different material. The analysis of the bill rate was:

$$\text{Face shovel: 1 m}^3 \text{ @ £4.73 per hour including driver:}$$

In peat will take 0.014 hours/m^3 = 71.43 m^3 per hour			
Deduct 10% for waiting on lorries	7.14	64.29	
Deduct 10% down-time (inclement weather)	6.43	57.86	
Price per m^3 = $\dfrac{4.73}{57.86}$ =			£0.0817

6-ton lorries: taking 2.95 m^3 (in situ) peat
(NB bulking, cf sand etc) @ £4.33 per hour
including driver:

Hours for round trip of 3.2 km	0.36		
Add standing to load	0.08		
Add waiting to load/offload	0.08	0.52	
Allow 10% down-time as before		0.05	0.57
Price per m^3 = $\dfrac{4.33}{2.95}$ × 0.57 =			0.8366
			0.9183
Add site overheads 15%			0.1378
			1.0561
Add HO overheads and profit 8%			0.0845
			£1.1406

This needed to be applied to the excavation of gravelly sand and cartage for a distance of 3.5 km. The calculation for this was as follows:

Face shovel will take say 0.021 h/m³ (average of sand and gravel)

= m³ per hour of	47.62			
Deduct 10% waiting	4.76	42.86		
Deduct 10% down-time		4.29	38.57	

$$\text{Price per m}^3 = \frac{4.73}{38.57} = \qquad\qquad £0.1226$$

6-ton lorries taking 3.69 m³ (average as before)

in the solid @ hours per round trip	0.38		
Add standing to load	0.08		
Add waiting	0.08	0.54	
Allow 10% down-time		0.05	0.59

$$\text{Price per m}^3 = \frac{4.33}{3.69} \times 0.59 =$$

	0.6923
Add site overheads 15%	0.8149
	0.1222
	0.9371
Add HO overheads and profit 8%	0.0750
So the claim becomes:	£1.0121

10,000 m³ @ £1.01 = £10,100.

(b) Excavation in the carr

It was agreed that as regards excavation of peat, the contractor had had to allow for the varying degrees of difficulty in the proportions that the contract originally required. Here conditions were worse than the worst that could otherwise have been expected. None of the overlying material was quite so liquid to the extent of considering pumping. This could be allowed for and included in a new average rate for the whole of this type of excavation ('peat') but it was accepted as being simpler and more straightforward to deal with it as a separate entity. The times had indeed been recorded and 'agreed as to fact without prejudice to liability for payment' for both labour and plant.

It was necessary to enhance the nett cost of wages to include such matters as bonus payments, National Health and Unemployment Insurances, Workmen's Compensation Insurance, holidays with pay and the like, plus site and Head Office overheads to make the 'cost' comparable with the Bill rate.

The contractor had said (in his letter of 5 July) that site overheads at 15 per cent and Head Office overheads and profit of 8 per cent had been included in his tender. This also affected claim (d), and he was asked how these figures had been applied. At first he was inclined to say that 23 per cent of the tender total was the appropriate amount. This worked out to £488,322 which, if spread over twenty months, gave £24,416 per month, which differed from the figure in claim (d). It was also pointed out that this was not the normal way to apply these figures and he was asked if a sight of the tender build-up could be given. This shewed that the 15 per cent had been added to the direct costs of labour, plant, materials and sub-contract and the 8 per cent added to the whole of these, i.e. (x + 15%) + 8%. It was also observed that Preliminary Items in this category (insurances, contractor's accommodation and the like) had been priced separately in the tender build-up and not included in these percentages for overheads. These could therefore be ignored in dealing with the present problem of overheads. Working on the basis shewn in the tender build-up, the HO overheads and profit were therefore (8/108) × 3,427,486 = £253,888 and the site overheads were (15/115) × (3,427,486 − 253,888) = £413,947.

So far as this claim regarding excavation in the carr was concerned, it was therefore proper to add 15 per cent to the nett cost for site overheads. Regarding HO overheads it was not so clear that these were affected by this variation order, but on the footing that had this work been included in the B/Q in the first place, the contractor would have allowed HO overheads and profit in his price, and this would seem appropriate under Clause 52.

The claim could therefore be valued at:

Nett direct costs	25,200	
Add 15% for site overheads	3,780	28,980
Add 8% for HO overheads and profit		2,318
		£31,298

(c) Average haul

The contractor had in fact both at tender stage and following the variations gridded the site and calculated the volume of cut/fill in each square and indicated the nearest point at which the excavation could be accommodated. He agreed that some 240,000 m³ were unaffected by the variation order but pointed out that the revised average distance took account of the whole quantity. If one were to calculate the haul for the remaining quantity only, this would give a longer haul for a smaller quantity and so the end result would be the same.

When the details were checked, an error was found in the calculation which reduced the average to 468 m, i.e. 20 m less than calculated. The new rate had been arrived at on the basis of (386/488) × the output at 386 m. For scraper work this seemed acceptable, but it was corrected to 386/468. Allowing 8.25 m³ per load and a difficulty factor (gravel) of 1.1, the calculation was (see Spence Geddes 6th edn p 185):

(a) Basis of tender: $\dfrac{386}{360}$ × 0.016 hours = 0.0172

(b) For revised haul: $\dfrac{468}{480}$ × 0.020 hours = 0.0195

(this had been taken at $\dfrac{488}{480}$ × 0.020 hours = 0.0203).

The extra time required for additional haul is $\dfrac{0.0195 - 0.0172}{0.0172}$ × 0.49 = 0.07 (not as

the contractor had taken it, i.e. $\dfrac{0.0203 - 0.0172}{0.0172}$ × 0.49 = 0.09).

It was agreed that as the average haul was calculated over the whole quantity in both cases, it was correct to base the claim on 790,000 m³ except that 10,000 m³ needed to be deducted for the haulage of that quantity from the hillock to the extension which was done by lorry and included *in toto* in claim (a).

The end result would therefore be 780,000 m³ at £0.07 = £54,600.

(d) Site overheads

This has been included in the contractor's claim of 11 June at £25,706, but as pointed out in connection with claim (b) his method of calculation was wrong. It was accepted that most of the site overheads would be time-related (e.g. supervisory staff, etc.) but it was pointed out that the amounts included under claims (a), (b) and (c) themselves contained provision for overheads as follows (taking the revised figures):

Claim (a) £10,100:

HO overheads and profit content = $\dfrac{8}{108}$ × 10,100 =   748

Site overheads content $\dfrac{15}{115}$ × (10,100 − 748) =   1,219

Claim (b) £31,298:
HO overheads and profit included   2,318
Site overheads included   3,780

c/f 4,999

Claim (c) £54,600:

$$\text{HO overheads and profit content} = \frac{8}{108} \times 54{,}600 = \qquad 4{,}044$$

$$\text{Site overheads content } \frac{15}{115} \times (54{,}600 - 4{,}044) = \qquad \underline{6{,}594}\,\underline{£11{,}593}$$

It was being claimed that there was four months' delay because of these variations but the engineer had decided that only three months would be accepted until the out-turn could be seen. On the basis of the tender, the HO overheads and profit element was £253,888 and the site overheads were £413,947 (see page 203).

It was pointed out that the contract period was 2 years (24 months) but the contractor maintained that it was perfectly feasible to do this work in 20 months *provided* the excavation resources were geared to complete excavation before the onset of the second winter. The RE had to agree that the programme seemed reasonable and that progress up to November 1979 was in keeping with it. It was therefore agreed that site overheads could be taken as 413,947 ÷ 20 = £20,697 per month, giving £62,091 for the three months. Site overheads to the value of £11,593 had been included in claims (a), (b) and (c). The additional site overheads attributable to the delay therefore amounted to £50,498.

Regarding HO overheads, the RE considered it was not appropriate to add a blanket percentage, as little if any of the HO facilities had been affected. There were perhaps extra visits (one per month for three months?) of certain HO staff, but nothing else. The contractor was inclined to dispute this but in fact could produce no evidence of anything specific. He did, however, claim the profit element on the basis that this was really extra time for extra work consequent upon the variations. The RE was inclined to regard it as delay and therefore to accept only 'cost' in the sense defined in Clause 1(5). The contractor did not agree but was prepared to accept the figures now arrived at on the understanding that prompt payment would be made.

A revised claim was therefore submitted as follows:

(a) Additional cost of excavation in the hillock	10,100
(b) Extra cost of excavating lower part of carr	31,298
(c) Increased average haul	54,600
(d) Site overheads for extended period due to extra work	50,498
	£146,496

Points of principle involved

The main point here is the applicability of B/Q rates and prices to varied work and the consequence to the cost of non-varied work.

ICE5 Conditions of Contract provide expressly that Bill rates apply only 'where work is of similar character and executed under similar conditions', otherwise Bill rates 'shall be used as a basis for valuation so far as may be reasonable'. It also makes specific provision for consequential effect in Sub-clause (2): 'Provided that if the nature or amount of any variation relative to the nature or amount of the whole of the contract work or any part thereof . . . shall be such that . . . any rate or price contained in the Contract for any item of work is by reason of such variation rendered unreasonable or inapplicable . . . the engineer shall fix such rate or price as in the circumstances he shall think reasonable or proper.'

There is no doubt that in the case cited the extra time was a direct consequence of the variation and affected all the other items of work. It was considered that the method of calculation indicated in the case under claim (d) is a proper assessment of the effect. If it were to be maintained that the engineer's powers were to 'fix rates or prices' and that the value arrived at above should be spread over B/Q items affected, the point might need to be conceded, but if the result were to be precisely the same (as it should) then literal interpretation of the clause might be waived, though strictly speaking the employer's agreement should be sought.

The JCT Forms (63/77 and 80) specifically refer to similarity of character and of conditions and the latter now adds (in 13.1.1.1) a qualification as to a significant change of quantity. Also in 13.5.5.3 specific reference is made to the addition to or reduction of Preliminaries. This is really (though properly and probably necessarily) expressing the obvious, because in any terms rates and prices against Preliminaries are no more nor less than 'rates or prices set out in the Contract Bills' and are no different in principle from any other rates or prices in the Bill (yet some persist in maintaining otherwise). Clause 13.5.5 provides 'If compliance with the instruction requiring a variation … substantially changes the conditions under which any other work is executed then such other work shall be treated as if it had been the subject of an instruction of the architect … which shall be valued in accordance with the provisions of Clause 13.' This would have the same effect as ICE 52(2), though there could well be an argument as to what constitutes 'substantial'. In practice this would probably have to be construed as 'significant in relation to the circumstances'.

GC/Wks 1 Edition 2 says in Condition 9(1): 'The value of alterations in, additions to and omissions from the Works shall be ascertained (a) by measurement and valuation at the rates and prices for similar work.' It is submitted that 'similar' here must mean similar in all respects as set out in ICE and JCT. The effect of dissimilarity of conditions is so often overlooked in valuing variations and this gives rise to many claims. The clause goes on: '(b) if such rates and prices do not apply … at rates and prices deduced therefrom in so far as it is practicable to do so.'

The process of deduction is not defined but it must be presumed to involve an analysis of the rates and prices on the generally accepted assumptions so as to obtain the constituent components of labour, plant, materials, overheads, profit, etc. Reference to and comparison with other rates would presumably be included in the process of deduction.

As regards consequential effects of a variation on other prices and rates in Edition 2 a proviso to Condition 9 allows the adoption of fair rates and prices where it would not be reasonable to use B/Q rates because of the content of the variation or the timing of its issue. This does not go so far as Clause 11(4)(b) of JCT 63/77 (13.5.1 of JCT 80), nor is it comparable with Clause 11(4)(d) of JCT 63/77 (13.5.1 of JCT 80). If, however, a variation has had an effect on other work (as in the case illustrated) then such effect cannot but be part of the variation and so fall to be reflected in the price. Problems may arise as to the items to which such an effect is applicable but this is a matter of deduction from the construction of the rates and the physical circumstances of the work.

The above remarks about Preliminaries apply as equally here as to the JCT Form.

CASE 7.3 CLAIM FOR ADJUSTMENT OF PRELIMINARIES

Pertinent particulars of contract

The contract was for the erection of a factory, including access roads and hard-standings for storage. The documents comprised:

Drawings, Specification, Bills of Quantities based on SMM 6.
Conditions of Contract: JCT 63/77 with *ad hoc* amendments to incorporate a specification.
Tender dated 4 April 1979 in the sum of £375,088, amended for the correction of errors of extension and cast to £375,488.
Acceptance dated 7 May 1979. Possession of Site 21 May 1979.
Time for completion 16 months (20.9.1980).
Date of actual completion 20.3.1981.

The B/Q contained Preliminary Items as required by SMM 6 including:

Insurance against injury to persons and property (Cl 19) Insurance against damage to the works Provisional Sum for fees and charges Provisional Sum for rates on temporary buildings Access to site, provision of Hoardings, provision of Temporary accommodation for C/W Site administration Water, lighting and power Provision of temporary accommodation for contractor Safety, health and welfare	43,500
Plant, scaffolding, transport of work people, protection of work, temporary roads and hardstandings, traffic regulations, drying the works, control of pollution	all priced as 'included'

The background of the case

The work proceeded much as usual with the issue of a fair number of variations. Work on these was in hand during the progress of the work and the site QS was inclined to take a rather narrow view of Clause 11(4)(a) and (b) regarding similarity of character and conditions. He considered that if the same words could be used for a description then the same rate must apply, although properly speaking the heading to a given group of items indicated differences of sequence, timing, etc. He was, however, persuaded to adopt a more reasonable (and correct) view but when the contractor sought, as a matter of compiling the final account, to require adjustment of Preliminaries, the site QS became adamant that this was not allowable. The contractor had in fact bracketed all the items together and put a single sum against them of £43,500. He declined to shew how he had arrived at the figures but claimed adjustment on the total proportionate to the increased value.

Delay in completion for which extension of time had been given amounted to 26 weeks due to extra work (fifteen weeks), strike (three weeks), exceptionally inclement weather (five weeks), and delay due to issue of instructions (three weeks).

The contractor eventually entered a claim:

Contractor to QS — *8 May 1981*

With reference to the final account for this contract, we have reached agreement as follows:

To amount of contract sum	*375,488*		
Deduct contingencies	*20,000*	*355,488*	
Adjustment of PC Sums as B/Q	*78,219*		
Add total of various final accounts	*81,484*	*3,265*	
Adjustment of Provisional Sums: B/Q	*60,000*		
Add work as executed	*64,227*	*4,227*	
Variations: add	*84,467*		*66,971*
omit	*21,723*	*62,744*	
		£425,724	

The last two items are at nett B/Q rates without any adjustment of Preliminaries. This we now require to be added. The Preliminaries in the B/Q represent 20.02 per cent of the measured work (375,488 less 158,219 = 217,269: 43,500 ÷ 217,269 = 20.02%) and we therefore claim £66,971 × 20.02% = £13,408.44.

We would point out that we have been given an extension of time of 26 weeks, so that if we were to take time as a basis we should be paid an extra 37 per cent of Preliminaries and our claim is therefore reasonable.

This is somewhat naive. To bracket all the Preliminaries together and price them at one sum, refuse to provide the build-up and then to expect pro-rata adjustment is expecting rather a lot. In face of this it is perhaps a little surprising that he did not take the alternative course of seeking adjustment pro-rata to time. Maybe he is not too sure of his ground, maybe he does not want to offend the architect or QS.

It would seem, however, from the reply that the QS partner does not support the line his site man has taken and has used this point to get the claim onto a proper basis.

> *QS to Contractor*   *18 May 1981*
>
> *This matter of adjustment of Preliminaries has been discussed between my site QS and yours and it has been made quite clear that an arithmetical adjustment of the Preliminaries proportionate to value cannot be entertained. Similarly adjustment pro-rata to time is equally inappropriate.*
>
> *Your QS has been asked to provide a breakdown of this sum and a sight of your tender build-up to provide some substantiation, but so far this has been refused. Unless and until this is provided I regret nothing can be done.*

Contractors are often disinclined to produce their tender build-up but given the assurance that it will be treated in strict confidence for the purpose of this job only and that no copies will be taken, they really should not refuse to disclose this information. Should a case ever get to arbitration and this information were required, it would have to be produced on discovery of documents when it might get a much wider circulation and considerations of confidentiality would take second place. In this case the QS's letter produced the following reaction:

> *Contractor to QS*   *26 May 1981*
>
> *We enclose a list of the items building up to the figure of £43,735 which we rounded down to £43,500 in our priced B/Q. We regret that it is against the policy of the firm to allow inspection of our tender details as these are highly confidential.*

> *QS to Contractor*   *29 May 1981*
>
> *Thank you for the information forwarded with your letter of 26 May. This is helpful but not sufficient for the proper computation of the sum due. For example, some items are not affected in any way by the extra work (hoardings, access to site, etc). The Provisional Sums are in any case already adjusted in the final account; items such as your temporary accommodation presumably include the capital element of providing, erecting and dismantling, which again are unaffected by the extra work. The cost of servicing this accommodation will be time-related.*
>
> *You will therefore see that it is essential for me to be provided with the details of these figures. I can assure you that the information will be treated in the strictest confidence and used for the purpose of this contract only. I may add that in arbitration cases this information has to be produced on discovery of documents — though it is not suggested that there will be any need to resort to arbitration in this case.*

The last sentence is somewhat unnecessary but was presumably put in to persuade the contractor to be sensible.

> *With reference to your letter of 29 May, as discussed by telephone if you could arrange to visit this office, the information you require will be made available.*

The alternative of making the information available in the contractor's office is not unusual. Contractors are understandably concerned that details of their pricing should not be leaked to their competitors. Perhaps, also, the presentation may be a bit rough and ready and generally not likely to strengthen confidence in the contractor's pricing system. On the other hand, any evidence of it having been 'tidied up' or otherwise produced for the purpose of inspection should be viewed with suspicion. In this case the information was made available and appeared to be authentic. The QS was able to arrive at the following:

Insurances (£2,800 and £375): increasing according to the policy in proportion to the value of the final account (including 'claims'), cf the Contract Sum. These will therefore need to be left until other figures are agreed.

Provisional Sums for LA fees (£500) and rates (£1,500): already adjusted in the final account.

Access to site: provision (£1,500), maintenance (seventy weeks at £20 per week = £1,400). The access was in fact kept in use for an extra fifteen weeks over what was anticipated. Strictly, this should be proportioned to the causes of delay and extra work should take no more than (15/26) × 15 =, say, nine weeks. This at £20 =

£ 180

Hoardings: provision £1,500, servicing forty weeks at £20. These were in fact kept up longer, for an additional ten weeks of which period the strike accounted for three, leaving seven at £20 =

£ 140

Servicing temporary accommodation for C/W: provision £1,500, servicing seventy weeks at £15 = £1,050. (15/26) × 15 =, say, nine weeks. This at £15 =

£ 135

Site administration: this was put in at seventy weeks at £268 per week. The items included in it (largely salaries) were virtually all time-related. The amount attributable to extra work was thus nine weeks at £268 =

£ 2,412

Water was taken at 0.4 per cent of the value, lighting and power had been put in at £500. It was agreed that both should be adjusted proportionate to value (because the bigger one, water, is usually charged on this basis), say 0.5 per cent of £66,971 =

£ 335

Temporary accommodation for the contractor: provision £3,500, servicing and maintenance seventy weeks at £100 = £7,000. The latter apparently included some wages not included under Site administration. Again the amount attributable to extra work would be nine weeks at £100 =

£ 900

Safety, health and welfare had been priced at seventy weeks at £15 per week but rounded down to £1,000. Allow nine weeks at £15 =

£ 135

£ 4,237

Value of variations as previously arrived at   66,971
Add adjustment of Preliminaries as foregoing   4,237 £71,208

				b/f	£71,208

Add insurance, third party at
   — 0.75% of wages, say 60% × 0.75   0.45%
   — damage to works   0.10%   0.55% =   £ 392

£71,600

The value of extras was agreed in this sum but the contractor was somewhat aggrieved that the twenty weeks' delay had been whittled down to only nine. It was pointed out that he was entitled to no compensation on account of the strike or the inclement weather, leaving a period of three weeks for delay due to the issue of instructions. He considered he was entitled to a further three weeks of Preliminaries on this account. It was agreed that he was entitled to compensation under Clause 24, but that this would be at cost, not at the prices put in the B/Q. This would have involved further research into his books which he was not prepared to permit and so he chose to forgo the claim.

Points of principle involved

There are some people who contend that Preliminary Items are not adjustable at all but there would seem to be no logic to this contention. There is nothing in the B/Q or in the Conditions of Contract to distinguish Preliminaries from any other items in the B/Q. Of course not all of them are necessarily adjustable, only those which have been affected by variations (as with any other B/Q items). There would be no need to adjust time-related items where, say, hardwood had been substituted for softwood (an increase in value only). Like other Bill items, Preliminaries need to be analysed to identify time-related, value-related and fixed elements, so that those elements affected may be appropriately adjusted. Better of course if time-related items are billed separately.

Contractors do themselves a disservice in bracketing items together as in this case and can hardly complain if thereby they get less than their entitlement.

Some contractors tend to 'load' Preliminaries for various reasons — to secure early finance (although this should be usually nipped in the bud by provisions spreading lump sum items over the contract period unless justified by proof of specific expenditure), to facilitate the tendering process by pricing indirect costs against a limited number of items, or to avoid the effects of deliberately over-measured quantities. There is no implied rule against such pricing, but it ought to be picked up during the examination of tenders and, if possible, the basis established as part of the contract to simplify any subsequent adjustment. If the principle is followed of valuing variations as they would have been priced in the original tender, subject to any adjustment for the effect of their later introduction and any other special factors, the proper approach to Preliminaries and non-standard pricing is relatively straightforward.

It follows that in valuing variations, the A/E/QS should not presume that the prices against Preliminary items necessarily correspond to the item descriptions. On the other hand, the A/E/QS can help reduce this problem (even if not avoid it altogether), by ensuring that Preliminary items in the B/Q are for definitive and priceable requirements or risks, where appropriate, permitting separate pricing for static costs and time-related costs and do not include such vague, almost meaningless items as 'Complying with the requirements of the Specification', and much less the howler of including in the list of items to be priced Condition 55 of GC/Wks 1 Edition 2 (Corrupt Gifts). Blanket items (more or less camouflaged) should not be used to cover deficiencies in the Bill.

CASE 7.4   CLAIM IN RESPECT OF EXTRA TIME FOR EXTRA WORK

Pertinent particulars of contract

The contract was for the construction of an office block. The documents comprised:

Drawings (no Specification), Bill of Quantities, Conditions of Contract (JCT 63/77).
Tender dated 8 May 1978 in the sum of £542,144.
Acceptance dated 16 June 1978.
Possession of site 1 July 1978. Time for completion 2 years. Due date for completion 30 June 1980 (extended by 27 weeks to 5 January 1981).

210

Development of the claim

Work progressed much as usual but there were rather more variations than normal. They numbered 243 and involved the addition of £75,171 and the omission of £12,140, giving a nett extra of £63,031 (including the adjustment of Provisional Sums but excluding the adjustment of PC Sums on which they were in any case only a small increase).

There were extensions of time in respect of exceptionally inclement weather in the winter of 1978 (3 weeks), strikes (3 weeks) and extra work (21 weeks).

The nett extra cost of £63,031 included for the adjustment of Preliminary Items, which were individually priced in the B/Q and totalled £49,187.

The first intimation of a claim was the following letter:

Contractor to QS　　　　　　　　　　　　　　　　　　　　　*7 May 1981*

We are in receipt of your draft account which may be summarized as follows:

Contract Sum		*542,144*	
Adjustment of PC Sums			
as B/Q	*128,774*		
as accounts	*131,286*	*2,512*	
		544,656	
Adjustment of Provisional Sums			
as B/Q	*40,000*		
as measured	*40,827*	*827*	
Variations: add	*74,344*		
omit	*12,140*	*62,204*	*£607,687*

We note that included in the variation account is an adjustment for certain Preliminary Items which have been varied on a time basis except for insurances which have been adjusted proportionate to value. The amount you have included is very much less than we asked for but we accept the arguments which your site man has put forward and therefore agree the figures as stated.

We must, however, point out that no allowance has been made in respect of general overheads which we incurred over the delay period of twenty-seven weeks. Overheads were included in our tender at 22 per cent, i.e. £119,272 for a contract period of 104 weeks = £1,147 per week. For twenty-seven weeks we therefore require a further 30,969 (27 × 1,147), which we claim under Clause 24 of the Conditions of Contract.

The contractor was right of course to put his claim in writing, though it is rather a pity this was not brought up with the site QS during the preparation of the account. Perhaps it was the fact that the adjustment of Preliminaries fell short of what the contractor hoped for that led him to cast around for something further. However, to pursue the matter by correspondence would be somewhat protracted and the QS therefore called a meeting.

First, attempt was made to establish the validity of the 22 per cent. The Contract Sum was analysed as follows:

Preliminaries		*49,187*	
PC Sums	*120,679*		
Attendance (sums)	*4,876*		
Profit 2½%	*3,219*	*128,774*	
Provisional Sums		*40,000*	
Measured work		*324,183*	*542,144*

211

From the build-up of the tender it was apparent that the overhead rate was indeed 22 per cent and that this had been included in the sum for measured work (£324,183).

The overhead element in the tender was therefore (22/122) × 324,183 = £58,459 (not £119,272 as claimed), which over 104 weeks = £562.1 per week. Overheads could therefore be regarded as a function of turnover.

Next, it was pointed out that the extra work under variation orders and all the work in connection with Provisional Sums was being paid for at B/Q prices or prices analogous thereto. This must include the 22 per cent for overheads. The problem therefore boiled down to a question of whether the turnover for the work as executed differed from that envisaged by the contract. At the risk of some slight oversimplification (i.e., ignoring Preliminaries and PC Sums), one could say that the turnover was originally expected to be 364,183 ÷ 104 = 3,501.76 per week. (324,183 ÷ 104 would give 3,117.14.)

From this it could be argued that, so far as overheads are concerned, an economic time for the varied work and work in connection with Provisional Sums would be (40,827 + 62,204) ÷ 3,502 = $29\frac{1}{2}$ weeks.

In fact the extra time required for extra work had been put at twenty-one weeks, so that there was in fact no case for recovery of additional overheads.

Had there been in fact no Provisional Sums, the economic time for varied work would have been 62,204 ÷ 3,117 = 19.9, say twenty weeks. In such case there would have been an under-recovery of one week which for practical purposes could be valued at the weekly rate of overheads included in the tender (£562).

The claim does not, however, lie under Clause 24 but under Clause 11(6). On the actual facts of this case, where the additional time required twenty-one weeks, cf thirty-three weeks 'paid for' in the rates, one might expect a counter-claim on behalf of the employer but Clause 11(6) contemplates no such adjustment.

Ponts of principle involved

In evaluating variations, consideration must be given to all aspects. First, it is paramount in terms of labour, plant and materials that B/Q prices apply only if the work is of similar character and executed under similar conditions (JCT63/77 Clause 11(4)(a); JCT80 Clause 13.5.1; ICE5 and ICE6 Clause 52). Second, it is essential in computing such prices that account be taken of factors proportionate to time, of those proportionate to value and of any that are fixed. Third, in such valuation it is proper to include adjustment of such Preliminary Items as have been affected by the variation(s). Fourth, overheads are very real costs although they may have been expressed as a percentage of turnover (whether this be in £s per annum for the firm as a whole or £s per week for a given job). If the varied work is to be no less remunerative than the contract work on which its prices are based, then consideration must be given to this factor also. Fifth, rates for the varied work should take account of any agreed measures to expedite the work required to limit the consequent extension of time.

It might seem that there should be some negative adjustment of rates where the value of variations etc gives a higher turnover ratio than was the case for the contract originally. It is doubtful, however, if this can be read into JCT63/77 Clause 11(6) or JCT80 Clause 13(5). So far as ICE5 and ICE6 are concerned, Clause 52(2) allows for adjustment either way, but an employer will probably be grateful in such circumstances to escape a claim for acceleration.

CASE 7.5   CLAIM IN RESPECT OF CHANGE OF RATES BY
AUDITOR AND DELAY IN PAYMENT

**Pertinent particulars
of contract**

The contract was for the laying of a sewer, constructing a sewage treatment plant with access road, fencing and outfall. The contract documents included:

Drawings, Specification, Conditions of Contract ICE 5 (though this is strictly immaterial to the case, the position being similar with any of the Standard Forms of Contract, including JCT and GC/Wks 1).

Bill of Quantities on the basis of CESMM, totalling £871,245.
Tender dated 21 September 1978. Time for completion 18 months.
Acceptance dated 27 October 1978.

The contract was under seal and was dated 15 January 1979. Minimum amount of interim certificates (Clause 60(2)) £30,000.

**Development of the
claim**

The engineer gave his order to commence under Clause 41 on 12 November 1978 and the contractor started work on site quite soon after. By the end of the month he had erected the site accommodation for the RE and for himself, and he had started site clearance and temporary fencing, all of which were covered by priced items in General Provisions.

On 8 December 1978 the engineer certified an interim payment in the sum of £28,500. Five days later it was returned to him by the departmental auditor:

Departmental Auditor to Engineer   *13 December 1978*

In connection with the attached certificate your attention is drawn to the fact that this is for less than the minimum amount of interim certificates as provided for in the Appendix to the Form of Tender (£30,000).

I would also point out that the contract has not yet been sealed. Until there is a contract, no payments on account may be made.

The intervention of auditors in this fashion raises very serious problems, both for the employer and for the A/E/QS. The need for audit where public money is being spent is not questioned in the least, but there are proper ways and times for it to be done. The employer has, by virtue of his contract with the contractor, appointed the engineer to perform certain functions under the contract, and has conferred certain powers and discretions on the engineer as part of those functions. It is an implied, if not an express[16] term of the employer's contract with the contractor, that the engineer will be permitted to perform those functions without hindrance, threat, collusion, or other improper interference, and that the employer will not countermand the engineer's exercise of his certification powers nor dispute such certificates except through the procedures laid down in the contract.[17]

That is not to say that the employer may not draw to the attention of the engineer any matters which he believes ought to be considered by the engineer in the exercise of a power or discretion — the employer has as much right as the contractor to be heard by the engineer. But if the employer or those for whom he is responsible overstep the mark, he will be in breach of contract. The auditor is not entitled under the contract to usurp the functions of the engineer, rarely indeed is he qualified to do so. If the auditor wishes to raise a matter during the currency of the contract, he should raise it with the engineer. If he is unable to obtain satisfactory responses from the engineer he may, if he considers it necessary, advise the employer that the engineer should be surcharged (if the conditions of engagement permit)

---

16. For example, FIDIC4 Clauses 2.6 and 69.1(b).
17. The certificate of an A/E/QS is still subject to the right of equitable set-off: *Gilbert Ash (Northern) v Modern Engineering (Bristol)* [1974] AC 689.

or even that the engineer should be dismissed and a new person be appointed in his place.[18] But the auditor must not seek to override or prevent the engineer's performance of his functions under the contract, so long as the engineer is in post.

> *Engineer to Departmental Auditor*　　　　　　　　　　　　　*December 1978*
>
> *Your attention is drawn to Clause 60(2) of the Conditions of Contract, to which the entry on the Appendix to the Form of Tender is but a reference. You will see there that 'The engineer shall not be bound to issue an interim certificate for a sum less than that named in the Appendix to the Form of Tender.' There is thus no ban against a lesser amount. In the present case I consider it to be in the employer's interest to make this payment. The Council is very anxious to spend the amount voted this financial year and I am urging the contractor to press on with the work. Work in excess of the sum certified has in any case been executed.*
>
> *Regarding para 2 of your Memo, I appreciate that the contract has not yet been sealed, I have been pressing the Legal Department to get this formality completed. However, there is indeed a valid contract in that the Tender dated 21 September was accepted on 27 October 1978. Your attention is drawn to para 4 of the Form of Tender.*
>
> *Will you please forward this certificate to the Finance Dept forthwith for payment. Their routine normally takes 14–21 days to complete. The certificate was in my office for checking and verification for five days, your Department retained it for five days, leaving eighteen days before payment is due without incurring interest (see Clauses 60(2) and 60(6)). Should this become payable no doubt you will explain to the Finance Committee.*

This may seem a somewhat crusty reply but the engineer is right to point out the facts of the matter and to demonstrate that under the contract he is the one who has to take responsibility. There seems to have been no reply, the certificate was paid a few days late but the contractor made no claim.

Hereafter things went along smoothly for a number of months, though an auditor was seen on site occasionally. However, in July 1979 an auditor went to the contractor's site office for the purpose of checking some daywork sheets. As these had already been signed by the inspector and the RE the agent asked the latter if he had any second thoughts and, if not, why the sheets were being queried. The RE of course knew nothing of it and contacted the auditor as to what he was doing, receiving the reply that it was only routine. The RE let the matter go though he would have been advised either to take it up with the Audit Department (the auditor should at least have informed the RE of what he was doing) or, better, get the engineer to do so (apparently he did not know of the first encounter).

The final account was being prepared as the job progressed and so rates for varied work were included in interim certificates in respect of work finally measured and agreed. It was with some surprise that the engineer received the following Memo:

> *Departmental Auditor to Engineer*　　　　　　　　　　　　　*29 January 1980*
>
> *I refer to Certificate No 14 dated 8 January and in particular to the section dealing with the additional retaining wall ordered under Variation*

---

18. Recent decisions, such as *Merton LBC v Stanley Leach Ltd* [1985] 32 BLR 51, appear to put a positive duty on the employer to consider the possibility of dismissing the architect, engineer, or quantity surveyor if they are not performing their respective roles under the contract with due skill, care or diligence. That is not, however, a licence for the employer to threaten dismissal because the A/E/QS is exercising a discretion contrary to the employer's opinions or wishes.

No 42 dated 14 June 1979. This variation specifically refers to one of the contract drawings and says that this new retaining wall at Chainage 442−604 of the Access Road is to be of identical design as Retaining Wall RR at Chainage 040−166 on the same road.

It is, however, observed that the prices included in this certificate differ significantly from those in the B/Q, though the description remains the same. The certificate has accordingly been reduced by the sum of £1,750.44 and passed for payment.

The auditors seem not to have learned the lesson of the first exchange of correspondence (or perhaps there was a change of personnel, which is not unusual in this work). In this instance, the auditor has *prima facie* justification for questioning the payment for the work. The RE has perhaps been remiss in not including as a heading to this part of the account some preamble to indicate why the prices were different. The auditor's proper course of action, however, is to raise the matter with the engineer and seek an explanation. He had no right to alter an amount certified by the engineer and, not surprisingly, the contractor complains somewhat strongly.

Contractor to Engineer   *4 February 1980*

We refer to Certificate No 14 dated 18 January 1980. We were surprised to find that payment was £1,750.44 less than the amount certified and notified by you. We were not given any reasons for this reduction and must ask that we be informed immediately which items in the agreed Statement were altered and why.

There must have been some delay between making the alterations by Departmental Audit and passing the account for payment and the Departmental Audit's Memo of 29 January to the engineer. The contractor has become aware of and challenged the amendment before the engineer can take remedial action with the Departmental Audit. It is not just the £1,750 at stake, it is the principle of whose responsibility it is under the contract to agree or approve or 'fix' rates. If the engineer's position is being undermined, the contractor will not know where he stands, nor to whom he has to look for agreement or approval — and there are still matters for the final account to be agreed as well as some claims in the offing. With whom is he to negotiate, if not the engineer?

Engineer to Contractor   *6 February 1980*

With reference to your letter of 4 February, I have to inform you that the reduction in Certificate No 14 was in respect of the retaining wall constructed under Variation Order No 42. There has been no change in the agreement reached between us in respect of these prices, the deduction was inadvertently and incorrectly made in another department in the course of processing this certificate. Appropriate action has been taken to prevent recurrence and the amount of £1,750.44 will be added to Certificate No 15 now being prepared for certification on 8 February. The delay in making this payment is regretted.

Engineer to Departmental Auditor   *6 February 1980*

I refer to your Memo dated 29 January in connection with Certificate No 14 and enclose copies of correspondence with the contractor for your information.

Had you sought some explanation of this apparent error before taking the drastic and, if I may be permitted to say so, improper action of reducing an amount certified by me under the contract, I should of course have been quite prepared to provide it. As it is, relations with the contractor have been jeopardised at an inconvenient stage when I am about to negotiate prices for other varied work where much more than £1,750 is involved. Further, the contractor is entitled to claim interest under Clause 60(6) for overdue payment of this sum, though he has not as yet intimated his intention to do so.

Regarding the subject of your query, I have to point out that Variation Order 42 was issued on 14 June 1979 as a result of a slip between Chainages 442–604 along the Access Road, which required the construction of an additional retaining wall. This new wall is indeed identical in design to three others along this road, all of which had been completed before the slip occurred. The contractor therefore had to bring back plant and new formwork, and divert labour from other work in order to construct this additional wall, all of which cost more than would have been the case had the work been done in sequence with the other walls. Your attention is drawn to Clause 52(1) which reads:

'The value of all variations ... shall be ascertained by the Engineer (sic) ... in accordance with the following principles. Where work is of similar character and executed under similar conditions to the work priced in the B/Q ... it shall be valued at such rates and prices contained therein as may be applicable. Where work is not of similar character or is not executed under similar conditions ... the rates and prices in the B/Q shall be used as a basis.'

In this case, the conditions under which the work was executed were by no means similar and the third sentence quoted above therefore applies. To remove any doubt about the matter I will arrange for the relevant items in the account to be suitably annotated. As you will see from my letter to the contractor dated 6 February, the amount has been included in Certificate 15.

I fully accept your Department's right to inspect and criticize the work of my Department but, with respect, I must point out that I have been appointed Engineer under the contract and in that capacity I have certain duties and obligations which may not be interfered with without risk of putting the Authority in breach of contract. If this matter could be properly understood by your staff, I can assure you of the fullest access to the work of my staff and their co-operation in facilitating the carrying out of your responsibilities. At the same time I must point out that much of my work is technical and that your staff are not technically qualified to comment on contractual or engineering matters. Also, I must insist that the intervention by your Department must be carried out ex post facto, *as it is my responsibility to ensure that the terms of the contract are complied with.*

Points of principle involved

This is not only an important matter of principle but it affects the relationships of the engineer and RE with the contractor and agent, which are sometimes subject to stress and always important to maintain on a good co-operative basis. On the other hand, it is equally important that the engineer should listen to and take into consideration any matters properly raised by or on behalf of the employer — indeed, a prudent engineer would seek to ensure for his own self-interest that the employer was given the opportunity to raise matters at times when appropriate action could be taken. That is not to say that the A/E/QS should attempt to avoid his own responsibility by seeking approval from auditors or anyone else in respect of what are his duties under the contract. It was established in *Panamena v Frederick Leyland*[19] that it does not constitute improper interference for the engineer to supply

---

19. *Panamena Europea Navigacion v Frederick Leyland & Co* [1947] AC 428 at p 444.

information to or consult with the employer, nor even for the employer to supply the opinion of his lawyers, so long as the engineer makes up his own mind at the end of the day on matters which are for his decision.

The *Panamena* decision was considered by the Australian courts in *Perini Corporation v Commonwealth of Australia*,[20] a case of particular interest in that the engineer was the Director of Works, an officer of the employer's organization. It was held that in making decisions as engineer the Director was entitled to consider Departmental policy, but he would be wrong to consider himself bound by that policy if it happened to conflict with the terms of the contract. It was also held that there were implied terms that the employer would not interfere with the performance by the Director in his function as certifier and that the employer would ensure that the Director performed his duties as laid down in the contract.

The more recent English decision of Vinelott J in *Merton LBC v Stanley Leach*[21] held that similar obligations were to be implied in relation to a local authority employer, not only to allow, but also to ensure, the proper performance of his duties by an architect who was not an officer of the Council. The implication was based on the power of the employer under the JCT contract to appoint an architect to replace the one named in the contract.

20. *Perini Corporation v Commonwealth of Australia* [1969] 12 BLR 82.
21. *Merton LBC v Stanley Hugh Leach Ltd* [1985] 32 BLR 51.

Chapter 8
Claims concerning time

GENERALLY

This chapter deals with claims concerning time. It deals primarily with claims for monetary compensation or reimbursement of time-related costs arising out of delay or disruption, whether in connection with an extension of time for completion or not. It also deals with claims for extension of time for completion. These two aspects of time need to be taken together, but there is a risk of confusion unless a couple of points are clearly registered. The first point is that claims for payment for delay are not necessarily linked with extensions of time. The second, apparently contradictory, point is that a claim for additional payment for delay may be inextricably linked with a claim for extension of time if they stem from the same cause.

In none of the Forms of Contract in common use[1] do the extension of time clauses make any provision for payment. Nor do delay and disruption clauses in these Forms make

---

1. The ICE New Engineering Contract, as issued for consultation, adopts a rather different approach. Time and money are treated as interdependent and no mention is made of extensions of time.

entitlement to extension of time a condition precedent to entitlement to money. Accordingly, various situations occur. A contractor may be entitled under the provisions of the contract to extension of time in respect of events such as exceptionally inclement weather, strikes and the like, but the grant of an extension of time in respect of such delays does not entitle him to additional payment for loss and expense. For other delays, for which the employer is either responsible or has accepted the financial risk, the contractor will, if such delay has affected operations along the critical path, be entitled to both extension of time and, if he can shew consequential loss or expense, to compensation also. If such other delays only affect operations not on the critical path but the contractor can shew consequential loss or expense, then he will not be entitled to an extension of time but he may well be entitled to compensation. Where extra work is ordered, the contractor may be entitled to extension of time to carry out the work and he may be entitled to additional payment either by way of compensation for delay and disruption or through adjustment of the rates, depending on the provisions of the contract. (This last category of claims is dealt with primarily in Chapter 7, but it is also considered here in relation to concurrent causes of delay.)

It follows that a contractor does not establish entitlement to payment by insisting on an extension of time. His entitlement to payment (if any) stems from the cause of delay — as does his entitlement to extension of time. By the same token, the A/E cannot thwart a claim for payment by denying an extension of time. On the other hand, time and money should not be considered in isolated compartments. They may be inter-dependent variables (where, for example, time effects can be reduced by agreement to pay for additional resources as part of the costs of the delay) or claims for time and money may be dependent on the same facts. In the latter case, a fact admitted in respect of one claim generally cannot be denied for the other,[2] despite the temptation to be more sympathetic in granting extensions of time than in certifying additional payment. The tendency to yield to this temptation, coupled with confusion over the inter-relationship between time and money, has led to the anomalous and unsatisfactory situation where contractors expect to be paid more for protracted projects than for prompt performance. Means of redressing the situation, to the advantage of all parties, are discussed below.

EXTENSIONS OF TIME

The primary effect of extension of time provisions is to relieve the contractor from liability to liquidated damages, but historically such provisions were introduced into construction contracts for the benefit of the employer, to keep in place a date for completion and the right to deduct liquidated damages. The employer's need derives from the principle established in *Holme v Guppy*,[3] that in the absence of explicit power to adjust the date for completion on account of employer-caused delay, a contractor would be released entirely from his obligation to complete the work by the time set by the contract, if he were prevented to any extent by the employer or his agents. The contractor would be released in respect not only of delay caused by the employer but also any delay for which he was himself responsible. In the words of Parke B., in that case the contractor would be 'left at large'. Some later judgments have said that the time for completion is at large. Once the time for completion set by the contract ceases to bind there is no implied power to substitute a new date. The contractor's obligation to complete is relegated to completion within a reasonable time; furthermore, any damages claimed for failure to complete within such reasonable time must be proved, the liquidated damages cannot be applied.

Subsequent cases have established that any power to extend the time for completion must clearly cover the event,[4] and the power must be exercised in accordance with the contract, including any stipulations as to timing of its exercise.[5] Otherwise the contractor or date

---

2. There may be situations, however, where different views of the facts are justified by the changing state of knowledge, for example, where an extension of time is granted prospectively but the entitlement to payment is evaluated retrospectively.
3. *Holme v Guppy* [1838] 3 M & W 387.
4. *Wells v Army & Navy Co-op Soc Ltd* [1906] 86 LT 764.
5. *Miller v LCC* [1934] 50 TLR 379.

for completion will again be left at large. There is, however, no requirement for the contract to provide any financial compensation for the delay. A bare extension of time suffices to keep a date for completion intact. Many of the older contracts were drafted to provide just that. This may help to explain the hostility to extension of time clauses exhibited by the courts in the older cases.

Unfortunately, the hostility of the courts to EoT clauses has persisted, although modern Forms of Contract commonly provide for financial compensation in respect of delay and disruption for which the employer is responsible. Most modern Forms (though not all[6]) are also drafted by committees representing all sides. The extreme view was stated by Salmon LJ in *Peak Construction (Liverpool) Ltd v McKinney Foundations*[7] that 'liquidated damages and extension of time clauses in printed forms of contract must be construed strictly *contra proferentem*'. It has been pointed out by Terence Burke[8] that no authority was cited for this proposition. In addition, according to the case headnote, the contract involved was a special form drafted by one of the parties, it was not a standard Form of Contract. It is submitted that the proposition ought not to be applied to standard Forms of Contract, agreed by all sides, with provision for compensation for employer-caused delay. Such Forms of Contract ought to be construed instead with due regard to the presumed common purpose of the parties. In particular, as a contract is to be read as a whole, the fact that entitlements to time and money are dealt with in separate clauses does not prevent the two aspects being considered together.

Extension of time provisions also provide relief against specified classes of events or circumstances outside the control of either party. Events for which the employer is not responsible do not, as a rule, carry entitlement to recover loss or expense.[9] There may, however, be financial consequences which flow from all extensions of time, for example, in relation to price fluctuation clauses and Preliminary items measured by reference to units of time, where the time fixed for completion is stipulated as a cut-off.

The relevance of the date for completion set by the contract is not limited to liquidated damages; the date also operates as a target for the purposes of programming and resource allocation. Thus in ICE5 and ICE6 Clause 14, the contractor is required to submit a programme or revised programme 'to ensure completion of the Works or any Section within the time for completion as defined in Clause 43 or extended time granted pursuant to Clause 44(2)/44'. Similar provisions are found in JCT 80 and GC/Wks 1.[10]

If the contractor is to take account of an extension of time in his programming and resource allocation it is necessary that the entitlement should be ascertained and granted at a sufficiently early stage to enable him to do so. In *Amalgamated Building Contractors v Waltham Holy Cross UDC*[11] Lord Denning MR said it was not essential that extensions of time should be fixed to give a date for the contractor to aim at in the future, but he was, of course, referring just to what was essential for the purposes of preserving the right to deduct liquidated damages. The absence of a general rule as contended in that case does not affect explicit provisions. Lord Denning MR also observed that there was a difference in principle between employer-caused delay and other delays.

As the contractor is expected to adjust his programming and resources to meet the time for completion as currently set, all the Standard Forms provide for entitlement to be assessed not only in respect of delays which have already occurred, but also delays which are expected

---

6. Exceptions include GC/Wks 1 and the Hong Kong Government Conditions of Contract.
7. *Peak Construction (Liverpool) Ltd v McKinney Foundations* [1970] 1 BLR 114.
8. Terence Burke, 1985 'The Liability of the Contractor for Late Completion' in *The Liabililty of Contractors* 71 at 80. Ed. H. Lloyd, Centre for Commercial Studies, Queen Mary College and Longman Group UK Ltd.
9. An exception is Clause 12 of the ICE and FIDIC Conditions, which provides entitlement to the costs of delay and disruption in the event of unforeseen physical conditions being encountered, irrespective of whether the employer would be liable at common law.
10. JCT 80 Clauses 23.1 and 25.3.4.1; GC/Wks 1 Ed 2 Condition 6; GC/Wks 1 Ed 3 Conditions 33, 34 and 35; also FIDIC4 Clause 14.2.
11. *Amalgamated Building Contractors Ltd v Waltham Holy Cross UDC* [1952] 2 All ER 452.

to occur. They also provide for interim assessments to be made. Failure to comply with such provisions for interim assessments can mean that the contract time for completion ceases to be applicable and there is no date from which liquidated damages can run.

The problems of the architect or engineer in dealing with interim assessments are twofold. Firstly, he usually has no access to the contractor's programming system, which would provide the most rational means of evaluating the entitlement. If the contractor exaggerates the claim or does not co-operate in the evaluation, the A/E is at a disadvantage, particularly on complex projects. This lack of access could be remedied for future contracts by amendment to the Conditions of Contract or specification; otherwise the A/E needs to set up his own programming system.

Secondly, most of the Forms of Contract are singularly unhelpful as to the basis on which entitlements to extension of time ought to be evaluated. JCT80 Clause 25.3.1 refers to the architect fixing a new Completion Date 'as he then estimates to be fair and reasonable'; this must be read in the light of Clause 23.1 by which the contractor undertakes to proceed 'regularly and diligently' with the works. ICE5 Clause 44 is even more reticent, saying only indirectly that the entitlement is to be 'fair'; Clause 41 stipulates that the contractor shall proceed with the works 'with due expedition and without delay in accordance with the contract', while Clause 51(1) empowers the engineer to order 'changes in the specified sequence method or timing of construction' as a variation. In ICE6 the wording of Clause 44(2) has been modified so that the Engineer is to assess 'the delay (if any) that has been suffered by the Contractor as a result of the alleged cause'. He is then to grant an extension of time if he considers that 'the delay suffered fairly entitles the Contractor to an extension of time'. This is easier to follow, but, arguably, it means that no EoT can be granted until after the delay has been suffered.

Only GC/Wks 1 faces squarely up to the question. In Edition 2, Condition 28(2) proviso (iv) states:

> 'It shall be the duty of the Contractor at all times to use his best endeavours to prevent any delay being caused by any of the above-mentioned circumstances and to minimise any such delay as may be caused thereby and to do all that may reasonably be required, to the satisfaction of the SO, to proceed with the Works.'

In GC/Wks 1 Edition 3, Condition 36(7) is similar.

Duty to mitigate

In the absence of such an explicit duty to mitigate the time effects, what is the contractor's duty in the event of a delay? The corollary question is whether the contractor is entitled to recover compensation if he takes steps to mitigate the delay; and if he is so entitled, whether his claim is for loss and expense or for a variation. A source of confusion in this connection is that other provisions[12] empower the engineer or architect to order the contractor to bring in additional resources at his own cost to make up for delays for which he is responsible. The situations need to be clearly distinguished, but there is a very difficult area where an extension of time in respect of delay for which the employer is responsible would also cover delay for which the contractor is responsible. In such a case mitigating the effects of the first delay would necessarily involve the contractor also in accelerating (in the sense of increasing the rate of progress) to mitigate the second.

Reference is sometimes made to a general duty to mitigate, but if such a duty exists, what does it entail? At common law there is an implied duty on a claimant to mitigate his loss or damage suffered due to breach of contract. The effect of the implied duty is that the measure of damages recoverable is abated to the extent that the loss or damage was, or could reasonably have been, mitigated by the claimant. If the doctrine applies to a delay

---

12. As in ICE5 Clause 46 and ICE6 Clause 46(1).

situation it would mean, first, that the employer is obliged to mitigate the damage suffered by him due to late completion by the contractor — such an obligation is avoided by the stipulation of liquidated damages. Second, the contractor would be under an obligation to mitigate the additional loss and expense which he incurs as a result of delay or disruption for which the employer is responsible. There is some authority[13] for applying the common law doctines by analogy to interpret contractual provisions, but the doctrine would not impose an obligation on the contractor to mitigate the time effects of delay except as necessary to mitigate the financial effects for which he claims. Any obligation to expedite the works in the event of delay must therefore be found in the express terms of the contract itself.

There are further ramifications of the doctrine. If a party reasonably takes steps in mitigation of damage suffered and thereby incurs additional cost instead of saving, he is entitled to recover his actual loss. If he does make savings by taking steps in mitigation, his recovery is limited to his actual loss whether or not he was obliged to take those steps. This is subject to a further rule that steps in mitigation are only to be taken into account in so far as they form part of a continuing process. In *Hussey v Eels*,[14] Mustill L J quoted a passage, which he said epitomized the law, as follows:

'When once the Court has arrived at the conclusion that the measure of damages is x, which in that particular class of case was the cost of putting the premises into repair, no outside circumstances will be taken into consideration for the purposes of reducing x to x−a. But here the measure of damages never was x, but was x−a, that is to say, the price of the new machines less the value of the additional advantages derived from their use.'

This principle that entitlement once accrued cannot be reduced by operation of law is probably also of application to extensions of time. For example, if possession of the site has been delayed for two days the entitlement to extension of time is necessarily two days without any question of making up the time. But where there is reasonable opportunity to take steps to expedite the works to avoid a potential delay effect and the contract provides for compensation for costs incurred as a result of such a delay, there appears to be no reason why such steps should not be taken, paid for as part of the costs of delay. If the costs of such steps are paid by the employer, there is no reason why they should not be taken into account in assessing the entitlement to extension of time. This principle applies equally where extra work is ordered as a variation and the effect on costs can be allowed through re-rating or fixing of new rates. Under some Forms of Contract, it may be possible to make payment for such steps under a power to order variations as to timing.

The only qualifications are that if an engineer or architect intends to take increased resources into account in assessing entitlement to extension of time, it is essential that he informs the contractor promptly and confirms that he will certify the additional cost involved, in order that the contractor can take the appropriate steps. It must also be reasonably practicable for the contractor to implement the steps involved within the timescale and any other practical constraints. An extension of time which necessarily involves accelerated working may amount to such information from the A/E, providing the contractor responds accepting the EoT on that basis.[15]

The possibility of accelerated working within the contract has been denied by Duncan Wallace I N QC. He has asserted[16] an assumption that a contractor will have priced on the basis of the optimum labour and plant organization, within the exigencies of the prescribed contract period, and asserted that no element of acceleration can be ordered as a contractor

13. *Minter v WHTSO* [1981] 13 BLR 1.
14. *Hussey v Eels* [1990] 2 QB 227 at p 234.
15. This corresponds to the American doctrine of 'constructive acceleration', see Burke T 1982 'Delay under Australian law'. In *Selected Problems of Construction Law: International Approach* 5 at pp 30−31. Sweet & Maxwell, London.
16. Duncan Wallace I N QC, *Construction Contracts Principles and Policies* (1986) para 8−48. Sweet & Maxwell, London.

in actual or apprehended delay will normally have the 'right' to weigh the consequences in liquidated damages and extended time-related costs on the one hand, against his loss in unproductive working and additional capital employed, if he increases his plant or labour force on the other. This view appears to enjoy considerable popularity amongst contractors, but the argument contains a number of flaws. Firstly, the contractor's original programme may well reflect an assumed labour and plant organization corresponding to the circumstances set out in the tender documents. It does not follow that, in changed circumstances, the programmed resourcing is to be regarded as either sacrosanct or necessarily appropriate. Secondly, a contractor can, as a matter of free will, choose to complete works late and suffer liquidated damages. It does not follow that he has a 'right' to do so, any more than he has a right to perform defective work and pay for it to be rectified later. Both examples represent breaches of contract. The architect or engineer assessing entitlement to extension of time is concerned only with performance which complies with the contract.

The difficulty in this area is partly a matter of language. 'Acceleration' has two meanings. It can be used in the sense of increasing the rate of progress, as in 'accelerated working'. It also has a second meaning of hastening the occurrence of some event, as in 'accelerated completion'. Acceleration in the first sense can be within the contract as part of expediting the Works or carrying out the Works with due expedition or diligence. The second may require explicit contractual provisions or a supplementary agreement, at least where it involves advancing the date for completion already set by, or fixed under, the contract.

If the contractor is content to accept an arrangement of being paid to accelerate to reduce the effect of a compensatable delay and for the extension of time to be limited accordingly, there should be no problem, so long as it is recognized that the payment is for implementing the acceleration measures, not for achieving the required completion date. The question remains whether there is a duty on the contractor either to adopt such an arrangement of his own instigation or to accept the instruction of the engineer or architect to do so. That is really a matter that ought to be clarified by explicit provisions in the Conditions of Contract.

In relation to causes of delay such as inclement weather or strikes, where there is commonly no power to make additional payment, or in situations where the extension of time is to be considered as having accrued, any payment for acceleration of completion can only be authorized by a supplementary agreement or under an explicit power to order accelerated completion as a variation. A supplementary agreement could not be implied from the acts or omissions of the engineer or architect unless the engineer or architect had apparent authority outside the contract to make such an agreement.

In ICE6 Clause 46(3), a special provision for accelerated completion has been introduced as follows:

> 'If the Contractor is requested by the Employer or the Engineer to complete the Works or any Section within a revised time being less than the time or extended time for completion prescribed by Clauses 43 and 44 as appropriate and the Contractor agrees to do so then any special terms and conditions of payment shall be agreed between the Contractor and the Employer before any such action is taken.'

GC/Wks 1 Edition 3 Condition 38 also provides for acceleration to provide completion of the Works or any relevant Section before the Date or Dates for Completion. The basis of the Condition is similar to ICE6 in that the Contractor is to submit priced proposals which the Authority may accept.

Both these provisions suffer from the drawback that the Engineer/Employer or the Project Manager/Authority under the respective Forms of Contract cannot order acceleration without first obtaining agreement of the Contractor to terms for doing so. It is a significant drawback because effective acceleration requires measures to be implemented at short notice. Such reliance on obtaining the prior agreement of the contractor is alien to the normal principles of construction contracts and the use of the provisions may be better avoided if possible. They are only essential where a supplementary agreement would otherwise be necessary to advance the date for completion.

EVALUATION OF DELAY CLAIMS

In evaluating delay claims, five aspects must be taken into account:

(a) the effective duration of delay,
(b) the effect of delay on work intended to be done,
(c) the costs attributable to the delay,
(d) the nature of costs/expenses,
(e) resources and acceleration/expediting measures.

Effective duration of delay

Contractors often give notices of delay aggregating considerably more than the period by which it is apparent that the time for completion will be exceeded. This may be due in some measure to overestimation but it is often also due to the fact that some delays overlap and some do not lie on the critical path. In this chapter we are concerned to consider all causes of delay so as to distinguish between those which are the responsibility of the contractor, those which may give entitlement under the Conditions of Contract to extension of time but no compensation (inclement weather, strikes, etc), and those which are the responsibility of the employer both in terms of extension of time and (if cost has resulted) to compensation as well.

The simplest of cases is where all work is stopped completely by a single cause. In such a case the period of delay would be equal to the duration of the cause plus some allowance for regaining the proper tempo of work. Frequently, however, different causes overlap. Where they give rise to similar entitlement in terms of extension of time and compensation, there is no problem. But individual, relatively short overlapping periods of delay may stem from different causes, see Figure 8.1 below.

Figure 8.1 Concurrent delays

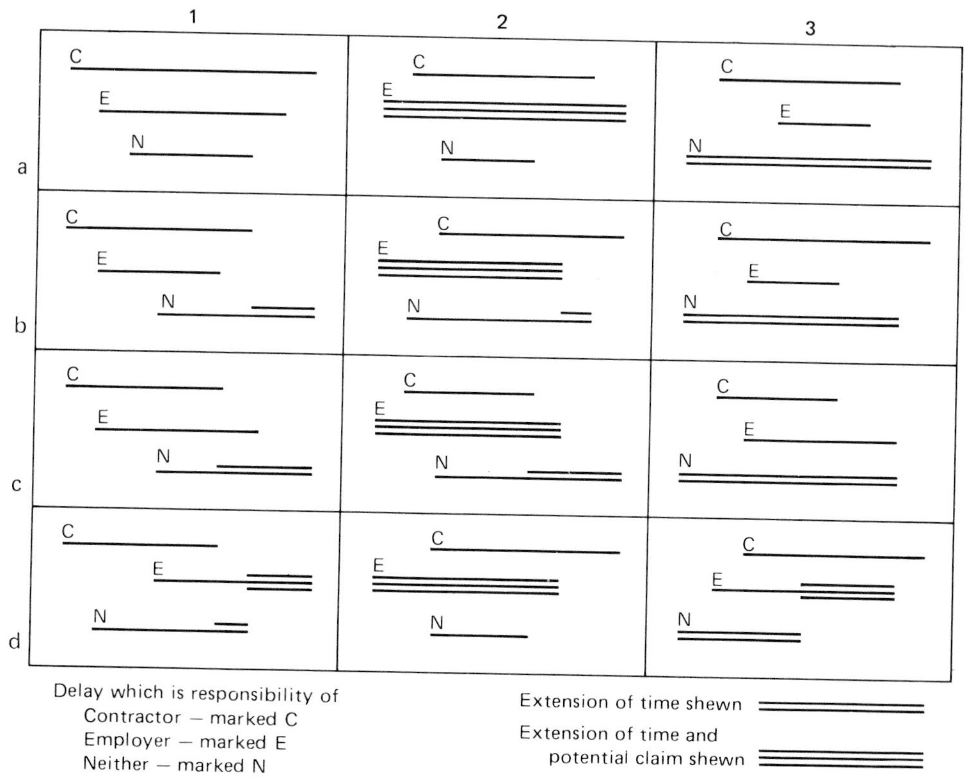

Delay which is responsibility of
  Contractor — marked C
  Employer — marked E
  Neither — marked N

Extension of time shewn
Extension of time and
  potential claim shewn

The consequences in the different situations are as follows:

(i) Where an initial delay is caused by the contractor, then any cause of delay by the employer commencing subsequently will be of no effect (if the job is stopped it cannot be any more stopped by another event) unless and until it continues after the contractor's delay has ceased (see Figure 8.1, diagrams (1a) to (1d)).

(ii) This situation will not be affected by delay caused by circumstances not the responsibility of either contractor or employer if they too commence subsequently to delay already existing. In Figure 8.1 diagrams (1b), (1c) and (1d) the contractor would be entitled to an extension of time for the period indicated and to compensation in the case of diagram (1d).

(iii) Conversely, where the initial delay is caused by the employer or his agents, then concurrent delay by the contractor will not relieve the employer of liability (though it might reduce the extent of damages). Again the contractor will be entitled to extension of time from commencement of the employer's delay to the end of delay by 'other' causes (see Figure 8.1, diagrams (2a) to (2d)).

(iv) Where the initial delay is due to causes for which neither contractor nor employer is responsible but the contractor is entitled to extension of time only, then neither the contractor nor the employer can be blamed for any concurrent delay.[16a]

The above refer to individual periods of delay considered separately and a diagram must be built up for the whole period to shew the interaction of causes, so that costs arising from them may be properly allocated. Extension of time considerations will apply only to those on the critical path (or a path made critical as a result of delays).

The foregoing diagrams (Fig. 8.1) illustrate the situation where the job is stopped by a given cause. More frequently delays cause a retardation, and to illustrate these graphically it is necessary to quantify progress, in terms of money if the project is being viewed overall or in some other unit of output if separate operations are being considered (cubic metres of excavation, concrete etc).

This may be done by indicating such quantities on a bar-chart or, more conveniently, by plotting time horizontally against quantities plotted vertically.

In Figure 8.2 the required rate of progress is represented by line O−A. A week's stoppage for, say, exceptionally inclement weather represents nil progress and is indicated by line B−B[1]. Assuming a resumption of work at the former tempo, further progress would be as B[1]−A[1]. If, however, the required rate of progress is not being achieved (say because of circumstances for which the contractor is responsible), then the 'programme' would be O−A but actual progress O−X. The week's inclement weather would then be shewn as Y−Y[1], and if the work is resumed at its former tempo completion will be achieved at X[1].

Figure 8.2

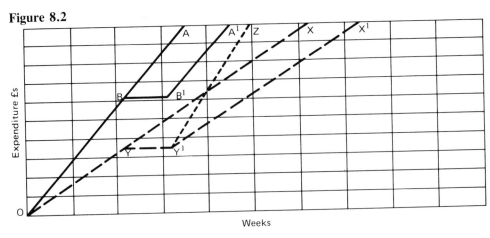

16a. cf *Fairweather v LB Wandsworth* [1987] 32 BLR 106, see p 260 *infra*.

If, however, the contractor took steps to mitigate his delay, he would still be entitled to one week's extension of time but would complete somewhere between A^1 and X^1 (say Z).

The result would be the same if the delay $B-B^1$ were the responsibility of the employer, except that he would be financially responsible.

Figure 8.3

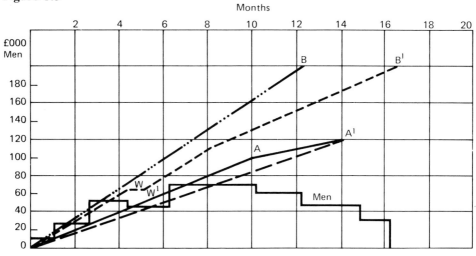

Figure 8.3 illustrates the beginning of a comparison between delays and the events and circumstances in which they are occurring. The required progress is represented by line $O-B$ and the actual progress by line $O-B^1$. Along the latter, the period $W-W^1$, being horizontal, depicts a complete stoppage and the remainder a retardation. By superimposing on this other factors such as the numbers of men employed, hours worked, plant in use or broken down, rainfall and temperature, one can begin to see a picture of delay in the context of the circumstances in which it is occurring.

Effect of delay on work intended to be done

Such a diagram as Figure 8.3 may well illustrate what happened, but claims are usually concerned to compare what happened with what was intended to happen. So far as construction contracts are concerned, this can be by way of comparison with the original programme. There seems to be some doubt, on the part of architects and engineers on the one hand and contractors on the other, as to the validity or purpose of such programmes. There is, or there is felt to be, an element of 'gamesmanship' both in preparing them and in commenting on them.

Standard Forms of Contract give no real guidance as to the content or purpose of programmes. This is no doubt due to the diversity of jobs for which they are used and of the widely differing requirements needed to be shewn. Where particular requirements are included in specifications there is usually a little more information, particularly as to monitoring progress and the purposes which monitoring may be required to serve.

Programmes produced in a short time after acceptance (e.g. ICE Clause 14 in 21 days) cannot be expected to shew great detail. Their main purpose is to ensure that the contractor understands what is required technically to comply with the contract but for most other purposes some form of quantification is needed so that the actual output may be compared with the target output. This may be by way of quantities shewn in successive periods (weeks or months) along the bar representing a given operation or by way of 'cascade' diagrams where quantities are plotted vertically against a horizontal time scale. The relative merits of these will not be discussed here as the choice depends partly on personal preference and partly on the nature of the work being illustrated.

The contractor is entitled to complete within the time stipulated and generally he will aim at a time which he considers is the most economic for him, and which allows a margin

227

of safety for unforeseen overrun. The contractor is responsible for certain types of delay (ordinary inclement weather, shortage of labour and materials (but see JCT 80 Clause 25.4.10), delay in obtaining or breakdown of plant and of course his own inefficiencies), and generally will have built into the programme some element of 'float time' as a hedge against these risks. This float time is not to be confused with 'float' as used in connection with critical path analysis, where it is used to indicate 'spare' time along a non-critical path pending completion of contingent work on another, longer path or indeed the critical path itself. In assessing the effects of delay one cannot take advantage of any float time which the contractor has built in against risks he has to carry, but where delay occurs on a non-critical path it will have little or no effect until the 'float' has been used up and the path becomes temporarily or wholly critical.

Progress may also be affected by other events, e.g. the supply of further drawings or information, the letting of nominated sub-contracts, work by Statutory Undertakers in connection with their plant, supply of key materials etc, etc. All these must be shewn on the programme if progess (or lack of it) is to be properly monitored.

In examining programmes at the start of a job, an architect or engineer should therefore first be concerned with the technical requirements of the contract (has the appropriate time been allowed for striking formwork, are the sequences correct, has proper allowance been made for weather-susceptible operations etc?). If these are not right then of course the programme must be suitably amended. Otherwise, comment must be more in terms of opinion than simple acceptance or rejection. If any period seems too short, then perhaps one might enquire what labour force is expected to be employed, what plant used and so forth. There is a feeling amongst architects and engineers that unduly short periods are sometimes shewn in programmes with the intention of establishing grounds for claims (when such periods overrun the contractor will allegedly find reason to blame the A/E). This may sometimes be the case but it may be defeated by asking for details of labour, plant, methods etc, or a further breakdown of the offending section of the programme. As grounds for claim it can also be negatived to some extent, if not entirely, by expressing the opinion (provided, of course, that such opinion is soundly based and honestly expressed) that the times shewn appear optimistic.

How correct a forecast the programme proves to be will be a matter of careful monitoring, the more so when events causing potential or actual delay require to be taken into account. The fact that delay coincides with an overrun of a period in the programme may be indicative of cause and effect, but at times it may not, but only careful and continuous observation will establish the fact.

It is against this background therefore that actual progress must be plotted. It is the only yardstick available by which the effect of delay can be judged. In order to do this adequately one needs a fair amount of detailed information: the duration of operations and the quantities involved, the numbers of men employed, arrival, use and disposal of plant, particulars of the extent to which inclement weather actually impeded work, of allowances built in to the programme, the need for and supply of information, the letting of nominated sub-contracts etc, etc.

The approach to retrospective evaluation of completed delays is different from evaluation of prospective or continuing delays. Prospective evaluation, as required for assessment of interim extensions of time, involves making assumptions as to rates of progress and therefore assumptions as to resources to be applied.

The costs attributable to delay

It will be seen therefore that whilst the duration of the delay is not without significance, it is the effect of the delay which requires to be determined. In the case of delay from a single cause (e.g. a strike) where the whole job is stopped, the effect of the delay is simple and obvious. The contractor would be entitled to an extension of time for the period of the strike, plus a small margin to allow for regaining tempo. Similarly with inclement weather, where the whole job is stopped. In neither of these cases is the contractor entitled to compensation. If there were a case where the whole job is stopped by some act or default for which the employer is responsible then the contractor could be entitled to an extension of time plus the cost he unavoidably incurred as a result (standing time of labour and plant, including that of any sub-contractors similarly affected); also the actual cost of his site overheads (staff, depreciation on huts etc, and such maintenance costs as could not be avoided).

If a stoppage of work were caused by the employer to operations on the critical path, the whole of the work would not necessarily be brought to a standstill. In such a case the contractor would be entitled to be paid standing time for such labour and plant as he could not employ on other operations. If the labour and plant could be economically employed, so well and good, but if it could not be, then the contractor would be entitled to such loss of productivity as he could demonstrate. There could also be consequential effects on other operations.

If a stoppage of work were caused by the employer to operations on a path which was not critical then there would be no need for an extension of time but the contractor would be entitled to compensation for such cost as he was able to demonstrate (again standing time on labour, plant etc). In such a case it would be unlikely that overhead costs would be affected. The possibility of utilizing the labour and plant elsewhere would need to be considered, as in the preceding paragraph.

The more usual case is, however, one of retardation rather than actual stoppage, and this could apply in any of the situations indicated above. There are two ways in which this can be considered:

(i) Converting the retardation into a period when work was 'as if' stopped, in which case one could assess the cost in terms of standing time of labour, plant etc, as indicated above. Just when this method could be employed would depend upon circumstances, but generally it would probably be restricted to relatively simple cases where the delay in question was short and the consequential effects minimal.

(ii) Evaluating the loss of productivity of labour and plant which has been caused by retardation. This is extremely difficult to do as clearly it will depend very much on the records being kept, not only those of the work as done but also comparable ones of similar work carried out before the supervening delay occurred. It is also difficult to avoid comparing the cost as executed (when by definition the work is being carried out in circumstances of delay) with the tendered prices (which may be underestimated or distorted by a variety of factors).

The nature of costs/expenses

Forms of contract

The various Forms of Contract differ as to what is payable to the contractor in the event of delay due to causes for which the employer is responsible.

(a) ICE5 Clauses 7(3), 13(3), 14(6), 31(2) and 42(1) all provide for entitlement according to a formula that '... if the Contractor incurs cost due to (event or circumstance of type X) the Contractor shall subject to Clause 52(4) be paid in accordance with Clause 60 the amount of such cost as may be reasonable'. Clause 1(5) says 'The word "cost" when used in the Conditions of Contract shall be deemed to include overhead costs whether on or off the Site except where the contrary is expressly stated.' This leaves open the question whether overheads must be shown to be incurred in order to be recoverable, or whether they are, by their nature, presumed on a conjectural basis to be incurred (as with general damages), either on a time or turnover basis.

(b) ICE6 is similar except that the corresponding clause references are 7(4), 13(3), 14(8), 31(2) and 42(3). 'Cost' has been redefined in Clause 1(5) to mean 'all expenditure properly incurred or to be incurred whether on or off the Site including overhead finance and other charges properly allocatable thereto but does not include any allowance for profit'.

(c) GC/Wks 1 Edition 2 refers in Condition 53 to 'expense'.

(d) GC/Wks 1 Edition 3 also refers in Condition 46 to 'expense', which it defines to mean 'money expended by the Contractor, but shall not include any sum expended, or loss incurred, by him by way of interest or finance charges however described.'

(e) JCT63/77 refers in Clauses 11 and 24 to 'direct loss and expense'.

(f) JCT80 Clause 13 (replacing Clause 11 of JCT63/77) no longer refers to 'direct loss and expense', but says 'a fair valuation shall be made'. Clause 26 (replacing old Clause 24) continues to use the words 'direct loss and expense'.

In *Minter v WHTSO*,[17] it was held that the words 'direct loss and expense' in JCT63/77 should be given the same meaning as they would have in a case of breach of contract in a legal context. The reasoning behind the decision may be simply that the words are commonly used in relation to common law damages, therefore the contract draughtsman is presumed to have intended to convey the same meaning. A broader view is that while a construction contract provides compensation under the contract as a substitute for damages for breach of contract, in the absence of clear words showing a different intention, it is intended that the financial outcome should be substantially unaltered. It is submitted that the broader view is to be preferred. Applying the well-developed common law principles[18] provides a more satisfactory approach than attempting to extract precise meaning from the very general words used in the contract.

Total cost

It is often difficult to identify precisely the additional cost or loss and expense which has been incurred as a result of a delay. In such circumstances a contractor may contend that all costs which he has incurred in excess of those anticipated by him at time of tender are to be attributed to the delay or other causes for which the employer is responsible. He might wisely concede that allowance must be made for any element of under-bidding and any other costs for which he is responsible to arrive at a proper evaluation. Subject to that qualification, the 'total cost' approach has some legal authority where it is not otherwise possible to evaluate the cost or loss and expense incurred. In *Crosby & Sons v Portland UDC*[19] Donaldson J (as he then was) upheld an award by Sir Harold Harding as arbitrator, of a lump sum covering a number of claims under different provisions of the ICE Conditions. Donaldson J said that in cases where the claim is complex and the various components interact so that it

> 'may well be difficult or even impossible to make an accurate apportionment of the total extra cost between the several causative events ... so long as the arbitrator does not make any award which contains a profit element, this being permissible under Clauses 51 and 52 but not under Clauses 41 and 42, and provided he ensures that there is no duplication, I can see no reason why he should not recognize the realities of the situation and make individual awards in respect of those parts of individual items of the claim which can be dealt with in isolation and a supplementary award in respect of the remainder of these claims as a composite whole.'

The validity of such an approach was supported by Vinelott J in *Merton LBC v Leach*[20] subject to limits. He said:

> 'In *Crosby* the arbitrator rolled up several heads of claim arising under different heads and indeed claims for which the contract provided different bases of

---

17. *Minter v WHTSO* [1981] 13 BLR 1.
18. See Chapter 2.
19. *Crosby & Sons v Portland UDC* [1967] 5 BLR 121 at p 136.
20. *Merton LBC v Stanley Hugh Leach* [1985] 32 BLR 51 at p 102.

assessment. The question accordingly is whether I should follow that decision. I need hardly say that I would be reluctant to differ from a judge of Donaldson J's experience in matters of this kind unless I was convinced that the question had not been fully argued before him or that he had overlooked some material provisions of the contract or some relevant authority. Far from being so convinced, I find his reasoning compelling . . .

I think I should nonetheless say that it is implicit in the reasoning of Donaldson J, first, that a rolled up award can only be made in a case where the loss or expense attributable to each head of claim cannot in reality be separated and secondly that a rolled up award can only be made where apart from that practical impossibility the conditions which have to be satisfied before an award can be made have been satisfied in relation to each head of claim.'

There is a risk of the *Crosby* approach being interpreted as an invitation to submit claims without attempting to correlate grounds of claim with their specific alleged consequences. Any such interpretation has been firmly quashed by the Privy Council in *Wharf Properties v Eric Cumine Associates*,[21] where the court struck out the claimant's statement of claim on the grounds that it failed to particularize the claim. *Crosby* and *Merton v Leach* were acknowledged without dissent, but their significance on this point was described as follows:[22]

'Those cases establish no more than this, that in cases where the full extent of extra costs incurred through delay depend upon a complex interaction between the consequences of various events, so that it may be difficult to make an accurate apportionment of the total extra costs, it may be proper for an arbitrator to make individual financial awards in respect of claims which can conveniently be dealt with in isolation and a supplementary award in respect of the financial consequences of the remainder as a composite whole. This has, however, no bearing upon the obligation of a plaintiff to plead his case with sufficient particularity to alert the opposite partly to the case which is going to be made against him at the trial.'

Lord Oliver concluded:[23]

'It is for the plaintiff in an action to formulate his claim in an intelligible form and it does not lie in his mouth to assert that it is impossible for him to formulate it and that it should, therefore, be allowed to continue unspecified in the hope that, when it comes to trial, he may be able to reconstitute his case and make good what he then feels able to plead and substantiate.'

American cases provide additional guidance. I N Duncan Wallace QC notes[24] an American decision where a change was valued by reference to 'the difference between the contractor's actual and originally estimated cost, after making adjustment for other costs, as shown by the record, for which the contractor was responsible and which were not attributable to the changed conditions'. A number of other American cases are quoted by Myers,[25] but he points out that the total cost approach is only accepted where other means of evaluation fail. It is not sufficient for a claim submission merely to identify a delay on the one hand and total costs incurred in excess of those anticipated at time of tender on the other, and hope the A/E/QS or arbitrator will find causation from the association. It is incumbent on a claimant generally to prove or at least demonstrate that the loss or expense flowed from the delay.

21. *Wharf Properties v Eric Cumine Associates* [1991] 52 BLR 1.
22. Ibid at pp 20, 21.
23. Ibid at p 23.
24. Duncan Wallace I N QC, *Construction Contracts Principles and Policies* (1986) paras 4–14. Sweet & Maxwell, London.
25. James J. Myers, 'Some Thoughts on Measuring and Proving Construction Damages' (1989) ICLR p 66.

The classification of cost/loss/expense

Generally the main headings under which extra cost, loss or expense falls in respect of delay etc are as follows:

(a) *Labour* — The total amount payable to the men together with all those payments in respect of bonus, travelling expenses and allowances (subsistence or lodging allowances), guaranteed time, plus rates and all statutory charges such as National Insurance, Employer's Liability Insurance, Non-contributory Sick Pay Scheme, Redundancy Payment contributions etc.

(b) *Plant* — If hired, the hire charge or the cost of sending the plant away and returning it to the site (whichever is the less), or if owned by the contractor, a depreciation rate (for which there are several methods of calculation but it will probably approximate to two-thirds of the long-term hire rates).

(c) *Materials* — These should not be affected by delay, though storage charges, special delivery costs and the like could be involved.

(d) *Sub-contracts* — Their component costs would be parallel to those for the main contractor.

(e) *Insurance* — This may be treated separately from other overheads.

(f) *Site overheads* — The actual costs of staff (not to be confused with any item under this description in the Preliminaries which may not correspond to actual costs for a variety of reasons); depreciation of all temporary buildings and equipment, unavoidable costs of servicing accommodation and unavoidable maintenance.

(g) *Head office overheads* — There are two views on the proper evaluation of entitlement to head office overheads in the event of delay. The first is that only identifiable costs incurred as a result of the delay are reimbursable. The second postulates that the contractor is entitled to a contribution to head office overheads, calculated on the basis of the original contract price and time for completion, total company turnover and total head office overheads. There is support for both approaches and it may be wrong to insist that there is a unique standard answer. It may be that the proper approach in a particular case depends on the circumstances, perhaps taking a robust and pragmatic view. For example the appropriate basis of entitlement may depend whether the delay occurs before the contractor has entered on the site, or in the middle of the work, or when he has virtually finished.

(h) *Escalation* — On contracts without provision for automatic reimbursement of cost escalation, delay may cause increased escalation costs to be suffered.[26]

(j) *Financing charges* — In *Minter v WHTSO*[27] it was held that additional financing charges incurred were recoverable as 'direct loss and expense'. Ackner LJ explained 'financing charges' as:

> 'What the appellants here are seeking is not interest on a debt, but a debt which has as one of its constituent parts interest charges which have been incurred.'

The requirement of the courts for realism and proof in ascertaining entitlements may be illustrated by an example from the law reports. A contractor claimed £577 at 1940 prices for standing time for a scraper in respect of a week's delay. The claim was in damages for breach of contract. The Court of Appeal commented:[28]

> 'As £577 for a week is at the rate of £30,000 a year for the use of a machine of which the cost price was £4,500 and formed part of the plant to earn £23,385

26. See Chapter 10, pages 323–326.
27. *Minter v WHTSO* [1981] 13 BLR 1.
28. *Bernard Sunley & Co v Cunard White Star* [1940] 1 KB 740.

on this job, this claim is obviously extravagant. . . . Unhappily, very little of the contractor's evidence was in the least relevant . . . the plaintiffs appear to have neglected to give any material evidence of their real damages. . . . There was no evidence of any loss of profit on the Guernsey contract; the only real evidence was that the capital cost of the machine had been £4500 and its life was three years. Beyond this there was nothing but the vague evidence about a hiring price of £30 a day.'

In the absence of specific loss being proved, the Court awarded £30 against four possible heads of damage — depreciation, interest, maintenance and expenditure of wages thrown away — for the week.

Quantum meruit

A *quantum meruit* approach[29] to evaluating financial entitlement for delay may be justified in place of loss and expense where the cause of the delay is a variation or where expenditure is instructed to overcome the delay.

Resources and acceleration

Where the time effects of delay are mitigated at the request or instruction or with the agreement of the A/E/QS, by acceleration measures such as additional resources or extended working hours, the additional costs incurred should be recoverable under the contract. Recoverable costs might include, for example, additional mobilization costs, premium time, additional supervision, special curing, heating or cooling of concrete, extra construction joints etc. They might also include the effects of reduced efficiency due to compression, but these are particularly difficult to prove.

Disruption

This is not a very precisely defined term but is generally understood to mean costs or loss and expense in the nature of uneconomic working or loss of productivity of labour and plant due to works not being carried out in their planned or logical sequences. Labour or plant may be working uneconomically or additional cost may be incurred (such as overtime or weekend working or the provision of additional formwork and the like) in order to maintain a required level of output or rate of progress. It is more often than not associated with delay but this need not necessarily be the case. It is very similar to retardation where work is slowed down either as a result of some instruction from the A/E or lack of some required instruction.

It is a most difficult matter to assess with any precision and there are two major difficulties to be faced in making any assessment. First there is always the possibility that the contractor's tender was low and so any comparison with cost would overcompensate. Secondly, there is always the possibility of inefficiency in operation (even with the best contractors) but of course the very problem being investigated is one of inefficiency imposed upon the contractor.

Regarding the first problem, some indication of general tender level can be obtained by comparison with other tenders received for the same job — by no means conclusive but possibly indicative. Close tendering would tend to indicate that the tender was not unduly low. On the other hand a tender significantly lower than the others might indicate an underestimation or it might merely mean that the contractor has seen more efficient and cheaper ways of doing the job or that he has plant or equipment available he wants to make use of, for which he is prepared to charge low rates in order to keep his organization together rather than allow it to disperse. He may yet make a profit if the plant has in effect paid for itself on previous jobs. The point here is to try to find the reason for the tender being 'low'. So far as sections of the work within the whole or different types of work are concerned, experience shews that there is a greater variability of pricing these than is reflected in the tender total. There is an even greater variability (statistically speaking) in prices for B/Q items for similar work. This is because B/Q rates are indeed the prices the contractor is choosing to put upon the items and their relationship to cost is more notional than actual. However, this information is really the starting point from which one is obliged to work.

---

29. See Chapter 2, page 34.

Regarding the second problem, efficiency or lack of it on a job is unavoidably a somewhat subjective judgment. Nevertheless it is usually not to be ignored. It must be recognized, however, that the situation being investigated is by definition one of inefficiency, so the best one can do is to make some allowance for any 'built in' inefficiency one may consider to exist independently of the circumstances. If the contractor has given notice of claim (as he should) the engineer is entitled under ICE Clause 52(4)(c): 'Without necessarily admitting the Employer's liability, the Engineer may upon receipt of a notice . . . instruct the Contractor to keep such contemporary records . . . as are reasonable and may be material to the claim . . .'

When one speaks, as here, of records, one automatically thinks of records of hours or labour and details of plant employed, but less frequently is any record of output kept. If this were done it might be possible on occasion to obtain something like unit costs from which one might be able to form a judgment as to what the costs should have been.

The sad truth is, however, that even if such unit costs were produced, in the vast majority of cases the contractor would have no records of comparable costs taken on the job before the onset of retardation or disruption.

Care would have to be taken to ensure that all costs were included. Unless systematic 'unit costing' is being undertaken (i.e. an allocation of all costs incurred on a job to small groups of B/Q items) there is a real risk of secondary or ancillary costs being overlooked. Comparison with B/Q prices is, even so, generally unreliable because these are rarely derived from actual feedback of costs from previous jobs.

The task of assessing the cost of disruption is therefore very much a case of looking at all factors and considering all the information which might have a bearing.

CASE 8.1 CLAIMS ARISING OUT OF DELAYS

Pertinent particulars of contract

The contract was for the construction of a small pumping station. The amounts of earthworks and pipework involved for which firm quantities could not be given were quite small and it seemed a waste of effort to remeasure the whole when a relatively few items could be made 'provisional'. It was therefore decided to prepare the contract on a lump-sum basis but using the ICE Conditions of Contract.

The contract documents comprised:

Drawings, Specification, Bill of Quantities (based on CESMM). Conditions of Contract ICE5 with the following amendments:

The Conditions of Contract referred to in the Tender shall be the Conditions of Contract for use with Works of Civil Engineering Construction (5th Edition) commonly known as the 'ICE Conditions of Contract' dated 1973, modified and added to as follows:

Clause 1(1)(j) — delete and substitute: 'Tender Sum' means the sum named in the Tender which sum is subject to such addition thereto or deductions therefrom as may be made under the provisions hereinafter contained.

Clause 10 — delete reference to 'Tender Total' and substitute 'Tender Sum'.

Clause 52(1) — in line 3 after 'principles' add: 'and shall be taken into account in arriving at the Contract Price by way of addition to or subtraction from (as the case may be) the Tender Sum'.

Clause 55(1) — in line 1 after 'quantities' add 'designated Provisional'.

Clause 55(2) — in line 1 after 'any error in description' add 'or in quantity'.

Clause 56(1) — delete and substitute: 'In respect of any items or quantities designated 'Provisional' in the Bill of Quantities the Engineer shall ascertain and determine by admeasurement the value in accordance with the Contract of the work actually executed in accordance with the Contract. The value so ascertained shall be included in the Contract Price in substitution for the amount annexed to such quantities and included in the Tender Sum.'

Clause 56(2) — in line 1 after the word 'item' add 'designated Provisional'.

Clause 58 — add the following as sub-clause (2) and renumber remaining sub-clauses: '(2) Provisional as applied to items and quantities in the Bill of Quantities means those items and/or quantities so designated which shall be used for the execution of such work as may be ordered or approved by the Engineer.'

Clause 60(3) — line 3, after 'detail' delete rest of line and substitute: 'all those additions to and deductions from the Tender Sum due to be made in accordance with the Contract'.

Tender dated 1 May 1979 in the sum of £148,486. Acceptance dated 1 June 1979. Time for completion 15 months.

Possession of site given 1 September 1979.

Liquidated damages were set in the Tender at £500 per week.

Events giving rise to claims

The employer could not get possession of part of the site and then in November 1979 there was a spell of very bad weather which affected the earthworks rather badly and about the same time there was delay in resiting a gas main. There was a succession of variation orders, not great in value but taking a relatively long time to carry out (due partly to delay in obtaining special valves and fittings). Certain bending schedules which the contractor needed by mid-April 1980 were not in fact forthcoming until mid-May. There was a week of exceptionally wet and windy weather in July 1980 and the work was not finally completed until 21 May 1981.

Contractor to Engineer   *19 July 1979*

We shall be glad if you would let us know when we may expect to be allowed to start work on this project.

Even in a letter as simple and obvious as this it is preferable to use the terms in the contract. What is being asked for, an order to commence under Clause 41 or possession of site under Clause 42? There was some delay in replying but eventually the engineer wrote:

Engineer to Contractor   *15 August 1979*

I refer to your letter dated 19 July and have to inform you that the site will be available for you on 1 September 1979.

Similar remarks to those above apply to this letter also. Is the engineer acting under Clause 41 where he is given powers to give an order to commence or under Clause 42 where it is the employer who should be giving possession of site? Work started in September and one is left to wonder what, in the absence of an order to commence, is the due date for completion. From this point of view one may perhaps argue that in the circumstances the engineer's letter of 15 August amounted to an order to commence — a rather sloppy way of starting a job, if one may say so.

> *As you know, there was a three months' delay in giving possession of*
> *site and thereafter work on site was held up for three weeks for*
> *exceptionally inclement weather in November and December. Then the*
> *work was stopped completely for the whole of December because of delay*
> *in resiting the gas main.*

> *In accordance with Clause 44 we request an extension of time of 19*
> *weeks and reserve our rights to claim for the additional cost.*

Taking the facts as they appear, the delays because of the inclement weather and the Statutory Undertakers overlap. But from when does the time run? According to Clause 43, time begins to run from the 'Date for commencement notified under Clause 41'. The only notification given concerning commencement was that dated 15 August 1979, referring to the site being available on 1 September 1979. Despite the imprecise wording used, both parties have acted on the basis that the Works should be commenced on that date, so the letter can be treated as effective notification.[30] Neither acceptance by the contractor of the notification, nor the non-availability of the site and the consequent difficulty in complying with Clause 42 excuses the lateness of the order to commence under Clause 41. We have not heard the last of this as we shall see.

The tail-end of the contractor's letter of 9 January is not satisfactory. Clause 52(4)(b) requires notice to be given of intention to claim any additional payment. When such notice is given, certain additional rights, obligations and duties are immediately introduced affecting both contractor and engineer. It may not be absolutely necessary to refer to the clause by number if the wording of a notice makes the purpose clear, but it is doubtful whether 'reserving rights' constitutes notice of intention to claim unless it was actually accepted as such. In any case why use one phrase when something else is meant?

A number of small but time-consuming variations were issued and then the contractor wrote:

Contractor to Engineer   *18 March 1980*

> *As we informed the RE at the last progress meeting, we urgently require*
> *the steel bending schedules for the beams of the roof. Unless we get these*
> *very soon we shall be delayed.*

Engineer to Contractor   *1 April 1980*

> *The delay in issuing the bending schedules is regretted. There has been*
> *some difficulty in accommodating the steel in certain columns and beams.*
> *It is expected that revised drawings and schedules will be ready in*
> *mid-May.*

In fact the drawings and schedules were not issued until the end of May 1980, and there was some further delay in obtaining the necessary steel. The contractor took no action regarding extension of time. Work continued and was delayed for a further week of exceptionally wet and windy weather in July 1980. In November the engineer wrote:

Engineer to Contractor   *3 November 1980*

> *Your attention is drawn to the lack of progress on this job and in*

---

30. Both parties would be restrained from challenging the effectiveness of the notice in legal proceedings under the doctrine of 'conventional estoppel', see p 116 *supra*.

*accordance with Clause 46 of the Conditions I must request you to take
such steps as are necessary to expedite progress.*

The contractor reacted characteristically. Clause 46 notices are always resented, the more so when it is believed they are unwarranted.

Contractor to Engineer   *6 November 1980*

We were astonished to receive your letter of 3 November invoking Clause 46. You are aware of the delays which have occurred. Our request dated 9 January 1980 for extension of time has not been granted. Since then there have been delays of five weeks because of non-issue of the revised bending schedules (and the consequent two weeks' delay in getting steel) and another week for exceptionally inclement weather in July, not to mention the many variations involving extra work for which we require an extra twelve weeks.

We formally request an extension of time of 39 weeks.

The contractor was remiss in not giving notice progressively and in allowing his request of January 1980 to be ignored. Notwithstanding that, the engineer could have taken action under Clause 44(2) and indeed should have done so if he wished to operate Clause 46 because that clause opens with the words: 'If for any reason which does not entitle the contractor to an extension of time . . .' Failure to extend the time for completion at the proper time can also jeopardise the employer's rights to recover liquidated damages.

Engineer to Contractor   *20 November 1980*

I hereby extend the time for completion by 24 weeks to 18 May 1981 in respect of delay notified to date.

Contractor to Engineer   *26 November 1980*

We cannot accept your extension of time of only 24 weeks. Will you please let us know how you arrive at this.

Engineer to Contractor   *1 December 1980*

I have allowed 6 weeks for delay due to inclement weather and resiting the gas main, 5 weeks in respect of late issue of bending schedules, 2 weeks for delay in delivery of steel, 1 week for inclement weather in July 1980 and 10 weeks for extra work.

Contractor to Engineer   *15 December 1980*

We consider your allowance for some of the delays are somewhat short but we are most concerned with your failure to recognize the initial delay in possession of the site. We submit herewith our claim for compensation in respect of the extension of time to which we consider ourselves entitled and we should be glad of an early payment on account.

CLAIM

Increased costs and extended overheads for 3 months due to late possession of site	4,500.00
24 weeks' delay consequent upon extension of time as per letter of 1 December 1980 at £342 per week	8,208.00
	£12,708.00

This is quite useless and it is the sort of thing that causes so much irritation in connection with claims. One can only draw the conclusion that the contractor does not know where his entitlement lies and has no idea how to formulate a claim. He gets the sort of answer he deserves and might have expected.

Engineer to Contractor   *23 December 1980*

> *It is accepted that three months elapsed between acceptance and your being given possession of the site, but that does not necessarily give grounds for claim. You do not quote any Clause of the Conditions to support your contentions, nor do you give any details of how the amount is arrived at.*
>
> *As for the extension of time, I must point out that 4 weeks are in respect of inclement weather and 2 weeks are in respect of delay in obtaining delivery of materials. The extra work has in any case been paid for by way of rates and prices in or based on the B/Q. Since September delay has been solely your responsibility.*
>
> *If you would reconsider the matter in the light of the above comment perhaps it would facilitate matters if a meeting were arranged to discuss matters.*

Nothing happens until the end of March 1981 when the following appears on the file:

Note of meeting held on 27 March 1981

> *The matter of the extension of time was discussed. The contractor pointed out that the difficulty was that under Clause 42 delay in possession of site had to be reckoned from Date for Commencement. In this case no such date had been given. The engineer replied that in simple fact that was so but effectively Date for Commencement was given with possession of site.*
>
> *Contractor:*
> *Agreed, but from that it follows that the Date for Commencement was not given in a reasonable time as required by Clause 41.*
>
> *Engineer:*
> *Well, you cannot expect an order to commence with the acceptance.*
>
> *Contractor:*
> *Perhaps not — but certainly in less than three months.*
>
> *Engineer:*
> *But what difference can it make? You have price fluctuation and you had no overheads on site.*
>
> *Contractor:*
> *In fact we had an agent and a foreman standing by with nothing to do for eight weeks.*
>
> *After further discussion it was agreed that the contractor had a valid claim under Clause 41 on grounds that an order to commence was not given in a reasonable time and was thus entitled to be paid the cost of staff standing by:*

8 weeks agent at £127.50 per week	*1,020.00*	
8 weeks foreman at £97.50 per week	*780.00*	*£1,800.00*

The contractor's claim to a percentage addition of overheads was refused because the items of Head Office overhead cost alleged to be involved could not be identified. His claim for profit was also refused on the grounds that as this was basically a claim for damages in breach, profit was not allowable. As this was extra-contractual, it would have to be put to the employer for approval.

Turning next to the twenty-four weeks' delay:

(a) Weather, first period — this did not rank for compensation at all.

(b) Diversion of gas main — this was four weeks late being completed and the job was stopped in consequence but it overlapped the period of inclement weather when work was stopped anyway. The nett effect was therefore three weeks.

The contractor considered this should be four but the engineer pointed out that the commencement of this work was itself held up by the weather. The contractor reluctantly agreed and said that he had to pay the men minimum wages and there were also his site overheads for which he had allowed 15 per cent in his tender.

He had on site eight tradesmen plus seventeen labourers (some with plus rates). Their normal pay ranged up to £136 per week for tradesmen and £120 per week for labourers. He was actually paying them £110 and £90 per week respectively.

The engineer considered he could pay only the minimum guarantee and offered £96.50 and £82.50 respectively. This was eventually accepted:

8 tradesmen 3 weeks at £96.50 =	2,316.00	
17 labourers 3 weeks at £82.50 =	4,207.50	£6,523.50

Regarding overheads, the contractor produced the build up of his tender, which certainly shewed an addition of 15 per cent for overheads — but to direct costs, not as a content. The tender should be analysed as follows:

Contract Sum	148,486			
5% profit	7,071	141,415		
$8\frac{1}{2}$% Head Office overheads		11,079	130,336	
15% site oncosts			17,000	£113,336

The constituents of the £17,000 were almost all time-related and were therefore the equivalent of £261.54 per week. At this rate, 3 weeks would cost £784.62

(c) The revised drawings and bending schedules: five weeks. The contractor refused to agree this, claiming also the two weeks' delay in obtaining steel and one week's inclement weather.

The engineer said that these could not rank for compensation, being a contractor's risk. The contractor said this might normally be so but in this case they had arisen as a direct consequence of the delay in the bending schedules. The engineer eventually accepted this but asked what costs flowed in any case. The contractor claimed the following:

3 carpenters ⎫
2 steel fixers ⎬ all required for constructing the roof of the pumping
5 labourers ⎭ station for whom no alternative work could be found.

These men's wages were normally about £140, £135, and £120 respectively. He had had to pay them £120, £110 and £95.

The engineer offered £100, £90 and £85, subject to a check on what the Working Rules actually laid down. For the time being the claim would be included at:

8 weeks for 3 carpenters	at £100	2,400	
8 weeks for 2 steel fixers	at £90	1,440	
8 weeks for 5 labourers	at £85	3,400	£7,240

Again there would be no addition for site overheads (because other work was in fact proceeding) or for profit as the claim fell under Clause 7 in respect of which payment was due at 'cost' — see Clause 1(5).

In addition the contractor had to buy some part of this steel from stockists rather than wait for delivery from the mills. This involved:

13.78 tonnes 12 mm diam at 20% premium	53.54	737.78
17.22 tonnes 16 mm diam at	47.93	825.35
21.10 tonnes 25 mm diam at	47.05	992.76
		£2,555.89

(d) Extra work. Work was still proceeding, so this could not be finalized but perhaps the principles could be agreed.

Engineer:
Surely one must start with the premise that the extra work was being paid for at Bill rates (including adjustment of Preliminaries) which themselves included overheads.

Contractor:
Agreed, but in this case there has been a large number of small variations taking a disproportionate time to execute.

Engineer:
How do you arrive at that conclusion?

Contractor:
The value of extra work, based mainly on actual measurement and partly on estimate, will amount to £12,450 for which you have allowed ten weeks. This represents a turnover of £1,245 per week. Our original contract turnover was:

Gross (£148,486) — £2,284.40 per week or
Direct costs (£113,336) — £1,743.63 per week.

One could therefore say that the extra work was sufficient to carry overheads for 12,450 ÷ 2,284.4 = 5.45 weeks.

Therefore we are entitled (on the basis of similarity of conditions which is stipulated in Clause 52) to 10 − 5.45 = 4.55 weeks of site overheads plus HO overheads and profit on those site overheads.

Engineer:
As this is in respect of extra works and had we calculated new rates to take account of that attenuation, then I must agree we would have added these.

The claim was therefore accepted in principle as follows, but this would have to be recalculated when the work was finally measured:

4.55 weeks site overheads at £261.45	*1,190.00*	
Add 8½% Head Office overheads	*101.15*	*1,291.15*
Add 5% profit		*64.56*
		£1,355.71

Points of principle involved

Notice of delays should be given in definitive terms. Whenever possible those on the critical path should be distinguished as only these affect the extension of time.

Notice of intention to claim additional payment should be given in explicit terms and not in ambiguous euphemisms such as 'we reserve our rights'. Further, the clause of the Conditions under which additional payment is claimed should be identified.

Clause 52(4)(d) also requires the notice of intent to be followed up 'as soon as is reasonable in all the circumstances' by quantification of the claim to date and particulars of the grounds upon which the claim is based. Prompt identification of grounds of claim is not always undertaken in practice, but it is in both parties' interests, both to enable steps to be taken to mitigate losses and to ensure that relevant records are kept. The relevance of specific records may only become apparent when the grounds of claim are analysed.

Clause 41 does not state what shall happen should delay in notification occur. Such a delay constitutes a breach of contract. The contractor's claim is in damages for breach rather than for adjustment under the contract. It is therefore extra-contractual. Under ICE5 the engineer has power to deal with extra-contractual claims under Clause 66 once a dispute or difference has arisen and the matter has been referred to him under Clause 66, but the matter may be resolved without a dispute arising if the agreement of both employer and contractor can be obtained to a settlement, based on what would be awarded. Accordingly the essential first step is to seek agreement with the employer.

The measure of damages in contract is to put the claimant, so far as money can do so, in the position that he would have been if the contract had not been breached. Taking the limit of a 'reasonable time' as 4 weeks, the delay in breach is 8 weeks. As the whole contract was merely deferred by 8 weeks, there was no automatic loss of profit or additional Head Office overheads incurred. In the absence of any identifiable special loss of profit or additional overheads, none was recoverable.

Whilst delay due to inclement weather may give entitlement to extension of time, it does not normally give entitlement to compensation. Where, however, events which do give such entitlement (such as delay in issue of drawings and instructions) push the work into a period of inclement weather which would otherwise have caused no extra cost, then the extra cost attributable to such inclement weather period may also rank for compensation.

The principle of similarity of character and similarity of conditions referred to in Clause 52 must include all conditions.

CASE 8.2 CLAIM FOR DELAY ARISING OUT OF ERROR IN DESIGN

Pertinent particulars of contract

The contract is for the construction of roadworks for a housing estate, including one road-bridge and one footbridge. Contract documents comprise:

241

Drawings; Conditions of Contract JCT63/77.
Bills of Quantities based on SMM 6.

Tender dated 5 March 1979 in the sum of £2,428,977.
Time for completion 2 years.

Acceptance dated 2 April 1979. Possession of site 17 April 1979.

Comment

The choice of JCT Conditions of Contract and SMM 6 is not perhaps the best for the purpose but they can function quite adequately given that the necessary amendments are made to the SMM to accommodate a number of items not normally covered, which may require a method of measurement to be defined. The main point to watch is to amend Clause 12 of the Conditions, preferably by the deletion of the last two and a half lines of Sub-clause (1): 'but save as aforesaid nothing contained in the Contract Bills shall override, modify, or affect in any way whatsoever the application or interpretation of that which is contained in these Conditions.' All the documents should be construed together without any one of them taking precedence. An amendment such as that suggested here would be even more necessary with JCT80, where any departure from the SMM seems to be regarded as a correctable error.

Background to case

In the absence of a specification, the B/Q contains a provision calling for a programme to be submitted after acceptance. This the contractor does, shewing completion in 18 months. The architect queried this but the contractor said he had men and plant available and was in a position to complete in that time although the contract period would remain at two years.

Events leading to claim

Work started normally and excavation and road formation were in progress when an error in the design of the footbridge was found and it was necessary to issue revised drawings.

Architect to Contractor   *4 July 1979*

I regret to inform you that an error in the design of the footbridge has been found and the drawings already issued to you must not be worked to. Revised drawings will be issued in about three weeks.

The contractor acknowledges, and six weeks later revised drawings are ready.

Architect to Contractor   *16 August 1979*

Herewith revised set of drawings for the footbridge. Please mark all existing drawings as superseded. The quantities remain unaltered and the weight of steel reinforcement remains the same.

Contractor to Architect   *20 August 1979*

We acknowledge receipt of revised drawings for the footbridge. Although the design appears to be much the same and the quantities remain unaltered, we consider that this bridge will take about two weeks longer to construct.

Will you please extend the time for completion to allow for this and also the six weeks' delay in issuing the drawings.

Architect to Contractor   *29 August 1979*

It is not intended to extend the time for completion at this stage. In any case, it is doubtful if this is necessary as your programme shews completion within eighteen months, so it would appear to be unnecessary to extend.

Contractor to Architect   *3 September 1979*

> *We must protest at your letter of 29 August. We were about to start work on this bridge when your instruction of 4 July was received and we have had plant standing idle on site in consequence. We need this extension of time in order to facilitate our claim for the extra costs involved.*

There is no reply to this letter and the job continues. In the course of the next few months there is delay of some 3 weeks because of exceptionally inclement weather and another 6 weeks because of varied work. The contractor tries again.

Contractor to Architect   *20 March 1980*

> *We hereby give notice that over the winter period up to the beginning of this month we have suffered exceptionally inclement weather which has delayed work by three weeks. Your Clerk of Works has also kept records and has agreed this period with our agent.*
>
> *There have also been a number of variations for which we will require six weeks' extension of time and there was three weeks' delay by the Electricity Board. This, plus the eight weeks we originally requested in connection with the footbridge, will make fourteen weeks in all.*

Architect to Contractor   *26 March 1980*

> *Even accepting the total delay is as much as you claim, this is still less than the six months which, according to your programme, you expected to save.*
>
> *We therefore do not propose formally to extend the time.*

Contractor to Architect   *1 April 1980*

> *We must again protest at your failure to extend the time for completion. We need your formal extension of time because of claims we intend to submit in connection with the footbridge and extended overheads because of varied work.*

In one sense the architect is correct in not extending the time for completion because it seems that the actual time required will not overrun the contract period. As, therefore, there seems no likelihood of liquidated damages being recoverable, extension of time is not needed.

On the other hand, there is often a problem in situations such as this where later events may render an extension of time necessary. If then all the circumstances are taken into account, so well and good, but it is always possible that some will be overlooked.

Why do contractors persist in asking for extension of time merely in order to provide a basis for a claim for additional payment? Equally, why do some architects, engineers and quantity surveyors adopt the position that no payment can be due for delay and disruption unless an extension of time is granted? The extension of time clause makes no provision for payment. The delay and disruption clauses do not make entitlement to extension of time a condition precedent to entitlement to money. The two aspects are related, but they are not Siamese twins.

Architect to Contractor   *9 April 1980*

> *I am at a loss to understand your letter of 1 April. Work on the footbridge is now nearing completion so clearly this will provide no*

grounds for claim. There remains other contract work to be done and there is every indication that you will complete within the contract time. Therefore there is no reason why you should seek to claim extended overheads.

Contractor to Architect *14 April 1980*

Our tender was based on our being able to complete the work in eighteen months. This we shall not be able to do. We are aware that we shall in all probability complete well within the contract time for completion, yet the fact remains that we have been delayed and require compensation.

We enclose herewith our claim.

STATEMENT OF CLAIM

1. *Delay because of redesign of footbridge*
   We were about to start work on this bridge when instructions were received not to proceed. We had on site certain items of plant which were required only for this bridge. We expected instructions within three weeks and therefore considered it better to retain plant on site in case we could not get it later when required.

IR compressor 250 ft³	*£207 per week × 6 =*	*1,242.00*
Crane 3–5 tonne crawler	*£246 per week × 6 =*	*1,476.00*
Concrete mixer 14/10	*£64 per week × 6 =*	*384.00*
		£3,102.00
Add overheads 12½%		*387.75*
		£3,489.75
Add profit 5%		*174.49*
		£3,664.24

2. *Extra work*
   The extra work we were required to do took an additional six weeks. We claim additional site overheads for this period.

   Overheads were included in our tender at 12½%.
   Tender Sum £2,428,997 × 12½% = 303,624.63
   This spread over 78 weeks = 3,892.62 per week.
   Therefore six weeks' overheads = *£23,355.72*

3. *Delay by Electricity Board*
   This delay arose through the failure of the Board to move their cable from the route of the main spine road. This caused nine weeks' delay (of which your Clerk of Works has records) when very little work could be done at all and we estimate delay to the job as a whole at six weeks.

6 weeks' overheads at £3,892.62 per week	*23,355.72*
Add profit at 5%	*1,167.79*
	£24,523.51

The architect is highly incensed at receiving this claim and sends it to the quantity surveyor with the following letter:

> *I enclose a claim from the contractor totalling some £51,543.47 which I consider quite preposterous.*
>
> *He is claiming for delay allegedly arising out of an error in the design of the footbridge. The location of the reinforcement had been wrongly shewn. There was no difference in the quantities, or in the design of the bridge itself, so there was no variation. In any case the bridge was completed long before other work on the contract.*
>
> *He is also claiming for additional overheads on extra work. You will know the value of these. If these are being paid at B/Q rates or similar I do not see what else he can claim.*
>
> *Then he is claiming for the delay in moving the electric cable. This is correct so far as the facts are concerned and to assess the effective delay at six weeks is, I think, not unreasonable. But I do not see how he can justify overheads when he planned to do the job in six months less than the contract period. This was for two years and he must be presumed to have allowed in his tender overheads for this period.*

Obviously a hasty letter, it is better to ask for comment and advice before giving an opinion, unless one is sure of one's grounds. This letter reveals three commonly held misconceptions.

Regarding the footbridge, from what the architect says it could not have been on the critical path. Nevertheless, there was delay on this item of work and the contractor says he had plant standing idle in consequence. The architect was warned of this in the letter of 3 September. Although that was not in explicit terms it would be difficult to argue that it was not a notice. If therefore plant was in fact standing idle in consequence, and if the contractor acted reasonably in the circumstances in not removing it, then the employer would be liable to pay. There is no need for extension of time, either in itself or to validate a claim. Whether the rates claimed are reasonable is another matter.

The second misconception concerns additional overheads for extra work. Certainly B/Q rates, one way or another, contain provision for site overheads. If they are all contained in the Preliminaries, then adjustment of these as part of the valuation process under Clause 11 may well suffice. Overheads may, however, be included in the rates and prices. Then, on the basis that similarity of character and of conditions is an essential term of the contract, if the extra work is of small value relative to the time required to do it the contractor may well be entitled to something extra. Site overheads are generally related to turnover, so that if turnover in relation to variations is less than that for contract works generally, some adjustment is called for.

The third misconception concerns the 'spare' time beyond the end of the contractor's programme to the contract date for completion. Some argue, as the architect here is arguing, that the contractor will have or should have allowed overheads for the whole period. But this is to ignore the terms of Clause 23 of the Conditions which say: 'and who shall complete the same on *or before* the Date for Completion . . .' If a contractor sees a way of completing the work more quickly then he economises not only on direct costs but also on overheads, particularly site overheads. Presumably this saving is reflected in his tender (and so he got the job and his competitors lost it). If delay occurs then the criterion is the same in all cases: did the contractor suffer damage? If he did he is entitled to compensation. If a job goes on beyond the contract date then clearly additional site overheads are being incurred. But if a contractor has planned and tendered on the basis of doing it in a shorter time, then equally clearly any extension of his overheads represents damage (assuming the delay to be the fault of the employer).

In this case the quantity surveyor reports as follows:

Quantity Surveyor to Architect   *20 May 1980*

Regarding the contractor's claims:

1.   Whether or not there was an 'error' in design, it seems to me quite clear that in terms of the working drawings as issued there was an 'alteration or modification of the design ...' within the meaning of Clause 11(2). I cannot think it is your intention to hold the contractor responsible for the design.

The items of plant were in fact on site (your C/W has records). As he was expecting revised instructions in three weeks, I think it reasonable that he retained the plant on site.

He has charged daywork rates which are unacceptable and I have informed him he is entitled to no more than depreciation rates. This he is prepared to accept, except for the crane which he hired. I have therefore agreed to accept the hire charge for this item. This would fall under Clause 24(1)(a).

2.   Regarding the extra work, the value is almost exactly £100,000. At the contract rate of turnover, this should have taken no more than 3.21 weeks. He has claimed six weeks which your C/W considers reasonable. In that case he would in my opinion be entitled under Clause 11(4) to 2.79 weeks of additional site overheads. He has, however, calculated them incorrectly. The $12\frac{1}{2}$% is right but this was added to his direct costs, it was not the overhead content. The Contract Sum needs to be analysed as follows:

£2,428,977		
£ 115,666	*less 5% profit*	
£2,313,311		
£ 161,394	*less $7\frac{1}{2}$% HO overheads*	
£2,151,917		
£ 239,103	*less $12\frac{1}{2}$% site oncosts ÷ 78 weeks =*	3,065.42
£1,912,814	*Direct costs*	

2.79 weeks at £3,065.42 =		8,552.52
In the same manner as he applied HO overheads in his tender, the same method should be applied here	$7\frac{1}{2}$%	641.44
		9,193.96
Similarly with profit	5%	459.70
		£9,653.66

3.   Delay by Electricity Board
The contractor produced his programme to you at the outset shewing completion in eighteen months. He has satisfied me by a sight of his original papers that he has based his tender on this. If therefore he was delayed beyond this period for a cause which is the responsibility of the employer (as in this case) then he is entitled to compensation as a matter of damage under Clause 24(1)(d). Site overheads were undoubtedly involved, but he could produce no evidence of any expenditure in the nature of HO overheads. He would not be entitled to profit.

Site overheads for a period of 6 weeks at £3,065.42   £18,392.52

Points of principle involved

These have been set out in the comment following the architect's letter of 25 April 1980 (ante).

CASE 8.3   CLAIM FOR ACCELERATION

Pertinent particulars of contract

The contract was for the construction of an office block with shops on the ground floor in the centre of a provincial city. A youthful and energetic developer bought a block of property from which existing buildings had been demolished to ground level. It was the intention of the developer to let off parts of the premises to separate tenants. The contract documents comprised:

Drawings (for the structure only, the internal partitioning to be arranged by tenants). Conditions of Contract JCT 63/77, Clause 31F applicable, Bills of Quantities.

Tender dated 4 June 1979 for the sum of £482,144. Tender accepted 18 June, possession of site given 25 June 1979.

Formal contract completed and dated 26 June 1979. Time for completion 18 months (24 December 1980).

Liquidated damages £600 per week.

Events giving rise to the claim

A certain amount of difficulty had been encountered in excavating the basement, a situation not unusual or unexpected in redeveloping old property, but delay had also been caused by the discovery of some old wells which had to be investigated for archaeological interest before being filled in.

In the course of the erection of the steel frame part of a party wall collapsed and proved to be only half-brick thick in places. This had to be replaced to conform to local bye-laws and, together with protective work to the adjoining property, again caused delay.

The heating system was to be gas-fired and there was delay in getting delivery of the boiler and with the installation generally by the nominated sub-contractor. This firm had been rather 'pushed' onto the contractor (being a business acquaintance of the employer) and without the sub-contract being properly formulated. The contractor had given notice of delay.

There had also been delay in the issue of certain drawings and instructions concerning the basement steelwork which caused the contractor expense for which he had put in a claim.

The contractor had applied for an extension of time about which the architect informed his employer, purely as a matter of keeping him informed, but the employer immediately became irate and instructed the architect not to give any extension of time. It transpired that he had prospective tenants lined up and had signed agreements with them giving them occupation from the original date.

The employer than took the unusual and unethical, if not improper, step of writing to the contractor, saying that if completion by the original date were not achieved, he would sue for damages which would be heavy because of these contracts with prospective tenants.

The contractor replied with a copy to the architect.

Contractor to Employer   *18 February 1980*

We are in receipt of your letter dated 14 February 1980. We would draw your attention to Clause 23 of the Conditions under which the architect is required to give us an extension of time in certain circumstances.

We have notified the architect of delay under Sub-clauses (b), (f) and (g)

247

*and understood from him that he was about to issue an appropriate
extension of time. We still expect this to be issued.*

*We would also draw your attention to Clause 22 under which liquidated
damages can be recovered in the event of delay for which we are not
entitled to extension of time. It is therefore not open to you to recover
unliquidated damages.*

A difficult letter for a contractor to write to his client, but he is right to take a firm stand both as to his rights and the standing of the architect. Wisely, he takes the architect's copy by hand and explains his point of view. He also says that he would not be unwilling to oblige the employer in getting earlier completion, at a price of course.

The employer was rather foolish to write as he did. Not only was he going over the head of his appointed agent to whom he had given certain authority by way of the contract, but he had revealed to the contractor that he was in a position of difficulty and so probably susceptible to some pressure.

The architect saw the employer and protested at the unwarranted action of writing directly to the contractor without taking his (the architect's) advice as to his position under the contract. He suggested that the contractor might be willing to accelerate (for a consideration). This the employer would not hear of and demanded that the architect write to the contractor insisting on completion by the original date. This the architect refused to do, broke off the discussion and returned to his office to write the following letter:

Architect to Employer   *19 February 1980*

*I refer to our meeting this afternoon when you instructed me to inform
the contractor that he was required to complete the contract by the original
date for completion. This I refused to do because clearly under the contract
he is entitled to an extension of time. You have offered no reasons to
dispute this. It is my duty under the contract to make a proper assessment
of the contractor's entitlement to extension of time; failure to do so would,
in this case, have completely the opposite effect to that which you intend,
in that the time for completion fixed by the contract and your right to
deduct liquidated damages for late completion would both be lost. It might
also affect the authority of other decisions that I have made under this
contract.*

*I fully appreciate and understand your position and the necessity for
getting the building complete by the original date but, as I have explained,
there is no provision in the contract to enable this to be done.*

*The contractor is willing to attempt what you require and I have
consulted the quantity surveyor as to how it might be achieved. He advised
that a Supplementary Agreement is necessary and he is willing to negotiate
such an agreement if you so require.*

*For my part, I must inform you that if you find my advice on this matter
unacceptable, I shall have no alternative but to resign my appointment
forthwith.*

Again a difficult letter to write but the architect must avoid getting himself into a false position. Such a letter must be courteous, straightforward, but unequivocal. Clearly he too would consider the consequences *vis-à-vis* a client, but there are some clients one cannot afford to work for.

Similarly in the case of the central or local government employment, architects, engineers and quantity surveyors sometimes have to tell their 'administrative' colleagues what the technical facts are, for they will not be thanked if the authority is landed into trouble through lack of sound professional advice.

In this case, this somewhat blunt but not unhelpful letter seems to have done the trick for the architect is invited to meet the employer again to discuss the situation. During the meeting the QS is called in to discuss what a Supplementary Agreement would involve and then invited to negotiate with the contractor.

Quantity Surveyor to Contractor (by telephone)　　　　　*22 February 1980*

We have been asked by the employer to discuss with you what arrangement can be made to complete this building by the original contract date and whether it would be possible to complete the shops on the ground floor say one month earlier to catch the Christmas trade. Can we meet to discuss the matter? What about Monday 25th at 10 am? That's a date!

Notes of meeting held 25 February 1980

QS:
Well now, you know what the employer wants, what can be done?

Contractor:
We know what he wants, but he cannot have it under the terms of this contract.

QS:
Quite so. I have already advised him that a Supplementary Agreement is required and he has asked me to negotiate this with you.

Contractor:
That sounds more promising than his letter to us of 14 February. I don't mind telling you we are very concerned about what he may try to do. Until we get an extension of time he may take it into his head to deduct liquidated damages. We have some claims for delay we would want settling, for we would not want to put ourselves in a position of having accelerated and then he refuse to pay our claims or at least hold out for a long time before we get our money. We have rather lost confidence over this extension of time business.

QS:
I understand your feelings but can we jot down the heads of a Supplementary Agreement so that we know what we are aiming for? You can then go away and work out what can be done, and how, and how much it will cost. Whilst you are doing that I will draft an Agreement that you can look at. Agreed?

Now, let us start from the premise that you are entitled to, and get an extension of time. How long do you require?

Contractor:
We have asked for twelve weeks but the architect is not prepared to give more than ten.

QS:
So the employer wants ten weeks' acceleration for the whole of the works and fourteen weeks' for the ground floor.

You had better let the architect have your proposals on this to make sure they are acceptable to him.

Contractor:
Yes, we will need to work overtime including weekends. We shall have to ask the heating and the lift people what they can do. The plasterers may prove a problem too. We shall want the architect to settle the sanitary fittings, ironmongery and so forth.

QS:

Right! Now what about your claims? Have you given the architect notice of them and have you got them formulated?

Contractor:

So far as the troubles with these old wells and with the party wall are concerned, yes, we have got them ready but have not put them in, otherwise you would have seen them for sure. Then there is this delay on the heating, and the late issue of some drawings and instructions early on. I could have them ready in, say, three or four weeks.

QS:

Well, let me have them and send a copy to the architect at the same time. But three or four weeks won't do. We have less than ten months left for acceleration and I shall want to have a look at your claims before recommending payment. What about one week from now? After all you have had quite a long time so far to get them ready.

Contractor:

We can but try. It will take us at least a week to work out how to accelerate and what it will cost. We will have to contact the heating and lift people by telephone.

QS:

Right. Let us meet again today week.

Notes of meeting held 31 March 1980

QS:
Well, what have you got for me?

Contractor:
I have worked out how this acceleration could be achieved, I have seen the architect and discussed my proposals with him and they would be acceptable to him.

I have worked out what it would cost in terms of overtime, some additional plant, extra costs for the sub-contractors (plasterer, lifts and heating) and special drying out measures. I reckon these would cost £8,400 to save fourteen weeks on the shops and £12,000 to save ten weeks on the offices, a total of £20,400, plus a bit of bonus for the extra risk, say £21,000.

QS:

That sounds a lot of money, rather more than I thought it would come to. You had better leave me your figures and I will go through them. But you would not suggest, I think, that you have not allowed for some margin within the £20,400 which you hope to save?

Contractor:

Well perhaps not, but we are taking a risk if we are going to be liable to liquidated damages from the new dates.

QS:

Quite. I will come to that in a moment. Now what about these claims?

Contractor:
There are really only four:

1. The old wells — stopping some work whilst the archaeologists investigated and then filling them in   2,515

2. Delay in the issue of instructions on the basement steelwork and our claim for formwork and working space to the ground beams   4,874

3. The work to the party wall, including temporary protection inside adjoining premises, and delay to all work in the staircase well   5,286

4. Delay due to heating sub-contract   2,259   £14,934

QS:
I shall have to have a look at those. Have you all the papers and figures there?

Contractor:
Yes, they are not very presentable but it is all there.

QS:
Leave that too with me, but first what is in them regarding time?

Contractor:
Well, they overlap a bit but I have amended our original claims so as to arrive at a total delay of ten weeks, which is all the architect is prepared to approve. We had $12\frac{1}{2}\%$ in our tender for site overheads, and those over seventy-eight weeks equal £687 per week.

QS:
Right. I take it the $12\frac{1}{2}\%$ is the overhead content, not the addition to direct costs?

Contractor:
Yes, it worked out at £53,500. So, taking it the other way round, $12.5 \div 112.5 \times 482,144 = 53,571 \div 78 = $ £687 per week.

QS:
So $10 \times 687 = 6,870$ is the cost you would incur if the work overran the due date for completion?

Contractor:
That is right.

QS:
Then if you accelerate, and if your acceleration estimate covers all your costs, you will save those overheads?

Contractor:
No ... well ... maybe ... I suppose so ... yes!

QS:
There is no catch in that. You would need the £6,870 if you overran ten weeks, but not otherwise. So, whatever figure we can agree upon for the claims, £6,870 would be deductible for non-incurred site overheads. Let us leave that there until I have had a look at the claims. Here is a copy of a draft Supplementary Agreement I have prepared. It looks rather involved but if you take it a clause at a time you will find it not too difficult to

*follow. Take that away and have a look at it, take advice on it if you wish
and let us meet again on Thursday 6th and see if we can reach agreement.*

Notes of meeting held on 6 April 1980

*First, the matter of your claims. I have had a look at these and I think
there is some overlap between them. Also you have charged daywork rates
for standing time on plant; these I cannot accept, depreciation rates are, I
think, appropriate. As you will see from my revised figures, I get a total of
£11,289.*

It is not proposed to illustrate the claims here in detail. It is to be presumed that they are
similar in general terms to the cases set out in other chapters. Obviously there would have
to be a full discussion of all the points but it must be accepted that in a climate of haste
such as is usually associated with acceleration situations the time is not available for exhaustive
investigation. It is to be assumed in this case that after some debate the QS's figures were
accepted.

QS:
*On the basis of the revised figures for the claims, if you accelerate and get
paid the full costs for so doing, then the sum to be added to the
acceleration costs is £11,289 − 6,870 = £4,419.*

*Your estimate (or may I say offer?) for acceleration is £21,000, which
plus 4,419 gives £25,419 and that is the total to be paid you?*

Contractor:
Call it £25,500 and we would agree.

QS:
*I can only put it to the employer but I would be prepared to recommend
that. Now, what about the Agreement? Let us go through it and discuss
anything you wish.*

The following represents the draft of the Agreement (which would of course have to be
modified to suit the circumstances of any particular case). The interspersed comment
represents partly discussion and explanation to our contractor in this example and partly
comment on the principles or reasons involved.

Supplementary Agreement

ARTICLES OF AGREEMENT
made the . . . . day of . . . . 19. . .
BETWEEN . . . .
of . . . .
(hereinafter called 'the Employer') of the one part and
. . . . .
of . . . .
(hereinafter called 'the Contractor') of the other part.

*WHEREAS under a Contract dated 26 June 1979 the Contractor has
agreed to carry out and complete the construction of an office block known
as Norwich House, Old Bank of England Court in the City of . . . .
by the 24th day of December 1980 plus such further period as determined
in accordance with Clause 23 of the Conditions of Contract of the said
Contract and*

It is important to retain the terminology of the head contract so far as possible.

WHEREAS pursuant to Clause 23 of the Conditions of the said Contract the Contractor is entitled and the Architect has made a fair and reasonable extension of time of ten weeks for completion of the Works in respect of all those events and circumstances of the kind referred to under the headings (a) to (l) inclusive of the said Clause 23 which have occurred or existed before 1st April 1980 and

It is important to write in the entitlement to and amount of extension of time due under the head contract so that the objective of this Supplementary Agreement can be defined. In this case it resolves the apparent conflict between employer and architect as to the contractual entitlement.

WHEREAS the Employer is desirous that the Works shall be completed on or before the 24th day of December 1980 except for the work on the ground floor which shall be completed on or before the 24th day of November 1980 and

WHEREAS the Contractor has made application dated .... for additional payment over and above that already certified in respect of the valuation of variations under Clause 11(4) and for direct loss and expense not reimbursable under that sub-clause in respect of work done prior to 1st April 1980 and also in respect of direct loss and expense for which he would not be reimbursed by a payment under any other provision in this Contract by reason of the regular progression of the Works or any part thereof having been materially affected as provided for in Clause 24 for events and circumstances occurring prior to 1st April 1980.

These are known as the recitals and it is important to include in them reference to any claims the contractor may have. These often overlap, particularly as regards site overheads, with the cost of acceleration and unless they are all considered as a package it would easily be possible for duplication to occur.

NOW IT IS HEREBY AGREED AS FOLLOWS
In this Agreement the following words and expressions shall have the meanings hereby assigned to them.

In the case of ICE or GC/Wks 1 Forms it may be convenient to incorporate the whole of the definitions clause.

The 'Contract' means that Agreement dated 26 June 1979 between ......
.... of ....
and .... of .... for
the construction and completion of an office block.
The 'Conditions' means those conditions annexed to the Contract and clause means clause of the said conditions.
The Employer means .... of ....
The Contractor means .... of ....
The Architect means .... of ....
The Quantity Surveyor means .... of ....
The Works means those works shewn on the Contract Drawings referred to in the Contract and described by or referred to in the Contract Bills and in the Conditions of the said Contract.

IT IS FURTHER AGREED that the following clauses shall apply to this Supplementary Agreement:
25 — Determination by Employer
26 — Determination by Contractor
32 — Outbreak of hostilities
35 — Arbitration

Definitions of terms such as these help to avoid lengthy repetitions in the text. The term 'Contract' distinguishes this Agreement from the head Agreement.

THE CONTRACTOR COVENANTS that he shall complete the whole of the Works on or before the 24th day of December 1980 with the exception of the work on the ground floor which shall be completed on or before the 24th day of November 1980 (hereinafter referred to as the prescribed dates) in accordance with Clause 21 as amended hereunder and shall pay to the Employer a sum calculated at the rate stated in the Appendix as amended hereunder to the said Conditions as Liquidated and Ascertained Damages in accordance with Clause 22 as amended hereunder if he shall fail to complete the work by the prescribed dates or such amended dates as determined in accordance with Clause 23 as amended hereunder.

Provided that the Employer shall allow the Contractor access to the upper floors by way of the Entrance Hall the lifts and staircase to permit work there to be carried out and completed.

Provided further the Employer shall contrary to the provisions of Preamble ... to the Bill of Quantities permit overtime to be worked at night and/or Saturdays until 8 pm and/or on Sundays until 5 pm as the Contractor may require.

It is important that any prohibitions or restrictions on working which may be contained in the specification or elsewhere be removed or amended as necessary otherwise the Contractor may be put into a situation of breach unintentionally.

IT IS FURTHER AGREED that clauses in the Contract shall be amended as follows:

Clause 21:
21(1) The Contractor having been given possession of the site and having begun the Works and carried out and completed part thereof shall complete the whole of the Works and that part located on the ground floor on or before the prescribed dates subject nevertheless in both cases to the provisions for extension of time as may be determined in accordance with the provisions of Clause 23 as amended hereunder in respect of events or circumstances occurring or existing after 31 March 1980 but without any further extension of time under Clause 23 or 31(1)(c) for any delay whatsoever in respect of events or circumstances which occurred or existed prior to 1st April 1980.

The object here is to draw a distinct cut-off line so that neither contractor nor employer can go back over prior events for the purpose of seeking either a further extension of time or recovery of liquidated damages in respect of those prior events.

Clause 22 and the Appendix to the Conditions:
22 If the Contractor fails to complete the work by the prescribed dates or within any extended time fixed under Clause 23 as amended hereunder or Clause 31(1)(c) and the Architect certifies in writing that in his opinion the same ought reasonably so to have been completed then the Contractor shall pay or allow to the Employer a sum calculated at the following rates:
for that portion of the work located on the ground floor £200 per week,
for the whole of the Works (except the aforesaid portion) £400 per week,
as Liquidated and Ascertained Damages for the period during which the work shall so remain or have remained incomplete and the Employer may deduct such sum from any monies due or to become due under the Contract.

Such an amendment is required if the original liquidated damages are to be altered in any way or, as here, they need to be apportioned between self-contained sections each of which has to be completed by a given date.

> *Clause 23:*
>
> *23 Upon it becoming reasonably apparent that the progress of the Works and/or that portion located on the ground floor as the case may be is delayed the Contractor shall forthwith give written notice to the Architect of the cause of the delay and if in the opinion of the Architect the completion of the Works and/or portion as the case may be is likely to be or has been delayed beyond the respective prescribed dates for completion or beyond any extended time previously fixed under this clause or Clause 33(1)(c) for events or circumstances occurring after 31st March 1980 and of the respective kinds set out under sub-paragraphs (a) to (l) inclusive of Clause 23 then the Architect shall so soon as he is able to estimate the length of the delay beyond the dates aforesaid make in writing a fair and reasonable extension of the respective times for completion.*
>
> *Provided always that the Contractor shall use constantly his best endeavours to prevent delay and shall do all that may be reasonably required to the satisfaction of the Architect to proceed with the work.*

Great care is required in amending clauses. It is usually better to write the new clause *in extenso* rather than add words here and there.

> *IN CONSIDERATION WHEREOF the Employer covenants to pay to the Contractor a sum hereinafter referred to as the 'Acceleration Payment' to be ascertained and paid in the manner and according to the following conditions namely:*
>
> *THAT the total sum of the Acceleration Payment shall be £25,000 (hereinafter referred to as the 'Maximum Payment') subject to reduction of*
>   *(a) £170 for each day after 24th December 1980 (or later date prescribed by Clause 23 as amended) for completion of the Works and*
>   *(b) £85 for each day after 24th November 1980 (or later date determined under Clause 23 as amended) for completion of that portion of the work on the ground floor*
> *by which the contractor fails to complete the said Works or work respectively provided that the Acceleration Payment shall not be reduced to less than £12,500.*
>
> *THAT the Acceleration Payment shall be in full and final settlement of all claims for additional payment whether under Clause 11 in respect of work done prior to 1st April 1980 or under Clause 24 in respect of events and circumstances prior to 1st April 1980 including all compensation, damages or other loss, cost or expense which might otherwise be recoverable under any other rights and remedies referred to in Clause 24(2).*

This may seem somewhat harsh but the object is no more than to prevent claims being brought up after the Acceleration Agreement has been signed and is taking effect. When negotiating the contractor will need to consider very carefully whether he has any potential and legitimate grounds for claim, if he has he will need to bring them out and get them dealt with. If he cannot or is not prepared to do this then the above clause will need to be amended. Depending upon how much the employer needs the acceleration it may be necessary to consider whether in a given case claims can be left outside the Supplementary Agreement and how far that could leave the door open to such matters being raised later, with possibly dire results.

This is in a sense the key clause. The various sums have been arrived at as follows:

Acceleration Payment (maximum) is the £21,000 (£12,000+8,400) the contractor estimated for acceleration plus £4,419 in settlement of his claims, which he rounded up to £25,500.

The £12,000 may be said to be the cost of saving ten weeks, i.e. £170 per day, and the £8,400 for saving four weeks, i.e. £85 per day (at seven days per week).

So these are the sums the contractor may be said to be working for. It may be argued that if he fails to save any time he will get no payment, but that is the risk he weighed up when he worked out his sums, and this is what the employer desires to be achieved. If the contractor requires otherwise then this is what would have to be put in the Agreement.

The £12,500 minimum payment really represents the value of his claims (£11,289) to which he would be entitled without any question of acceleration. It might be argued that the minimum payment should also include some part of acceleration costs proper, as clearly the contractor will have to spend money if he is to achieve the required result. This is a matter of negotiation and it depends on how much the employer wishes to achieve his aims and how far the contractor is prepared to take the risk. It is not possible to illustrate all the possible combinations.

> THAT subject to the certificate of the Architect that the progress of the work is sufficient to achieve completion of the work by the prescribed dates or later dates determined under Clause 23 as amended the Contractor shall be entitled to instalments of the Acceleration Payment as follows:
> (a) 20 (twenty) per cent of the Maximum Payment within 21 days of the date of this Supplementary Agreement.
> (b) Six instalments each of 10 (ten) per cent of the Maximum Payment at intervals of one calendar month thereafter, payment to be made within 21 days of the issue of the Architect's certificate. Provided that if the progress of the work is in the opinion of the Architect not such as to achieve completion of the work by the prescribed dates or extended dates, the Architect shall certify such lesser amount if any as appears to him to be fair and reasonable.
> (c) The outstanding balance of the Acceleration Payment, if any, shall be paid to the Contractor
>   (i) as to 40 per cent of the said balance, if any, within 21 days of the issue of the Certificate of Practical Completion of the work located on the ground floor
>   (ii) as to 60 per cent of the said balance, if any, within 21 days of the issue of the Certificate of Practical Completion of the whole of the Works.
> If the total instalments paid to the Contractor exceed the amount of the Acceleration Payment as finally determined such excess shall be deducted from any sums due to the Contractor or recovered as a debt.
> (d) No retention shall be deducted under the Contract from any payments made under this Supplementary Agreement.
> (e) The provisions of Clause 31F (Adjustment of Contract Sum) shall not apply to the Acceleration Payment.

The rate of payment can be a key matter to the contractor but care must be taken not to arrive at a formula which will inevitably result in overpayment. The risks and probabilities must be weighed and a result potentially fair to both sides achieved. In no case should the offer to accelerate be in terms of a fixed sum for the saving of a stated time because this would constitute an 'entire' contract and if the contractor failed to achieve the stipulated date(s) by as little as one day he would be entitled to no payment at all.

In the case we are considering, it is to be assumed that the QS kept the employer and the architect informed of the progress of the negotiations.

It might be advisable to provide the employer with a copy of the draft Supplementary Agreement so that he too can take legal advice upon it should he consider it necessary. This step should not be left until agreement with the contractor is reached and everything otherwise is set for signing and steps to be taken in beginning the actual acceleration which is the object of the exercise.

It is also to be assumed that the contractor challenged or queried a number of matters affecting him and the situation as he saw it. He should at least appreciate that his entitlement to extension of time had been recognized and dealt with, that his claims to date were being settled without long delays in reaching agreement and getting the money. This is an area which can present particular difficulty, especially with the shortage of time usually obtaining in these situations. It is, however, very much in the contractor's interests to get them settled — and worth quite a bit in cash terms, which a QS negotiating would be aware of and use to curb a contractor's tendency to exploit the situation. At an appropriate point in the negotiations the QS will have obtained an offer in writing from the contractor, which would be on the following lines:

Contractor to Employer   *10 March 1980*

As you are aware, there has been ten weeks' delay to the Works in respect of which we are entitled to an extension of time pursuant to Clause 23 of the Conditions.

We understand that you wish to recover this lost time if possible and further to accelerate completion of the ground floor by one month so as to complete that portion by 24 November 1980.

We hereby offer to take such measures as are necessary to achieve completion by the dates you require for the sum of £25,500 or such other sum as may be ascertained in accordance with the terms of the attached Supplementary Agreement which has been prepared by your Quantity Surveyor.

Included in the sum of £25,500 is a sum in settlement of our claims for additional payment under the existing contract for delays and other matters as set out in our letter dated . . . . to the architect in respect of matters which have arisen prior to the signing of this Agreement.

We would appreciate early acceptance of this offer because the time remaining to us to achieve the required dates is already somewhat short.

There remains then the presentation of the case to the employer.

Quantity Surveyor to Employer   *12 March 1981*

You instructed me to negotiate with the contractor the terms of a Supplementary Agreement under which he would covenant to complete the whole of the Works by 24 December 1980 except for the ground floor which you require to be completed by 24 November.

I enclose a letter from him dated 10 March 1980 in which he offers to do so.

The sum of £25,500 may at first sight seem somewhat high but as he points out this includes settlement of his outstanding claims on the existing contract. These claims have been investigated in collaboration with the architect and the details of the claims themselves, the reasons for their being made and the contractor's entitlement to payment are set out in an appendix to this letter.

It will be seen that these claims as originally submitted totalled £14,934. After negotiation, the contractor has agreed to accept the sum of £11,289 in full and final settlement (see letter attached). It must be pointed out that this sum is in respect of events which have already happened and to which the contractor is therefore entitled whether the work is accelerated or not.

Settlement of these claims has been included in this Supplementary Agreement partly because the method of their computation necessarily has some interaction with the computation of the acceleration payment and partly to facilitate a clean cut-off line between matters outstanding prior to this Agreement and events which may happen after.

It does mean, however, that the additional cost of acceleration in real terms is £25,500 less £11,289, i.e. £14,211. There will also be a saving in respect of price fluctuations by reason of earlier completion being achieved.

You will see from the draft Agreement attached that this sum is reducible should the contractor fail to achieve the dates due to his own default. He would also be liable to pay liquidated damages as indicated. Periodic payments of this sum are required to be made subject to the architect being satisfied that adequate progress is being achieved.

We consider this offer to be fair and reasonable and we recommend its acceptance.

Points of principle involved

This case involved a situation where entitlement to extension of time had already accrued, even though it had not yet been granted. Acceleration was required to bring forward the date for completion from the date which was due to be fixed by the architect under the contract. In those circumstances the architect does not have the power under the contract to deal with acceleration. The matter needs to be dealt with by a supplementary agreement between the contractor and the employer. The architect may act on behalf of the employer as his agent for the purposes of reaching such agreement, but only if he is authorized by the employer to do so.

This is different from situations where the entitlement to extension of time has not yet accrued and the architect has power under the contract to grant entitlement both to extension of time and additional payment. In those situations, the architect may deal prospectively with matters under the contract, taking account of the interrelationship between time and money.

CASE 8.4   CLAIM FOR EXTENSION OF TIME REDUCED BY ALLOWANCE FOR EXTRA RESOURCES

Pertinent particulars of contract

The original contract was for the erection of four large oil storage tanks, an associated jetty and ancillary works on a coastal site with access only by sea. The documents comprised:

Drawings, Specifications, Bill of Quantities
Conditions of Contract: ICE5
Tender for £3,427,526 dated 17 February 1984.

Acceptance date 15 March 1984. Time for completion 36 weeks (date for completion 17 December 1984).

Liquidated damages £43,000 per week.

Events giving rise to claims

During construction, the employer required the addition of a control building at the root of the jetty. As the additional work was of a substantially different kind from that included in the existing contract, the contractor was invited on 2 May 1984 to submit a quotation. The quotation proved unacceptable to the employer, who then instructed that tenders be invited from others. One of these latter tenders was accepted on 25 June 1984 with commencement of work to be on 9 July 1984.

The contractor under the original contract agreed to give up possession of the part of the site required for the control building together with a working area for the building contractor, but he pointed out that loss of the area at the root of the jetty in front of the tanks would cut off his access along the seaward side of the tanks for his crawler crane. This would, he said, entail his crane travelling a much longer distance around the back of the tanks to service the site and he would thereby suffer a delay of 2 weeks.

Contractor to Engineer   *22 June 1984*

We acknowledge receipt of your letter dated 19 June 1984 requesting that we make available the area of the site between Tanks 2 and 3 and the Jetty for the proposed building contractor.

While we do not wish to make an issue of releasing this area, we must point out that it was not envisaged at the time of contract that this building would be constructed during our work on the site. Releasing the area will have the effect of stopping the normal route used by our crawler crane for travelling to service the site on either side of the Jetty. It will be necessary for the crane to travel instead around the back of the tanks. We estimate that the additional crane travelling time will result in a delay to completion of 2 weeks.

The instruction to release the area to the building contractor effectively constitutes a failure by the Employer to give possession of the Site within Clause 42(1) of the Conditions of Contract.

Accordingly we claim under Clause 42(1) an extension of time of 2 weeks to cover the delay, together with reimbursement of the additional costs (site and head office overheads and uneconomic working) which we will incur as a result of this change.

Engineer to Contractor   *28 June 1984*

I refer to your letter of 22 June 1984. I accept that neither the construction of the new building during your contract nor the requirement to release the area of the site were envisaged at the time of contract. In the circumstances, I accept that the instruction to release the area should be treated as a failure by the Employer to give possession in accordance with Clause 42(1).

It would appear, however, that the time effects of the delay could be avoided by bringing in a second crane to enable both halves of the site to be serviced without extended travelling. This would involve additional cost in mobilization and hire charges for the additional crane, but the net effect should be more satisfactory. Subject to agreement on the necessary hire period and hire and mobilization rates, and checking that there will be a

259

net saving after taking account of overhead costs which would otherwise be incurred, I would be willing to certify the additional mobilization and hire charges as costs for reimbursement under Clause 42(1). No extension of time would then be necessary.

Contractor to Engineer   *3 July 1984*

Thank you for your letter of 28 June 1984. Your proposal that we should bring in an additional crane will solve the problem of additional crane travelling and avoid delay.

The crane will be required for a period of 6 weeks, and the costs involved will be

Mobilization and Transport	*£1,500*
Hire Charges 6 weeks @ £1,050	*£6,300*
Demobilization and Transport	*£1,500*
Total	*£9,300*

The saving of site overheads which would otherwise be incurred, based on a period of 2 weeks, would be approximately £25,000, i.e. the hire of an additional crane would be cheaper by about £15,700.

Subject to confirmation of your agreement of these figures as costs reimbursable under Clause 42(1), we shall proceed to mobilize the crane prior to releasing the area.

Points of principle involved

Mitigating the time effects of delay by mobilizing additional resources or implementing other acceleration measures is not precluded by the Conditions of Contract. Indeed it probably accords with the common sense expectations and presumed intention of both parties, that reasonable measures should be taken to minimize the effects of delays providing payment is made by the Employer to cover any additional costs reasonably and properly incurred.

The trade-off between time and money involves a balancing exercise and the balance is best fixed by agreement. Different employers may put different values on time, so one should not expect a contractor unilaterally to implement such measures without any commitment to payment.

If steps are to be taken to reduce delay, prompt agreement is essential to allow the steps to be implemented while they can have effect.

The possibilities of mitigating time effects will rarely be aired in arbitration or litigation, or even in retrospective claim submissions. Steps have to be taken by one or both sides to invoke acceleration measures at the time. It is too late after the event.

Note: In *Fairweather v LB Wandsworth*,[31] a case under JCT 63/77, Judge Fox-Andrews QC had to consider, *inter alia*, whether an arbitrator had dealt correctly with extensions of time due to concurrent heads of delay. He said that he did not consider the 'dominant test' was correct and that 'an arbitrator has the task of allocating, when the facts require it, the extension of time to the various heads'. He did not, however, explain what he considered to be the proper basis of 'allocating'. *Keating*[32] points out that the comment was *obiter* (that is, not binding as precedent) and out of line with general legal principles.

31. *Fairweather v LB Wandsworth* [1987] 32 BLR 106 at p 120.
32. Sir Anthony May QC (1991), *Keating on Building Contracts* 5th edn, p 196, Sweet & Maxwell, London.

Chapter 9

Claims arising from breach or termination

GENERAL

No attempt to categorize contractual provisions can ever be completely definitive. A contract is to be read as a whole, so superimposed classifications must be of limited significance. They do not create strict boundaries. For example, a provision for the A/E/QS to certify payment for work completed in accordance with the contract could be classified as a payment provision, but it is equally relevant to ensuring the achievement of conformance to specification. This limitation is acknowledged in most Forms of Contract by an explicit provision[1] that the headings in the Conditions of Contract are not to be taken into account in interpreting the document. Nevertheless, some attempt at classification (while recognizing the limitation) is helpful as an aid to analysis. This chapter is concerned with a residual category of provisions dealing with breach or termination of the contract.

---

1. ICE5 and ICE6 Clause 1(3); FIDIC4 Clause 1.2; GC/Wks 1 Ed 2 Cond 1(5); GC/Wks 1 Ed 3 Cond 1(2). JCT 80 does not exclude headings from consideration but Clause 1(2) states that the Articles of Agreement, the Conditions and the Appendix are to be read as a whole.

The categories addressed in Chapters 4–8 are concerned with the normal working of the contract. Those chapters describe the operation of the machinery for adjustment, which is provided in the contract primarily to allow changes to be ordered or instructions to be given on behalf of the employer within the contract and to cure non-fulfilment of the employer's obligations.[2] The machinery is provided in order to keep the contract intact until completion. This chapter, on the other hand, is concerned with situations where the contract is either not intact or does not survive until completion. The first situation occurs where non-fulfilment of an obligation (which may be a contractor's or an employer's obligation) is not internally cured and therefore amounts to a breach of contract. The second occurs where the contract, or the employment of the contractor under the contract, is terminated before performance has been completed in the normal way. The two situations are linked in that breach of contractual obligations may provide grounds for termination.

Even in these situations, the Standard Forms of Contract generally make explicit provision for what should happen or what steps may be taken. For example, most Forms stipulate liquidated damages for breach of the term as to time of completion, and they provide powers and procedures for premature termination. These provisions are intended to avoid the potential uncertainty, delay and cost of reference to the courts or arbitration and, on contracts overseas, to escape the involvement of local law.

The provisions have several objectives. The first is to provide compensation to the innocent party. The second is to allow positive action to be taken promptly in certain events. The third is, indirectly, to provide motivation for the parties to comply with their contractual obligations. This last objective is, however, subject to a restrictive attitude by the courts. This raises questions in some instances as to whether contractual provisions will be upheld and how failure to comply strictly with the procedures will be treated.

As a related subject, in the light of this restrictive attitude, alternative approaches to motivation are considered.

BREACH BY CONTRACTOR

Liquidated damages

The stipulation of liquidated damages for late completion on construction contracts tends to conceal the fact that failure to complete the Works within the time prescribed by the contract is a breach of contract. The meaning of 'liquidated damages' is simply damages which have been fixed or settled by agreement, usually by stipulation in a contract. Although provisions for liquidated damages are incorporated typically in construction contracts in respect of failure to complete on time, there is no fundamental reason why they should not be stipulated in respect of other breaches of contract which result in loss or damage.

The important point is that liquidated damages are still damages. They are compensation for loss suffered or anticipated as a result of breach of a term of the contract. They are not compensation under the contract as, for example, additional payment claimed by the contractor and settled by the A/E/QS. One consequence of this is that although the A/E may issue the certificates of completion and ascertain and grant the extensions of time, which combine effectively to determine the delay to be compensated, the liquidated damages are deducted by the employer. The sum of money to be deducted is not usually certified by the A/E/QS.

In order for late completion to constitute a breach of contract for the purposes of liquidated damages, there must be a date for completion validly fixed by the contract. As described

---

Where provisions for secondary obligations are stipulated by a contract to arise on non-fulfilment of primary obligations, the provisions survive a repudiatory breach, see *Port Jackson v Salmond & Spraggon* (1981) 1 WLR 138.

2. The machinery for adjustment also provides for any agreed allocation of risk where the employer accepts responsibilities in excess of those imposed by law.

in Chapter 8,[3] this is subject to the doctrine of prevention. The date for completion ceases to apply in the event of an act or omission by the employer (or for which the employer is responsible) preventing completion by such date, unless there is a relevant power to extend the time for completion and that power is duly exercised. If the date for completion set by the contract, or the power to fix a date, is lost, the contractor is still obliged to complete within a reasonable time, and his failure to do so will constitute a breach of contract. In that case, however, only such loss and damage as can be proved will be recoverable, the right to deduct liquidated damages does not apply.

As liquidated damages are damages, the common law rules set out in Chapter 2[4] apply. In particular liquidated damages will not be enforceable if, by virtue of the amount or nature or basis of calculation stipulated, they constitute a penalty, intended as a coercive sanction rather than compensation. The description given in the contract is not conclusive on this point. Thus, liquidated damages might not be enforceable in respect of failure to meet a 'milestone' established solely for management control purposes during the contract. There would be no loss to be compensated unless the employer required a hand-over to himself or another contractor on that date.

The basis of calculating liquidated damages payable (or deductible) in the event of a breach should be consistent with the likely damage suffered. For example, in *Public Works Commissioners v Hills*,[5] the contract provided that all retention money should be forfeit in the event of default. It was held that this amounted to a penalty because retention money increased with progress, whereas the likely damage from default reduced; there was no correlation between the likely loss and liquidated damages. Similarly, a single lump sum for failure to complete by a given day would probably be regarded as a penalty unless, for example, the work was required to be completed for a specific event.

In construction contracts the amount of liquidated damages for late completion is normally stipulated at so much per day or per week or, sometimes, 'per week or part of a week' for the period of delay. This will be consistent with the likely averaged effect of the delay on the employer. Calculation of the amount of liquidated damages is subject to the rule that, in law, a fraction of a day is treated as a day[6] unless the contract requires otherwise. It is sometimes argued that the rule should be extended, so that, where liquidated damages are expressed as an amount per week, part of a week counts as a week, but the validity of the argument is doubted unless such an intention is stated explicitly in the contract. There are at least two grounds for doubt. Firstly, such an extension of the rule would be inconsistent with the objection to penalties; a fixed sum would be payable for a small part or the whole of a week, irrespective of the likely effect. Secondly, demurrage in shipping cases, which is the equivalent of liquidated damages in construction, is commonly calculated for fractions of an hour though expressed as a rate per hour. In any event, the rule would only apply to the calculation of the liquidated damages; it would not lead to a requirement that extensions of time must be granted in integral units of weeks.

The rate of liquidated damages should be a genuine pre-estimate of the loss likely to be suffered in the event of a breach, estimated at the time of tender. Some attempt should therefore be made to assess the probable actual loss, and a record kept of the calculation.[7] This estimated loss may include continuing finance costs arising out of lack of use of the facility, the cost of alternative accommodation, continuing supervision costs, and loss of actual income or profit if such were to apply. In this connection the loss must be that sufferable by the employer, which, in the case of a local or central government authority, would include the foregoing but would not include loss of benefit by the public (e.g. cost benefit from a road improvement). It is, however, no bar that the consequences of the breach are such as to make a precise estimation impossible. On the contrary, as stated in the leading case

---

3. See pages 220, 221.
4. See page 33.
5. *Public Works Commissioners v Hills* [1906] AC 368.
6. 'In law there is no fraction of a day': *Pugh v Duke of Leeds* [1777] 2 Cowp 714.
7. See, for example, the calculation described in *Robophone v Blank* [1966] 1 WLR 1428.

of *Dunlop v New Garage & Motor Co*,[8] that is just the situation when it is probable that pre-estimated damage was the true bargain between the parties.

Subject to these requirements, and to the date for completion being set by the contract and duly adjusted, where justified, by a proper extension of time, there is nothing esoteric about the recovery of liquidated damages. They are recoverable. Recovery does not depend upon being able to prove actual damage. There is no question of mitigation. There is no question of having to have a corresponding bonus for earlier completion; that is a quite separate matter. Liquidated damages are recoverable merely on proof of the breach.

If liquidated damages are found to be a penalty,[9] they will not be recoverable. They will be set aside, but actual (unliquidated) damages will be recoverable.[10] It is unlikely that a party which had stipulated the right to deduct liquidated damages could argue that they were a penalty in order to claim a greater amount as unliquidated damages,[11] but a respondent should beware of opening the gates by arguing that the liquidated damage provisions are a penalty. He might lose the protection, as a liquidated damage clause may equally be regarded as a limitation clause inserted for the benefit of the contractor.

The stipulation of liquidated damages in a contract will not preclude the recovery of unliquidated damages for delayed completion for reasons outside the contemplation of the contract, such as fundamentally defective construction.[12]

Bonuses

The efficacy of liquidated damages as an incentive to timely completion has been questioned. It has been suggested, for example, that doubling the rate of liquidated damages does not lead to a doubling of effort to complete on time, but only a doubling of the number of claims consultants employed to find grounds for extensions of time. The alternative approach to motivation through the contract is to provide positive incentives, for example, by including provisions for bonuses for timely completion. This may be extended to more sophisticated schemes to provide both incentives and sanctions, but the scheme must be devised so as not to offend the rule against penalties.

It has been relatively uncommon to provide for the payment of bonuses for timely or early completion. Public authorities appear to find it difficult to justify bonuses. The existence of bonus provisions puts pressure on the employer and designers to avoid change and provide details early, and on supervisors to provide prompt approval or disapproval. Unless the employer, designers and supervisors are willing and able to respond to that pressure, there is no corresponding benefit from providing a bonus. On the other hand, if the nature of the project lends itself to incentives, the possibility should not be overlooked.

There are significant potential benefits in bonuses. They are not subject to the strict rules on extensions of time or penalties as liquidated damages. The provisions can be framed much more freely. For example, bonuses can be attached to intermediate stages as milestones. Above all, attitudes induced by the prospect of a bonus are much more constructive than those induced by the threat of liquidated damages.

Care must be taken in granting extensions of time when bonus schemes are in operation to ensure that they are properly due and not granted merely to permit the contractor to earn a bonus. There is, however, no absolute requirement that extensions of time granted in relation to liquidated damages should be applicable to bonus provisions. The respective provisions may be drafted to be quite independent of each other.

---

8. *Dunlop v New Garage & Motor Co* [1915] AC 79.
9. The onus of proof is on the party alleging that it is a penalty: *Robophone v Blank* [1966] 1 WLR 1428.
10. *Jobson v Johnson* [1989] 1 WLR 1026.
11. Ibid.
12. *Chanthall Investments v F G Minter Ltd* [1975] per Lord Keith (Unreported).

An example of a more sophisticated incentive scheme is the 'lane rental' system introduced by the Department of Transport in the 1980s. The use of the 'lane rental' concept allows payment to be adjusted to cover both early and late completion, relative to a target date proposed by the contractor at time of tender, without falling foul of the rules on penalties. The target dates proposed are taken into account in evaluation of the tenders and then stipulated in the contract.

It is sometimes found appropriate to introduce bonuses or other incentive schemes after the original contract has been let, once the design and other details have been settled. There is, however, a difference in kind between an incentive scheme incorporated in the original contract, where tender prices take account of the potential bonus to be earned, and a scheme superimposed later by agreement.

Defective work

Talk of claims for payment and time tends to obscure the original purpose of construction contracts, which is the execution of the Works in conformance with the specified requirements. Failure to execute the Works in accordance with the specified requirements — a 'nonconformity' — constitutes a breach of contract.

The status of a nonconformity during the course of the contract is the source of some difficulty in law. One view is that a nonconformity is an inchoate breach of contract, that it does not become actionable as a breach of contract until the contractor submits that he has completed the Works. Up till that time, the contractor has the right to rectify the defective work. The alternative view is that the nonconformity is immediately a breach of contract, but that the employer's entitlement to recovery of damages is limited, by the doctrine of mitigation, to the amount which it would have cost the contractor to correct the nonconformity. This latter view was adopted by Judge Stannard in *William Tomkinson & Sons v St Michael PCC*,[13] where the employer had in fact gone ahead and rectified defects before practical completion. Judge Stannard declined to follow the dissenting judgment of Lord Diplock in *Hosier & Dickinson v P & M Kaye*[14] where Lord Diplock had said that prior to practical completion:

> 'Upon a legalistic analysis it might be argued that temporary disconformity of any part of the works with the requirements of the contract even though remedied before the end of the agreed construction period constituted a breach of contract for which nominal damages would be recoverable. I do not think that makes business sense. Provided that the contractor puts it right timeously I do not think that the parties intended that any temporary disconformity should of itself amount to a breach of contract by the contractor.'

If Judge Stannard's view is correct, it may well have solved the difficulties of the Parochial Church Council of Saint Michael but it creates a major problem in relation to the Limitation Act 1980, since the limitation period starts to run as soon as the right of action accrues. If a nonconformity is actionable as soon as committed, without any failure by the contractor to comply with an order to rectify the nonconformity, the limitation period runs from then. It may be that Judge Stannard's view is appropriate to the specific case of work on an existing building under the JCT Minor Works Form, but it is submitted that such an approach is inappropriate to new works carried out under the Standard Forms for major works.

Even if the employer does have the right to correct nonconformities during construction, he will not usually be able to do so at the same cost as the contractor.

To minimize eventual problems, the Standard Forms of Contract provide an extensive framework of powers for the A/E to inspect and approve the Works at all stages, and to require immediate replacement or rectification of materials or work not in accordance with

---

13. *William Tomkinson & Sons v St Michael PCC* [1990] 6 Const LJ 319.
14. *Hosier & Dickinson v P & M Kaye* [1972] 1 WLR 146.

the contract. The powers of the A/E differ between the various Standard Forms of Contract, but under all the Forms there is a significant change in the powers of the A/E once a certificate of substantial completion is issued, or becomes due to be issued, in respect of the whole or the relevant part of the Works. Thus, under the ICE and FIDIC Conditions, the Engineer has powers under Clause 39, prior to substantial completion, to order the removal and proper re-execution of any work which, in the opinion of the Engineer, is not in accordance with the contract. For a period of, typically, 12 months after substantial completion, the Engineer has a reduced power to order the execution of work of 'amendment, reconstruction and remedying defects, shrinkages or other faults'.[15] This period is variously called the Liability Period,[16] the Period of Maintenance,[17] and the Defects Correction Period.[18] JCT 80 and GC/Wks 1 provide similar powers before[19] and after[20] substantial completion.

After the defects notified by the A/E to the contractor during the stipulated period have been rectified and any final certificate issued, the contractual provisions for rectification by the contractor cease to apply. Under some Forms of Contract, the final certificate has the effect of releasing the contractor from further liability for defects,[21] or it may affect the basis of liability,[22] but this is not the normal position. The contractor generally remains liable for defects and the consequences of defects, but any claim by the employer in respect of defective work which only becomes apparent or noticed after the issue of the final certificate (usually referred to as 'latent defects') can only be pursued legally as a claim for damages (unless the parties agree that the contractor shall repair or rectify the defect and/or consequential damage). This book is not concerned with claims in connection with latent defects.

Breach of other obligations

In addition to the primary obligation of executing the Works in accordance with the drawings and specification and the instructions of the A/E, construction contracts also impose ancillary obligations on the contractor. For example, most Standard Forms of Contract include obligations to insure, to submit a programme, to submit returns of labour and plant, to employ a qualified agent or person in charge. While non-compliance with such ancillary obligations may contribute to late completion or defects in the Works, such consequences will rarely be the direct result of such non-compliance alone.

The Standard Forms of Contract provide some effective remedies in the event of non-compliance with specific ancillary obligations. A good example concerns insurance. The obligation to insure is commonly backed up by a clause allowing the employer, in the event of failure by the contractor to insure, to effect the insurances directly and to deduct the premiums from monies due to the contractor.[23]

An example where commonly no satisfactory means of enforcement is provided under the contract concerns the submission of programmes. In the event of failure by the contractor to submit a satisfactory programme, the A/E/QS is virtually powerless. Failure to submit a programme may constitute grounds for invoking the forfeiture provisions, but using a sledgehammer to crack a nut leaves little worth having in its trail. A possible extra-contractual response demands the involvement of the employer. The non-compliance constitutes a breach of contract. That only becomes significant if the employer incurs actual loss or expense as a result, but if the contractor fails to submit a programme in accordance with the contract, it might be reasonable for the employer, (having first given an appropriate warning to the contractor and received no satisfactory response) to employ a programming consultant to

---

15. FIDIC4 Clause 49.2. ICE5 and ICE6 Clause 49(2) are similar, but use different words.
16. FIDIC4 Clause 49.1.
17. ICE5 Clause 49(1).
18. ICE6 Clause 1(1)(s).
19. JCT 80 Clause 8.4 (and Amendment 5: 1988); GC/Wks 1 Ed 2 Cond 7(1)(c) & (d) and 13(4); GC/Wks 1 Ed 3 Cond 31 and 40(2)(c) & (d).
20. JCT 80 Clause 17; GC/Wks 1 Ed 2 Cond 32; GC/Wks 1 Ed 3 Cond 21.
21. IEE/IMechE Model Form A (1966 Edition); see *Southern Water Authority v Carey* [1985] 2 All ER 1077.
22. Under GC/Wks 1 Ed 3, Cond 31(2) may have the effect of limiting the basis of the contractor's liability to breach of due skill and care, once the PM's powers expire.
23. ICE5 Clause 25; ICE6 Clause 25(3); FIDIC4 Clause 25.3; JCT 80 Clause 21.1.3; GC/Wks 1 Ed 3 Cond 8(4).

prepare a valid programme.[24] He could then deduct the cost of the consultant's fee from money otherwise due to the contractor, as a set-off. Such a remedy could equally be written into the contract as an explicit provision.

BREACH BY EMPLOYER

Breaches of contract by the employer are comparatively rare. Construction contracts are drafted to cover almost all situations which might amount to breach by the employer through adjustment provisions. The objective is to keep the contract intact for the benefit of the employer. Nevertheless, the possibility of breach of contract by the employer exists and it has become more prominent as a result of two decisions, *Wadsworth v Lydall*[25] and *Merton LBC v Leach*.[26] These cases are mainly concerned with issues of responsibility of the employer for the proper performance of the duties conferred by the contract on the A/E/QS, allegations of interference or collusion with the A/E/QS, and entitlement to recover financing costs as special damages. These matters are considered in Chapter 11. Another example of breach by the employer is illustrated in Case 8.1, concerning the withholding of the notice of commencement.

TERMINATION

Premature termination of performance obligations (and rights) under the contract may occur as a result of either some event which is outside the control of either party, or some act of one of the parties. It may occur through explicit contractual provisions or through common law. It may occur automatically or it may require the election of one of the parties to exercise a right of termination. This range of meanings was noted by Lord Radcliffe in relation to a hire purchase contract as follows:[27]

> 'For the purposes of these agreements, there is a distinction between terminating a hiring (which is all that clause 6 deals with) and terminating the agreement itself. "Terminate" is an ambiguous word, since it may refer to a termination by a right under the agreement or by a condition incorporated in it or by a deliberate breach by one party amounting to a repudiation of the whole contract.'

Construction contracts contain explicit provisions for termination to avoid the uncertainty inherent in reliance on the common law — it is impractical to wait several years while a court or arbitrator decides what the law is in any given situation. Also, this ensures standard rules for work in different countries. The contractual provisions are discussed below, but these do not preclude the possibility of termination at common law.[28] If the provisions for termination are not strictly followed, it may become necessary to resolve the outcome on the basis of the common law rules.

Determination by employer

Standard Forms of Contract confer on the employer the right to terminate the employment of the contractor under the contract in response to default by the contractor or the contractor becoming insolvent or in the event of corruption. This is commonly termed 'forfeiture' or 'determination of employment'. The reason for using these terms rather than 'terminate the contract' is that the contract itself survives. The parties are released from primary obligations but the secondary obligations provided by the contract come into play and the parties continue to be bound. In addition, some Forms confer special rights on the employer to determine the contract at will or in certain events for which the contractor is not responsible.

Forfeiture or determination of employment

Although civil law is mainly concerned with damages as compensation in the event of breach of contract, the law of contract also upholds a more direct response to serious breaches.

---

24. It is not uncommon in the US for the construction programme to be settled by an independent programme consultant.
25. *Wadsworth v Lydall* [1981] 1 WLR 598.
26. *Merton LBC v Stanley Hugh Leach* [1985] 32 BLR 51.
27. *Bridge v Campbell Discount Co Ltd* [1962] AC 600.
28. Ibid.

The innocent party is entitled to repudiate the contract, that is, to treat the contract as at an end in regard to performance of future primary obligations. In construction, there are complications, that the contractor is in possession of the site and has constructed works on it. Also interim payments will have been made. Standard Forms of Contract therefore provide an equivalent remedy in the event of serious breach of contract by the contractor. Such breaches include:

failure to proceed diligently
failure to comply with an instruction
failure to remove rejected work.

Detailed procedures are laid down[29] involving the certificate of the A/E, followed by determination by the employer. Strict compliance with these procedures is essential if it is decided to invoke the forfeiture provisions. Very substantial and expensive claims from the contractor can arise if either the grounds of determination are unjustified, or there is a failure to comply strictly with the procedure, in particular the timetable. Typical problems include the A/E saying that he will determine the contract, whereas it is the employer who has the power to determine. The A/E has to provide the certificate of grounds for determination. If the employer fails to follow the timetable after the issue of the relevant certificate, the certificate lapses and a fresh certificate is required.

Most Standard Forms also provide intermediate means of enforcement in the event of noncompliance with instructions, through the employer bringing in another contractor,[30] but this power is rarely used except, perhaps, at the end of the maintenance period or where there are several contractors already on site. The A/E must again be careful to avoid ordering, or threatening to order, the employment of other contractors without the specific authority of the employer.

The Forms generally provide for automatic determination in the event of the contractor becoming insolvent. Some forms provide particular powers of determination in the event of corruption.

In the event of forfeiture, the clauses in the various Forms of Contract[31] provide for the calculation and timing of further payment to the contractor, together with other matters such as the vesting of plant and materials, and rights to take over sub-contracts and hired plant. These provisions aim to compensate the employer for breach by the contractor. Typically, the contractor has no right to any further payment until the completion of the Works, and any additional costs incurred as a result of the termination and change of contractor are to be set off against monies which are calculated as due.

Special powers of determination

In contrast, where special powers of determination are conferred on the employer, the provisions for settlement and time of payment aim to compensate the contractor. As described below, special powers of determination are commonly conferred on the employer in the event of war. A much broader special power of determination by notice is conferred on the Authority by GC/Wks 1.[32] This is completely discretionary. Special powers of determination, exercisable by the employer on the occurrence of certain events, have been introduced into JCT 80 as Clause 28A by Amendment 4: 1987, where previously only the contractor had the right to determine the contract.

Determination by contractor

The attitude of the Standard Forms to determination by the contractor varies. GC/Wks 1 does not even mention the possibility of such determination, although this does not prevent

29. ICE5, ICE6 and FICID4 Clause 63; JCT 80 Clause 27; GC/Wks 1 Ed 2 Cond 45; GC/Wks 1 Ed 3 Cond 56.
30. ICE5 and ICE6 Clauses 49(4) and 62; FICID4 Clauses 49.4 and 62; JCT 80 Clause 4.1.2; GC/Wks 1 Ed 2 Cond 32(3) and 49; GC/Wks 1 Ed 3 Cond 21(3), 53 and 54.
31. ICE5, ICE6 and FIDIC4 Clause 63; JCT 80 Clause 27; GC/Wks 1 Ed 2 Cond 45; GC/Wks Ed 3 Cond 56.
32. GC/Wks 1 Ed 2 Cond 44; GC/Wks 1 Ed 3 Cond 56 and 58.

the operation of any common law rights. FIDIC4, on the other hand, contains a significant provision[33] entitling the contractor to terminate his employment under the contract on equitable terms if the employer fails to honour any certificate, obstructs the issue of certificates, becomes insolvent, or withdraws from the project. Payment in those situations is as provided by the war clause. ICE5 and ICE6 provide, in Clause 40(2), for the contractor to treat the contract as abandoned by the employer in the event of undue delay in permitting resumption of work after suspension. There is no provision under the contract for the consequences of such abandonment.

JCT 80 gives entitlement to the contractor to terminate his employment under the contract on even broader grounds.[34] Clause 28 specifies grounds of termination including failure by the employer to honour certificates, interference or prolonged suspension for various causes. This last ground can catch the architect or employer unawares as it may provide the contractor an opportunity to withdraw from an unprofitable contract to cut his loss.[35]

Frustration

In Chapter 3, the doctrine of frustration was discussed in the context of its application to a claim for payment on a *quantum meruit* where the parties proceed to complete the project. The doctrine is also relevant, though rarely invoked, as a basis for premature termination of the contract where the project is abandoned. The principles involved are the same. Entitlement to a *quantum meruit* depends on the original contract being terminated by frustration before a new contract can be implied in its place.

The term 'frustration' is used in the ICE Conditions, but no definition or explanation is given of its meaning. Clause 65 merely provides what is to happen in the event of frustration. It is, therefore, necessary to refer to the common law for enlightenment.

FIDIC4 includes an equivalent provision, but does not use the term 'frustration', presumably because the term is peculiar to common law systems. Clause 66.1 talks instead of release from performance 'if any circumstance outside the control of both parties arises . . . which renders it impossible or unlawful for either party to fulfil his contractual obligations, or under the law governing the Contract the parties are released from further performance . . .' Other Standard Forms do not make special provision for frustration, but they contain provisions which may be used to deal with such situations. If the provisions are not used, the common law rules apply.

The doctrine of frustration was described by Lord Radcliffe as follows:[36]

'The theory of frustration belongs to the law of contract and it is represented by a rule which the courts will apply in certain limited circumstances for the purpose of deciding that contractual obligations, *ex facie* binding, are no longer enforceable against the parties.'

In the event of a contract being frustrated, the contract is discharged in relation to the future performance obligations of both parties. Occurrence of the frustrating event brings the contract to an end forthwith, without more ado automatically,[37] but accrued rights and liabilities survive, as does any arbitration clause.[38]

The attitude of the courts towards what constitutes a frustrating event has varied considerably. The origin of the doctrine can be traced to rules that a contract for personal services was discharged by the death or incapacity of the individual even where, as in apprenticeship, another person (the father) was the party to the contract.[39] In *Taylor v*

---

33. FIDIC4 Clause 69.1.
34. JCT 80 Clause 28 (and Clause 28A — see Amendment 4: 1987).
35. *John Jarvis Ltd v Rockdale Housing Association Ltd* [1987] 36 BLR 48.
36. *Davis Contractors v Fareham UDC* [1956] AC 696.
37. *Hirji Mulji v Cheong Yue Steamship Co Ltd* [1926] AC 497.
38. *Heyman v Darwins* [1942] AC 356.
39. As described in *Taylor v Caldwell* [1863] 3 B & S 826.

Caldwell,[40] this was extended to the perishing of things which make the performance of the contract impossible. A theatre, hired for a series of concerts and fêtes, was burnt down. It was held that the contract was discharged, but Blackburn J made clear that the doctrine did not apply merely because the contract had become more burdensome.

The doctrine of frustration has been extended to other examples of impossibility due to supervening events, including changes in legislation. It is essential to the doctrine that the impossibility should not have resulted from the act or election of either party.[41] It has also been applied to cases where it was no longer possible to provide the thing contracted for, such as a room to view a coronation when the coronation was cancelled,[42] but not if the change in nature was merely ancillary and the foundation of the contract could still be achieved.[43]

In *Davis Contractors v Fareham UDC*,[44] the House of Lords firmly rejected the application of the doctrine to mere increased difficulty. Lord Radcliffe stated:[45]

> 'It is not hardship or inconvenience or material loss itself which calls the principle of frustration into play. There must be as well such a change in the significance of the obligation that the thing undertaken would, if performed, be a different thing from that contracted for.'

The effect of the strict requirements for frustration may be seen in *Tsarikoglou & Co v Noblee Thorl*,[46] where a shipper who had entered into a contract to ship goods from Port Sudan to Hamburg was held to be bound by the original fixed price, although he had had to ship the goods around the Cape of Good Hope instead of through the Suez Canal as expected, after the Suez Canal was closed. It was held there was no implied term that shipment would be via Suez. 'A man may habitually leave his house by the front door to keep his appointments; but, if the front door is stuck, he would hardly be excused for not leaving by the back,' said Lord Radcliffe.[47]

Where a contract is frustrated, the parties are discharged from future performance, but accrued rights and liabilities stand. At common law, this could work harshly either way, as it depended whether or not entitlement to payment had accrued. For example, in *Appleby v Myers*,[48] it was held that no payment was due on an 'entire' contract despite the work having been largely completed. On the other hand, in *Blakely v Muller*,[49] another coronation case, the time for payment had accrued before the coronation was cancelled and it was held that the party could not recover the payment.

In *Fibrosa v Fairbairn*,[50] the House of Lords attempted to find a more acceptable solution, but legislation was required. The Law Reform (Frustrated Contracts) Act 1943 was enacted to provide for a more equitable distribution of losses in the event of frustration,[51] but the Act only applies to the extent that it is consistent with any express provisions of the contract intended to cover the effects of frustration.

Under the ICE Conditions, Clause 64 provides expressly for the consequences of frustration, as regards obligations performed before the frustrating event, by reference to the war clause. FIDIC4 Clause 66.1 does likewise.

---

40. *Taylor v Caldwell* [1863] 3 B & S 826.
41. *Maritime National Fish Ltd v Ocean Trawlers Ltd* [1935] AC 524.
42. *Krell v Henry* [1903] 2 KB 740.
43. *Herne Bay Steam Boat Co v Hutton* [1903] 2 KB 683.
44. *Davis Contractors v Fareham UDC* [1956] AC 696.
45. Ibid at p 728.
46. *Tsarikoglou v Noblee Thorl* [1962] AC 93.
47. Ibid at p 123.
48. *Appleby v Myers* [1867] LR 2 CP 651.
49. *Blakely v Muller* [1903] 2 KB 760.
50. *Fibrosa v Fairbairn* [1943] AC 32.
51. The Act was considered in detail by the House of Lords in *BP Exploration Co (Libya) Ltd v Hunt (No 2)* [1983] 2 AC 352.

JCT 80 confers a right of termination on the contractor (and, where Amendment 4: 1987 is incorporated, on the employer) following suspension in the event of *force majeure* or loss or damage to the Works through the special perils.[52] These cover most potential frustrating events other than changes in legislation. Under GC/Wks 1, frustrating events can be dealt with by the Authority under the special powers of termination, but the contractor must rely on the common law.

War clauses

The outbreak of war may constitute a frustrating event if it prevents the further execution of the works. The ICE Conditions expressly mention war as a possible frustrating event.[53] More generally, war does not prevent the execution of the works, but it makes the work more onerous for the contractor, it brings additional risk of damage to the works, and it may make the work irrelevant for the employer. Two possibilities exist — that the work should continue under the more difficult circumstances and the special risk of damage due to military action; or the contract might be terminated. Standard Forms provide for both possibilities. In the event of termination, the forms mostly treat the effects of war as closely analogous to frustration, but deal with it separately.

The ICE Conditions contain very detailed provisions[54] relating to the outbreak of war 'in which Great Britain shall be engaged on a scale involving general mobilization of the armed forces of the Crown . . .'. This narrow preoccupation with war of a specific nature reflects the origins of the ICE Conditions which were first published in 1945. The war clause is unchanged, except for very minor points, since the first edition.

FIDIC Conditions, although derived from the ICE Conditions, recognize the effects of war much more widely. The relevant provisions are mostly in clause 65, but the issues are addressed in two halves. Sub-clauses 65.1 to 65.5 are concerned with the risk of damage to the works. Sub-clauses 65.6 to 65.8 deal with the possibility of termination of the contract as a result of the outbreak of war. Sub-clauses 65.1 to 65.5 apply to all 'special risks', which are listed as certain 'Employer's risks' as defined in Sub-clause 20.4 and include 'war, hostilities (whether war be declared or not), invasion, act of foreign enemies'. The contractor is indemnified by the employer against liability in consequence of the special risks including, under Sub-clause 65.5, increased costs of execution of the Works arising from special risks.

The FIDIC termination provisions have a separate definition of war, which is also much wider than that in the ICE Conditions. It covers any situation where there is 'an outbreak of war, whether war is declared or not, in any part of the world which, whether financially or otherwise, materially affects the execution of the Works'.[55]

Both the ICE and FIDIC Conditions share a feature, however, that it is only the employer that has the right to terminate the contract in the event of war. Subject to the right to indemnity by the employer against increased costs and risks as stipulated in the Conditions, the contractor is otherwise obliged to continue unless the contract is frustrated by the war.

JCT 80 also contains specific provisions relating to the outbreak of war. It is closely similar to the ICE Conditions in that it is limited to the special case of 'outbreak of hostilities (whether war is declared or not) in which the United Kingdom shall be involved on a scale involving the general mobilization of the armed forces of the Crown'.[56] There is a difference, however, that in the event of such war, either the employer or contractor has the right to serve notice terminating the contract. Clause 33 deals with the alternative position where the contract is not terminated.

GC/Wks 1 does not provide explicitly for termination in the event of war. However, the

---

52. JCT 80 Clause 28, or 28A as inserted by Amendment 4: 1987.
53. ICE5 and ICE6 Clause 64.
54. ICE5 and ICE6 Clause 65.
55. FIDIC4 Sub-clause 65.6.
56. JCT 80 Clause 32.

situation can be dealt with by termination by the Authority under the special powers of determination. In addition the 'Accepted Risks' as defined[57] include war. The definition has changed between the editions. Edition 3 includes as an accepted risk, 'war, invasion, act of foreign enemy, hostilities (whether or not war has been declared), civil war, rebellion, insurrection, or military or usurped power'.[58] Under both editions, the contractor is entitled to be indemnified against loss or damage to the Works due to the accepted risks, but Edition 3 has extended this to include loss or damage which arises out of or is in any way connected with the execution or purported execution of the Works.[59]

CASE 9.1   CLAIM FOR RECOVERY OF LIQUIDATED DAMAGES WRONGLY DEDUCTED

Pertinent particulars of contract

The contract was for the construction of a length of motorway and was based on ICE4 Conditions of Contract. Time for completion was 2 years.

Tender dated 22 January 1972.
Order to commence given 13 March 1972.
Date for completion 12 March 1974.
Date of actual completion 29 August 1974.
Liquidated damages £1,400 per week.

Events giving rise to claim

Various delays occurred during the course of the work, as is not unusual, including delay in giving possession of the site (2 weeks); by exceptionally inclement weather (a total of 9 weeks claimed, 6 allowed); extra and additional work (6 weeks claimed, 4 allowed); a strike (2 weeks) and two specific instances of delay (one week in each case) by want of drawings or details to be supplied by the engineer. The total delay was 24 weeks. Shortly after the certificate of completion had been issued, the engineer granted an extension of time of 16 weeks and informed the employer and contractor accordingly. From an interim certificate issued shortly thereafter the employer deducted £11,200 in respect of liquidated damages for eight weeks' delay.

Engineer to Contractor   *20 September 1974*

With reference to the various notifications of delay which you have given from time to time during the course of the work, these totalled twenty-one weeks but I consider the periods claimed for exceptionally inclement weather (nine weeks) and additional work (six weeks) are both overstated and I have reduced them to six weeks and four weeks respectively, thus extending the time for completion from 12 March 1974 to 2 July 1974.

Work was due to be completed by 12 March 1974 whereas it was not in fact completed until 29 August 1974, a delay of twenty-four weeks. It is therefore considered you are responsible for eight weeks' delay, liquidated damages for which amount to £11,200 at £1,400 per week.

Contractor to Engineer   *25 September 1974*

With reference to your letter of 20 September, will you please confirm that you have taken account of the delay caused by the late issue of instructions regarding pile lengths to Bridge No 4 and in the issue of drainage details from Ch 1100−1300?

---

57. GC/Wks 1 Ed 2 Cond 1(2); GC/Wks 1 Ed 3 Cond 1(1).
58. GC/Wks 1 Ed 3 Cond 19.
59. GC/Wks 1 Ed 3 Cond 19(1).

Engineer to Contractor   *30 September 1974*

> *It is confirmed that these delays did occur and one week has been allowed in each case.*

Contractor to Engineer   *3 October 1974*

> *Thank you for the information contained in your letter of 30 September. We have to point out, however, that under Clause 8 of the Conditions, no provision is made for extension of time nor is there any other provision in the contract under which time for completion may be extended in respect of delays for which the Employer is responsible.*
>
> *We are advised that in such a case the liquidated damages clause is inoperable.*

Engineer to Contractor   *14 October 1974*

> *I cannot accept the contention set out in your letter dated 3 October that the liquidated damages clause is inoperable.*
>
> *Clause 44 of the Conditions of Contract provides that the time for completion may be extended in case of 'other special circumstances of any kind whatsoever'. This clearly includes delays caused by the late issue of instructions under Clause 8. If you insist upon your contention it would mean that the extension of time granted should have been for only fourteen instead of sixteen weeks. You cannot seriously be contending this, for this would have increased your liability for liquidated damages, not reduced it to nil.*

Contractor to Engineer   *17 October 1974*

> *We are advised that provisions for extension of time are generally for the benefit of the contractor and that should the employer wish to make provision for extending the time in the event of his causing delay then express provision must be made, as is in fact the case with Clause 42.*
>
> *We are further advised that in the event of the employer being responsible for any delay, however slight, for which no provision is made for extension of time, then liquidated damages provisions are totally inoperable.*

This is of course a matter for the employer in that it is he who deducts liquidated damages: yet it is extremely important that architects, engineers and quantity surveyors should be aware of this principle as it affects recommendations they may need to make to their employers. This situation still applies in respect of the FIDIC Conditions and some *ad hoc* Forms of Contract.

In this case, the employer evidently sought legal advice as the deduction for liquidated damages was restored.

Points of principle involved

The line of cases supporting the contractor's contention has been reviewed in Chapter 8 above.[60] The cases suggest that extension of time provisions are as much for the employer's benefit as for the contractor's, but the point does not affect the argument. Whilst the defect on which this case is based has been remedied in ICE5 (see Clauses 7, 13, 14 and 31) the problem may still be encountered in *ad hoc* Conditions of Contract or amendments to Standard

---

60. See pages 220, 221.

Forms, prepared by individuals or authorities for their own use (as was the case in *Peak v McKinney Foundations*[61]). Even Standard Forms may still have gaps (e.g. supply of materials by employer).

Care is also necessary to operate the extension of time provisions at the proper time. If the contract provides that entitlement to extension of time is to be ascertained and granted to the contractor at stages during the progress of the works, it must be done at those stages. Failure to do so may defeat the power of the A/E later to extend the time for completion and consequently defeat the power of the employer to deduct liquidated damages for late completion.[62] Once defeated the powers cannot be revived within the existing contract.

It is therefore dangerous to leave granting of extensions of time to a sort of sweeping-up operation when the date of actual completion is known, except insofar as the contract may permit or require further or final review of the EoT at that stage. Any final steps required by the contract, such as issue of a certificate of non-completion must also be fulfilled or the right to deduct liquidated damages may be lost.[63]

If the power to extend the time for completion is defeated, a term will be implied instead that the contractor should complete within a reasonable time.[64] Breach of that implied term will entitle the employer to recover unliquidated damages, but he will be required to prove both the breach (involving questions of what is a 'reasonable time') and the actual loss suffered as a result of the breach, subject to the duty to mitigate that loss. Reports of cases on the topic have tended to shy away from the question of damages once the express contractual provisions have been defeated but, in *Jobson v Johnson*,[65] the Court of Appeal held that in setting aside the application of a penalty provision, the court could still award damages representing actual loss for breach of the primary obligation; or it could enforce the penalty clause subject to such conditions or relief as ensured that the claimant recovered no more than his actual loss.

The employer probably cannot recover unliquidated damages greater than he could have recovered as liquidated damages. At least he could not set up his own failure to comply with the contract as grounds for overriding the liquidated damages provisions: it is an axiom of English law that a person cannot profit from his own default.[66] The position might be otherwise if it were the contractor who had argued that the extension of time provisions were defeated.

CASE 9.2 CLAIM IN RESPECT OF LIQUIDATED DAMAGES AFTER ISSUE OF A VARIATION ORDER IN THE DELAY PERIOD

Pertinent particulars of contract

The contract was for the erection of five steel-framed buildings clad externally with corrugated steel sheeting. Foundations and floors had already been put in by another contractor. The documents comprised:

Drawings, Specification, Bill of Quantities.
Conditions of Contract: GC/Wks 1 Edition 2.
Tender (lump-sum) for £528,486 dated 10 January 1978.

Acceptance dated 27 January 1978. In the circumstances of the case, time for completion

---

61. *Peak Construction (Liverpool) Ltd v McKinney Foundations* [1970] 1 BLR 114.
62. *Miller v LCC* [1934] 50 TLR 379.
63. *A. Bell & Son (Paddington) Ltd v CBF Residential Care & Housing Association* [1989] 46 BLR 102.
64. See Sir Patrick Garland QC 1989 'Contract policy for time.' In *Construction Contract Policy, Improved Procedures and Practice* at p 195. Centre of Construction Law and Management, King's College, London.
65. *Jobson v Johnson* [1989] 1 WLR 1026,
66. *Alghussein Establishment v Eton College* [1988] 1 WLR 587.

dated from acceptance, possession of site being available for the contractor when he required it. Time for completion 15 months (date for completion 27 April 1979).

Liquidated damages £880 per week.

Events leading to claim

There was delay in delivery of the steelwork and further delay in obtaining supplies of steel sheeting, added to by a general shortage of labour. There were (for once) no variations . . . so far.

The whole situation was aggravated by the contractor's lack of drive and poor organization and the nett result was a delay of twelve and a half months.

On 25 March 1980 a variation order was issued for rehanging five doors to the opposite hand, work to the value of only a few pounds and taking just two weeks for three men to do. This work was completed by 8 April and the whole of the work was certified complete on 9 May 1980.

The question then arose as to the extension of time due and the entitlement to recover liquidated damages.

> *Contractor to Superintending Office*   *27 March 1980*
>
> *We acknowledge receipt of your variation order to rehang the five side doors. We hereby give you notice of delay pursuant to Condition 28(2).*
>
> *Superintending Office to Contractor*   *16 April 1980*
>
> *I refer to your letter of 27 March. The work was completed on 8 April, i.e., two weeks after the issue of the variation order. I have therefore recommended an extension of time of this amount.*

Under GC/Wks 1 Edition 2, extensions of time are made by the 'authority', not the Superintending Officer. In terms of the foregoing letter, the intentions of the SO are not as clear as they might be as to the date from which the two weeks were to operate. In the meantime liquidated damages amounting to £35,200 (forty weeks at £880 per week) had been deducted up to the last certificate for interim payment, dated 1 February. There had of course been strong protests from the contractor but as up to that date at least he had no grounds for extension of time, there was little he could do. The next letter was as follows:

> *Authority to Contractor*   *23 April 1980*
>
> *I have to inform you that an extension of time of two weeks is hereby allowed in respect of delay caused by the work in rehanging the doors.*
>
> *The revised date for completion is therefore 11 May 1979.*
>
> *Contractor to Authority*   *25 April 1980*
>
> *Thank you for your letter of 23 April. We think, however, there must be some mistake in the date given as the revised date for completion. Surely this should be 1980 not 1979.*
>
> *We would point out that liquidated damages amounting to £35,200 have been deducted to date, and we now claim repayment of that sum.*
>
> *Authority to Contractor*   *7 May 1980*
>
> *With reference to your letter of 25 April, there is no mistake in the date quoted, i.e. 11 May 1979.*

It is pointed out that apart from the matter of the variation, the delay is wholly your responsibility and there is no entitlement to further extension of time.

Allowing two weeks beyond the original date for completion for the work in rehanging the doors, the revised date for completion thus becomes 11 May 1979.

That being so, there is no question of refunding liquidated damages, indeed further sums are due from you in respect of the period 1 February to 9 May 1980 less two weeks. This will be deducted from the next certificate.

Contractor to Authority   *16 May 1980*

We cannot accept your interpretation of the contract as contained in your letter of 7 May. The variation order in question was dated 25 March 1980 and it was agreed that two weeks were required to do the work and that this was completed on 8 April.

Therefore there cannot possibly be any question of giving an extension of time in May 1979 for an event which occurred in May 1980.

Point of principle involved

The correct answer on the point raised needs to be reconsidered in the light of a new case, *McAlpine Humberoak v McDermott International.*[67] On a claim for unliquidated damages under a non-standard form of contract Lloyd LJ, delivering the sole judgment of the Court of Appeal, rejected a contention similar to that advanced by the contractor in the case above. He said;

'If a contractor is already a year late through his culpable fault, it would be absurd that the employer should lose his claim for unliquidated damages just because, at the last moment, he orders an extra coat of paint. On the facts of this case and the conditions of this contract the ordering of extra work on 11th June did not have that effect.'

It remains to be seen whether the judgment on this point is treated as of general application, or confined to the particular facts and conditions of contract. The position under various forms of contract in different jurisdictions has previously been reviewed by Terence Burke.[68] It may still be arguable that the A/E must elect whether he wishes to treat the construction period as continuing, with unfettered freedom to issue variation orders, or closed, in which case the A/E is only free to order variations found necessary for the completion of the works. The answer may still depend on whether the necessity for the extra works ordered could have been discovered before the contractor reached that stage of construction. In any event, the issue of the late order by the authority in this case has put the employer in a very disadvantageous position, and would have been better avoided.

A more satisfactory outcome may be obtained if the matter is dealt with explicitly in the Conditions of Contract, as recommended by IN Duncan Wallace QC.[69] In ICE6, a new provision has been incorporated for this purpose in Clause 51(1) that 'Variations . . . may be ordered during the Defects Correction Period'. Clause 44, dealing with extensions of time, makes no reference to this, but a new Clause 47(6) provides that the employer's entitlement to liquidated damages is suspended in the event of a delay caused by issue of a variation order or by a Clause 12 situation being encountered after liquidated damages have become payable. The suspension continues until the delay ceases. The employer's entitlement to liquidated damages which had already accrued is, however, protected.

67. *McAlpine Humberoak Ltd v McDermott International* [1992] unreported.
68. Burke T 1984 Prevention by Variation of the Works after Date for Completion. 2 ICLR 8.
69. Duncan Wallace I N QC 1986 *Construction Contracts Principles and Policies* App 1, Cl 24(3); App 2—12. Sweet & Maxwell, London.

Chapter 10
Compound claims

This chapter deals with what may have come to be regarded as 'traditional' in the way of claims. These are usually voluminous, and in this form usually appear later rather than earlier in relation to either the execution of work or the production of what is otherwise regarded as the 'final account'.

GENERALLY

Claims in this category require on occasion some hundreds of pages to set out their detail (causes, grounds, effect) and their valuation. They require drawings, charts, schedules and the like in their substantiation. They require copies of or at least copious reference to the contract documents, to possibly hundreds of letters, variation orders, minutes of meetings etc, plus substantiation by way of tender build-up, records of costs etc, etc. Clearly it is not possible within the compass of a single chapter in a book such as this to reproduce all this documentation *in extenso*. Something will inevitably be lost in the process of condensation and some degree of oversimplification. Yet it is hoped sufficient will remain to provide a useful precedent.

When matters arise during the course of a job, in respect of which a contractor seeks additional payment, each may be regarded as a separate claim, individually numbered and progressively resolved (or withdrawn). Alternatively a number of such matters may, by circumstances or by choice, be collected together in one submission and whether this is dealt with as a number of separate claims or a single claim with a number of parts is immaterial.

Situations frequently occur where claims arising from separate causes tend to overlap or interreact with one another and it is this aspect which may determine how the claim is dealt with. It is to this situation that the term 'compound claim' is here applied.

Such claims may occur because, at first sight, the several components appear to be inseparable or maybe it transpires that individual matters thought to have been self-standing (and possibly dealt with in the course of the job) affect or are affected by other matters arising subsequently and so require reconsideration.

Discussion or negotiation may have caused a contractor to change the grounds on which he is basing his claim, and this he is fully entitled to do. Indeed, should the matter get as far as arbitration he may then, or again, change his grounds (possibly as a result of legal advice). This may be somewhat annoying to the A/E/QS having to reconsider a mass of different points and circumstances and apply to them for a second time a different basis, but this is by no means reprehensible. It could be that had the same A/E/QS been as certain of the correct grounds (or their absence) as he now considers the contractor should have been, perhaps the contractor would have been enabled to deal with the matters more expeditiously.

Rates and prices agreed for varied work may have included some allowance for overheads and/or the disproportionate time compared with its value which such work involved, and subsequently it may have become apparent that this is overlapped by a claim for delay. A claim for disruption and loss of productivity may be significantly affected when the out-turn of final measurement becomes known. When causes of delay are considered collectively, it could become apparent that delay from one cause was contemporaneous with that from another, resulting in no additional damage. Alternatively, delay may have a 'knock-on' effect long after the initial cause of delay has ceased. In yet other ways, delay can have a disruptive effect in altering sequences of work and causing them to be done out-of-phase with other work, with consequent loss of productivity.

Another problem often associated with this type of claim is whether or not the proper notices have been given. In the interests of both the employer and contractor, it is important that the contractor should give notice of the happening of events which may give rise to a claim and for the A/E/QS to recognize this and not condemn a contractor for doing what the contract requires him to do. It is important that such matters be discussed when a notice is first given, with a view to considering whether any instructions ought be given or actions be taken by the A/E, and to identify the grounds on which any claim might validly be based and the records that ought to be kept accordingly for the substantiation or otherwise of such a claim.

SEPARATION AND AMALGAMATION OF INDIVIDUAL CLAIMS

Strictly speaking, each separate ground for claim needs to be isolated and the value of damage suffered from each to be assessed and allocated separately. Certainly every effort should be made to do this as otherwise the interaction and possible overlap between them will not become apparent. The contractor is entitled only to what he can demonstrate (prove to an arbitrator or in a court of law) he has suffered or incurred.

In some cases, however, this is more easily said than done. Different delays become intermingled and their effects become complex and impossible to disentangle. Is then the contractor to be deprived of compensation simply because of this complication when, clearly, taking each individual point separately he would be entitled to compensation? In *Crosby v Portland UDC*[1] one of the matters in dispute and submitted to arbitration was the contractor's general claim for delay attributable to a number of factors. The arbitrator, Sir Harold Harding, awarded the contractor compensation on a global basis in respect of 31 weeks out of a total delay of 46 weeks. He did not give a breakdown in his award between the various causes of delay. The Council challenged the award in the High Court by way of the case stated procedure (which is no longer available in England). Donaldson J (as he then was) held that provided 'the arbitrator does not make any award which contains a profit element, this being permissible under Clauses 51 and 52 but not under Clauses 41 and 42, and provided he ensures that there is no duplication, I can see no reason why he should not recognize the realities of the situation and make individual awards in respect of those parts of the individual items of the claim which can be dealt with in isolation and a supplementary award in respect of the remainder of these claims as a composite whole'.

That extract from the judgment should not be treated as an invitation to submit all claims on a rolled-up basis. Donaldson J made clear that if heads of claim can be isolated and costs allocated to them individually, that ought to be done. The point is that genuine and substantial claims may not be defeated or frustrated on a technicality, for example, by calling for allocation of costs to individually short delays occurring on unrealistically short lengths of road. Using a rolled-up approach may mean that the contractor will have to forgo his profit on some parts (as where variations are involved in conjunction with delay for which only bare cost is payable), but that should clearly be preferable to forgoing the claim as a whole.

The permissible scope of the *Crosby* approach should be considered in the light of the comments of Vinelott J in *Merton LBC v Leach*[2] and, more particularly, the Privy Council in *Wharf Properties v Eric Cumine Associates*[3] as discussed above in Chapter 8.

References giving details of American decisions to similar effect have been quoted in Chapter 8.[4]

CASE 10.1 CLAIMS IN CONNECTION WITH NEW ROAD CONSTRUCTION AND CONCERNING RESPONSIBILITY FOR USE OF SPECIFIED MATERIAL AS FILL, DELAY CAUSED BY STATUTORY UNDERTAKERS, EXTRA WORKS AND LATE POSSESSION OF ONE PART OF THE SITE, INCLUDING ADDITIONAL FINANCE COSTS

Pertinent particulars of contract

The contract was in respect of the construction of about eight miles of motorway with a grade separated interchange at one end. The contract documents comprised:

Drawings, reasonably comprehensive but lacking details of certain bridges and culverts.

---

1. *Crosby v Portland UDC* [1967] 5 BLR 121.
2. *Merton LBC v Stanley Hugh Leach* [1985] 32 BLR 51. See pp 230, 231 *supra*.
3. *Wharf Properties v Eric Cumine Associates* [1991] 52 BLR 1. See p 231 *supra*.
4. See p 231 *supra*.

Figure 10.1.1 (a)

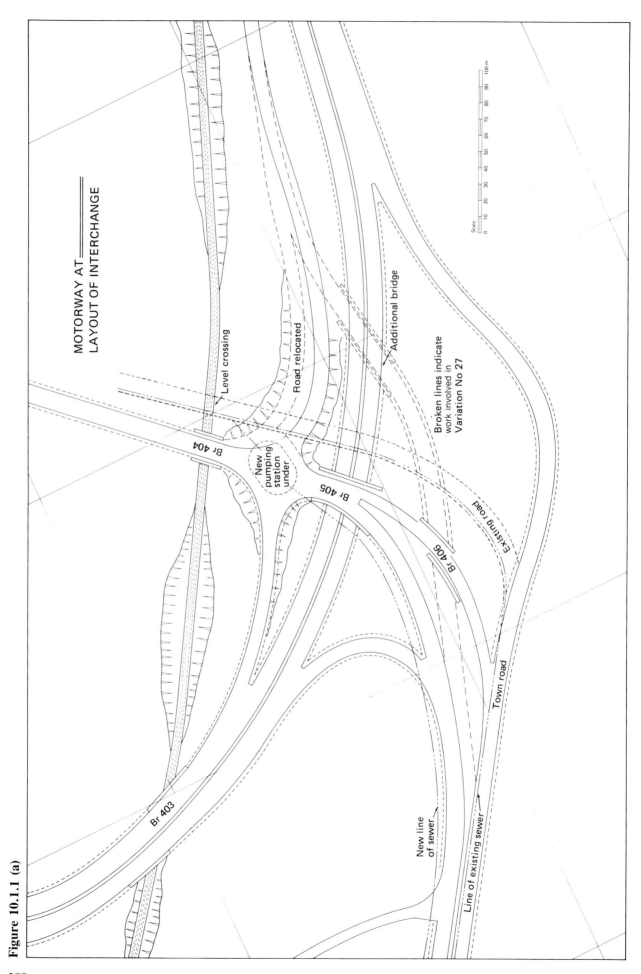

MOTORWAY AT
LAYOUT OF INTERCHANGE

Level crossing

Road relocated

Additional bridge

Broken lines indicate
work involved in
Variation No 27

Br 404

New
pumping
station
under

Br 405

Br 406

Existing road

Town road

Br 403

New line
of sewer

Line of existing sewer

Scale
0 10 20 30 40 50 60 70 80 90 100 m

Figure 10.1.1 (b)

MOTORWAY AT ━━━━━━ COMPARISON OF PLANNED PROGRAMME WITH ACTUAL

Specification comprising MOT (standard) Specification for Road and Bridge Works 1969 (with metric Addendum) together with a Particular Specification amending clauses in the standard document and introducing additional clauses required for this contract.
Bill of Quantities based on Method of Measurement for Road and Bridge Works 1971.
Conditions of Contract: ICE5 with price fluctuation.
Tender dated 16 December 1975, with a tender total of £8,238,613.
Liquidated damages were set at £6,500 per week.

Correspondence issued as circular letters to tenderers, amending certain clauses of the Specification and requiring a programme to be submitted with the tender.

Correspondence occurring between Tender and Acceptance dealing with apparent errors of prices in B/Q and engineering queries as to methods (to ensure contractor's proposals met with contract requirements).

Acceptance dated 3 February 1976 with qualifications, i.e. in effect a counter-offer.

Contractor's reply dated 6 February 1976 accepting one qualification but refusing another.

Reply accepting dated 11 February 1976.

Contract period $2\frac{1}{2}$ years. Order to commence dated 29 April 1976. Possession of site given 13 May 1976.

The following matters are of particular application and note:

Drawings

These included diagrammatic representation of borehole logs and there is a Supplementary Condition 11(1).1 referring to the Soils Report.

A part of the layout drawing of the interchange is shewn in Figure 10.1.1(a).

Specification

The following amendments were made to the 'standard' Specification:

Clause 105 — add para 3: The information shewn on the drawings regarding water, gas, electricity and other services has been obtained from the relevant Statutory Authorities. The Employer shall not be held responsible for any additional mains, cables, services, chambers, sewers, pipes or drains or for those shewn on the plans. The Contractor shall be responsible for co-ordinating his programme of work with the authorities concerned as regards any resiting of services required in connection with the works and shall allow in his tender for any delays which may occur due to any alterations to public services.

Comment: Disclaimers as to the existence and location of public utility services are not uncommon. Information concerning location, even if obtained from the relevant Statutory Undertaker, is known generally to be unreliable. The disclaimer therefore does no more than shew that the information given does not purport to be any more accurate.

Attempt is sometimes made to put responsibility for delay caused by SUs (which is all too common an occurrence) upon the contractor. If a clause really does that then the contractor would be advised to query it when tendering rather than risk having to claim. Many clauses are unclear as to what they mean, of which the above is an example. There is a clear responsibility for co-ordination but it is doubtful if there is anything more. The loose terminology of the last sentence might almost be taken to refer to buses or trains rather than pipes and cables, which illustrates the danger of using different words for the same thing.

Clause 601.1(iv) — 'Rock' shall mean Sandy Mudstone.

Clause 601.1(vii) — Selected Fill shall be crushed rock, broken brick, broken concrete, or gravel, well graded from a maximum size of 6 in. with 55–25% passing a $\frac{3}{4}$ in. and not more than 10% passing a No 200 sieve prior to compaction.

Clause 601.2 — amend as follows:
  (i) Cohesive soil . . . with a moisture content of that fraction of the soil which pases a $\frac{3}{4}$ in. BS sieve shall not be greater than 1.2 times the value of the plastic limit . . .
  (ii) Well graded granular and dry cohesive soils . . . with a moisture content of that fraction of the soil which passes a $\frac{3}{16}$ in. BS sieve shall not be greater than 2% above the optimum moisture content determined in accordance with BS 1377 Test No 13, well graded sands . . .
  (iii) Uniformly graded material . . . The moisture content (except for PFA) of that fraction of the soil which passes a $\frac{3}{4}$ in. sieve shall not be greater than 15% or less than 8% when measured in accordance with BS 1377.

Clause 608 — add to paragraph 1: Unweathered Sandy Mudstone from site excavation shall be used in the upper layers of embankments and immediately below formation in filling any over-excavation or soft spots in cuttings. It is expected that there will be a shortfall of this material on site but surplus material of the same kind arising from an adjacent contract will be stockpiled at . . . . and shall be available to the contractor (without charge) for use on this contract.

Add to paragraph 4: (iv) provide at his own expense an equal quantity of the same unweathered material from his own resources or an equal quantity of imported fill material as Clause 601.1(vii).

Bill of Quantities

There was included in the Preambles relating to earthworks the following clause:

'Rock': In this Bill of Quantities the word 'Rock' shall in the context of excavation mean Sandy Mudstone and unweathered Keuper Marl. This definition applies only to measurement for payment purposes and shall not of itself be construed as referring to material specified to be used for any given purpose or having any particular properties.

Comment: It may well be that some materials (as for example Keuper Marl) may be very hard and rock-like to excavate and should be segregated so that the contractor can price accordingly, but obviously care must be taken not to conflict with any definitions or stipulations in the Specification. This clause appears to meet this requirement and should itself cause no difficulty.

A Preamble was also included as follows:

Adjustment Item
Provision is made in the Grand Summary of this Bill of Quantities for the insertion of a lump sum to be added to or deducted from the total of the preceding Bills in arriving at the Tender Total.

Such sum shall be paid or recovered (as the case may be) by instalments in interim certificates in the proportion that the total of such certificates less any amount in respect of Provisional and PC sums but before the application of the provisions of the Price Fluctuation Clause and before the deduction of any retention moneys and before the addition/deduction of any part of this Adjustment Item bears to the corresponding amount of the Tender Total. Provided that the total amount added to or deducted from the final account shall not exceed the sum stated in the Bill of Quantities.

Figure 10.1.2

BILL OF QUANTITIES – GRAND SUMMARY

Preliminaries			1,192,250
Site clearance			17,620
Fencing			248,722
Drainage and service ducts	Interchange	206,619	
	Road	618,582	825,201
Earthworks	Interchange	280,411	
	Road	1,201,589	1,482,000
Carriage-way			
Sub-base and road base	Interchange	163,966	
	Road	718,181	882,147
Flexible surfacing	Interchange	92,604	
	Road	471,615	564,219
Kerbs and footways		59,587	
		282,749	342,336
Traffic signs and markings		5,000	
		23,780	28,780
Structures			
Bridge No 403		638,164	
Bridge No 404		174,825	
Bridge No 405		205,803	
Bridge No 406		297,940	
Bridge No 511		202,125	
Bridge No 628		254,793	
Retaining wall A		56,281	
Retaining wall B		22,447	
Culverts		144,442	1,996,820
Testing			21,241
Accommodation Works			37,277
Provisional and PC Sums (including daywork)			200,000
			£7,838,613
Add/deduct lump sum (if any)		Add	400,000
		Tender Total	£8,238,613

The Summary of the Bill of Quantities and the Preliminaries Bill are shewn at Figures 10.1.2 and 10.1.3 respectively.

Conditions of Contract

There was a Supplementary Condition regarding the Soils Survey:

> Clause 11(1).1 The Contractor shall be deemed to have inspected the Soils Survey Report prepared by Messrs . . . . dated October 1973 for the Employer. The information contained therein is believed to be correct but is not guaranteed. The Contractor shall be responsible for any deductions he may draw from such information.

Comment: Clauses such as this, sometimes amounting to complete disclaimers, are not uncommon. The meaning and effect of such a clause will obviously depend on the precise

Figure 10.1.3

BILL OF QUANTITIES – PRELIMINARIES (GENERAL ITEMS)

Item				£		
A1	Provision of Bond (Clause 10)		Item		34,000	00
A2	Insurance of Works (Clause 21)		Item		72,000	00
A3	Insurance against Third Party Damage		Item		31,500	00
A4	Provision and removal of accommodation for Engineer		Item		21,500	00
A5	Servicing accommodation for Engineer	Wk	130	200	26,000	00
A6	Provision and removal of accommodation for Contractor		Item		35,000	00
A7	Servicing accommodation for Contractor	Wk	130	300	39,000	00
A8	Provision, maintenance and running of transport for the Engineer	Wk	195	100	19,500	00
A9	Progress photographs, sets of 20	No	20	40	800	00
A10	Additional progress photographs	No	50	3	150	00
A11	Contractor's site supervision	Wk	130	5560	722,800	00
A12	Traffic safety and control		Item		21,000	00
A13	Provision and removal of temporary diversion of traffic and new level crossing		Item		145,000	00
A14	Maintenance of temporary diversion and level crossing	Wk	60	400	24,000	00
					£1,192,250	00

wording, but it must also be read in conjunction with relevant provisions of the Conditions of Contract. In particular Clause 11 of ICE5 says, 'The Contractor shall be deemed ... to have satisfied himself before submitting his tender as to the nature of the ground and sub-soil (so far as is practicable and having taken into account any information connected therewith which may have been provided by or on behalf of the Employer) ...'. The effect of information provided being qualified by a disclaimer is not mentioned. If information is provided, it is not necessary that it be warranted or guaranteed; it is still deemed to be taken into account.

The effect of any disclaimer may be limited, irrespective of the Conditions of the Contract, by the Misrepresentation Act 1967 s3 (as amended by UCTA),[5] which limits the effect of clauses excluding liability for misrepresentation. The Act only applies, strictly speaking, to claims for misrepresentation but its provisions may reasonably be taken into account in interpreting and applying contractual provisions dealing with misrepresentation-type situations.

Scenario

We now have the documentary skeleton — the props as it were — of a drama (or should it be tragedy?) of which this case is typical. Neither the size of the contract nor the size of the claim makes any difference, divide both by ten and one can find the same situation. Let us now attempt to put some flesh on the skeleton, to indicate something of the action, and see if we can discern why the characters acted as they did (perhaps at times see how they should have acted) and discover what the outcome was, or should have been. Fiction

5. See p 43 *supra*.

this is in the sense that it refers directly to no actual case but in substance it may be found, at least as regards individual aspects, in the experience of many.

It may be that the job got off to a rather unfortunate start (there was delay in giving an order to commence) and the giving of notice of a claim (as required under Clause 42) almost at once did not endear the contractor to the engineer. Personalities on the site tended to be somewhat abrasive and attitudes unhelpful. In other respects, the contractor tended to complain about the contract documents and the unhelpful reaction of the RE by way of evasive and defensive response rather than attempt to establish what if anything he was entitled to and why. His eventual recourse to experts was somewhat late in the day. There is always difficulty when consulting experts, legal or otherwise, in putting the right questions and also in getting engineers and quantity surveyors to understand the legal implications of documents and events and lawyers to understand the engineering or other considerations involved. In the meantime everyone (on both sides) struggled to get the job completed, more concerned with the physical problems presenting themselves and not sufficiently appreciating that (as Lord Denning said in *Gilbert Ash v Modern Engineering*[6]) 'There must be cash flow in the building trade. It is the very lifeblood of the enterprise.' It is hardly surprising that the engineer should be concerned at the prospect of substantial claims, but they do not lend themselves to being swept under the carpet. Nor is it surprising that the contractor's financial position eventually obliges him to claim for everything he can think of regardless of overlap and totalling a sum greatly in excess of what he can hope to recover in order (as he sees it) to substantiate enough to cover his costs.

This is the sort of situation which has come to be regarded as typical of Claims (with a capital C) where the contractor gives the appearance of being unscrupulous and the A/E/QS of being intractable; where the contractor is finding the cost of financing his losses to be crippling and the A/E/QS dreading the day when he must apprise his employer of the sorry story and he in turn taking on the worry of finding additional finance and looking for heads to roll. The primary means of avoiding such situations developing is in attention to pre-contract preparation, tendering, planning and timely performance on both sides; but it is no less important that all those involved should play their parts in dealing with matters that do arise on a proper and professional basis. This requires a proper understanding by all concerned of what contracts impose on the parties to them (and the limit of those impositions) and on those 'creatures of the contract' (as the law ponderously dubs them), the architect, engineer and quantity surveyor, in the administration of such contracts.

Events and circumstances leading to the claim

The tender was accepted on 3 February 1976 but was in effect a counter-offer. The contractor's counter-counter-offer was accepted on 11 February. The engineer gave Date for Commencement as 29 April (6 weeks later than the contractor had indicated on his T & P chart accompanying his tender — see Figure 10.1.1(b)) and possession of site was not given until 13 May.

There were a number of relatively minor variations from the start but on 21 June 1976 Variation Order No 27 involved a major change. The entry to the motorway from Bridge No 404 was deleted and diverted to a point south of Bridge No 405, with a new roundabout and new bridge over the motorway. This was shortly followed by a request from the Water Authority for a new pumping station on the sewer being relocated and it was decided to put this beneath the new roundabout. This seriously delayed road works in the area of the interchange. The work had to be designed to suit the plant to be installed and Variation Order No 141 for this work was not issued until 23 March 1977.

The contractor started the earthworks of the motorway proper at the end of May 1977 but almost immediately encountered difficulties with the Sandy Mudstone. The situation developing from this and the associated drainage became very protracted. It was not until about September 1978, when the earthworks were well advanced, that the contractor sought

---

6. *Gilbert Ash v Modern Engineering* [1973] 1 BLR 83 (CA). The decision of the Court of Appeal was reversed by the House of Lords, but Lord Denning's comment is still a valid observation.

expert advice on the matter of the Sandy Mudstone but it was not until 3 months later that he got the advice he should have had almost 20 months earlier. There was a further complication in that occupants of premises on the site of Bridge No 628 had not vacated and possession was delayed by about 2 months whilst the necessary legal procedures were invoked.

The contractor gave notice of most of the delays as he saw them but the engineer was unwilling to extend the time for completion in respect of some of the causes, contending that the effect of the delays in question was not yet fully established. One of the outcomes of this was that from about mid-1979 the employer deducted liquidated damages from interim certificates.

In the meantime somewhat spasmodic progress was made with the final measurement and preparation of the final account. Both sides were inclined to regard this as a 'fall-back' job. The contractor had rather more staff available than had the engineer but the former contended that under Clause 56 it was the engineer's responsibility to measure.

At some stage, which the contractor must consider opportune either because he has completed preparation of his claims or because his need for ready cash has driven him so to complete them, he must submit a formal claim to the engineer. That this must be complete goes without saying; it weakens credibility if some later claims have to be put in, they tend to look rather manufactured. They should also state the grounds on which the various claims are based and give full particulars both as to the events leading to the claims and the effect of such events in terms of the additional costs resulting. They should be accompanied by all the documentation necessary to substantiate the facts being alleged and the computation of the amounts being claimed.

In the following example, the documentation is unavoidably abridged but it must be emphasized that in reality it must be comprehensive if delay in consideration is to be avoided.

The negotiation of the claims

It is to be assumed that with his letter of 10 March 1980 (post) the contractor did supply all that he thought necessary and that this somewhat massive document took the engineer some time to examine and to form even a preliminary opinion of what substance there was in the claims, to decide what further information was needed and whether it would be better to seek at least some further information prior to arranging a meeting or whether it would be better to have a meeting first to gauge the attitude of the contractor and probe a little as to where the strengths or weaknesses may lie. Such a meeting will of course be equally revealing to the contractor. On the whole, however, this course is probably better than trying to accept some small matters, reject others, and call for a bit more information on yet others, because in so doing one is in danger of reducing the problem to a hard core where there is, or seems to be, no room for manoeuvre. Individual claims are sometimes totally acceptable or totally unacceptable, but this is not the usual case. There are often constraints or mitigating (or aggravating, depending on one's point of view) circumstances on one side or the other and endeavour must be made to reach some agreement within the terms of the contract provisions.

In the following example it is therefore to be assumed that the engineer took about two months to examine these claims and that he then called a meeting at which all the claims would be discussed in some degree. The following narrative sets out the statements of claim but deals with each as they might be discussed at a series of meetings.

Contractor to Engineer *10 March 1980*

CLAIMS

We have intimated to you from time to time throughout the currency of this job a number of matters in connection with which we consider we are entitled to additional payment. These have met with very little or no response and in some cases we have been told that nothing can be done

Figure 10.1.4

HEADS OF CLAIM

1. Extra costs due to delayed Order to Commence	22,240
2. Extra costs of placing and compacting Sandy Mudstone, including delay	1,282,581
3. Extra cost of laying part of drainage out of sequence, causing delay	138,074
4. Delays by Statutory Undertakers (66 KVA cable and diversion of main sewer)	87,322
5. Disruption and loss of productivity caused by 1, 2 and 3	250,608
6. Delay in possession of site of Bridge No 628	13,987
7. Delay and extra cost in connection with Variation Order for roundabout and additional bridge and approach road	29,030
8. Delay and disruption caused by Water Authority requirement for pumping station at low level at roundabout	109,889
9. Increase in Adjustment Item	36,000
10. Wrongful deduction of liquidated damages	212,895
11. Interest on outstanding monies	513,468
	£2,696,094

---

until the work is complete. This has now been achieved and we must now formally submit our claims in connection with these outstanding matters.

We are and have throughout been in some difficulty in formulating these claims as we have not been given the extensions of time for which we have applied. Not only have liquidated damages been wrongfully deducted, but we have been deprived of substantial sums of money which have caused us financial difficulty and embarrassment.

We therefore ask that these claims be given your urgent attention. We shall be glad to give you any further information you may require and are ready at any time to attend any meeting you may wish to arrange to discuss the matter

The Heads of Claim are shewn in Figure 10.1.4.

Any attempt to shelve consideration of a claim is foolish and counter-productive. It could also be in breach of Clause 60(2)(a) under which the contractor is entitled to payment in 'respect of (a) the amount which in the opinion of the engineer on the basis of the monthly statement is due to the contractor' (see Clause 60(1)(d)). Of course the engineer is entitled to sufficient information to enable him to be satisfied (see Clause 52(4)(f)) but that is not to say he can arbitrarily postpone examination.

The presumption that entitlement to extension of time is essential to entitlement to payment is fallacious, as is the presumption that extension of time necessarily leads on to payment in direct proportion to the period of time granted. A contractor may be entitled to additional payment for delay to operations not on the critical path and for which no extension of time is required. He may be entitled to additional payment for delay even if he has completed within the contract period, provided of course that the delay can be substantiated and that additional cost has been incurred. He may be entitled to payment of cost incurred in reducing the extension of time required. He may be entitled to extension of time for causes which give no entitlement to additional payment.

On the other hand the granting of an extension of time does have significance for payment in that it involves acknowledgement or admission of the facts on which the entitlement is based. Those facts may be relevant to entitlement to payment. The submission of a claim to an extension of time may also be significant as an essential step if a contractor intends to claim payment for steps taken to make up time. The relationship between extension of time and additional payment is complex and needs careful understanding. Oversimplification leads to misunderstanding.

CLAIM NO 1   EXTRA COSTS DUE TO DELAYED ORDER TO COMMENCE

Statement of claim

Our tender was finally accepted on 11 February 1976 but we were not given an order to commence until 29 April, although we had indicated on the programme accompanying our tender that we had planned our work on the basis of starting in mid-March.

We did not get possession of the site until 13 May, and whilst we were able to catch up some time in getting established on site and with site clearance the latter was not complete until the end of July, i.e. one month late. More important was the fact that the earthworks to the interchange could not be started until towards the end of July. These were further delayed by the sewer diversion and alterations to layout under Variation No 27.

We have therefore found it difficult to separate the costs attributable to late commencement but your QS has insisted that this must be done. We accordingly claim the following:

(a) Extension of time of four weeks (which gives you the benefit of the period we were able to catch up)
(b) Compensation for extended overheads:
    Preliminaries Item A11, 4 weeks at £5,560 = £22,240

Claim No 2 followed immediately on this, but for clarity, comment and response on each claim will be interposed.

The contractor has quoted no contract conditions on which he bases his claim, nor any argument except that the start was later than he programmed.

The costs attributable to various heads of claim should be separated as far as practicable to enable proper consideration of each claim, but the possibility of a rolled-up claim cannot be excluded absolutely if separation is impracticable.[7] The QS was wrong to do so.

After usual introductions and courtesies, and some general comment on the job as a whole and the problem of claims, detailed discussion starts, dealing with each claim separately. The narrative is set out in the form of a skeleton of the discussion. Although all the remarks are attributed to 'engineer' or 'contractor', it is to be assumed that members of their respective teams made their contribution.

First meeting 17/6/89

Engineer:
Clause 41 says that the order to commence is to be given within a reasonable time after acceptance. I do not agree that the time taken in this case was unreasonable.

In any case, time for completion runs from order to commence and two weeks for possession of site after such order is surely not unreasonable.

---

7. *Crosby v Portland UDC* [1967] 5 BLR 121.

Your claim for both extension of time and compensation is therefore rejected.

Contractor:
We see your argument, but you must agree that eleven weeks from acceptance to order to commence and another two before possession of site is given is hardly reasonable, particularly in view of the earthworks involved. However, we will not press this claim at present but reserve our right to bring it up again if we cannot reach an overall settlement.

What is reasonable depends upon the circumstances in any given case. Here, the *locus standi* of the programme submitted with the tender is not clear. It is presumed that it is not contractual (though this should have been made clear in the tender). The engineer is in any case stretching things somewhat to take eleven weeks before giving an order to commence and then two more before possession of site is given. The potential effect on earthworks and drainage is the danger, but the contractor has made nothing of this, perhaps because it was more seriously affected by later events.

The contractor could not in any event claim in terms of Preliminaries. If he could sustain a contention that thirteen weeks' 'delay' (or some part of it) was unreasonable he might then claim that he had engaged an agent and other staff for the job for whom he had no other employment. He would then need to claim the cost involved.

CLAIM NO 2   EXTRA COST OF PLACING AND COMPACTING SANDY MUDSTONE

This is not the next event occurring in time sequence but the choice of how to present his claim is the contractor's. The merits of this claim may well stand independently but, in considering the effects, preceding events may affect the situation on which this present circumstance has impact. Further, such a circumstance may well have directly consequential effects.

Statement of claim

There has been much correspondence and many meetings over a long period and we append a list of letters, minutes of meetings etc in connection with this matter.

We based our tender on the information contained in the contract documents and we contend that the material we encountered and were required by the Specification to use in certain embankments and in filling below formation level in cuttings was different from what we could have expected and that the various instructions we received as to its use were variations under Clause 51 of the Conditions. As you will know, the difficulty with this material was in fact the major cause of delay and the earthworks took almost twice as long to execute as we planned for. The facts may be briefly recapitulated as follows.

In Specification Clause 601.1(iv) Sandy Mudstone was defined as 'rock' and was directed to be used in the upper layers of embankments (Specification Clause 605) and in filling soft spots below formation levels in cuttings. This clause also stated that similar material from another contract would be stockpiled for our use.

In Specification Clause 601.1(vii) 'Selected Fill' was defined as crushed rock, broken brick or concrete and is to be read as being synonymous with and to be used as an alternative to Sandy Mudstone.

The B/Q defined rock as being Sandy Mudstone and unweathered Keuper Marl. This was of course for measurement only of excavation but at least it reinforced our view of the nature of the Sandy Mudstone in question.

The Soils Report which was available for our inspection referred to the Sandy Mudstone as a generally well cemented series of micaceous fine sandstones, generally more arenaceous than the overlying marl. It also drew attention to the fact that Keuper Marl can slake and disintegrate but made no such nor any qualification regarding Sandy Mudstone.

There was a note on Drawing No 14/2877/75 that the Sandy Mudstone was a hard, fine-grained micaceous sandstone.

There was no prohibition about using the surface of embankments in Sandy Mudstone for haul traffic other than that which applied to any other material.

Specification Clause 601.1(iv) defines 'rock' and para(v) defines 'rock fill' and says that 'this may comprise rock as defined in this Clause'.

All these things taken together led us to believe that there would be no undue difficulty in either handling or compacting this material.

Turning now from the basis on which we formed our opinion when tendering to the situation we encountered, the material proved to be hard and rock-like when dug but disintegrated under the effects of even a light shower and under compaction. In use in embankments, some material was rejected by the inspector there as not being Sandy Mudstone yet it had been accepted as such by the inspector at the dig. The overlying marl and any lenses of soft material had been removed and only the underlying rock was used. In general, we were being blamed for mishandling the material but we were never told how we were going wrong.

In many locations material was condemned as being 'too wet', but when we asked for an indication of the permitted moisture content we were told that this was not applicable to rock. With this we were inclined to agree but it is clearly inconsistent with material being rejected as 'too wet'.

On other occasions material was condemned under Specification Clause 608.4 because it was said it had deteriorated in stockpiles which we had arranged. We pointed out that you yourselves had arranged for a stockpile of material for our use and there was no stipulation about this having to be used quickly. Our own stockpiles were generally standing about two weeks, which was surely too short to expect any 'weathering' of the material.

It was certainly not practicable to use the top of embankments where Sandy Mudstone had been used as haul roads and this caused serious problems, much delay and increased the length of the haul.

On one occasion when this matter was being discussed at a progress meeting, the RE pointed out that although certain geological strata were referred to as rock, it did not necessarily follow that the material was suitable for rock fill. In view of the fact that the material was undeniably heaving under the roller (even in cases where the material when excavated was dry and there was no rain whilst being transported and compacted), this may indeed have been so, but so far as the contract is concerned Specification Clause 601.1(v) says that 'rock fill' may comprise rock as defined in this clause.

It is quite apparent therefore that this material was not behaving as we had every right to expect it to behave. Put another way, the material we were being required to use was different from that specified and its use therefore constituted a variation. Added to this, the piecemeal manner in which we were instructed as to its use and the lack of information as to the criteria for its rejection resulted in hand-to-mouth working more in keeping with jobbing work than a major civil engineering project.

We therefore claim reimbursement on the basis of the cost of labour and plant necessarily expended (by our sub-contractor) together with compensation for the delay which has retained our organisation on site for some fifteen months longer than would otherwise have been necessary.

Evaluation

This work was wholly sub-let on the basis of appropriate extracts from the Main Contract together with FCEC 'Blue Form', and was on a fixed price basis for completion in twenty-two months. The tender was dated 11 December 1975.

Total value	1,482,000	
Less work in interchange	280,411	£1,201,589

The actual time taken was thirty-four months, with two breaks of three months each over the winters of 1977/78 and 1978/79.

There were three main factors involved, loss of productivity compared with what we expected, additional increased costs and extended overheads over the longer period.

Regarding loss of productivity, our plant and labour force were in fact very similar to that on which we based our estimate but it was of course on site for the much longer period.

Regarding increased costs, as you will appreciate these increased sharply in 1977–79. We had allowed for increases of 10 per cent in respect of labour and materials and 12 per cent in respect of plant. We have calculated amounts representing the actual increases which form part of our total costs using the National Economic Development Office (NEDO) formula.

Regarding overheads, we calculated our site requirements based on a twenty-two month period. Our site organisation had to remain for the whole period although we closed down actual work for two three-month winter periods.

We set out in Appendix 1 [Figure 10.1.5] an analysis of our sub-contractor's tender so as to shew the figures for labour, plant and materials required on the main road section.

In Appendix 2 [Figure 10.1.6] we shew in bar chart form the actual progress in terms of time and money and the payments received compared with what had been expected (allowing for time-lag in preparing statement, certification and payment).

In Appendix 3 [Figure 10.1.7] we shew the additional increased costs incurred. We shew the payments received month by month from which we have deducted increased costs at the rate included in the tender. We have then calculated the increased costs actually incurred using the NEDO formula applied to the nett amounts.

In Appendix 4 [Figure 10.1.8] we shew the actual cost of labour, plant and materials as incurred. We have distributed increased costs proportionately between these elements so as to arrive at nett costs which can be compared with corresponding elements in our tender to shew the loss of productivity. We consider materials to be properly included here because they are almost entirely fuel and timber, i.e. all consumable and therefore also increased as a factor of lost productivity.

We therefore claim the following amounts:

1. Per our sub-contractor		
Loss of productivity	378,857	
Increased costs	343,141	
Site overheads	48,508	
Additional Head Office overheads	79,817	
Profit	42,543	892,866

2. Our own costs and expenses		
Increase in bond premium (pro rata to value)	4,210	
Increase in CAR insurance (ditto)	8,914	
Increase in third party insurance (ditto)	3,899	
Increase in servicing accommodation 48 weeks at £300	14,400	
Increase in site supervision 48 weeks at £5,560	266,880	
	298,303	
HO overheads (average for the period) 10.17%	30,337	328,640
		1,221,506
Profit 5%		61,075
		£1,282,581

We must wait and see what the engineer's reaction is to this tale of woe and whether the contractor has anything more to his defence, but perhaps one may be allowed to comment here that reliance solely on information given in the contract is unwise to say the least and unsafe in view of Clause 11 of the Conditions. Regarding the stockpile of material being arranged from another contract, the situation might have been different had it been there for the tenderers to see.

First meeting

> *Engineer:*
> *The misunderstanding concerning the Sandy Mudstone seems to be a matter of your responsibility under the Contract. Material identified as being Sandy Mudstone was approved for excavation but the fact remains that when placed and rolled it was unsatisfactory. The material is indubitably Sandy Mudstone and there would seem to be no alternative to the conclusion that the material had deteriorated in handling and transport. Specification Clause 608.4 makes provision for what is to happen if the material '... subsequently reaches a condition such that it cannot be compacted ...' This is what happened and you were accordingly required to remove the material and replace it.*

The engineer seems to be somewhat obtuse, but whether or not this is a tactical defence is as yet not clear. He has not put forward the point where it would seem the contractor is most vulnerable.

> *Contractor:*
> *We cannot agree with your contention that we allowed the material to deteriorate. The contract documents described the material as Sandy Mudstone, defined it as rock and specified its use as rock fill. We have drawn your attention to all the information contained in the contract and we maintain we were entitled to rely on that information and tender accordingly. If the material requires special methods of handling or different methods of compaction than that to be expected for rock and defined in the contract then obviously this constitutes a variation.*

Really, this does not advance matters at all, unless perhaps the contractor is hinting, gently and tactfully, at possible misrepresentation.

> *Engineer:*
> *In what way does this material differ from that which seems to be envisaged in Specification Clause 609.6?*

293

Figure 10.1.5

Claim No 2 – Appendix 1

Analysis of sub-contractor's tender

	Nett	Increased costs	Total	Percentages		
Labour	396,636	39,664	436,300	37.95	29.44	*Increased costs*
Plant	495,286	59,434	554,720	48.25	37.43	$\dfrac{127,189}{1,172,829} = 10.84$
Materials	144,158	14,416	158,574	13.79	10.70	
Total	1,036,080	113,514	1,149,594	99.99		$\dfrac{127,189}{1,300,018} = 9.78$
Site oncosts (calculated for job) = 13.08% of above total costs	136,749	12,675	150,424		10.15	$\dfrac{127,189}{1,482,000} = 8.5823$
	1,172,829	127,189	1,300,018			
HO oncosts (percentage of direct costs)		8.57%	111,411		7.52	
'Turnover'			1,411,429			
Profit, taken on turnover		5%	70,571		4.76	
			1,482,000		100.00	

Distribution between interchange and main road

Total of B/Q items for interchange					280,411	
Ditto for main road					1,201,589	£1,482,000
Analysis for main road						
Labour	321,588	32,159	353,747			
Plant	401,572	48,189	449,761			
Materials	116,882	11,688	128,570			
	840,042	92,036	932,078			
Site oncosts	110,875	11,087	121,962			
	950,917	103,123	1,054,040			
HO oncosts 8.57%			90,331			
			1,144,371			
Profit 5%			57,218			
			£1,201,589			

Figure 10.1.6

Claim No 2 – Appendix 2
EARTHWORKS

	Planned	As done
Interchange	280,411	239,581
Main road	1,201,589	1,339,992
	£1,482,000	£1,579,573

Comparison of planned and actual progress

1976

	May	June	July	August	September	October	November	December
INTERCHANGE Work planned			75,000	110,000	95,411			
Payments expected 000's					70	100	90	
Actual progress				65,000	70,000	24,700	11,000	9,000
Actual payments 000's						60	65	20

1977

	January	February	March	April	May	June	July	August
INTERCHANGE P'ments expected	20,411							
Actual progress			28,000	31,881				
Actual payments	15		15		25	25		14,581
MAIN ROAD WORKS Work planned				65,000	95,000	120,000	120,000	100,000
Payments expected 000's						60	90	115
Actual progress								
Actual payments 000's								75

1977 / 1978

	September	October	November	December	January	February	March	April
Main road work planned	125,000	110,000	85,000	75,000	75,000	70,000	80,000	81,000
Payments expected 000's	115	125	110	85	75	75	75	65
Actual progress	75,000	60,000	50,000					
Actual payments 000's	75	65	70	55	50		10	15

1978

	May	June	July	August	September	October	November	December
Payments expected 000's	90	100		21,589				
Actual progress	85,000	95,000	100,000	90,000	85,000	70,000	60,000	
Actual payments 000's	50	65	80	90	95	90	80	60

1979

	January	February	March	April	May	June	July	August	Sept
Actual progress			60,000	80,000	75,000				
Actual payments 000's	60	20	15		55	75	70	10	9,992

Figure 10.1.7

Claim No 2 – Appendix 3

Additional increased costs by reason of delay in payments as expected compared with those actually made

Certificate dated	Amount	Increased costs @ tender rate 8.58%	Nett	Price fluctuation factor	Actual increased costs	Additional increased costs
August 1977	75,000	6,435	68,565	0.2836	19,445	13,010
September	75,000	6,435	68,565	0.2893	19,836	13,401
October	65,000	5,577	59,423	0.2916	17,328	11,751
November	70,000	6,006	63,994	0.2965	18,974	12,968
December	55,000	4,719	50,281	0.2894	14,551	9,832
January 1978	50,000	4,290	45,710	0.3001	13,718	9,428
March	10,000	858	9,142	0.3045	2,784	1,926
April	15,000	1,287	13,713	0.3152	4,322	3,055
May	50,000	4,290	45,710	0.3244	14,828	10,538
June	65,000	5,577	59,423	0.3275	19,461	13,884
July	80,000	6,864	73,136	0.3419	25,005	18,141
August	90,000	7,722	82,278	0.3540	29,126	21,404
September	95,000	8,151	86,849	0.4064	35,295	27,144
October	90,000	7,722	82,278	0.4121	33,907	26,185
November	80,000	6,864	73,136	0.4224	30,893	24,029
December	60,000	5,148	54,852	0.4253	23,329	18,181
January 1979	60,000	5,148	54,852	0.4278	23,466	18,318
February	20,000	1,716	18,284	0.4337	7,930	6,214
March	15,000	1,287	13,713	0.4394	6,025	4,738
May	55,000	4,719	50,281	0.4563	22,943	18,224
June	75,000	6,435	68,565	0.4643	31,835	25,400
July	70,000	6,006	63,994	0.4972	31,818	25,812
August	10,000	858	9,142	0.6018	5,502	4,644
September	9,992	857	9,135	0.6339	5,701	4,934
	1,339,992	114,971	1,225,021		458,112	343,141

Contractor:
That clause refers to a rock which 'contains' sufficient soft material for satisfactory compaction. The stuff we were being asked to use does not contain soft material, it degrades under the rollers and with the slightest addition of moisture. It was quite different from what we were led to expect from the contract documents.

Engineer:
I do not accept that the contract documents were in any way incorrect. Apart from the information with which you were supplied you were required, indeed you were 'deemed' to have satisfied yourselves 'as to the nature of the ground and subsoil ...' Have a look at Clause 11(1).

Here it is at last. Apart from requiring the tenderer to look — or be presumed to have looked even if he has not — this provision makes it more difficult to plead misrepresentation if the contractor is deemed to have satisfied himself.

Contractor:
We do not dispute this but Clause 11(1) goes on to say 'so far as is practicable'. The time available to us for tendering was much less than that available to the engineer in preparing the design. Of course we visited the site and made such enquiries as we could.

In quoting conditions of contract, people are apt to read the phrases that seem to help their arguments. Always make sure what follows.

Figure 10.1.8

Claim No 2 – Appendix 4

Actual cost of labour, plant, materials etc, cf Analysis of Final Account (Main Road Section Only)

	Actual costs			Final account		
	Gross	Increased costs App 3	Nett	Nett	Increased costs at tender rate	Total
Labour	653,081	153,747	499,334	358,640	35,854	394,394
Plant	830,339	195,477	634,862	447,834	53,725	501,559
Materials	237,363	55,880	181,483	130,348	13,031	143,379
	1,720,783	405,104	1,315,679	936,822	102,610	1,039,432
Site oncosts	225,164	53,008	172,156	123,648	12,361	136,009
Total direct	1,945,947	458,112	1,487,835	1,060,470	114,971	1,175,441
HO overheads	180,584	(at 9.28% average for period)			(as at Tender)	100,767
	2,216,531					1,276,208
Profit	106,327					63,786
	2,232,858					1,339,992

Summary

Cost of labour, plant and materials actually incurred (nett)		1,315,679
Cost as estimated in tender (nett)		936,822
Loss of productivity	£	378,857
Increased costs as Appendix 3		458,112
Less allowed in tender		114,971
Additional	£	343,141
Site overheads, actual cost (nett)		172,156
Tender allowance		123,648
Extra cost	£	48,508
Head Office overheads (@ average rate for period)		180,584
Less at tender		100,767
Extra	£	79,817
Profit		106,327
Less in tender		63,786
	£	42,543

Engineer:
I still maintain you were at fault in your handling and also your method of construction. You did not start the drainage until the embankments had been brought up to formation level and there were several instances where the Sandy Mudstone fill had been affected by the ingress of water at levels above those of the drains, so that had these been laid earlier such damage would not have occurred.

Contractor:
We do not agree. Our sequence of operations in this connection was perfectly normal, particularly in the case of rock fill. The programme submitted with our tender indicated what we had in mind and you did not disapprove. Further, it was clear that you envisaged this method when preparing the contract documents because the B/Q measures these drains in terms of the depth from formation.

Engineer:
I do not accept that the programme has anything to do with it. It was not a contract document and in any case, even if it were approved, Clause 14(7) leaves you with the responsibility. I am sorry, I cannot accept that the employer is in any way responsible for the massive costs which you allege you have incurred.

Contractor:
We cannot accept your rejection of our claim. We still hope that this matter can be resolved without recourse to arbitration but there is obviously a fundamental difference of opinion between us as to whether the nature of the material met with was the same as was envisaged in the contract documents or about which we could have satisfied ourselves in the time available to us. We must go away and see whether we can produce any further arguments which will persuade you of the justice of our claim.

The contractor has exposed a slightly weak point here. So far as we know, he made no application for an extension of the tendering period. Had he done so and had this been refused his argument would have been stronger. He must have used the intervening period to seek legal or other expert advice for when the discussion is resumed he changes his argument in a small but highly significant respect.

Second meeting 21/7/80

Contractor:
We have now had opportunity to look at this whole matter again and take advice as to the strength of our case. Without spelling out in detail all the points we made earlier about the provisions in the contract, we would particularly draw your attention to the following:

(a) *Specification Clause 601.1(iv) in which Sandy Mudstone was stipulated as rock.*

(b) *The note on Drawing 14/2877/75 to the effect that the Sandy Mudstone was 'a hard, fine-grained sandstone'.*

(c) *The Soils Report referred to the Sandy Mudstone as 'a generally well cemented series [sic] of micaceous fine sandstones'.*

(d) *Specification Clause 601.1(v) defines rock fill and says this may include Sandy Mudstone. Rock fill is generally understood to consist of pieces of stone that require their interstices to be filled with smaller material (which would be consistent with hard, well cemented fine sandstones) but which do not themselves disintegrate under compaction.*

(e) *Specification Clause 608(iv) equates Sandy Mudstone with 'Selected Fill' (601.1(vii)).*

As you are no doubt aware, the Keuper Sandstones, Mudstones and Marl comprise a number of closely related materials which are not always easy to classify as between one category and another. At the one end of the scale there are the marls, which can be difficult to handle. At the other end are the fine-grained sandstones, which have the characteristics conventionally associated with rock, i.e. hard, dense and unaffected by water.

From the information available at time of tendering, we expected the Sandy Mudstone to come from the harder end of the scale and consequently present no difficulties in handling and no susceptibility to moisture. We took the reference 'unweathered' to mean unweathered in the bed and the use of material in fill as referring to its origin rather than its condition upon placing. We certainly would not expect anything in the category of rock as indicated in the contract to 'weather' in the short period between excavation and placing, not even if stockpiled for several weeks or even months. Your own reference to providing a stockpile for our use tended to confirm this.

We visited the site when tendering and consider we took such steps as were practicable in the time available to satisfy ourselves as to the material we were being called upon to handle.

We do not accept that in excavating, transporting and placing this material as we did, we 'allowed the material ... to reach a condition where compaction ... is impracticable ...' What happened to this material was degradation or disintegration under the processes of excavation, transport and compaction and hence susceptibility to moisture.

This is the key problem of the claims and no doubt the engineer required time to appreciate fully the import of this latest statement before continuing discussion.

Third meeting 6/8/80

Engineer:
We have had opportunity to consider the further information you tabled at our second meeting and also to take advice ourselves.

We are inclined to concede, though reluctantly, that the information contained in the contract documents did not match as closely as it might the actual material with which you had to contend. We do consider, however, that you might have taken other steps to ascertain the nature of the Sandy Mudstone in this locality, and there are several matters in the substance of your claim with which we do not agree.

One could hardly have expected complete surrender. The circumstances determining entitlement are rarely black and white and it is unusual to find the injured party entirely blameless. However, there seems to have been a breakthrough.

In the course of your original claim, you made one reference to Clause 51, but I am not too sure that this matter comes within the ambit of an unauthorized variation.

Contractor:
We think it does in that you clearly instructed us to use the material we met with rather than the fine-grained sandstone indicated in the contract, though we must admit there is no formal Variation Order as is normally the case for extra work.

We did consider Clause 12 but this does not seem to fit the circumstances precisely. We also considered Clause 8 in that the specifying of this material was a matter of design, but if one accepts that the design was based on the material originally expected, then that is not at fault and one is brought back to Clause 51 as being the proper basis.

Engineer:
Very well, let us debate the matter on that basis, using Clause 52 for the purpose of valuation.

We must accept that there are no prices in the Bill which can be used as a basis but I am reluctant to work on the basis of cost because the original tender may have been too low and there is no safeguard against inefficient working.

Contractor:
We accept that but as to the last point, we must remind you that acceptance or rejection of material was entirely in the hands of your inspectors on an almost continual basis.

Engineer:
Agreed, but what evidence can you produce concerning the tender? Can we see the other tenders you received at the time?

Contractor:
We no longer have the actual tenders but we do have a log of the tenders received, if that will help.

Engineer:
When we get that we can look at the figures as a whole. I am not prepared to accept the allowances in the tender for increased costs and I would like this looked into using the NEDO indices to find out what increased costs the sub-contractor would have incurred in any case to compare with what was actually incurred calculated on the same basis. I would like our respective quantity surveyors to look into these matters and let us have a Note.

Regarding your own part of the claim, I would prefer to postpone consideration until we have had a look at the other claims, as it seems to me we must take the question of delay and site overheads as a whole.

CLAIM NO 3   EXTRA COST OF LAYING PART OF THE DRAINAGE OUT OF SEQUENCE WITH CONSEQUENT LOSS OF PRODUCTIVITY AND DELAY

Statement of claim

This claim is directly consequent upon the use of Sandy Mudstone which is the subject of Claim No 2. We had planned to excavate trenches for the drains after the embankments had been completed and compacted. We showed this in our original time and progress chart by indicating the drainage to the road starting some three months after commencement of earthworks.

The fact that we had, in the case of embankments with Sandy Mudstone in the top layers, to install some of the drains before completion of the embankment meant not only out-of-sequence working, but also some damage to the drains, which would not otherwise have occurred, and problems also in providing temporary outfalls in some places.

Evaluation

		Tender		Final a/c
Total of drainage bill		*825,201*		*840,728*
Less interchange		*206,619*		*194,457*
		£618,582		*£646,271*

Comparative analysis of tender, final account and actual costs

		Tender	Final a/c	Actual cost	Increase
Labour	24.66%	152,542	159,370	201,190	41,820
Plant	15.24%	94,272	98,492	121,738	23,246
Materials	32.88%	203,390	212,494	243,187	30,693
		450,204	470,356	566,115	95,759
Site supervision	18.66%	115,427	120,594	145,152	24,558
		565,631	590,950	711,267	120,317
HO overheads $\dfrac{8.56}{100.00}$ %		52,951	55,321	66,503	11,182
		618,582	646,271	777,770	131,499
Profit	5%	30,929	32,314	38,889	6,575
		£649,511	£678,585	£816,659	£138,074

We claim the sum of £138,074 shewn in the last column.

Note: Delay overlaps with that included in Claim No 2.

This is really a matter consequential upon the Sandy Mudstone problem but has been kept separate perhaps at the instigation of the QS that each aspect of a claim must be separately substantiated.

First meeting

Contractor:
The problem of Sandy Mudstone had two effects on the drainage. First we were required in certain areas to lay the drains before the top layers of embankment were placed and formation level reached. Second, the whole of the drainage work was attenuated over a period of twenty-four months compared with the twelve months we allowed in our programme. The interchange was not affected in this respect and our claim is therefore in respect of the roadworks only.

Engineer:
As I told you in correspondence, in choosing to lay the drains after completion of tipping to embankments, you were not making proper allowance for the material with which you were having to deal.

Contractor:
And as we pointed out in reply, we indicated this sequence on our programme which we submitted with our tender. Moreover it would seem from the B/Q that you had this sequence in mind in that drain trench depths had been measured from formation level.

Engineer:
Well, this matter follows consequentially out of the Mudstone problem, so I think we had better wait until you produce further argument on that.

This interchange took place before the Sandy Mudstone debate was resolved. At the third meeting, this claim was brought up for further discussion.

Third meeting

Engineer:
Now that we have taken the Sandy Mudstone matter so far, let us look again at Claim No 3.

301

Contractor:
Our claim is based on a loss of productivity of about 25 per cent overall plus of course the cost in terms of overheads attributable to the delay.

Engineer:
I do not understand why there should be such a substantial increase in the cost of materials. Surely this should not be affected by loss of productivity?

Engineer's QS:
I think maybe this is due to the fact that the drainage is not fully measured. The contractor has not yet produced his final account for the drainage. I doubt whether this will account for the full amount here; but there is something yet to come on measurement.

Engineer:
I thought the measurement was complete.

Contractor:
We understood from site that this was practically complete. We will look into this and come back to you.

It is extremely important that final measurement be kept up to date all along. Contractors look to make good their shortfall between expenditure and income by way of claims if not by measurement.

Engineer:
I am not satisfied about the inclusion of overheads here. Surely this overlaps the Sandy Mudstone claim? I think we must look at the delay as a whole and decide where extra overheads (if any are due) are to fall.

Engineer's QS:
I agree. Apart from overlap of claims, there has been a significant increase in the value of work done (Variation Order No 27, for example), the rates and prices for which will be carrying a share of the overheads.

CLAIM NO 4   DELAY BY WATER AUTHORITY IN RELAYING SEWER AND BY ELECTRICITY BOARD IN RELAYING 65 KVA CABLE

Statement of claim

This claim is in respect of delay and disruption to the work of reconstructing Town Road, including major complications in connection with the diversion of traffic. It does not take into account the later delay in diverting the sewer to a new route and constructing the pump-house which had such a disastrous effect on the construction of the roundabout (see Variation Order No 27). The delay in relaying the cable was approximately coincidental with that of the sewer but affected other earthworks.

The effect of these delays was to disrupt about one-third of the earthworks and one quarter of the drainage, sub-base and road-base work to the interchange. There was also some delay to Bridge No 406. We assess the delay in this area at two months.

Evaluation

	Tender	Final a/c	Amount affected
Value of earthworks in interchange	280,411	239,581	79,860
Value of drainage in ditto	206,619	194,457	48,614
Value of sub-base and road-base ditto	163,966	157,228	39,307

Analysis Earthworks (sub-contract)
(See Appendix 1 to Claim No 2 — Figure 10.1.5)

		Amount affected	25% loss of productivity		
Labour	29.44%	23,511	5,878		
Plant	37.43%	29,892	7,473		
Materials (mainly fuel) 10.70%		8,545	2,136		
		61,948	15,487		
Site oncosts 13.08% of above total		8,104	2,026		
		70,052	17,513		
HO overheads 8.57% ditto		6,004	1,501		
		76,056	19,014		
Profit	5%	3,804	951		
		79,860	19,965		19,965
Drainage and road-base (own work)					
(48,614 + 39,307 = 87,921)					
Labour	24.66%	21,681	5,420		
Plant	15.24%	13,399	3,350		
Materials	32.88%	28,908	—	8,770	
Increase in bond premium (£34,000)			36		
Ditto CAR insurance (£72,000)			76		
Ditto third party insurance (£31,000)			33	145	
Servicing contractor's accommodation	8 weeks @ £300			2,400	
Site supervision	8 weeks @ £5,560			44,480	
Traffic safety and control — additional measures over					
prolonged period			say	2,000	
				57,795	
Add HO overheads	9.35%			5,404	63,199
					83,164
Add profit	5%				4,158
					£87,322

First meeting

Engineer:
I agree there was very substantial delay here but I would not have thought it had quite the effect you suggest. In any case, what provision of the contract are you relying upon here?

Contractor:
We consider we have a claim under Clause 31.

Engineer:
But what about Clause 105 of the Specification? You were specifically warned that you would be responsible for co-ordinating your programme with the authorities concerned and to allow in your tender for any delays which may occur due to alterations in public services.

Contractor:
Yes, but surely we did everything possible by way of co-ordination. Whenever there was a choice between who could work where, we had to allow the Water Authority or Electricity Board priority. As for delays, you know as well as we that a contractor has no control whatever over Statutory Undertakers. Neither, with respect, do you. Yet they are your contractors and so surely come within the ambit of Clause 31. In any case, we contend that the last sentence of Clause 105, para 3, is quite

303

ambiguous and does not in our view refer to these major re-alignments which were particular requirements of this contract rather than any general effect of 'alterations to public services'.

Engineer:
I do not entirely agree with you about Clause 105 but I must admit that the present case goes beyond even what is usually to be expected from Statutory Undertakers, especially when it comes to the pump-house. I think it might be more convenient and perhaps more appropriate to consider the prolongation here in conjunction with the other aspects to which we have already referred. Otherwise we shall inevitably get overlap with these various delays and the overheads you are claiming in respect of them.

Responsibility for delays caused by Statutory Undertakers is a very difficult area, primarily because of the lack of proper contractual relationship between the Statutory Undertakers and either party. There is an essential difference between two situations. The first is where the Statutory Undertaker or his pipes or cables are just in the way, without any involvement of the employer. In that situation, the employer has no responsibility at common law for delay or disruption suffered by the contractor,[8] unless he has misrepresented or expressly warranted the position of the utilities. Indicating utilities on a drawing does not automatically amount to a representation.

It is quite different where the Statutory Undertaker is performing either new work or diversions in connection with the employer's scheme. Such work is generally not included in the main contract as most Statutory Undertakers will not agree to become sub-contractors to the main contractor. Usually such work is 'ordered' by the employer directly on the SU. Whilst they may be unwilling to enter into a contract with the employer or give any undertaking as to time or programme, they are, so far as the contractor is concerned, working on behalf of the employer and are therefore his responsibility. Where possible such work should be carried out before the main contract is commenced. If it is not possible and the work has to be carried out in parallel with the main contract work, and if the contractor has to wait for the Statutory Undertaker to carry out diversions or new work, it may amount to a denial of possession for which the employer would be liable, unless stipulated otherwise in the contract.

This distinction between the two situations is recognized in Clause 31 of ICE5 which refers to facilities for statutory bodies 'who may be employed in the execution on or near the site of any work . . . in connection with or ancillary to the Works'. In that situation, the employer is liable for delay and disruption beyond that which the contractor was required to allow for by the contract at the time of tender. The employer may also, through the contract, impose a special duty on the contractor to mitigate delay and disruption by requiring the contractor to liaise and co-ordinate with the Statutory Undertakers.

Clause 105 of the Specification amounts to an exclusion clause. Any ambiguity, such as contained in the last sentence of the clause, should therefore be interpreted strictly *contra proferentem*. It would thus not cover delays due to changes introduced after the time of tender. In a case like this it might be wise of the engineer to advise the employer of the problem and give his recommendation.

Contractor:
We would not be averse to that, but what about the loss of productivity?

Engineer:
Your claim is in terms of cost compared with what you estimated. I am always worried that that form of claim can make good deficiencies of low tendering and inefficient working. In any case in a claim for delay, and

---

8. *Porter v Tottenham UDC* [1915] 1 KB 776.

assuming you are relying on Clause 31(2), you can expect only those overheads you have expended, and no profit.

Contractor:
We understand your aversion to reimbursing cost but you will know how our tender compared with others and whether it was unduly low. You have asked us for similar information concerning the earthworks' sub-contract. We can produce for you a log of what our men and our sub-contractor's men and the plant were doing day by day in this area and can indicate on a drawing which earthworks and roadworks were affected. We see no reasons for refusing us profit.

Engineer:
Clause 31 refers to cost and Clause 1(5) defines cost as including overheads but does not refer to profit. Clause 12 is the only one where reference is made to profit as well as cost.

If this information is available, it is a pity it was not produced as part of the claim documentation. The engineer was obviously aware of the position but whether the contractor gave formal notice of a claim is not clear (it should not be assumed that the matter was so obvious that no notice is required). The 'Returns of labour and plant' required under Clause 35 should be helpful.

Engineer:
Well, we have a certain amount of information from the Daily Returns but you put in no information for my people to check at the time.

Contractor:
We started by putting in Daywork Sheets 'for record purposes only' but your inspectors refused to sign them because the work had not been ordered on daywork.

Engineer:
I did not know of that. It should have been brought up at a progress meeting. But even had you done so, there would have been no information as to the quantities being produced.

Contractor:
This is so, but if you look at our original T & P chart, on our working copy we shewed the quantities needed to be produced to achieve the programme and we also shewed the plant we intended to use. We in fact used the plant we intended and we can allocate output from information we have concerning bonuses so that you can compare and see that there was a substantial reduction.

Engineer:
The delay here was taken into account in the second extension of time and was put then at six weeks, i.e. the effect on the job as a whole. I think two months is an overstatement. In any case, as we have said in connection with previous claims, this matter of delay must be looked at as a whole.

CLAIM NO 5   DISRUPTION AND LOSS OF PRODUCTIVITY ON WORK GENERALLY OTHER THAN THAT WHICH IS THE SUBJECT OF CLAIMS 2, 3 AND 4

Statement of claim

We have set out in Claim 2 the effect on earthworks of the use of Sandy Mudstone as encountered, and in Claim 3 the effect on the drainage work of having to do this in a sequence other than as planned. Claim 4 concerns delays and disruption to certain works in the interchange area caused by Statutory Undertakers' works.

All this had a consequential effect on all the other work which was not affected by Sandy Mudstone or Statutory Undertakers.

There was a significant drop in productivity on all the bridges and all the other work except perhaps the flexible surfacing. This last came on very late and was the subject of a separate sub-contract. As you will see from the evaluation of our claim some M£3.3 worth of work was affected. We have left the delay aspect as being covered by other claims.

This work was programmed to be done in twenty-six months but in fact Bridge No 628 was not completed until seven months and the sub-base and road-base fourteen months after it was planned to be completed. As you will see from the T & P chart, from the beginning of the fencing to the completion of the sub-base and road-base there was a period of some thirty-seven months and completion of all work took forty-four months.

We have not had from you a final determination of the extension of time but allowing for periods of strike and inclement weather (for which we can claim no compensation) we consider the extra time attributable to matters which are the employer's responsibility to be sixteen and a half months.

The proportion of lost time was thus about 37 per cent and as you will see from our Claim Evaluation the actual loss of productivity of our labour and plant is 17.67 per cent. We consider this a not unreasonable result of such prolongation.

Evaluation

Value of work affected:
Preliminaries — dealt with in other claims — —
Site clearance — not affected — —
Fencing — 248,722
Drainage and earthworks — included in Claims 3 and 4 — —
Sub-base and road-base — 882,147
  Less included in Claim 4 — 163,966 — 718,181

Flexible surfacing — not affected — —
Kerbs and footways — 342,336
Traffic signs and markings — not affected — —
Structures — 1,996,820
Testing — not affected — —
Accommodation works — negligible — —
Provisional and PC Sums — —

£3,306,059

Analysis

	Tender	Proportions	Final a/c	Actual cost	Increase
Labour	815,274	24.66%	876,862	1,036,789	159,927
Plant	503,843	15.24%	541,537	632,218	90,681
Materials			No increase attributable to loss of productivity		
	1,319,117		1,418,399	1,669,007	250,608

$$Increase = \frac{250,608}{1,418,399} = 17.67\%.$$

First meeting

Engineer:

I must say I find this claim somewhat removed from the direct causes of trouble on which you have based your other claims. Again, you quote no contract condition on which you rely.

Contractor:

This is indeed a consequential loss arising out of those other matters and the basis of this claim is in the clauses we quote for them. It is not possible to allocate this general loss of productivity between the individual causes.

Engineer:

Accepting that for a moment, it seems to me entirely circumstantial and is equally consistent with a degree of underestimating in the first place and a degree of inefficiency of working in the second. I doubt whether you would claim that your site organization worked 100 per cent efficiently, even allowing for the problems they had to cope with.

Contractor:

No, we would contend that our organization is good if not very good, but we would not claim it to be perfect. But it is a recognized phenomenon that an attenuation of the time for construction inevitably leads to loss of productivity even in those areas not directly affected. The attitude of the men working under difficulties permeates those who are not and there is a knock-on effect.

Engineer:

I do not accept that that need be so and in any case I do not accept that it is any responsibility of the employer. Are you sure there are no explanations of this apparent loss?

Engineer's QS:

I think I may suggest one such explanation. There is a column of figures in the Evaluation headed 'Final account'. The total there is certainly the total reached so far but there is still a good deal to be finished. I would think there is still around £100,000 to be picked up. That is in terms of value of work of course, not just labour and plant, but there is some daywork.

Contractor:

We agree the final account is still not complete, but even with the figure just quoted there will still be a shortfall. There has been some research on this in America which shews that loss of productivity or increase in costs is proportionate to delay or acceleration. According to that a delay of 27 per cent would result in additional costs in excess of 13 per cent. This seems to be in the field of our experience here.

Engineer's QS:

I do not know the authorities to which you refer but I would doubt their applicability here. First because there seems to be no definition of an optimum time against which delay can be gauged. Second, practice in America differs greatly from that here. Not only is the majority of their contract work more akin to lump-sum than measure and value as we know it, but American contractors do much more in the way of unit costing than do English contractors and so have greater control of their costs.

Engineer:
I am not satisfied that there is any entitlement but even if there were I do not accept your statement as any demonstration, much less proof, of the costs you say you have incurred. I am sorry, I see no way in which this claim can be entertained.

CLAIM NO 6   DELAY IN POSSESSION OF SITE FOR BRIDGE NO 628

Statement of claim

This is a claim under Clause 42 of the Conditions of Contract in respect of delay in possession of part of the site for Bridge No 628. There was no indication in the contract that the site for this bridge would not be available but in fact we were not given possession of land for the south abutment until 12 July 1977, some three months after we had planned to start.

It was not until we had our pile rig, a compressor and a crane on the north abutment that we were aware that the area on the south side was still in the occupation of a farmer.

We therefore claim standing time for our plant as follows:

Evaluation

Diesel hammer 4,000 lb at £226.00 per week × *13 weeks*	*2,938.00*
Hanging leaders, rectangular section 2' × 2', nominal length 50 ft at £101.50 per week × 13 weeks	*1,319.50*
Compressor, portable 321–380 ft³ with 2 tools and hose at £240 per week × 13 weeks	*3,120.00*
Crane, mobile, crawler 8–10 ton at £250 per week × 13 weeks	*3,276.00*
	10,653.50
Add overheads 25.63%	*2,730.50*
	13,384.00
Profit 6%	*603.00*
	£13,987.00

First meeting

Engineer:
I accept that possession of site of this bridge was delayed as you state but I do not accept the claim for standing time on plant for three months. After you had possession you did not start for another month and in any case, in view of the progress of the work generally, there was no need to put plant here so soon.

Contractor:
We do not agree. We were already in some difficulty because of the additional bridge and we wanted to get this one started to release the pile rig for Bridge No 511. Your inspector has signed for the fact that the plant was there.

Engineer:
I appreciate that but I am concerned with whether it need have been there. QS, what have you to say about the rates charged?

Engineer's QS:
These rates look to me like daywork rates which are quite inappropriate to be applied to standing time. They are intended to apply to odd hours of work and in any case they include fuel.

Contractor:
What would you consider appropriate?

Engineer's QS:
Well, Clause 42 refers to cost and in this context I would interpret that to mean depreciation rates. In my view this should be about two-thirds of long-term hire rates and again, as was said in connection with Claim No 4, profit in this context is not allowable.

Contractor:
But that would be about half what we are claiming.

Engineer's QS:
Maybe so, but you cannot possibly justify daywork rates in a situation like this. Further, Clause 42 refers to cost which is defined in Clause 1(5) as including overheads but I fail to see what overheads could be involved here. There should certainly be no provision for profit.

Contractor:
We think that is very poor compensation but may we leave that to be worked out into a definitive sum so that we can look at it in the context of what is being offered in respect of our other claims?

CLAIM NO 7   DELAY AND EXTRA COST IN CONNECTION WITH VARIATION ORDER NO 27 FOR REVISED ACCESS TO THE NORTHERN CARRIAGEWAY AND THE CONSTRUCTION OF A ROUNDABOUT

Statement of claim

In the main, the work in connection with this variation has been paid for under Clause 52 but we claim adjustment of Preliminaries on account of this extra work and also an element of delay, though the latter is in fact compounded by the further complication of the Water Authority pumping station which is the subject of Claim No 8. The value of additional work measured and included in the final account to date is as follows:

Additional bridge	*225,480*
Roadwork to new alignment, less the value of roadwork in original B/Q	*52,726*
Work at roundabout (exclusive of work in pumping station)	*53,142*
	£331,348

Roadwork in the interchange was expected to take about five months but in fact was spread over nearly fifteen months (with the pumping station following after that). Our claim is therefore as follows:

Adjustment of Preliminaries	
Additional premium on bond (p/r value)	*1,367*
Additional CAR insurance (ditto)	*2,896*
Additional third party insurance (ditto)	*1,267*
Servicing accommodation for engineer 43 weeks × 200	*8,600*
Servicing accommodation for contractor 43 weeks × 300	*12,900*
Traffic and safety control	*2,000*
	£29,030

The matter of delay is contained in Claim No 8.

First meeting

Engineer:
I was not aware of any dispute in respect of adjustment of General Provisions. QS, what is your comment on this?

Engineer's QS:
It is true that nothing has yet been included in the final account in respect of these Preliminaries. I was waiting until the final account was complete before making adjustment in respect of the variations as a whole. There is no dispute and the contractor can be assured that these figures or something like them will be included.

Contractor:
We would be content with that.

CLAIM NO 8 DELAY AND DISRUPTION CAUSED BY WATER AUTHORITY REQUIREMENT FOR PUMPING STATION AT ROUNDABOUT IN ACCORDANCE WITH VARIATION ORDER NO 141 DATED 7 JANUARY 1977

Statement of claim

Variation No 27 for the roundabout was issued on 21 June 1976 and work was in hand with approach earthworks and drainage when the Water Authority required a pumping station. The work we could do in advance of the design being completed was therefore limited and it was not until 23 March 1977 that Variation No 141 was issued, shewing the pumping station beneath and as an integral part of the roundabout.

The value of the work involved as measured and included in the final account is £152,490 and in terms of straightforward work should have taken no more than about three months to complete. Our work was, however, delayed as regards:

(a) *foundation bases for the pumps and other plant which were to be installed by a contractor employed by the Water Authority;*
(b) *final closing in of the roof of the pumping station and completing the waterproofing until their plant had in fact been installed, which was not until February 1978.*

In Claim No 4 we have dealt with the delay (put at two months) by the Water Authority and Electricity Board in repositioning their services, as this affected earthworks. In this claim we seek reimbursement for the remainder of the period, i.e. from the end of July 1976 to the end of April 1978. The difficulty is, however, that this work affecting the interchange overlaps with the delay to the main roadworks which was caused by the Sandy Mudstone. We have therefore arbitrarily allocated three months' delay to this claim, which is therefore made up as follows:

Evaluation

Adjustment of Preliminaries	
Additional insurance and bond premiums (p/r value)	2,545
Servicing accommodation for engineer 13 weeks × £200	2,600
Servicing accommodation for contractor 13 weeks × £300	3,900
Contractor's site supervision 13 weeks × £5,560	72,280
Traffic safety and control	1,000
Successive temporary diversion of traffic to permit work to proceed and maintain flow of traffic	12,480
	94,805
Add HO oncosts 9.35%	8,864
	103,669
Add profit 6%	6,220
	£109,889

First meeting

Engineer:
Again we get this claim for adjustment of Preliminaries.

Engineer's QS:
And again so far as valuation under Clause 52 is concerned this will be picked up in the final account.

Engineer:
As to delay, I am now quite unclear where this has reached. It seems to me on the information given that there is real danger of overlap, and I cannot properly consider a claim in this respect until I am satisfied that there is in fact no overlap.

Contractor:
We are not wanting to claim twice for the same thing. As this matter of Preliminaries is one which needs to be dealt with in the final account I suggest that our respective quantity surveyors get together and resolve this and also prepare a statement of the overall effect of delay, but to do that we should first need you to determine the extension of time under Clause 44(4).

Engineer's QS:
I appreciate that the engineer will need to deal with the question of extension of time but I suggest he may need information from the investigation it has been suggested we do. Payment is not dependent upon extension of time though both may stem from the same basic causes. I suggest we get together on this matter as soon as possible and advise the engineer of our findings. He can then decide how this affects the extension of time position.

Contractor:
That would be agreeable to us.

CLAIM NO 9   INCREASE IN ADJUSTMENT ITEM IN RESPECT OF EXTRA WORK UNDER VARIATIONS ETC

Statement of claim

In recent applications for further interim payment we have included a large part of the work as finally measured. In respect of this we have sought an addition to the Adjustment Item but this has been consistently refused.

It has been pointed out to us that the relevant preamble in the B/Q refers to a 'lump-sum' and no provision is made for amendment. We note the wording of the last sentence of this preamble but consider this to refer to the summation of the instalments.

It is our general practice to price our B/Q's nett of profit and to add this at the end by way of the Adjustment Item. If no amendment is to be allowed, it will mean that we shall have carried out a substantial amount of additional work without any profit. This cannot have been intended.

There is an increase in the value of work executed of something considerably in excess of £600,000 and our profit on this should be 6 per cent, i.e.   <u>£36,000.</u>

First meeting

Engineer's QS:
That I have refused to include an amended amount for the Adjustment Item in the final account is true but in my opinion the wording of the preamble is quite clear.

That you have used this item to represent your profit is your choice. The Adjustment Item is purely a figure to permit last-minute adjustments to tenders without recourse to wholesale repricing.

Contractor:
The preamble makes no reference to its purpose. It must be construed as it stands.

Engineer:
I agree with that last remark but I consider that the preamble is quite clear and I agree with the QS that no amendment can be made.

Contractor:
Amendment has in fact been made in other contracts.

Engineer's QS:
That may be, but the wording of the preamble clause was changed subsequently to this contract to allow for amendment pro-rata to the value of measured work. But that does not help us in this case. I am sorry, but I have no alternative but to reject this claim.

The process of interpreting or construing a contract is an art rather than a science. Assistance may be obtained from textbooks or commentaries, or from domestic literature such as Practice Notes, Notes for Guidance or Circulars, but the parties are not bound by such sources, nor by Departmental Policy,[9] nor by comparison with other forms of contract.[10] It is the words of the particular contract that have to be interpreted. Previous interpretation of the particular Form by the courts provides an effective precedent. Some inference may be drawn from changes in Conditions of Contract but caution is required. The rules of construction relating to changes in statutes do not apply to contracts. A change of words may represent a deliberate modification of intention, but it may equally be a clarification of an existing intention.[11]

CLAIM NO 10 REIMBURSEMENT OF LIQUIDATED DAMAGES WRONGFULLY DEDUCTED

Statement of claim

We have from time to time given notice of delays and applied for extension of time. In fact only two such extensions have been given, the second of which dated August 1978 extended the time to 31 May 1979. No assessment was made at the due date for completion (28 October 1978) in accordance with Clause 44(3) or upon the issue of the Certificate of Completion (22 December 1979).

We claim that we are entitled to an extension of time up to the actual date of completion (22/12/79).

As a result of no extension of time having been given liquidated damages have been deducted by the employer at the rate of £6,500 per week for $29\frac{2}{5}$ weeks (£191,100).

9. *Perini Corporation v Commonwealth of Australia* [1969] 12 BLR 82.
10. *Mitsui v A-G for Hong Kong* [1986] 33 BLR 1.
11. For example, Clause 52(1) in ICE5 is arguably a clarification of the same clause in ICE4.

We claim reimbursement of such liquidated damages pursuant to Clause 47(5), together with interest at Bank Rate plus $\frac{3}{4}$% from the dates deducted up to the present date or such time as we are given the extension of time to which we are entitled.

Evaluation

Note: Bank Rate/Minimum Lending Rate (MLR) applicable:

Up to 12/6/79	*12%.*
From 31/6 to 14/11	*14%.*
From 15/11 to end	*17%.*

Recovery of liquidated damages plus interest at Clauses 47(5) and 60(6):

	Damages at £6,500 per week	Cumulative	Interest Rate	Interest Amount
From 1 June to 12 June 1979				
2 weeks	*13,000*	*13,000*	*12$\frac{3}{4}$%*	*63.75*
From 13 June to 14 November				
22 weeks	*143,000*	*156,000*	*14$\frac{3}{4}$%*	*9,735.00*
From 15 November to 31 December				
5$\frac{2}{5}$ weeks	*35,100*	*191,100*	*17$\frac{3}{4}$%*	*3,520.64*
From 1 January 1980 to 31 March				
13 weeks	*—*	*191,100*	*17$\frac{3}{4}$%*	*8,475.63*
	191,100			*21,795.02*
				191,100.00
				£212,895.02

First meeting

Engineer:

As you know, liquidated damages are deductible by the employer, they are not shewn as part of the certificate. I was not aware that this deduction was being made. Why did you not inform me?

Contractor:

We thought you must know and our reply took the form of a further request for extension of time.

It is a pity when simple facts are not made clear. The whole situation might have been avoided had the contractor made the point that liquidated damages were being deducted.

Engineer:

I said earlier that I was waiting until I could see the effect of the Sandy Mudstone problems and hence the completion of the roadworks and any other factors of delay. I will need to look at this matter at once and determine your entitlement (if any).

Engineer's QS:

May I point out that a number of variations minor in value but nevertheless requiring some time to complete were issued as late as November 1979. I would have thought that for the purposes of extension of time only, these constituted an overriding cause of delay which would entitle the contractor to an extension of time up to actual completion date.

Engineer:

That seems rather unfortunate but if it is so then I agree the contractor is entitled. I shall have to inform the employer of the position.

The engineer now has the problem of explaining why he did not take action earlier; he should have done so at least as soon as the extended date for completion was reached. He must also point out that the employer was in error in deducting liquidated damages when Clause 44 says:

'(4) If the Engineer shall under Clause 44(3) or (4) have determined and certified any extension of time to which he considers the Contractor entitled or shall have notified the Employer and Contractor that he is of the opinion that the Contractor is not entitled to any or any further extension of time the Employer may deduct . . .'

As it is the contractor has been stood out of a substantial sum of money and the interest accruing is not insignificant. This might well cause an auditor to ask how it came about, for the payment of this interest could have been avoided.

CLAIM NO 11 CLAIM FOR INTEREST ON MONIES OUTSTANDING OVER LONG PERIODS, ARISING OUT OF THE VARIOUS MATTERS WHICH ARE THE SUBJECT OF THE FOREGOING CLAIMS (EXCEPT CLAIM 10)

Statement of claim

As you will see from the Heads of Claim [Figure 10.1.4 at p 288], we are seeking reimbursement of a sum in excess of M£2, which is the extra cost and expense we have been put to, or the amount we consider we are entitled to be paid under the contract in connection with the events and circumstances indicated.

During the course of the work we were reimbursed under Clause 60 for work executed under the contract, but only to the extent that such work could be valued in accordance with rates contained in the Bill of Quantities. Our claim to be reimbursed additional costs in connection with Sandy Mudstone (M£1.3) and indeed all the other matters have not been met even in part. The result has been that we have been stood out of a very substantial sum of money for a considerable period of time.

We therefore claim interest on this outstanding money at currently prevailing overdraft rates (which are significantly in excess of 'Bank Rate $+ \frac{3}{4}\%$' as referred to in Clause 60(6)).

We attach a graph [Figure 10.1.9] shewing our actual income and expenditure compared with our expected income and expenditure. As you will see, expenditure has exceeded income throughout, whereas we had expected to break even by the end of 1976 and get into a positive cash flow situation.

We also attach a statement [Figure 10.1.10] shewing month by month the excess of expenditure over income compared with what we anticipated when tendering and formulating our programme. We also shew the overdraft rate applicable for each month and finally the cost to us of the overdraft.

First meeting

Engineer:
I do not see how you can claim interest on overdue payment before you have established your entitlement to the money.

Contractor:
Well, we have spent the money and we were entitled to recover our expenditure much earlier. Take for example the Sandy Mudstone. Had the difference in the material been recognized from the outset, you would have issued a variation under Clause 51 and we could have recovered payment in interim certificates under Clause 52. As it is we have had to finance the extra cost of doing this different work by way of wages and plant hire (in

Figure 10.1.9 Claim No 11. Comparative receipts/expenditure – planned/actual

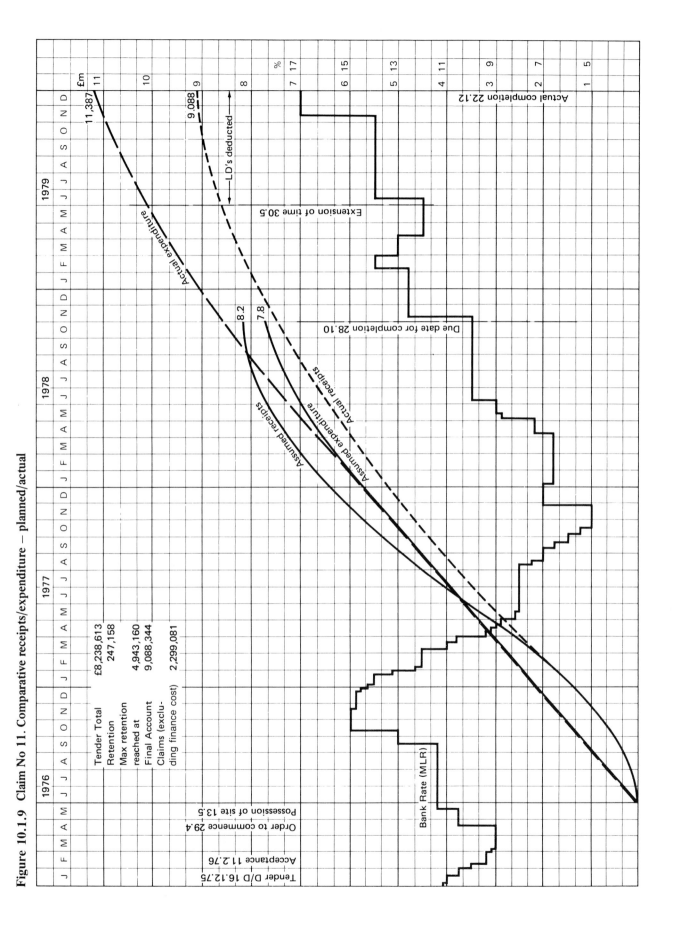

Figure 10.1.10

EVALUATION [see also Figure 10.1.9]

COMPARISON OF RECEIPTS AND EXPENDITURE

Date	Planned			Actual			Difference	Int rate %	Overdraft cost £
	Receipts	Expenditure	Surplus/ deficiency	Receipts	Expenditure	Deficiency (all minus)			
1976									
June	–	150,000	–150,000	–	150,128	150,128	–128	12	–1
July	200,000	450,000	–250,000	251,000	500,877	249,877	+113	13	+1
Aug	350,000	750,000	–400,000	349,500	748,996	399,496	+504	13	+5
Sept	500,000	1,050,000	–550,000	501,000	1,051,214	550,214	–214	13	–2
Oct	650,000	1,350,000	–700,000	648,500	1,347,685	699,185	+815	14	+6
Nov	1,000,000	1,650,000	–650,000	1,002,000	1,652,014	650,014	–14	13¾	–
Dec	1,350,000	1,950,000	–600,000	1,348,000	1,948,962	600,962	–962	13½	–11
1977									
Jan	1,700,000	2,200,000	–500,000	1,710,000	2,201,443	491,443	+8,557	16	+114
Feb	2,200,000	2,500,000	–300,000	2,199,000	2,501,928	302,928	–2,928	14	–34
Mar	2,600,000	2,800,000	–200,000	2,501,000	2,798,630	297,630	–97,630	13	–1,058
Apr	3,100,000	3,150,000	–50,000	2,708,500	3,151,221	442,721	–392,721	11	–3,600
May	3,450,000	3,400,000	+50,000	3,102,000	3,402,765	300,765	–350,765	10	–2,923
June	4,200,000	3,800,000	+400,000	3,410,500	3,861,286	450,786	–850,786	10	–7,089
July	4,600,000	4,050,000	+550,000	3,759,000	4,108,928	349,928	–899,928	10	–7,499
Aug	5,100,000	4,400,000	+700,000	4,108,500	4,456,780	348,280	–1,048,280	9	–7,862
Sept	5,500,000	4,650,000	+850,000	4,401,000	4,707,654	306,654	–1,156,654	8½	–8,193
Oct	5,850,000	5,000,000	+850,000	4,712,000	5,092,381	380,381	–1,230,381	7½	–7,690
Nov	6,200,000	5,400,000	+800,000	5,004,000	5,452,188	448,188	–1,248,188	9	–9,361
Dec	6,500,000	5,700,000	+800,000	5,299,500	5,748,927	449,427	–1,249,427	9	–9,371
1978									
Jan	6,800,000	6,000,000	+800,000	5,602,000	6,121,316	519,316	–1,319,316	8½	–9,345
Feb	7,000,000	6,200,000	+800,000	5,799,000	6,402,279	603,279	–1,403,279	8½	–9,440
Mar	7,250,000	6,500,000	+750,000	6,011,000	6,609,217	598,217	–1,348,217	8½	–9,550
Apr	7,500,000	6,750,000	+750,000	6,251,000	6,950,882	699,882	–1,449,882	9½	–11,478
May	7,700,000	7,000,000	+700,000	6,448,000	7,197,357	749,357	–1,449,357	11	–13,286
June	7,850,000	7,200,000	+650,000	6,701,500	7,502,468	800,968	–1,450,968	12	–14,510
July	8,000,000	7,400,000	+600,000	6,898,500	7,799,211	900,711	–1,500,711	12	–15,007
Aug	8,100,000	7,550,000	+550,000	7,102,000	8,101,953	999,953	–1,549,953	12	–15,500
Sept	8,150,000	7,700,000	+450,000	7,249,500	8,350,324	1,100,824	–1,550,824	12	–15,508
Oct	8,200,000	7,800,000	+400,000	7,438,500	8,598,410	1,159,910	–1,559,910	12	–15,599
Nov				7,710,000	8,809,842	1,099,842	–1,099,842	14½	–13,290
Dec				7,851,000	9,100,943	1,249,943	–1,249,943	14½	–15,103
1979									
Jan				8,000,500	9,401,427	1,400,927	–1,400,927	14½	–16,928
Feb				8,149,000	9,598,865	1,449,865	–1,449,865	16	–19,332
Mar				8,302,600	9,703,104	1,400,504	–1,400,504	15	–17,508
Apr				8,401,000	9,948,791	1,547,791	–1,547,791	14	–18,058
May				8,499,500	10,187,568	1,688,068	–1,688,068	16	–22,508
June				8,610,000	10,409,222	1,799,222	–1,799,222	16	–23,990
July				8,699,000	10,498,864	1,799,864	–1,799,864	16	–23,998
Aug				8,799,500	10,648,106	1,848,606	–1,848,606	16	–24,648
Sept				8,850,000	10,801,727	1,951,727	–1,951,727	16	–26,023
Oct				8,931,000	10,980,933	2,049,933	–2,049,933	16	–27,332
Nov				8,994,500	11,145,480	2,150,980	–2,150,980	19	–34,057
Dec				9,088,344	11,387,425	2,299,081	–2,299,081	19	–36,402
									–£513,468

this case through our sub-contractor). Similarly with the other items of claim. It makes no difference whether the basic cost is recoverable under Clause 52 or Clause 31, we still have to finance the cost.

Engineer:
But that is something different. The cost of finance to do the work is one thing and interest on overdue payment is another. Claim No 10 is in this latter category for which the contract specially provides.

Contractor:
We appreciate that and we may have used the wrong term in referring to this claim. What we are referring to is the cost of finance. We normally finance these jobs by way of overdraft arrangements with the bank and the cost is of course taken up in our Head Office overheads. Overheads are specifically referred to in Clause 1(5) and we contend this is a proper element of cost.

Engineer:
I understand your argument so far, but there is no reference to overheads in Clause 52.

Contractor:
That is so, but here we contend that these costs come within the ambit of Clause 52(2) which says: 'Provided that if the nature or amount of any variation relative to the nature or amount of the whole of the contract work or any part thereof shall be such that in the opinion of the Engineer or the Contractor any rate or price contained in the Contract for any item of work is by reason of such variation rendered unreasonable or inapplicable either the Engineer shall give to the Contractor or the Contractor shall give to the Engineer notice before the varied work is commenced or as soon thereafter as is reasonable in all the circumstances that such rate or price should be varied and the Engineer shall fix such rate or price as in the circumstances he shall think reasonable or proper.'

Admittedly, we have not put our claim for Sandy Mudstone in terms of price per cubic metre, though this could be done if it were required to establish this claim. Similarly these finance costs could be distributed through the Bill rates by way of a revised overhead content, but that would be only an arithmetic exercise and would not affect the principle involved.

Engineer:
That may be so but you are required to give notice of these matters, as indeed you are also in connection with Clauses 7(3), 42(1) and 31(2), through Clause 52(4)(a) and (b).

Contractor:
We may not have made reference to finance charges but we have repeatedly asked for a variation in connection with the use of Sandy Mudstone. In connection with other matters we have claimed extension of time or given specific notice of claim.

Engineer:
Giving notice of delay or claiming an extension of time has nothing to do with claiming payment. I do feel I have not been warned, as a notice is intended to warn, of the possibility of a claim of this magnitude.

Contractor:
We did not realize ourselves that it was so big until we came to formulate

these claims and compared our actual receipts and expenditure with what we had planned for. As soon as we saw this we tranlated it into terms of money and our overdraft charges. There is no doubt, however, that we have incurred these heavy bank charges and we are quite willing to give you every facility for checking them.

Engineer:
I am still not happy about the principle. QS, have you any views on this?

Engineer's QS:
I consider there is a fundamental difference between interest on overdue payments and finance charges. I would like the opportunity to have a look at the ICE Conditions with this point specifically in mind. Also, there was a legal case in the first half of 1979 on this matter. It concerned the JCT contract I believe, but the case may clear the matter of principle.

Engineer:
Very well then. Look into that and we will call another meeting to discuss it. Would you also look into this general question of delay and overheads in conjunction with the contractor and prepare some statement on the overall position.

Third meeting

Engineer's QS:
I have had a look at the ICE Conditions but I have not yet been able to prepare a Note, nor have I been able to get a Report on the case I was looking for. It is F G Minter Ltd *v* Welsh Health Technical Services Organisation *and it was in respect of a contract on the JCT Form. I hope to have more information soon.*

It is not unusual to have a series of meetings in connection with a claim such as this. There must, however, be a predisposition to make progress. In this case, the second meeting dealt with little else but the Sandy Mudstone matter, but this is not surprising considering the size and complexity of this matter. By the end of the first meeting, three claims had been rejected, two had been accepted and two more accepted in principle; by the end of the third meeting two more (the biggest) had been accepted in principle and for the remainder a definite line of enquiry had been agreed.

The following is a condensed representation of the discussions between the Engineer's QS and the Contractor's QS as a result of which each prepared a Note for the fourth meeting.

EQS/CQS DISCUSSIONS

Extension of time

The first thing to be considered was the extension of time. The T & P chart was agreed as representing actual progress cf the original programme. In respect of several items that had obviously been delayed the delays were overlapping. There was little point, however, in pursuing these individually because, as had been said in connection with Claim No 19, there had been variations issued in November 1979 which required two weeks to execute and so postponed the clearing of the site for two weeks. These constituted an overriding delay for which the contractor was entitled to extension of time to 22 December 1979.

The agreed position regarding variation orders issued late in the day may no longer always be valid in the light of subsequent case law, see page 276 *supra*. The only qualification to note here is that if, as a matter of fact, the necessity for a variation could not be discovered until the contractor had reached that particular stage of construction, then probably the extension could be given to run from the date when the contractor should have reached that stage — but the onus is rather on the engineer to prove.

Figure 10.1.11

SUMMARY OF FINAL ACCOUNT

Preliminaries				1,282,088
Site clearance		18,221		
Fencing		227,405		
Drainage – Interchange	194,457			
Road	646,271	840,728		
Earthworks – Interchange	239,581			
Road	1,339,992	1,579,573		
Carriageway:				
Sub-base and road-base	787,486			
	157,228	944,714		
Flexible surfacing		565,470		
Kerbs and footways		341,636		
Traffic signs		29,220		
Structures:				
Bridge No 403	639,464			
Bridge No 404	173,285			
Bridge No 405	207,001			
Bridge No 406	298,449			
Bridge No 511	202,521			
Bridge No 628	257,397			
Retaining wall A	57,444			
Retaining wall B	23,218			
Culverts	145,876	2,004,655		
Testing		25,776		
Accommodation works		40,181		
Provisional and PC Sums		151,290	6,768,839	
Variation No 27		331,348		
Variation No 141		152,490		
Other variations		128,138	611,976	7,380,815
Add Balancing Item				400,000
				£9,062,903

In the present case, delays caused by exceptionally inclement weather, strikes etc are not relevant to the matter of cost.

The next thing to consider was the effect of the delay arising from the several causes. It was clear that the critical path ran through the earthworks and road construction of the main road. Delay by the Statutory Undertakers, plus VO No 27 for the roundabout and particularly VO No 141 for the pump-house was serious but was not the ultimate cause. The delay to the sub-base and road-base should really be considered as contingent on the earthworks and not as a separate entity. If that is accepted, then the delay arising from the use of (the different) Sandy Mudstone should be put at seventy and a half weeks (the period from 16/8/78 which is ten and a half weeks prior to the due date and was when the contractor planned to complete to 22/12/79). The only things to be set against that were periods of exceptionally inclement weather and strikes, which would have caused delay in any case. These occurred as follows:

Exceptionally inclement weather			Strikes		
Winter 1976/77	1 week				
Summer 1977	2 weeks		Autumn 77	2 weeks	
Winter 1977/78	3 weeks			3 weeks	
Spring 1978	2 weeks	8	Summer 78	2 weeks	7
Winter 1978/79	4 weeks			1 week	
Summer 1979	1 week	13			8

The main item of damage arising from this delay was the cost of the site organization which the contractor had to keep on site until 22 December 1979. That organization would have been unproductive in any case for the period when the job was stopped by exceptionally inclement weather and strikes, so the Sandy Mudstone problem was not a cause of damage for these periods. It would seem therefore that the employer should accept responsibility for those overheads for a period of $70\frac{1}{2}$ weeks less $8 + 7 = 55\frac{1}{2}$ weeks.

Against this, the employer would be entitled to set off such overheads as the contractor might have been paid for in respect of extra work executed in the same period.

Adjustment of Preliminaries

The final account [see Figure 10.1.11] is now completed except for the matter of Preliminaries. As will be seen from the attached summary, the value of measured work amounts to £6,768,839, cf £6,646,363, in the B/Q (an extra of £122,476 arising solely from the difference in quantities); the value of variations is £611,976.

Contractor's QS:
Dealing first with the increased value of work, we are looking for adjustment of certain Preliminaries under Clause 56(2).

Engineer's QS:
But that refers only to differences of cost of executing the work solely because of an increase or decrease in quantity.

Contractor's QS:
Precisely. Because of these increases we shall have to pay additional premium for the bond and for insurances and Clause 56(2) does refer to 'an appropriate increase or decrease of any rates or prices rendered unreasonable or inapplicable in consequence thereof'. These costs are undoubtedly in consequence and we are entitled to adjustment.

Engineer's QS:
Agreed. Now, these three items are affected similarly, i.e. pro rata to value, by the variations. So let us take these together.

Value of measured work and PCs in final account	6,768,839
Value of variations	611,976
	7,380,815
Add Balancing Item	400,000
	£7,780,815

Contractor's QS:
But the Balancing Item should be added after we have made the adjustment.

Engineer's QS:
I think not, because surely you will have paid your insurance premium on the total value, will you not?

Contractor's QS:
Yes, I think that is right; the value of work in the B/Q without
Preliminaries is: *6,646,363*
  Add Balancing Item   *400,000*

                                            7,046,363
  Deduct this from   *7,780,815*

  The increase in value is   *£ 734,452*

And 734,452 ÷ 7,046,363 = 0.10423

Then:

Item A1 Provision of bond	*34,000 × 0.10423 =*	*3,543.82*
Item A2 Insurance of Works	*72,000 × 0.10423 =*	*7,504.56*
Item A3 Third party insurance	*31,500 × 0.10423 =*	*3,283.25*
		£14,331.63

A4 and A6 remain unchanged.
Items A5 and A7 require adjustment proportionate to time.

Engineer's QS:
Here again, I am not sure that these should be adjusted in respect of increased or decreased quantities.

Contractor's QS:
But if these warrant an extension of time under Clause 44 ('Should ... increased quantities referred to in Clause 51(3), i.e. differences of quantities not arising from a variation — or any other cause of delay ...') should they not also carry payment under Clause 56(2)?

Engineer's QS:
Yes, I think that is right, in which case we can again include variations. But there remains the question of how much extra time out of the total delay should be allocated to this.

Contractor's QS:
I think we should look at it as a matter of turnover. The measured work in the Bill totalled £6,646,363 — or £7,046,363 if you include the Balancing Item. This was to have been done in 130 weeks less the ten and a half weeks we expected to save, giving a turnover of £58,965 per week. If we assume that the contract envisages the same rate of turnover, ie we are not required to complete in the original time, then the extra time required for extra work would be:

    734,452 ÷ 58,965 = 12.46 weeks
                       B/fwd   *£14,331.63*

Engineer's QS:
That would give:
  Item A5 Servicing accommodation for engineer
  12.46 weeks at £200   *2,492.00*

  A7 Ditto for contractor 12.46 weeks at £300   *3,738.00*

  A11 Contractor's site supervision 12.46 weeks at
  £5,560   *69,277.60*

                                          89,839.23
  Add Preliminaries as B/Q   *1,192,250.00*

                                 £1,282,089,23

Figure 10.1.12

ANALYSIS OF TENDER

				Percentages		
Labour			1,568,151	33.89	24.66	19.03
Plant			968,469	20.93	15.24	11.76
Materials			2,090,559	45.18	32.88	25.37
			4,627,179	100.00		
Site oncosts						
In rates		251,610				
In Preliminaries						
Bond	34,000					
Insurance (Cl 21)	72,000					
Insurance (Cl 23)	31,500					
Accommodation	35,000					
Servicing ditto	39,000					
Supervision	722,800	934,300	1,185,910		18.66	14.39
Total direct costs			5,813,089			
HO overheads		@ 9.35%	543,524		8.56	6.60
			6,356,613		100.00	
Sub-contract			1,482,000			17.99
Turnover			7,838,613			
Profit @ 6%		470,317				
Less 10½ weeks saving						
on overheads @ £5,560		58,380				
		411,937				
Adjustment Item		say	400,000			4.86
			£8,238,613			100.00

Items A8, 9 and 10 have already been adjusted in the final account to take up actual supplies. A12 is a fixed item and any adjustment here should, I think, be left to be dealt with in the claims. A13 is not affected. A14 Maintenance of level crossing was increased but not because of extra work, because some of that was done after the level crossing was removed. We will look at this with the claims.

Let us now look at the claims. Obviously, from the basis you have used, it is clear we shall need an analysis of your tender. Can we have that and was it the one produced in compiling your tender?

Contractor's QS:
Yes, I have it here. You will appreciate it is a confidential document. [See Figure 10.1.12.]

Engineer's QS:
Yes, of course. It will be used only for this job and no copies will be kept.

CLAIM NO 1
This is not altered by any question of Preliminaries. It was rejected but you reserved your position.

CLAIM NO 2

This work was sub-let, but presumably you added a profit for yourselves before putting the rates in the Bill.

Contractor's QS:

No, if you look at the analysis you will see we added the total sub-contract tender in to our total costs before we added the Balancing Item, which is why we are seeking adjustment of that.

Engineer's QS:

Yes, I see, but that is a separate issue. So far as we are now concerned, for Claim 2 we deal with the figure of £1,579,573 in the final account. If we break that down between road and interchange we get

Total for road	1,339,992	
Total for interchange	239,581	£1,579,573

Now, how was this tender compiled?

Contractor's QS:

It was compiled from the bottom up so to speak, that is estimates were made of the value of labour, plant and materials, allowances were added for increased costs (this was a fixed price sub-contract, remember); then site oncosts were calculated as a total and added in, then the HO oncosts at the current rate for that year and finally a profit of 5 per cent.

For our purposes we shall have to work the other way round, which is why I have added a column of what you might call the 'constituent' percentages on the left. This will give slightly different answers but I think the differences are negligible.

Engineer's QS:

Let us do the sums and see what we get. It will be a check on the arithmetic at the same time.

		Contract	Road section only Tender	Final a/c
Labour	29.44%	436,300	353,748	394,494
Plant	37.43%	554,713	449,756	501,559
Materials	10.70%	158,574	128,570	143,379
		1,149,587	932,074	1,039,432
Site oncosts	10.15%	150,423	121,961	136,009
Total direct costs		1,300,010	1,054,035	1,175,441
HO oncosts	7.52%	111,446	90,359	100,767
Turnover		1,411,456	1,144,394	1,276,208
Profit	4.76%	70,543	57,195	63,784
		£1,481,999	£1,201,589	£1,339,992

These are certainly near enough to work on. (Refer to Evaluation of Claim — Figure 10.1.8 on p 297.)

Now, first the loss of productivity claim. We shall have to get our accountant to verify the costs, and we may have to look at it again when we see how the increased costs work out. Subject to that, I think it is right to consider the figures in the 'Nett actual cost' column, as the other matters have been dealt with separately.

Figure 10.1.13

EARTHWORKS – MAIN ROAD SECTION ONLY
Additional increased costs. Revised calculation — see Appendix 3 [Figure 10.1.7]

Total value of final account	1,579,573
Less interchange	239,581
	1,339,992

EV taken in this case to equate with certificate.

Certificates dated 30th of month or nearest.

PFF derived from 6 weeks prior to certificate, i.e. previous month.

Col 4 = split of payments expected (see App 2 [Figure 10.1.6]) against payments received.

Actual progress			Contractor's planned progress				Increased costs in tender	Nett contract value	Actual increased costs	Additional increased costs
Cert date	PFFc	Effective value	Effective value	Date	PFFp	$\frac{PFFp}{1+PFFp}$				
1	2	3	4	5	6	7*	8	4 – 8	2 × 9	10 – 8
Aug 77	0.2836	75,000	60,000	June 77	0.2390	0.1929	11,574	60,473	17,150	2,623
			15,000)	July	0.2452	0.1969	2,953			
Sept	0.2893	75,000	75,000)	July	0.2452	0.1969	14,767	60,233	17,425	2,658
Oct	0.2916	65,000	65,000	Aug	0.2836	0.2209	14,358	50,642	14,767	409
Nov	0.2965	70,000	50,000	Aug	0.2836	0.2209	11,045	54,467	16,149	616
			20,000)	Sept	0.2893	0.2244	4,488			
Dec	0.2894	55,000	55,000)	Sept	0.2893	0.2244	12,342	42,658	12,729	387
Jan 78	0.3001	50,000	40,000)	Sept	0.2893	0.2244	8,976	38,766	11,634	400
			10,000	Oct	0.2916	0.2258	2,258			
Mar	0.3045	10,000	10,000	Oct	0.2916	0.2258	2,258	7,742	2,440	182
Apr	0.3152	15,000	15,000)	Oct	0.2916	0.2258	3,387	11,613	3,660	273
May	0.3244	50,000	50,000)	Oct	0.2916	0.2258	11,290	38,710	12,557	1,268
June	0.3275	65,000	40,000	Oct	0.2916	0.2258	9,032	50,251	16,457	1,708
			25,000)	Nov	0.2965	0.2287	15,717			
July	0.3419	80,000	80,000)	Nov	0.2965	0.2287	18,296	61,704	21,097	2,801
Aug	0.3540	90,000	5,000)	Nov	0.2965	0.2287	1,143	69,324	24,541	3,865
			85,000	Dec	0.2984	0.2298	19,533			
Sept	0.4064	95,000	75,000	Jan 78	0.3001	0.2308	17,310	73,030	29,679	7,709
			20,000)	Feb	0.3037	0.2330	4,660			
Oct	0.4121	90,000	55,000)	Feb	0.3037	0.2330	12,815	69,016	28,441	7,457
			35,000)	Mar	0.3045	0.2334	8,169			
Nov	0.4224	80,000	40,000)	Mar	0.3045	0.2334	9,336	61,076	25,799	6,875
			40,000)	Apr	0.3152	0.2397	9,588			
Dec	0.4253	60,000	25,000)	Apr	0.3152	0.2397	5,993	45,436	19,324	4,760
			35,000)	May	0.3244	0.2449	8,571			
Jan 79	0.4278	60,000	55,000)	May	0.3244	0.2449	13,469	45,297	19,378	4,675
			5,000	June	0.3275	0.2467	1,234			
Feb	0.4337	20,000	20,000	June	0.3275	0.2467	4,934	15,066	6,534	1,600
Mar	0.4394	15,000	15,000	June	0.3275	0.2467	3,700	11,300	4,965	1,265
May	0.4563	55,000	55,000	June	0.3275	0.2467	13,569	41,431	18,905	5,336
June	0.4643	26,589)	5,000)	June	0.3275	0.2467	1,233	19,713	9,152	2,276
			21,589	Aug	0.3540	0.2614	5,643			
		48,411)	—	Average	0.2949	0.2277	11,023	37,388	17,359	6,336
July	0.4972	70,000	—		0.2949	0.2277	15,939	54,061	26,879	10,940
Aug	0.6018	10,000	—		0.2949	0.2277	2,277	7,723	4,648	2,371
Sept	0.6339	9,992	—		0.2949	0.2277	2,275	7,717	4,892	2,617
		1,339,992	1,201,589				305,155	1,034,837	386,562	81,407

* See x in Figure 10.1.14.

What about these increased costs; what did they allow in the tender?

Contractor's QS:
They allowed 10 per cent on nett costs for labour and materials and 12 per cent for plant.

Engineer's QS:
I think those are low and we could debate for ages whether they are and what they should have allowed. What I propose is that we make a table of certificates as might have been expected based on the original programme and calculate the increased cost content by reference to the NEDO indices. We can then put alongside that the certificates as they were paid, work out the increased cost content of those at the indices of the later dates and so we get the increase.

Contractor's QS:
I don't follow.

Engineer's QS:
I am not surprised, I have not put it very clearly. Let me explain by way of the table I propose to set up. I have roughed something out. [See Figure 10.1.13.]

   Look first at Column 3. There are the earthwork values in the certificates, as they were paid, with the dates in Column 1. Then in Column 5 we put the date when you expected to have had it, with the amount in Column 4. Where Column 4 is greater than Column 3, then the balance has to be set against the next certificate. This will take account of the alteration of the programme and the higher indices because of the delay.

   Then we work out the PFF obtaining when you expected to get paid and put that in Column 6. Taking the first payment you see in Column 4 — £60,000, now that includes increased costs, and at that date according to NEDO it was 14.95 per cent [see Figure 10.1.14, p 326] increase over tender date. So, the increased costs in the tender would theoretically be $0.2390 \div (1 + 0.2390) = 0.1929$ of the certificate value (Column 8). Take this from Column 4 and you get the core value, so to speak, to which we can apply the increased costs when you in fact get paid. The indices relate of course to a date six weeks before certificate which, as we were working to the last day of the month, means the previous month's indices. Take the increased costs at the later date from those of the earlier and you get the additional increased costs.

Contractor's QS:
I find it difficult to fault the logic of that because Column 8 represents the increased costs that should have been allowed in the tender. The contractor in fact allowed only about 11 per cent, so that if you take off what may by the look of your figures turn out to be 20 per cent or more on average, you will be applying the later, higher, factor to a figure which is really too small.

Engineer's QS:
Maybe so, but in the context of considering productivity you have produced a log of the other tenders to shew that this one was not unduly low. It therefore seems not unreasonable to assume (a) that the tender generally was about right and (b) if that is so that the proper allowance for increased costs has been included. I don't see how I can take any other line without risking giving your sub-contractor in effect an increase in his tender.

Figure 10.1.14

PRICE FLUCTUATION FACTORS
Calculation (first sixteen months only)

Base at Tender: date 13.12.75; Indices @ November 1975

Proportions		Indices	Weighted
Labour	0.50	218.9	109.45
Plant	0.375	213.5	80.06
Diesel	0.10	147.7	14.77
Timber	0.025	231.0	5.78
	1.000		210.06

Note: The proportions total 1.00, i.e. no fixed element, because in connection with a claim there is no surplus or deficiency from the formula to be taken up in the tender, as there is when tendering. In any case it applies to both calculations.

	August 1976		September 1976		October 1976		November 1976	
Lab 0.50	243.6	121.80	243.6	121.80	243.6	121.80	243.7	121.85
Pl 0.375	243.9	91.46	246.9	92.59	251.0	94.13	253.9	95.21
D 0.10	196.9	19.69	196.9	19.69	197.7	19.77	208.7	20.87
T 0.025	340.3	8.51	345.5	8.64	361.6	9.04	372.0	9.30
		241.46		242.72		244.74		247.23
		210.06		210.06		210.06		210.06
		31.04		32.66		34.68		37.17
PFF		0.1495		0.1555		0.1651		0.1770
'x'		0.1300		0.1346		0.1382		0.1504

	December 1976		January 1977		February 1977		March 1977	
Lab 0.50	243.7	121.85	244.9	122.25	245.2	122.60	245.7	122.85
Pl 0.375	255.1	95.66	258.4	96.90	260.9	97.84	266.6	99.98
D 0.10	211.3	21.13	217.0	21.70	217.0	21.70	218.0	21.80
T 0.025	376.3	9.41	381.7	9.54	382.5	9.56	385.3	9.63
		248.05		250.39		251.70		254.26
		210.06		210.06		210.06		210.06
		37.99		40.33		41.64		44.20
PFF		0.1808		0.1920		0.1982		0.2104
'x'		0.1531		0.1611		0.1654		0.1738

	April 1977		May 1977		June 1977		July 1977	
Lab 0.50	248.9	124.45	248.9	124.45	250.8	125.40	263.1	131.55
Pl 0.375	270.4	101.40	272.1	102.04	273.0	102.38	278.1	104.29
D 0.10	234.5	23.45	240.6	24.06	240.6	24.06	240.6	24.06
T 0.025	386.7	9.67	388.2	9.71	389.1	9.73	389.7	9.74
		258.97		260.26		261.57		269.64
		210.06		210.06		210.06		210.06
		48.91		50.20		51.51		59.58
PFF		0.2328		0.2390		0.2452		0.2836
'x'		0.1888		0.1929		0.1969		0.2209

	August 1977		September 1977		October 1977		November 1977	
Lab 0.50	263.5	131.75	263.5	131.75	263.5	131.75	263.5	131.75
Pl 0.375	280.0	105.30	282.8	106.05	286.1	107.29	287.6	107.85
D 0.10	240.6	24.06	240.6	24.06	240.6	24.06	240.6	24.06
T 0.025	389.3	9.73	377.9	9.45	370.0	9.25	363.5	9.09
		270.84		271.31		272.35		272.75
		210.06		210.06		210.06		210.06
		60.78		61.25		62.29		62.69
PFF		0.2893		0.2916		0.2965		0.2984
'x'		0.2244		0.2258		0.2287		0.2298

Contractor's QS:
Well, let us work out the whole thing and see what we get. *[Again see Figure 10.1.13.]* That will give him only £81,407 compared with £343,141 he was looking for. *[See Figure 10.1.7.]*

Engineer's QS:
True, but taking the average, he should have allowed for about 29.49 per cent increase, i.e. about £305,000 against £115,000. That, plus £81,407, would give a total of £386,500 to compare with his £458,000 odd. I think that is not too far adrift.

Contractor's QS:
I can only put it to them and see if they will accept.

Engineer's QS:
Well, I don't see how your sub-contractor can argue about it really because the NEDO formula has been accepted as giving a reasonable remuneration in the event, therefore it should be equally valid before the event, a sort of hind-sight as it were of what should have been allowed.

So far as the actual costs are concerned, including site oncosts and also the HO overheads, I would like our accountant to check those if you can please make arrangements.

I am not quite sure about the validity of claiming profit here.

Contractor's QS:
Why not? This is not a claim for damages. It has been accepted that there should technically have been a variation. It is therefore right to include profit. Even under Clause 12 this would be allowable.

Engineer's QS:
Yes, agreed. Let us then resummarize the claim using the figures we now have.

		Actual costs			Final account	
	Gross	Increased costs as Fig 10.1.12	Nett	Nett	Increased costs at tender	Total
Labour	653,081	129,735	523,346	292,080	102,414	394,494
Plant	830,339	164,946	665,393	371,350	130,209	501,559
Materials	237,363	47,152	190,211	106,156	37,223	143,379
	1,720,783	341,833	1,378,950	769,586	269,846	1,039,432
Site oncosts	225,164	44,739	180,435	100,700	35,309	136,009
Total direct	1,945,947	386,562	1,559,385	870,286	305,155	1,175,441
HO overheads	180,584	(at 9.28% average for period)		(as at tender)		100,767
	2,216,531					1,276,208
Profit	106,327					63,786
	2,232,858					1,339,992

Summarizing:

Loss of productivity: Costs	1,378,950		
Less in final account	769,586	609,364	
Increased costs	386,562		
Less in final account	305,155	81,407	
Site overheads: Costs	180,435		
Less in final account	100,700	79,735	
HO overheads	180,584		
Less in final account	100,767	79,817	
Profit now claimed	106,327		
Less in final account	63,786	42,543	£892,866

327

So, the total comes to the same. The reduction in increased costs mean that your loss of productivity has increased correspondingly.

This is going to worry the engineer because again it means that any underestimating in your tender is being made good.

Contractor's QS:
That is so, but we would deny any error in the tender. If you compare ours with the others there is no great difference and you must admit that dealing with this problem in such small pieces and periods — checking the material day by day, dependent on the lightest shower, almost lorry load by lorry load — was no way to run this job, yet that is what we had to do.

Engineer's QS:
Yes, well, we can only put that to the engineer and see what he has to say. Now, let us look at your part of the claim. We have agreed that the total delay ranking for compensation is $55\frac{1}{2}$ weeks, of which we have picked up 12.46 in the final account, leaving 43.04 to take up.

You have not in fact claimed the extra time of servicing the engineer's accommodation, but I see no reason why you should not.

So far as the earthworks claim is concerned, if this is accepted at £892,866, the first three items should be adjusted proportionally to £8,238,613, i.e. the tender total.

That would give:

Increase in bond premium (£34,000)	*3,685*	
Increase in CAR insurance (£72,000)	*7,803*	
Increase in third party insurance (£31,500)	*3,414*	*14,902*
Increase in servicing engineer's accommodation		
43.04 weeks at £200		*8,608*
Increase in servicing contractor's accommodation		
43.04 weeks at £300		*12,912*
Increase in site supervision 43.04 weeks at £5,560		*239,302*
		275,724
Add HO overheads (10.17 as average over period)		*28,041*
		£303.765

So far as HO overheads are concerned, I think this is acceptable, but again I would like our accountant to look at it.

So far as profit is concerned, I doubt whether we can include it, although I agreed just now that in principle it should be included. You see, if we were to translate all these extra costs back into terms of B/Q rates (which theoretically I think we should), then we would add the same allowance for profit as you had in your rates, i.e. nil. Then we would come to the Balancing Item (which you say represents your profit) and we find this is not adjustable.

I am afraid I cannot agree it. You can put it to the engineer again if you wish, but you know my views.

This, then, will give us a total for this claim of:

Sub-contractor (as claim)	*892,866*	
Main contractor	*303,765*	*£1,196,631*

CLAIM NO 3
I think there is nothing further to pick up here. Indeed, if we are now accepting site overheads in Claim No 2 and the extra works for the whole period of delay, it means, I am afraid, that the site supervision in this and probably the following claims must be deducted.

Contractor's QS:
I am afraid you are right. What does that leave us?

Engineer's QS:

Increase on labour, plant and materials as statement in Claim 3	*95,759*
Add Head Office oncosts at 9.35%	*8,963*
	£104,722

On the matter of the materials, the large extra cost here was queried at the third meeting.

Contractor's QS:
Yes, but I have had this checked and it seems mainly to have arisen from damage to drains when they were laid before placing and compacting embankments were complete. It is not a matter of underestimating; that I can confirm.

I am sorry to remind you but we still have profit to add.

Engineer's QS:
Agreed, but that takes the form in your case of a non-adjustable balancing or adjustment item!

CLAIM NO 4
This is a matter of delay and so the basis of the claim is in effect damages. The claim lies under Clause 31, so we are looking at 'cost'.

The 25 per cent loss of productivity seems high to me. If there really was such a loss, should you not have reduced your labour force?

Contractor's QS:
We did trim a bit, but by the very nature of the work and the need to keep the traffic moving, we could do no more. This claim does not overlap in money, but it is difficult to separate from the roundabout.

Engineer's QS:
This must be settled by the engineer.

I am afraid the 5 per cent profit must come out of the sub-contractor's claim. Look at Clause 1(5).

So far as your part is concerned, adjustment of all the Preliminary Items (except Traffic Control) has been picked up in Claim 2. On that item, it is a nice round figure, but have you any basis for it?

Contractor's QS:
We put in some record sheets to your inspector which he refused to sign, not because he disputed the times but because he said it had not been ordered as daywork.

Engineer's QS:
Let us look at those and see what they yield. I will then put it to the engineer as to whether he is prepared to accept them.

Contractor's QS:
As you will see from these sheets, priced at daywork, they total £1,987.40.

Engineer's QS:
I think we should now summarize this claim as follows:

Loss of productivity claimed by sub-contractor	19,014.00
Ditto by main contractor	8,770.00
Traffic safety and control measures	1,987.40
	£29,771.40

CLAIM NO 5

This was rejected, so there is nothing more for us to do with it. I think for your own satisfaction you should look at it again because the final account has now been completed and this will give you better figures than when you prepared your claim.

Contractor's QS:
I am not sure that that is so — apart from the Preliminaries, but there is one item I think does not belong here and should be in Claim 2: sub-base and road-base. I think if we could get that accepted, I might get my people to forgo the rest of the claim.

Engineer's QS:
I will put it to the engineer. What are the figures?

Contractor's QS:
I have abstracted these separately on the lines of Claim 2 and they are as follows:

		Tender	Final a/c	Actual cost	Increase
Labour	24.66%	177,103	194,194	229,612	35,418
Plant	15.24%	109,451	120,013	140,109	20,096
Materials	32.88%	236,138	258,925	—	—
		522,692	573,132	—	—
Site supervision	18.66%	134,013	146,945	—	—
		656,705	720,077	369,721	55,514
HO oncosts	8.56%	61,476	67,409	31,648	4,752
		718,181	787,486	—	60,266
Profit	5%				3,011
					£63,277

Engineer's QS:
I follow the figures and I am inclined to agree that this is in the same category as earthworks and should probably be included in Claim 2. I will put it to the engineer to accept £60,266. Again we are back to your non-adjustment item.

CLAIM NO 6
First we must get the rates right. There are several ways one can do this,
but I have done it on the basis of depreciation over the working life but
with allowance for higher cost at time of replacement. This would give:

Diesel hammer	*£150 per week × 13 =*	*£1,950*
Hanging leaders	*£67 per week × 13 =*	*£ 871*
Compressor	*£160 per week × 13 =*	*£2,080*
Crane	*£170 per week × 13 =*	*£2,210*
		£7,111

Contractor's QS:
That is a little better than I thought it might be. I can only put it to our
people.

Engineer's QS:
After what I have said previously about overheads and profit, I think you
will agree these must come out.

Contractor's QS:
To be consistent, yes; though I do not like it very much.

Engineer's QS:
CLAIM NO 7
Again, we have covered all these items of Preliminaries. That leaves the
question of traffic control.

Contractor's QS:
I am afraid that that item is a duplication of the one in Claim 4 and must
be deleted.

Engineer's QS:
That means the claim can be withdrawn.

Contractor's QS:
Yes.

Engineer's QS:
CLAIM NO 8
Again, we have dealt with the Preliminaries. So we are left with the last
two items.

Contractor's QS:
Yes. In connection with this traffic control item, we have record sheets
which we put in to your inspector at the time. These total £982.75 on a
daywork basis.

Engineer's QS:
I think they will be acceptable.

Contractor's QS:
Regarding the successive temporary diversions we have records and this
time they have been agreed and signed by your inspector. Really they
should have gone into the final account and not been included in the claim.

Engineer's QS:
So the claim now boils down to:

Traffic safety and control	*982.75*	
Successive temporary diversions	*12,480.00*	*£13,462.75*

CLAIM NO 9
I can sympathise over this, but on the wording of the preamble there is no way out.

Contractor's QS:
No, I agree. I can only say we shall watch out for this in future.

Engineer's QS:
So long as it is adjustable (given the revised preamble) you can perhaps use it rather more flexibly, but I think in preparing tenders you should know where it is likely to fall when adjusting variations. It is all very well to say that the Adjustment Item is variable in proportion to measured work but, as you will see from the exercise we have been doing, it can matter whether it is spread over labour and/or plant and/or material and/or site supervision or whatever.

CLAIM NO 10 *(Liquidated damages)*
There is nothing to do with this one.

CLAIM NO 11 *(Interest/finance charges)*
This is quite a complicated problem and I have prepared a Note about it. Here is a copy:

ENTITLEMENT TO FINANCE CHARGES IN RESPECT OF VARIATIONS ETC

The question is whether, in connection with the valuation of varied work or as a matter of cost in connection with delay, the contractor is entitled to be paid the cost of providing finance.

1. Variations
The principles of valuing variations are that where work is of similar character and executed under similar conditions it is valued at Bill rates. If the character or conditions are dissimilar, B/Q rates are to be used as a basis, otherwise a fair valuation is to be made.

Whether it be 'contract work' or 'varied work', it must be financed. That finance must be included in the B/Q rates, no doubt by way of the Head Office overheads. So that if the contractor is reimbursed at Bill rates or rates based thereon, he will be getting paid for the finance necessarily involved.

2. Delay
In case of delay arising from circumstances provided for in Clauses 7(3), 13(3), 14(6), 31(2) or 42(1), the basis of the reimbursement is to be 'cost' as defined in Clause 1(5), which includes overhead costs off site (presumably therefore Head Office), and again of necessity this includes for the cost of providing finance.

3. Period to be allowed for
When work is completed to an extent sufficient to enable it to be measured and valued, it can be included in interim certificates. The preparation of the statement (60(1)) takes some time so that the work may have been completed at least two weeks before. In terms of monthly certificates, the mid-point would be two weeks before that. So

that, for wages, the costs would be those incurred at least on average four weeks before the statement. Materials are rather more difficult. It is not a matter of when the price becomes fixed (as with the NEDO formula), but of when they are paid for. Assuming prompt payment, this could mean that materials are paid for at about the same time as the statement is prepared. Plant hire would probably be roughly similar, though these are probably the shortest periods possible. If that is right, then the total cost may be subdivided (see analysis of tender) as to 47 per cent labour (if labour on supervision and in oncosts is included), 20 per cent plant and 33 per cent materials, or, simplifying it to the two components, then 47 per cent labour and 53 per cent plant/materials. Therefore, so far as finance is concerned, 47 per cent would need to be laid out four weeks before the statement and 53 per cent at the time of the statement. This does not take into account retention. Then, if certificates are honoured when they are due, a further twenty-eight days are needed before payment, plus perhaps another three days before this is cleared through the bank. This means that finance is required as to:

$$47 - 1.41 = 45.59\% \text{ for labour for } 8\tfrac{1}{2} \text{ weeks} = \quad 3.875$$
$$\underline{53 - 1.59} = 51.41\% \text{ for material/plant for } 4\tfrac{1}{2} \text{ weeks} = \quad 2.313$$
$$3.00\% \qquad\qquad \text{retention for 104 weeks} = \quad \underline{3.120} \quad 9.308 \text{ weeks average}$$

On £100,000 at 15 per cent for 9.3 weeks, interest would amount to £2,740 or, say, 2.74 per cent of the outlay. This is of course an over-simplification but it may serve as a guide. The time arrived at is optimum, particularly if one takes account of the extent of under-measure.

4.   Minter v Welsh HTSO

There is a recent case, F G Minter Ltd (Drake and Scull) v Welsh Health Technical Services Organisation which was decided on appeal in March 1980 (see 13 BLR 1) and which deals with this matter, but the contract in question was on the JCT Form (1963) as amended in one important particular (twenty-one days to make application). It is a matter of opinion as to its applicability to the Standard ICE Form (1973/79) but there is one important point which Ackner LJ made in reply to an argument against the payment of interest per se. He said 'To my mind this seems to overlook that what the appellants here are seeking to claim, is not interest on a debt, but a debt which has as one of its constituent parts interest charges which have been incurred.' This accepts that finance charges are a component of cost.

*   The matter to be decided here was whether the contractor/sub-contractor was entitled to be reimbursed finance costs incurred:*

(i)   between the loss/expense being incurred and the making of a written application for reimbursement;
(ii)   during the ascertainment of the amount of the same;
(iii)   between the time of ascertainment and the issue of a certificate including it and in the case in question this was in respect of:

(a)   Varied work and in particular Clause 11(6) of the Conditions. This read:
    'If upon written application being made to him by the Contractor, the Architect is of the opinion that authorised variations . . . have involved the Contractor in direct loss and/or expense for which he would not be reimbursed by payment in respect of a valuation made in accordance with the rules contained in Sub-clause (4) . . . and if the said application is made within 21 days of the loss or expense being incurred then the Architect may ascertain . . . the amount . . .'
    Note that twenty-one days had been substituted for 'a reasonable time' of the original clause.

(b)   Disturbance of regular progress and in particular Clause 24(1) which reads:
    'If upon written application being made to him by the Contractor the Architect is of the opinion that the Contractor has been involved in direct loss and/or

expense for which he would not be reimbursed by a payment made under any other provision in this Contract by reason of the regular progress of the Works ... having been materially affected by:

> *(a) the Contractor not having received in due time necessary instructions drawings ... from the Architect for which he specifically applied in writing ...*

and if the written application is made within 21 days of it becoming apparent that the progress of the works ... has been affected as aforesaid then the Architect shall ... ascertain ... the amount ...'

Regarding (a), note that the agreement is to pay for the 'direct loss and/or expense' as a result of complying with the variation instruction. Ackner L J accepted that finance costs were part of the direct costs. Note that there was the problem that notice had to be given within twenty-one days of the cost being incurred, which might involve a series of notices unless the Employer was prepared to waive that necessity. However, this did not alter the fact that the cost of finance had to be part of the direct cost of the variation. The court was not concerned with determining the effect of their construction of the clauses but only to answer the question. This they answered in the affirmative so far as (i) above is concerned but in the negative so far as (ii) and (iii) were concerned. So that if the cost in question arises because of the time taken to consider the problem, the contractor has no claim.

The same ruling applies to (b) also.

Reverting now to the ICE Conditions, it seems that these are parallel to JCT in contemplating 'cost' or 'direct cost and/or expense' and that this refers to the costs involved in doing the work.

It therefore seems to me that if the contractor can point to any circumstances inherent in the variation or delay in themselves which cause additional finance costs, these could be reimbursed. Similarly, if the nature of the variation or delay were such as to increase the period for which finance has to be provided (if, for example, some materials had to be paid for in advance or if progress payments during manufacture were required before delivery to site and the contractor thus enabled to seek payment), then this too could be included.

But payment of the continuing cost of finance whilst the claim is being examined or following examination before certification is not allowable. In the latter case, if the amount were included in a statement under ICE Clause 60 and payment were delayed beyond twenty-eight days, then interest under 60(6) would follow.

The only alternative would appear to be to consider whether the engineer owes a duty of care to the contractor to deal with these matters expeditiously (Parker J in the High Court seems to suggest that a claim might lie against the architect).

In face of this judgment, I do not see how the engineer can recommend payment under the contract for costs which are not a direct part of the cost of the work.

This led in to the fourth and final meeting in the negotiation of these claims.

Fourth meeting

Engineer:
We now have the results of the work which our respective quantity surveyors have done and I propose to go through the claims one by one and see whether we can now reach agreement.

CLAIM NO 1
I see no reason to change my view on this. It is not admissible.

Contractor:
Reluctantly we agree, though we did have some staff standing by.

Engineer:
CLAIM NO 2
This was presented as the overriding cause of delay so far as the claims are concerned and if the overhead costs for this are met in full, then those attributed to Statutory Undertakers etc will fall away. The increased costs of Preliminaries for Variation Orders No 27 and No 141 have now been included in the final account.

As I have said, I am not happy about paying total costs. The increased costs are significantly reduced but the loss of productivity is correspondingly increased.

Contractor:
We promised to produce the log of the sub-contract tenders received. Here it is, from which you will see that the next lowest tender was £1,485,287, and the one above that is not too far away. I think that is fair indication that the tender was reasonable. And as for inefficiency on site, we agree that even contractors are not perfect but generally our estimating has to accord with our performance. Also, in this case, as we have said before, the control of the job was largely taken out of our hands, and a job run in as piecemeal a fashion as we were obliged to run this cannot possibly be efficient or economical.

Engineer:
Very well, let us put the new total in and we will look at the outcome as a whole.

CLAIM NO 3
This follows the principle of Claim No 2 and the amounts for site and HO overheads are deleted because these have now been dealt with overall. I agree the revised figure subject to the comment I made for Claim No 2.

CLAIM NO 4
I have no comment on the quantity surveyor's figures. I am prepared to accept this if you are.

Contractor:
Yes, we can see that our overheads have been picked up elsewhere but we do not really see why we should forgo profit.

Engineer:
The claim is based on Clause 31 and Sub-clause 2 refers to 'cost', which is defined in Clause 1(5).

Contractor:
Yes, we agree.

Engineer:
CLAIM NO 5
This was rejected but your quantity surveyor has raised the matter of the sub-base and road-base. On reflection, I am inclined to agree that this should be included in Claim No 2. Progress on that was certainly directly affected by the placing of Sandy Mudstone.

335

Contractor:
If you will accept that much, we will withdraw the rest of the claim.

Engineer:
CLAIM NO 6
Are the rates now proposed acceptable to you?

Contractor:
Reluctantly, yes. If we had hired the plant you would have paid hire charges, but for our own plant you will accept only depreciation rates.

Engineer:
That is so.

CLAIM NO 7
I understand this claim is now withdrawn.

Contractor:
Yes.

Engineer:
CLAIM NO 8
I have no further comment on this. I am prepared to accept the revised sum of £13,462.75.

Contractor:
We are agreeable to this.

Engineer:
CLAIM NO 9
This was rejected earlier. Have you any further comment?

Contractor:
Regretfully, no. We have since seen a copy of the revised clause used later and appreciate the difference.

Engineer:
CLAIM NO 10
No further comment.

CLAIM NO 11
This is the big one, after the Sandy Mudstone, that is. You have a copy of my QS's Note on this. It seems to me that he has been reasonably detached in forming his opinion.

On the face of it, we took much too long in coming to a view on this or perhaps it would be more correct to say took the wrong view for too long. I think, however, it would be fair to say that you too were taking the wrong line. If you could have made and substantiated the point earlier what sort of material you had expected (and that you were not relying solely on the contract documents) and why you considered you were entitled to expect it rather than ask my inspectors what you were to do, perhaps we could mutually have arrived at a decision much earlier which might have got a lot of this money paid earlier and so avoided these enormous finance costs.

Contractor:
Yes. We cannot at the moment fault the logic in the QS's Note. We have had a look at the Reports in the Building Law Reports and perhaps you will not be surprised to hear that in view of the amount involved we are taking further advice. But in the meantime we understand why you cannot accept our claim. Should we receive advice which suggests we might successfully pursue this claim we would propose to ask you for a decision under Clause 66. But this we hope to let you know about shortly.

The question of interest and finance charge claims is pursued further in Chapter 11. The law has changed since 1981, the date of the correspondence in the above claim. The Note by the Engineer's QS remains generally valid as a summary of *Minter*, and it has been left without reference to subsequent changes in the law because it also illustrates a fundamental point: the law changes and Forms of Contract change, but each decision has to be understood in the context of the relevant Form of Contract and the state of the law at the relevant time. That leads onto the question, what is the relevant time? In dealing with a contract, it is the specific edition of the Form of Contract that was incorporated in the contract, together with any Special Conditions, *ad hoc* amendments and entries in the Appendix, that applies. On the other hand, the substantive common law applies as it stands at the time of the decision, on the basis that judgments of the courts are merely declaratory of the existing law. Similarly any procedural rules, whether of statutory or common law origin, apply as at the date the matter is dealt with — this includes statutory rules on interest. Other Acts of Parliament generally only apply prospectively, but the precise scope of application must be found from the statute itself. In studying old cases it is important to identify both the Conditions of Contract and the date of the law applied.

In general, under contract, common law or statute, no entitlement to interest can start to accrue until the contractor has submitted his claim or at least given notice of the claim. ICE5 Clause 52(4)(e) says:

> 'If the contractor fails to comply with any of the provisions of this Clause in respect of any claim he shall seek to make then the Contractor shall be entitled to payment in respect thereof only to the extent that the Engineer has not been prevented from or substantially prejudiced by such failure in investigating the said claim.'

What all this boils down to is that a contractor cannot wait until the end of the day before recognizing his entitlement to claim, giving notice of his intention, formulating and evaluating the claim even on an interim basis, and formally submitting it; including interim valuations in his monthly statements under Clause 60 and, in the event of stalemate with the engineer, informing the employer. If that is right, it is not surprising that our contractor in the foregoing case decided not to proceed further in this aspect of the matter.

By the same token, architects, engineers and quantity surveyors must recognize what the contractor stands to lose if he fails to take what may seem to him appropriate action, and not take umbrage if served with notice of a claim. They should be able to distinguish the try on from the genuine even when in the latter case a claim may later be withdrawn. After all a claim is not validated by the notice of it but can well be invalidated by lack of it. If a contractor is not entitled, he is not entitled and can and should be told so. Either the claim will be disposed of or the contractor will be induced to look for a more correct basis or he may produce additional information which may persuade the engineer of its justice.

Engineer:
So, the result of these negotiations may be summarized as follows [see Figure 10.1.15].

The figures indicated as 'accepted' are subject only to verification of facts by our accountant. I understand arrangements have been made to visit your office next week.

Figure 10.1.15

CLAIMS — RESULT OF NEGOTIATION

		Claimed	Accepted
Claim No 1	Extra costs due to delayed order to commence	22,240	—
Claim No 2	a) add to final account for Preliminaries		89,838.23
	b) extra cost of placing and compacting Sandy Mudstone	1,282,581	1,196,631.00
Claim No 3	Extra cost of laying drainage out of sequence	138,074	104,722.00
Claim No 4	Delays by Statutory Undertakers	87,322	29,771.40
Claim No 5	Disruption and loss of productivity	250,608	60,266.00
Claim No 6	Delay in possession of site of Bridge No 628	13,987	7,111.00
Claim No 7	Delay and extra cost arising from VO for roundabout and additional bridge	29,030	—
Claim No 8	Delay and disruption by Water Authority pumping station	109,889	13,462.75
Claim No 9	Increase in adjustment item	36,000	—
Claim No 10	Wrongful deduction of liquidated damages	212,895	212,895.00
Claim No 11	Interest on outstanding monies	513,468	—
		£2,696,094	£1,714,697.38

Note: On 20 August 1981 the fixing and publication of 'Bank Rate' by the Bank of England ceased. In 1982 an amendment to Clause 60(6) of ICE5 was issued, changing 'Bank Rate' to 'Minimum Lending Rate'; this was incorporated in the 1986 Reprint. The amendment also increased the percentage over Bank Rate or MLR from $\frac{3}{4}$ per cent to 2 per cent. Rates of interest may also be fixed by reference to the lending rates of other banks or groups of banks. For example, ICE6 Clause 60(7) refers to 'a rate equivalent to 2% per annum above the base lending rate of the bank specified in the Appendix to the Form of Tender'.

Chapter 11
The finance claim pursued

INTRODUCTION

This chapter is partly by way of being a postscript to Chapter 10, continuing the saga into 1981 as the contractor pursues the claim for financing costs. We then look at developments in the law since 1981 in relation to interest and financing costs, as this has been a particularly active area of legal development. Finally we look at the provisions in the newer editions of the Standard Forms relating to interest and financing costs.

There is a risk that readers might be confused by the continued inclusion of an example which does not fully reflect the current state of the law, but the example still serves to demonstrate a number of points of principle, and the outcome would be the same on the facts ten years later. It also illustrates two fundamental points, which are often overlooked or inadequately appreciated. Firstly, the obligations, liabilities and entitlements of the parties are not solely to be found from the words of their contract; they may also derive from, and be supplemented by, statutes and common law. Secondly, while the terms of the contract are fixed at the time of agreement (and therefore it is essential to refer to the specific edition, amendments and *ad hoc* modifications made, not to the latest edition or amendments), the position of the 'legal supplement' may change during the course of the contract and even after completion, due to legislation and evolution of the common law. Statutes generally apply only with prospective effect but, occasionally, as in the case of the interest provisions, their effect can be back-dated. Common law rules stand as at the time when the matter is to be settled.

RE-SUBMISSION AND SETTLEMENT OF CLAIM

We pick up the narrative towards the end of the fourth meeting which may be assumed to have taken place on 14 October 1980. The contractor's final comment in respect of Claim

No. 11 ('Interest on outstanding monies' — subsequently recognized as finance costs) was:

'We have had a look at the Reports in the Building Law Reports and perhaps you will not be surprised to hear that in view of the amount involved we are taking further advice ... Should we receive advice which suggests we might successfully pursue this claim we would propose to ask for a decision under Clause 66. But this we hope to let you know about shortly.'

After taking advice the contractor resubmits the claim, reformulated on the basis of finance costs. Despite the previous mention of Clause 66, he makes no mention of the clause in the re-submission. In so far as the basis of the claim has changed, Clause 66 would arguably not be appropriate since there is not yet a dispute or difference. Submission under Clause 66 has several implications:

(i) It is an essential prerequisite under ICE5 to a reference to arbitration;

(ii) It starts the clock running. It requires the engineer to give a decision within a fixed period, and it requires the contractor and employer to refer the engineer's decision to arbitration within a further period or be finally bound by the decision;

(iii) It exhausts the engineer's powers to deal with the matter and therefore his obligation to consider the contractor's submissions. It is the last opportunity for the contractor to put his claim to the engineer.

It is not open to the engineer to elect to treat a submission as made under Clause 66 unless it is clear that it is. In cases where the submission is ambiguous on this point, it might be appropriate for the engineer to respond initially by asking the contractor to state whether the submission was to be considered as under Clause 66 or not. Where a claim is re-submitted without any fresh arguments, the engineer could decline to deal with it except under Clause 66.

Contractor to Engineer   *5 January 1981*

Motorway at . . . .

Claim for reimbursement of Finance Costs

Under our original Heads of Claim we included an Item 11 'Interest on outstanding monies' in the sum of £513,468. At our first meeting to discuss our claims, it was agreed that this claim was misdescribed and was in fact in respect of additional finance costs arising out of the varied work and the delays for which we were in no way responsible.

At the final meeting to discuss our claims, you indicated that you were unable to recommend acceptance mainly on the grounds that we had not stated our case sufficiently clearly as to our contentions about the nature of the Sandy Mudstone and our failure to particularise until we had formulated our claims about the effect on our financial position and the costs being incurred in that connection.

At that meeting we intimated to you that as there is such a large sum involved we felt impelled to seek legal advice on the matter. On the basis of that advice we now re-submit our claim for reimbursement of what are in fact finance costs to which we consider we are entitled under Clause 52 in respect of the varied work and Clause 31 in respect of delay by Statutory Undertakers.

We are further advised that the fact that we did not give notice specifically referring to finance costs in no way lessens our entitlement.

Clause 52(4)(e) certainly limits entitlement where the engineer has been 'prevented from or substantially prejudiced ... in investigating such claim'. The facts of the matter are as capable of being verified now as they would have been during the currency of the works. As regards the Sandy Mudstone, you have conceded (though not until the third claims meeting on 6 August 1980) that the instructions your representatives gave about the handling of this material amounted to variations under Clause 51. We contend that finance, as part of overheads, is one of the elements to be taken into account when considering the dissimilarities of varied work compared with contract work. Had these matters been recognized earlier, we should have been able to formulate our claim earlier. As it is we have had finance costs continuing right through 1980.

The contractor is protesting overmuch here. If he really believed that variations were involved in connection with the Sandy Mudstone, he could and should have so maintained and formulated his case accordingly. The engineer was at fault in not recognizing the fact but the contractor was also at fault.

We therefore re-present our claim as follows:

1. *Finance costs were incurred for the whole extra period required to carry out the extra work, for which 12.46 weeks was allocated.* [p. 321]

Costs of variations as final account	734,452
Add additional Preliminaries	89,838
	£824,290

The period of 12.46 weeks was in fact spread throughout the extended contract period and it is not possible to allocate this to any particular months.

We therefore claim the average overdraft rate which is:

From 0 to 2,299,081 in 43 months cost £513,468 [p. 316]

Average deficiency (2,299,081 ÷ 2) = 1,149,540

$$\frac{513,468}{1,149,540} \times \frac{100}{1} \times \frac{12}{43} \quad = 12.47\% \ p.a.$$

Claim

£824,290 at 12.47% for 12.46 weeks = £24,629.82

2. *Finance costs arising out of delay.*

The total costs involved as agreed in the Claims Settlement:

Total Claims 1 to 11	1,714,697.38
Less Claim 2 (Preliminaries)	89,838.23
	1,624,859.15
Less Claim 10 (L.D.s) (carried its own interest)	212,895.00
	£1,411,964.15

So far as the period is concerned, it was agreed that the total period of delay for which the employer was responsible was 55½ weeks. Of this 12.46 has been allocated to varied work leaving 43.04 for extra time (delay) attributable to Sandy Mudstone. This period also covered delays by Statutory [p. 320]

*Undertakers (which it overlapped) including the Water
Authority.*

> *We therefore claim the average overdraft rate on this
> amount for 43.04 weeks:*
>
> *£1,411,964 × 12.47% × 43.04 weeks = £145,733*

3. *These sums have remained outstanding for a further
period of a year (to the end of 1980).*

> *We therefore claim the cost of finance at the overdraft rates we had to pay
> as follows:*

Total of final account	9,062,903	[*p. 319*]
Add total of claims as agreed	1,714,697	[*p. 338*]
	10,777,600	
Less payments on account	9,088,344	[*p. 316*]
	£1,689,256	

£1,689,256 at 19% × 6 months (to 3 July)	160,479
£1,689,256 at 18% × 5 months (to 25 November)	126,694
£1,689,256 at 16% × 1 month (to end December)	22,523
	£309,696

SUMMARY

Finance costs attributable to variations	24,629
Finance costs attributable to delay	145,733
Finance costs in respect of both for further period	309,696
	£480,058

> *We shall be glad if you would deal with this matter at an early date for, as
> you will appreciate, these finance costs are continuing.*

The engineer called for a report from the QS who said:

1. *The sums referred to in the claim in respect of the VOs and the delay are those
settled and agreed at the fourth meeting on 14 October 1980.*

2. *The basic periods for the variations (12.46 weeks) and delay attributable to the
employer (43.04 weeks) were also those agreed. The claims in connection with
Sandy Mudstone (2b and 3) have been included in delay and not in variations.
This is not incorrect because in considering extension of time, it was accepted
that delay arising out of Sandy Mudstone overlapped and exceeded that by SUs
etc.*

3. *On the question of notice, I think it is true to say that clause 52(4)(e) is not a
complete cut-off as was the case in* Minter v Welsh HTSO.

4. *On the other hand, the contractor did not during the course of the work give the
proper grounds on which he was entitled to claim. If he considered he was
entitled to a Variation Order, he could have maintained it, substantiated it,*

formulated his claim accordingly and indicated the inclusion of finance costs. He gave no indication that finance costs were involved, much less the amount and he admitted during discussion on the claims that he was not aware of this until he had formulated his claim. If however it is conceded that the material met with and the instructions given in connection with the handling of it were 'variations', then it must be accepted that all dissimilarities must be taken into account and this must include prolongation, and the costs of finance going with it.

5. *The overdraft rate claimed has been arrived at by taking the cost of the overdraft attributable to this contract (£513,468 [see p. 316]) and assuming that this was in respect of an average between 0 and £2,299,081 for the whole period, i.e. 513,468 ÷ 114,954 × 100 for 43 months = 12.47% p.a.*

    It is not possible to identify the cost of variations or parts of the delay in relation to any given month and its concomitant overdraft. It is therefore considered that the method adopted is reasonable in the circumstances.

6. *Whatever the merits of the first two parts of this claim it is considered that the third part is not in fact the cost of financing the variations or the delay, but interest on a debt and is therefore outside the scope of the contract.*

The engineer called a meeting with the contractor which took place on 13 January 1981 and it required relatively brief discussion to accept:

(a) the sums on which the calculations had been based;
(b) the periods in question;
(c) the overdraft rates being claimed.

The matter of notice was rather more difficult. It was accepted that Clause 52(4)(e) did not provide a complete cut-off but the engineer contended that his consideration of the claim had been prejudiced by not having been made properly and making no reference to finance costs. It was no part of the engineer's duties to make the contractor's case for him.

The contractor responded that this was understood but it was not a valid argument since it had eventually been agreed that a variation had been involved as regards the Sandy Mudstone and the extent of the delay for other reasons had been established and remuneration therefore had been accepted and agreed. All that was now in issue was a relatively small element of cost which had so far not been recognized.

The *Minter* case established that finance costs were commonly incurred by contractors in construction to finance variations or the costs of delay and disruption, and that as such formed part of the 'loss and expense' referred to in the JCT form. In that finance charges form part of the overheads of an organization, amounts incurred to finance a reimbursable cost are surely to be included as part of that cost under ICE5 Clause 1(5).

After further discussion the engineer agreed to accept the first two items but rejected the third. He gave as his reasons:

(a) *The first item was concerned with the valuation of the variation(s) which had to take into account all aspects of dissimilarity — including any difference of time relative to value. This was now taken up by the 12.46 weeks. The B/Q prices must be deemed to include for the time involved between spending the money on labour, materials etc. and recovering it by way of payments on account. If that allowance has been exceeded, it is not because of the variation but of some failure on the part of the engineer or the contractor.*

(b) *Similarly with delay. The costs which the contractor is entitled to be reimbursed are those arising directly from that delay. In the Minter case, Ackner L J made reference to the case governing damage — Hadley v Baxendale, 1854 (13 BLR 23). Not until the cost has been determined and the employer notified (via the engineer) and has had opportunity to satisfy himself as to the correctness of the charge does payment become due. In this period it cannot be said that such costs are arising from the causative delay but from the time taken by the contractor to formulate his claim and the engineer to consider it.*

    (c) *In connection with both these matters the engineer has dealt expeditiously with the information which the contractor has supplied him.*

The contractor protested that this was not the case. The continuing finance costs were a consequence of the original events (i.e. the Sandy Mudstone and the delays).

The engineer replied that at no point during the progress of the work had he had a claim stating grounds he considered justifiable nor quantifying the compensation being sought. He could not substitute other (? correct) grounds for those put forward by the contractor. He could not calculate how much, if anything, was due, any more than an arbitrator was in a position to change the particulars of claim submitted by the claimant.

The contractor then said they had been advised that if they were to go to arbitration or litigation, they would be able to claim interest, which might differ technically from finance costs but would be substantially the same in amount. If this were so, could the engineer not so inform the employer and could he not then accept that that being the case he would find it reasonable to pay without actually going to the lengths of arbitration?

The engineer was quite prepared to put the matter to the employer but he could not recommend payment for the reasons just given. He was prepared to certify £170,362 in respect of the first two items and report the third to the employer on the lines already discussed.

The contractor agreed to this and the employer then paid the amounts agreed in respect of the claims (£1,689,256) plus £170,362. He declined to pay anything in respect of 'interest' as he considered that the engineer had acted properly.

POINTS OF PRINCIPLE INVOLVED

It is vital for the contractor to recognize his entitlement as soon as possible after the events giving rise to the situation. In the case of earthworks particularly costs can escalate in an alarming manner (see also Case 6.1) and matters of claim should not be allowed to drift in the urgency of getting on with the work.

It is important that the contractor identifies the grounds on which he bases his entitlement. It is indeed no part of the engineer's or quantity surveyor's duties to do that job for him.

It is equally important for the engineer/QS to recognize the potentiality for a claim and to discuss matters with the contractor at the time. If he is putting forward incorrect grounds he should be told so — and why they are considered incorrect. If as a result of discussion the contractor changes his grounds, so be it — even in arbitration he can change his points of claim if he has good cause.

The matters with which the A/E/QS is charged in this connection are determining the value of the variation (according to the rules or principles laid down in the contract) and the cost (or loss and expense as the case may be) arising out of the delay. It was established in *Minter* that entitlement to financing costs is to be calculated from the date when the primary loss and/or expense or the expenditure on a variation was incurred up to the date when the contractor submits his claim subject to any time limit for submission of such claims stipulated by the contract. The time limits under ICE5 Clause 52(4) allow some flexibility, unless the engineer states specific requirements for submission of accounts, but even on a generous interpretation, the account giving full and detailed particulars of the amount claimed is to be submitted within a reasonable time of the variation being completed or the delay ceasing. If the contractor takes a longer time to prepare his claim than allowed by the contract, he has only himself to blame. The financing costs incurred by the contractor between the time allowed by the contract for submission of the account and the actual date of submission are the result of his delay in submitting the claim, not a result of the original events. If the A/E/QS takes an unreasonable time to consider the matter, that is a separate and different cause from the originating cause and must be dealt with as a separate issue.

It is important that every effort be made by both sides to facilitate and make payments on account. For the contractor it is important to obtain the money to which he is entitled, and also to avoid prejudicing his situation later. As for the engineer he must certify everything to which the contractor is entitled, having regard to the proviso in ICE5 Clause 52(4)(f): that if the particulars submitted by the contractor are insufficient to substantiate the whole of the claim, the contractor is only entitled to interim payment of such part of the claim as the particulars submitted do substantiate.

Reference is made in Clause 52(4)(f) to what the engineer considers due and what is substantiated to the satisfaction of the engineer, but this is to be interpreted on the basis that the engineer is to apply objective standards commonly used by engineers in the exercise of their professional task.[1]

If the particulars submitted in fact substantiate more on such objective basis than the engineer certifies, this would amount to a failure by the engineer to certify and the contractor would be entitled to interest under ICE5 Clause 60(6) — which is to be paid by the employer without the certificate of the engineer.

SUBSEQUENT DEVELOPMENTS IN THE LAW

The common law has historically been averse to awarding financing costs or interest on debts prior to judgment. The old common law position established by the Court of King's Bench in 1829[2] was confirmed by the House of Lords in 1893 in *London Chatham and Dover Rly Co v South Eastern Rly Co*,[3] that a creditor cannot, in the absence of some express or implied agreement, recover damages for late payment of a debt. Thus a judge or arbitrator had no power at common law to include any element of interest or financing costs in an award unless it had been stipulated in the contract. The Court of Appeal in *Minter*, although drawing an analogy between the contractual entitlement under the JCT Form to 'loss and/or expense' and entitlement to damages at common law, explicitly declined to apply the common law restriction on interest or financing costs as damages. Stephenson LJ explained:[4]

> 'I do not think that today we should allow medieval abhorrence of usury to make us shrink from implying a promise to pay interest in a contract if by refusing to imply it we thereby deprive a party of what the contract appears on its natural interpretation to give him.'

The decision in *Minter*, therefore, only provided authority as to the interpretation of the specific JCT Form of Contract, although the principle might be extended to similar provisions in other Forms. The decision did not provide authority for any wider proposition as to the recoverability of interest or financing costs as damages. Since *Minter* was decided in March 1980, however, there have been substantial developments in the common law on recovery of financing costs as damages and, by legislation, on entitlement to interest on debt or damages. There have also been changes in some Standard Forms.

There is a distinction between entitlement to recover financing costs or loss of interest as an element of damages on the one hand, and entitlement to interest on damages or debt

---

1. *Sudbrook v Eggleton* [1983] 1 AC 444 at p 479.
2. *Page v Newman* [1829] 9 B & C 378.
3. *London Chatham and Dover Rly Co v South Eastern Rly Co* [1893] AC 429.
4. *Minter v WHTSO* [1981] 13 BLR 1 at p 17.

on the other. This was considered in *Minter* by Ackner LJ, who concluded[5] that what was being claimed was 'not interest on a debt but a debt which has as one of its constituent parts interest charges which have been incurred.'

Financing costs as element of damages

In considering whether any item of loss or expense is recoverable as damages, the starting point is the case of *Hadley v Baxendale*.[6] This established that damages are only recoverable in so far as the nature (as distinct from the amount) of the loss or damage suffered was in the contemplation of the parties at the time of contract as likely to result from the breach of it. The judgment went on to distinguish two 'rules' or 'limbs'. Under the first rule, loss or damage is presumed to have been in the contemplation of the parties at the time of contract if its nature was such as to be likely to arise in the usual course of things. Damages recoverable under this rule are termed 'general damages'. Under the second rule, damages are recoverable if the nature of the loss or damage was outside the usual course of things but was in the actual contemplation of the parties at the time of the contract as the likely result of a breach. Damages recoverable under the second rule are termed 'special damages'.

In *Minter*, Stephenson LJ based his judgment on the view that, since it was agreed between the parties that 'cash flow' is vital to the contractor in the construction industry, financing costs are part of general damages. He said:[7]

'The loss of the interest which (the contractor) has to pay on the capital he is forced to borrow and on the capital which he is not free to invest would be recoverable for the employer's breach of contract within the first rule in *Hadley v Baxendale* without resorting to the second . . .'

Ackner LJ agreed that financing costs came within the first rule of *Hadley v Baxendale*. He expressed the point as follows:[8]

'Direct loss and/or expense is loss and expense which arise naturally and in the ordinary course of things, as comprised in the first rule in *Hadley v Baxendale*. Building Contractors in the ordinary course of things, when they require capital to finance an operation, either have to pay charges for borrowing that capital, or if they use their own capital, lose the interest which it otherwise would have earned.'

Change to 'special damages'

The approach followed in *Minter* of interpreting contractual provisions by analogy with common law principles, but stopping short of applying the whole of the relevant principles, may be regarded as unsatisfactory, but the flaw in the argument has since been cured. In *Wadsworth v Lydall*,[9] the Court of Appeal found a way round the old common law restriction on recovery of interest as damages, by holding that the old cases only excluded recovery of interest or financing costs as general damages within the first limb of *Hadley v Baxendale*. The Court was accordingly free to hold, and did hold, that financing costs could be recovered as special damages within the second limb. Brightman L J dealt with the point as follows:[10]

'If a plaintiff pleads and can prove that he has suffered *special damage* as a result of the defendant's failure to perform his obligation under a contract and such damage is not too remote on the principle of *Hadley v Baxendale*, I can see no reason why such *special damage* should be irrecoverable merely because

5. *Minter v WHTSO* [1981] 13 BLR 1 at p 23.
6. *Hadley v Baxendale* [1854] 9 Ex 341.
7. *Minter v WHTSO* [1981] 13 BLR 1 at p 15.
8. Ibid at p 23.
9. *Wadsworth v Lydall* [1981] 1 WLR 598.
10. Ibid at p 603.

the obligation on which the defendant defaulted was an obligation to pay money and not some other type of obligation.'

The decision in *Wadsworth v Lydall* was approved by the House of Lords in *La Pintada*.[11] The decision in *La Pintada* makes clear, however, that interest is not recoverable as general damages. In order for the loss of interest or financing costs to be recoverable based on the general knowledge of the importance of cash flow in the construction industry, it is necessary to deploy the argument accepted by Hobhouse J in *IMCC v Helm*,[12] that the effect of damage being commonplace in a particular trade is not to bring it into the heading of general damage but to introduce an evidential presumption as follows:

> 'In the eyes of the law, those facts or circumstances are deemed to be special, whether in truth they are or not, and knowledge of them must be proved. Where, as in the present case, the relevant facts or circumstances are commonplace, the burden of proof will be easy to discharge and the Courts may well be willing to draw inferences of knowledge.'

Thus the line of argument in the *Minter* case should be revised to make the analogy with financing costs being recoverable as 'special damages' under the second rule of *Hadley v Baxendale*.

Unlike entitlement to interest under statute described below, the award of financing costs or loss of interest as special damages is not a matter of judicial discretion, nor does it depend on the primary sum still being outstanding at the date of the commencement of legal proceedings. It depends only on proof of breach of contract, that the financing costs or loss of interest were suffered as a result of the breach, and that the loss comes within the second limb of *Hadley v Baxendale*.

It can be argued, as a matter of principle, that the loss of interest or financing costs incurred must be specifically proved by the claimant. This could involve a detailed investigation of financing arrangements and other details, such as when relevant invoices were paid. It is, however, apparent from the judgment in *Minter*, as quoted above, that little distinction is drawn between loss of interest and financing costs incurred. Unless the claimant seeks to prove some special rate of interest, it is suggested that a notional figure of 2 per cent over Minimum Lending Rate may be assumed, as the typical overdraft rate paid by civil engineering contractors. It could be argued that any special higher rate of interest should not be recoverable, being excluded by the second rule of *Hadley v Baxendale* unless specific notice of it was given at the time of contract. This broad brush approach may be applied equally to contractual provisions interpreted by analogy with the common law entitlement to damages. Note, also, the contrary impact of contractual provisions, such as GC/Wks 1 Edition 3 Condition 47(6) (set out below), negating entitlement to financing costs as special damages.

Failure to certify as breach

The significance, in a construction context, of the recoverability of financing costs as damages for breach is that failure by the A/E/QS to certify monies properly due in accordance with the contract could amount to a breach of contract. The principal loss suffered by the contractor as a result of such failure to certify is in financing costs. Therefore, the breach — if it is a breach — can only be the subject of a claim if financing costs are recoverable either as damages or under the provisions of the contract.

For delay in fixing valuations or settling claims to constitute a breach of contract by the employer, the A/E/QS must be under a duty to fix the valuation or settle the claim properly and without delay *and* the employer must somehow be held responsible for his failure to

---

11. *President of India v La Pintada Cia Navegacion SA* [1985] AC 104.
12. *IMCC v Karl O Helm* [1986] 1 Lloyd's Rep 81; See Foyle A W 1988 *Recent Developments in the Recovery of Interest and Financing Charges* 4 Const LJ 3.

discharge the duty. The latter requirement is obviously satisfied where the employer has interfered with the issue of a certificate or exercise of a discretion by the A/E/QS. It is less obvious where the employer has not interfered. In *Rees & Kirby v Swansea City Council*,[13] Robert Goff LJ mentioned the employer's responsibilities in law for the acts or omissions of the architect as a 'matter open to question'. *Perini Corporation v Commonwealth of Australia*[14] provides authority for such responsibility in the case of an engineer who is an individual employee of the employer. Authority for a broader principle of responsibility has been provided recently by Vinelott J in *Merton LBC v Leach*.[15] He held in that case that the local authority employer would be liable in damages for breach by their architect of a duty to exercise a discretion or act as certifier, without any proof of collusion or interference. He dealt with the question as follows:[16]

> 'In so far as the architect exercises a discretion or acts (as it has been said) as a certifier the contractor is entitled to refer the matter to an arbitrator who (under clause 35(3)) will stand in the shoes of the architect and can review the matter in the same manner as if the certificate or decision had not been given. The arbitrator is himself part of the machinery for correcting any failure or mistake on the part of the architect. So it is said, there is no room for the imposition of any secondary obligation on the part of Merton to pay compensation for any such failure or mistake . . . In my judgment under the contract Merton undertook to ensure that there would at all times be a person who would carry out the duties to be performed by the architect and that he would perform those duties with reasonable diligence, skill and care and that where the contract required the architect to exercise his discretion he would act fairly.'

In *Lubenham Fidelities v South Pembrokeshire DC*,[17] on the other hand, the Court of Appeal declined to imply a term that the employer was bound to pay sums properly due to the contractor in excess of sums certified by the architect where the architect had admittedly made errors in the certificates. It does not appear that *Merton v Leach* was cited to the court — indeed May LJ specifically noted that counsel for the employer told the court 'that there seems to be no previous authority on this point and no real help can be obtained from the textbooks'.

It does not follow from *Merton v Leach* that the employer would be liable for financing costs as damages merely because the arbitrator disagreed with the decision of the A/E/QS. For a breach of contract, the A/E/QS must have failed properly to discharge his function under the contract.[18] Disagreement by the arbitrator with the decision of the A/E/QS may provide *prima facie* evidence that the A/E/QS failed to perform his duties with due skill, care and diligence or that he was unfair, but it is not conclusive.

Payment of interest | **Interest after award**

Although the law has been reluctant to award interest or financing costs as damages before judgment, it has long been the rule that a party to litigation or arbitration is automatically entitled to interest on judgment debts, that is, on awards made by the court (including the award of costs).[19] A successful party in arbitration is also entitled to interest on an award by an arbitrator[20] (subject to the power of the arbitrator to exclude such interest[21]). Interest runs from the date of the award at simple interest at rates set by Order in Council and

---

13. *Rees & Kirby v Swansea City Council* [1985] 30 BLR 1.
14. *Perini Corporation v Commonwealth of Australia* [1969] 12 BLR 82.
15. *Merton LBC v Stanley Hugh Leach* [1985] 32 BLR 51.
16. Ibid at p 107.
17. *Lubenham Fidelities v South Pembrokeshire DC* [1986] 32 BLR 39.
18. See Barber J N 1988 '*Rules of Conduct for the Engineer*' 5 ICLR 290.
19. Judgments Act 1838.
20. Arbitration Act 1950 s20.
21. Ibid.

published by Statutory Instrument[22] from time to time. The rate of interest applicable to a judgment debt is that in force at the date of the award, it does not vary thereafter.[23]

The entitlement to interest survives even agreement to accept the amount of the original judgment debt in instalments.[24]

Interest under statute

The common law position on interest was amended by statute, first by the Civil Procedure Act 1833, commonly referred to as Lord Tenterden's Act, and subsequently by the Law Reform (Miscellaneous Provisions) Act 1934, which conferred on judges a discretionary power to award interest on amounts which were the subject of an award. Arbitrators were held to have implied power to award interest by analogy with the 1934 Act.[25]

The 1934 Act was amended by the Administration of Justice Act 1969, but it has now been superseded by the Administration of Justice Act 1982, which went much further. The 1982 Act inserted new sections into various Acts[26] introducing a statutory discretion for judges and arbitrators to award simple interest not only on amounts included in an award, but also on amounts included in a reference but paid over before the award. The relevant parts of the statutory provisions as regards High Court and arbitration are as follows:

Supreme Court Act 1981 s35A
(1) Subject to rules of court, in proceedings (whenever instituted) before the High Court for the recovery of a debt or damages there may be included in any sum for which judgment is given simple interest, at such rate as the court thinks fit or as rules of court may provide, on all or any part of the debt or damages in respect of which judgment is given, or payment is made before judgment, for all or any part of the period between the date when the cause of action arose and — (a) in the case of any sum paid before judgment, the date of the payment; and (b) in the case of the sum for which judgment is given, the date of the judgment. ...

(3) Subject to rules of court, where — (a) there are proceedings (whenever instituted) before the High Court for the recovery of a debt; and (b) the defendant pays the whole debt to the plaintiff (otherwise than in pursuance of a judgment in the proceedings), the defendant shall be liable to pay the plaintiff simple interest at such rate as the court thinks fit or as rules of court may provide on all or any part of the debt for all or any part of the period between the date when the cause of action arose and the date of the payment.

(4) Interest in respect of a debt shall not be awarded under this section for a period during which, for whatever reason, interest on the debt already runs ...

(6) Interest under this section may be calculated at different rates in respect of different periods ...

Arbitration Act 1950 s19A
(1) Unless a contrary intention is expressed therein, every arbitration agreement shall, where such a provision is applicable to the reference, be deemed to contain a provision that the arbitrator or umpire may, if he thinks fit, award simple interest at such rate as he thinks fit — (a) on any sum which is the subject of the reference but which is paid before the award, for such period ending not later than the date of the payment as he thinks fit; and (b) on any sum which he awards, for such period ending not later than the date of the award as he thinks fit.

---

22. Judgment Debts (Rate of Interest) Orders, made from time to time under the Administration of Justice Act 1970 s44.
23. *Rocco Giuseppe & Figli v Tradax Export SA* [1983] 3 All ER 598.
24. *Foakes v Beer* [1884] 9 App Cas 605.
25. *Chandris v Isbrandtsen-Moller* [1951] 1 KB 240.
26. New provisions were inserted in the Supreme Court Act 1981, County Courts Act 1959 and Arbitration Act 1950.

(2) The power to award interest conferred on an arbitrator or umpire by subsection (1) above is without prejudice to any other power of an arbitrator or umpire to award interest.

The statutory provisions were interpreted and explained at length by Lord Brandon in *La Pintada*.[27] He identified three cases:

Case 1 — Late payment of debts before any proceedings for their recovery have begun.

Case 2 — Late payments of debts after proceedings have begun but before they have been concluded.

Case 3 — Debts not paid before judgment in proceedings for their recovery has been given.

Lord Brandon concluded that Parliament intended to confer a discretionary power to award interest in respect of Cases 2 and 3, but no discretionary power in respect of Case 1. Nor would the House of Lords seek to override the intentions of the Statute by imposing an entitlement to interest as of right.

In a later decision,[28] the House of Lords held that the new section in the Arbitration Act 1950 was inserted with retrospective effect so that it applied to all arbitration agreements made after 1950, rather than 1982, if the arbitration proceedings were commenced after the 1982 Act came into force.

The distinction between debt and damages was discussed in *Rees and Kirby v Swansea CC*,[29] a case under the Supreme Court Act. Robert Goff L J said there was a question whether in the absence of an architect's certificate, any sum recoverable was a debt or whether it could only be recovered as damages. He concluded that it was enough for the purposes of awarding interest to hold that the sum was due as debt or damages.

Date from which interest runs

Although the award of interest under these statutes is discretionary, the interest must be exercised judicially and for reasons which can be stated.[30] The courts have indicated that the rate of interest should normally be 1 per cent plus bank rate or minimum lending rate, but that in a commercial setting, it would be proper to take account of the manner in which and the time at which persons acting honestly and reasonably would pay.[31]

The Supreme Court Act s35A gives the earliest date from which the interest may run as the date when the 'cause of action arose'. S19A of the Arbitration Act appears to confer an open discretion as to the period, but Lord Brandon implied in *Lips Maritime*[32] that despite the difference in wording, the powers conferred on an arbitrator were to be construed as consistent with the powers conferred on the High Court.

Lips Maritime was a shipping case, involving a claim for demurrage. The main issue was whether currency losses could be recovered as special damages (the House of Lords held they could not), but Lord Brandon (with whom Lord Keith agreed) held[33] that the arbitrator was correct to calculate discretionary interest from the end of 2 months after the delay, on the basis that demurrage is usually settled and paid for within 2 months of the completion of discharge. This did not depend on an implied term.

In other cases it has been stated that, among other factors, unreasonable delay by a plaintiff

---

27. *President of India v La Pintada Cia Navegacion SA* [1985] AC 104.
28. *Food Corporation of India v Marastro Cia Naviera* [1987] 1 WLR 134.
29. *Rees & Kirby v Swansea City Council* [1985] 30 BLR 1.
30. *Panchaud Freres SA v Pagnan and Fratelli* [1974] 1 Lloyd's Rep 394.
31. *Shearson Lehman v Maclaine Watson (No 2)* [1990] 3 All ER 723.
32. *President of India v Lips Maritime Corp* [1988] AC 395.
33. Ibid at pp 422, 423.

in prosecuting a claim may lead a court not to award interest for the full period from the date of the loss.[34] Those cases must be treated with caution, however, in so far as they relate to claims for loss of non-profit-earning chattels.

INTEREST UNDER STANDARD FORMS

Interest under statute is only recoverable if arbitration or litigation is commenced, and then only on the amount still outstanding when the proceedings are commenced. This may provoke a radical change in thinking, since the early commencement of arbitration becomes advantageous if considerable monies are outstanding, unless there is provision for interest to be paid under the contract. The introduction of the new statutory rights to interest and the new common law position on recovery of financing costs as special damages has been reflected in, or pre-empted by, amendments to some Standard Forms, either to allow interest or to limit its recoverability.

The ICE Conditions have always provided, from the first edition in 1945, that interest is payable by the employer on overdue payments on certificates. The rate of interest in the first edition was 5 per cent per annum and it remained so until the fifth edition in 1973, when it was increased to $\frac{3}{4}$ per cent over Bank Rate. In the 1986 Reprint the rate of interest was increased to 2 per cent over Minimum Lending Rate.

ICE5 Clause 60(6) also extended the entitlement to interest to the event of 'failure by the Engineer to certify ... in accordance with sub-clauses (2) (3) and (5)'.

In a Scottish case, *Nash Dredging v Kestrel Marine*,[35] the First Division court held that the contractor was entitled to interest under Clause 60(6) where the employer had interfered with the issue of a final certificate by the engineer. The employer had terminated the employment of the original engineer when he refused to act on instructions not to certify sums agreed, and appointed a new engineer who issued a final certificate excluding the claim. The Opinion of the Court refers to arguments that the claim for interest was quite wrong in that it 'appeared to contemplate, quite wrongly, that all they had to establish to qualify for interest under Clause 60(6) was that the amount certified in the final certificate was smaller than it should have been'. The validity of the argument was not considered in detail, however, as the Court held that the claim did raise sufficiently the issue of interference.

In *Morgan Grenfell v Seven Seas Dredging Ltd*,[36] Judge Newey held that Clause 60(6) was not limited to cases where the engineer failed to form an opinion or did not act *bona fide* or failed to issue a certificate under ICE5 Clause 60(2). He said:[37]

> 'In my judgment, Clause 60(2) requires the engineer, who has been provided with a statement in accordance with Clause 60(1), to "certify" the amount which the contractor should be paid. Obviously, that amount should be the amount which in his "opinion" the contractor should be paid. If the word "opinion" had not been used in the sub-clause some similar word or words would have had to have been used. For the sub-clause to work the engineer has to decide how much the contractor should receive and that is a matter of "opinion", "judgment", "conclusion" or the like. If the engineer certifies an amount which is less than it should have been, the contractor is deprived of money on which he could have earned money.
>
> Clause 66(1) provides a means by which a contractor can obtain a review and, if appropriate, a revision of the engineer's certificate by an arbitrator. If the

---

34.   See *Metal Box v Curry Ltd* [1988] 1 All ER 341; *General Tire & Rubber Co v Firestone Tyre and Rubber Co Ltd* [1975] 2 All ER 173.
35.   *Nash Dredging (UK) Ltd v Kestrel Marine Ltd* [1987] SLT 641.
36.   *Morgan Grenfell v Seven Seas Dredging Ltd* [1990] 51 BLR 85.
37.   Ibid at p 99.

arbitrator revises his certificate so as to increase its amount, it follows that the engineer has failed to certify the right amount and the contractor becomes entitled to interest under Clause 60(6).'

It is submitted that while the increase in value of a certificate may provide *prima facie* evidence that the engineer failed to certify the right amount, it is not conclusive.[38] In particular Clause 66 explicitly provides that 'neither party shall be limited in the proceedings before such arbitrator to the evidence or arguments put before the Engineer for the purposes of obtaining his decision'. That applies to evidence put before the engineer for his decision under Clause 66. *A fortiori* the evidence put before the arbitrator by the contractor may be different from the evidence and arguments submitted to the engineer for a claim prior to Clause 66. Due regard should be had to Clause 52(4)(f):

'The Contractor shall be entitled to have included in any interim payment certified by the Engineer pursuant to Clause 60 such amount in respect of any claim as the Engineer may consider due to the Contractor provided that the Contractor shall have supplied sufficient particulars to enable the Engineer to determine the amount due. If such particulars are insufficient to substantiate the whole of the claim the Contractor shall be entitled to payment in respect of such part of the Claim as the particulars may substantiate to the satisfaction of the Engineer.'

Judge Newey also quoted in his judgment from the finding in the arbitrator's award that 'since the contractor was entitled to monthly payments in respect of overdue payments the contractor was entitled to have interest compounded monthly with the principal sum'. This appears to have been accepted as valid without argument — it was indeed the reason for the case, since the contractor was entitled to simple interest under the Arbitration Act 1950 s19A — but the validity of the proposition may be open to challenge. Clause 60(6) does not refer to monthly payments, so the argument must depend on the contractor being entitled to have the interest included in monthly interim certificates. It is arguable, however, that interest under Clause 60(6) is not dependent on certification in monthly certificates by the engineer under Clause 60(2).

Nevertheless, the principle of compound interest has been adopted in ICE6, together with the rest of the principles stated in the case. Clause 60(7) provides:

'In the event of
(a) failure by the Engineer to certify or the Employer to make payment in accordance with sub-clauses (2) (4) or (6) of this Clause or

(b) any finding of an arbitrator to such effect

the Employer shall pay to the Contractor interest *compounded monthly* for each day on which any payment is overdue or which should have been certified and paid at a rate equivalent to 2 per cent per annum above the base lending rate of the bank specified in the Appendix to the Form of Tender. If in an arbitration pursuant to Clause 66 the arbitrator holds that any sum or additional sum should have been certified by a particular date in accordance with the aforementioned sub-clauses but was not so certified this shall be regarded for the purposes of this sub-clause as a failure to certify such sum or additional sum. Such sum or additional sum shall be regarded as overdue for payment 28 days after the date by which the arbitrator holds that the Engineer should have certified the

38. This is consistent with a second Scottish decision, *Hall & Tawse Construction Ltd v Strathclyde Regional Council* [1990] SLT 774, noted at 51 BLR 87, where the Lord President, Lord Hope, said on Clause 60(6):

'Clearly a certificate which is revised later because of better or more complete information than was available originally does not indicate a failure by the Engineer in that regard. I agree with Lord Ross that there would not be a failure on the part of the Engineer to certify merely because the sums certified turned out to be less than the sum which the court or an arbiter considered was due.'

sum or if no such date is identified by the arbitrator shall be regarded as overdue for payment from the date of the Certificate of Substantial Completion for the whole of the Works.'

It is submitted that this clause is only compatible with the intention of ICE6 Clause 52(4)(f). If the words 'engineer should have certified' are interpreted to mean 'should have certified on the basis of the particulars then submitted to him', this may entail the arbitrator making a separate assessment of entitlements on the basis of the earlier particulars for the purpose of applying the clause.

JCT 80 does not provide explicit rights under the contract to payment of interest for late payment on certificates or late certification. Nor does GC/Wks 1 Edition 2. But GC/Wks 1 Edition 3 contains a new Condition 47, Finance Charges, as follows:

'(1) The Authority shall pay the Contractor an amount by way of interest or finance charges (hereafter together called "finance charges") only in the event that money is withheld from him under the Contract because, either —
(a) the Authority, PM or QS has failed to comply with any time limit specified in the Contract or, where the parties agree at any time to vary any such time limit, that time limit as varied, or
(b) the QS varies any decision of his which he has notified to the Contractor.

(2) Finance charges shall be calculated as a percentage of the amounts which would have been paid to the Contractor if any of the events mentioned in paragraph (1) had not occurred. The rate at which finance charges shall be payable shall be 1% over the rate charged during the relevant period by the Bank of England for lending money to the clearing banks.

(3) Finance charges shall be payable in respect of any period commencing with the date on which, but for a failure or variation mentioned in paragraph (1), money properly due under the Contract should have been certified, and ending with the date on which it was certified for payment under Condition 50 (Certifying payments).

(4) When calculating finance charges the QS shall take into account any overpayment made to the Contractor as a result of circumstances described in paragraph (1)(b).

(5) The Authority shall not be liable to pay any finance charges which result from —
(a) any act, neglect or default of the Contractor or any of his subcontractors,
(b) any failure by the Contractor or any of his subcontractors to supply the PM or the QS with any relevant information, or
(c) any disagreement about the Final Account.

(6) The Authority and the Contractor agree that, when they entered into the Contract, neither of them had knowledge of any special facts or circumstances which would entitle the Contractor to be paid interest or finance charges, except in the circumstances mentioned in paragraph (1).'

Note the deliberate exclusion of interest as special damages in paragraph (6).

FIDIC 4 Clause 60.10 provides:

'In the event of the failure of the Employer to make payment within the times stated, the Employer shall pay to the Contractor interest at the rate stated in the Appendix to Tender upon all sums unpaid from the date by which the same should have been paid. The provisions of this Sub-clause are without prejudice to the Contractor's entitlement under Clause 69.'

FIDIC 4 Clause 69 provides significant new provisions. Not only is the contractor entitled to terminate his employment under the contract for the employer failing to pay, or interfering with or obstructing or refusing any required approval to the issue of any certificate, the contractor has an alternative right to suspend the work, as follows:

'69.4 Without prejudice to the Contractor's entitlement to interest under Sub-clause 60.10 and to terminate under Sub-clause 69.1, the Contractor may, if the Employer fails to pay the Contractor the amount due under any certificate of the Engineer within 28 days after the expiry of the time stated in Sub-clause 60.10 within which payment is to be made, subject to any deduction that the Employer is entitled to make under the Contract, after giving 28 days' prior notice to the Employer, with a copy to the Engineer, suspend work or reduce the rate of work.

If the Contractor suspends work or reduces the rate of work in accordance with the provisions of this Sub-clause and thereby suffers delay or incurs cost the Engineer shall, after due consultation with the Employer and the Contractor, determine
(a) any extension of time to which the Contractor is entitled under Clause 44, and
(b) the amount of such costs, which shall be added to the Contract Price, and shall notify the Contractor accordingly, with a copy to the Employer.

69.5 Where the Contractor suspends work or reduces the rate of work, having given notice in accordance with Sub-clause 69.4, and the Employer subsequently pays the amount due, including interest pursuant to Sub-clause 60.10, the Contractor's entitlement under Sub-clause 69.1 shall, if notice of termination has not been given, lapse and the Contractor shall resume normal working as soon as is reasonably possible.'

Chapter 12
The process of negotiation

GENERALLY

Having looked at some technicalities attaching to claims, it might be helpful to consider the process of negotiation. It has been stressed from the beginning that claims do not generally appear in formal suits or couched in terms of contractor versus employer and having the air of near arbitration. Rather they tend to develop simply as one of the factors which have to be coped with in the course of construction. The process of negotiation will therefore often start as a matter of sheer routine, of asking for this or that information, the reason, the basis and so on. This may be accompanied or followed by letters covering the same sort of ground but requiring more information or more detail. Once a matter becomes complicated (as they often do) then it is necessary to resort to something more formal. Even so, this does not preclude discussion — getting together round the table is not necessarily confrontation. Negotiation at arm's length is not likely to lead to a conclusion quickly, particularly where the issues are not clear cut, where it is not a matter of 'yes' or 'no' — all or nothing. Some claims which cannot be resolved by ordinary correspondence and discussion may have to be dealt with rather more formally, especially if the argument is somewhat involved or the whole situation somewhat complicated.

It is at this stage that a matter may be regarded as a claim as the term is currently frequently used, at which the whole matter may have to be set out anew, formally stating the facts of the matter, the grounds upon which it is based, the conditions of contract or point of law being relied upon etc, etc, and attaching full supporting documentation of drawings, schedules, correspondence and so on. This has already been referred to in Chapter 3. It is at this stage too when negotiation may take on a more formal air.

The aim of this book is very much to encourage the resolution of claims through informed agreement, or through the decision of the A/E/QS with the assent of the contractor, but such agreement or assent will not always be forthcoming. The possibility should always be borne in mind that the A/E/QS may have to settle a claim by giving a decision unilaterally, as provided by the contract, and furthermore that such decision may be disputed and challenged in arbitration by either the contractor or the employer. Appreciation of these two possibilities should condition attitudes in a number of ways.

Firstly, both contractor and A/E/QS should be aware at any time whether they are negotiating, or whether the A/E/QS is in the process of making a unilateral decision. The position and attitude of the A/E/QS and the relationship between the parties is or should be different in the two situations. Some functions of the A/E/QS, such as certification that work has been properly completed, are essentially unilateral. Other functions, such as agreement or fixing of new rates, start as negotiations. It is a contradiction in terms to say that the A/E/QS should negotiate impartially; negotiation is a process conducted across the table. As negotiator the A/E/QS is acting as agent on behalf of the employer. If a mutually acceptable conclusion cannot be reached in negotiations, the A/E/QS must assume another role. Even while negotiating, however, the A/E/QS must be prepared to move on to the second stage. This requires him to anticipate his ultimate decision. He should not insist on a position in negotiation which he would not maintain in making a decision.

In all cases where the A/E/QS has to act unilaterally, he is required to exercise his skill and knowledge as it should be exercised.[1] If there is a legal discretion involved (as distinct from a practical one[2]), the A/E/QS is then under a duty to act impartially also.

Secondly, each party should ensure that he is prepared, in terms of full contemporaneous documentary records, to go to arbitration if necessary, whether as claimant, respondent or, in the case of the A/E/QS, as witness. The intention is to avoid arbitration, but arbitration is most effectively avoided by readiness for it.

Thirdly, each party should realize that, if the matter should go to arbitration, all documents relevant to the contract, including those marked or intended to be confidential, will come out and be disclosed. Even hand-written comments on incoming letters will be disclosed. Any instances where a party or his employees have been economical with the truth or indulged in any other less than professional conduct will probably become apparent.

---

1. *Sutcliffe v Thackrah* [1974] AC 727 at pp 756, 757.
2. Decisions, such as whether timber meets a contractual description of 'fair quality', may involve a practical discretion, but there is no legal discretion involved: *Hillas v Arcos* [1932] 147 LT 503.

INVOLVEMENT OF PEOPLE

Be that as it may, it is necessary to bear in mind at all times that although the problem may be technical in terms of liabilities and responsibilities, contract and law, and concern the physical realities of building and civil engineering construction, all these must be dealt with by people — people with more or less knowledge of one kind or another, more or less perception of what the problems are and what the answers should be, more or less experience of the matters in question and of negotiating a settlement, people with interests to serve whether it be their own or their employer's (or both) but who are not for that reason to be treated as necessarily having ulterior purposes. If they have, then this will be revealed soon enough and can be dealt with as it deserves. People have characteristics and foibles of their own, which of necessity become part of the problem of negotiation. It should be remembered too that all these characteristics, abilities or lack of them are not confined to 'the other side'. To them we are the other side.

PSYCHOLOGY

From these considerations it might almost appear that some dissertation on the 'psychological aspects of claims negotiation' is imminent. This might be slightly more profitable than attempting to determine the answers by statistical probability, but like so many other matters connected with claims, it is better to stick to the simple, straightforward, commonsense aspects in taking account of the human element. If the architect, engineer or quantity surveyor is the sort of person who likes to see a contractor's account well sprinkled with red ink to shew that he has done his job or who is constitutionally incapable of accepting the statement that $2 + 2 = 4$ at face value, then he may well expect claims put to him to be deliberately inflated so as to accommodate his predilection. It might even be unwise to disappoint him. But contractors too are not free from criticism. Speaking generally, they have earned themselves a reputation for overstatement (though the employer's advisers rarely face up to why this may be so). Some give the impression that they do not know what they are entitled to and therefore bid high and let their opponent make an offer. Clearly such an opening gambit could not risk bidding low, as rarely will an A/E/QS feel inclined — or indeed be able — to increase a contractor's bid.

Architects, engineers and quantity surveyors work for an employer and are paid to consider his interests, but they are not paid to be unfair to a contractor and their professional integrity should require them to seek a just solution. Too often they too give the impression of not knowing the answer or at least they seem unprepared to give reasons for holding the views they express. Some seem to think that a monosyllabic 'No' is expressive of decisiveness, but in this they are usually wrong.

GROUND RULES

Is it possible, therefore, to set down any ground rules, any guidelines which will help us to find our way through this tangled web and achieve a solution which is just to both sides and reduce the staff-effort involved in so doing? The idea that this might be done by statistical analysis on the basis of mathematical probability is naive almost to the point of being cynical. One must start from the premise that there is cause and the object is to ascertain the effect; there are matters of rights and obligations which override any possibility of a statistical approach.

Personal capabilities

First, what are the qualities required in those who take part in this field? It is important to have an understanding of the problem, of the circumstances, of the real objectives of both the employer and the contractor and where their best interests lie, and of the constraints within which one must work. One also needs the ability to convey that one has this understanding, and for this one needs some understanding of people — how they are likely to react to a given line of argument and how they may best be persuaded to your point of view. That is not to say that one should get sentimental or emotive; claims have probably suffered more over recent years from the emotion they have generated than from anything else.

357

Knowledge of industry   The next requirement is a sound knowledge of the industry in which we work (a sound and extensive knowledge of one's own profession goes without saying); and also a knowledge of the capabilities, functions and responsibilities of the other professions involved, including something of the law. Regarding the last mentioned, one needs to know enough of it to know the probably appropriate line to take and to know one's limitations in this direction. Lack of knowledge in any aspect must be remedied by seeking advice, and this involves knowing when it is needed. If one is normally in the position of advising the employer, it must be assumed that one understands his problems, but it is also necessary to know something of how the contractor functions and the business and financial considerations with which he is involved. Conversely, if one is usually acting for a contractor then it is necessary to have some knowledge of the scope, difficulties and responsibilities of the employer's professional advisers, and of course of the employers themselves. In all cases it should be knowledge, not half-baked ideas, which impels one to act on the premise that all contractors (particularly those who put in claims) are rogues whose sole aim is to exploit alleged discrepancies and weaknesses (loophole engineering) or conversely that all architects and engineers are stupid, impractical so and so's whose sole aim in life is to deprive the contractor of his just dues.

Integrity   The third attribute may be described as professional integrity or probity, and applies of course to both sides. It implies not merely honesty, but also balanced and sound judgment and the ability to be objective. Such an attribute, or lack of it, tends to get 'noised abroad' and becomes part of a person's reputation. People adjust their attitudes and conduct their dealings accordingly. A reputation for professional integrity is a precious asset, as is the mutual respect and trust that it engenders in relationships, but it is acquired only over a period of time.

Patience   The last of these qualities, yet still important, is patience. Many claims are complicated and suffer from a surfeit of documentation. It takes patience to wade through them meticulously so as not to miss something of importance. Argument is often involved and it takes patience to listen to it with concentration, particularly if it is repetitive and emotively charged. Coupled with this is tact, the ability to persuade a person he is wrong without damaging his self-respect, without giving a feeling of 'I know it all' or 'Holier than thou'. Also in this category is an ability to compromise. Some problems in the claims field are black or white, where the answer must be 'Yes' or 'No' and can be nothing else, but in such a complicated area as construction many situations are anything but black or white. One party may be at fault to some degree but the other may not be entirely without blame. One may have caused delay but this may have been compounded by some inefficiency of the other. Principles are extremely important but it is not always sensible to adhere to them at all costs. To some, anything other than an uncompromising 'Yes' or 'No' is 'horse-trading', as if that is necessarily despicable and to be avoided. That is not to advocate the easy course of splitting the difference between bid and counter-offer, it is merely making the point that the answer sometimes lies in that grey area between black and white. In this connection architects, engineers and quantity surveyors must bear in mind the power they carry. If they flatly reject a claim, particularly one where there may be some validity, a contractor will consider carefully before taking an employer to arbitration, not only from the point of view of considering the cost compared with the amount at issue but also from the point of view of the possible effect on future invitations to tender. The knowledge that a contractor is unlikely to take a matter to arbitration should not be allowed to influence one into giving an unjust decision.

PROCESS OF NEGOTIATION

Having considered some of the personal qualities and considerations required one may turn to the process of negotiation itself.

It will have been clear from the foregoing chapters that many claims arise in the ordinary course of dealing with interim payments, valuation of variations and preparation of final accounts. In such cases the process of negotiation will occur in the form of correspondence and discussion, i.e. in the relatively informal way. Nevertheless, the principles apply here also. They may be summarized as follows.

Know the problem

From the contractor's point of view know what you require, and know the basis on which your entitlement depends. Do your 'homework' in so far as it is necessary to check on the provisions of the contract. Take nothing for granted, particularly the conditions of contract. Editions change, *ad hoc* conditions are introduced and the application of conditions to given circumstances (which always differ from the last occasion) needs to be checked. Check the facts, there is nothing more damaging than alleging a fact only to find there is correspondence on the file clearly indicating the contrary.

Know your opposite number

Know the man with whom you are dealing. If you are not sure about how he wants things done or put, ask him. If he seems to want too much information, discuss the matter with him. He may be right or you may be able to persuade him that a crisp, concise summary, referring to letters or other papers of which he must have copies on his files, will suffice. Know what his authority is and to whom he is answerable. In an impasse you may have to get your boss to go to his boss to break it.

Use simple language

Do not dress up a claim or a rejoinder in long, seemingly-learned phrases when simple words and simple phrases will put the matter more clearly. Be concise and appreciate the difference between this and being brief. Be direct and not devious, the former is much more telling in the long run. Be logical and be prepared to say 'why', why one considers there is entitlement or why one considers there is not.

Be prompt

Delay and procrastination in following up either notice of a claim or a request for more information are damaging and cast doubt on the validity of the claim or response being made. To the other side delay may suggest a lack of knowledge about what to do or a lack of understanding of the importance of the matter at issue and the importance of finance and cash flow to contractors. More than one contractor otherwise financially solvent has been crippled by lack of liquidity arising from unsettled claims.

In more formal negotiations considerations are just the same. In the nature of things, if a claim has proved difficult to resolve then the handling of it may have to go higher up the tree. Perhaps one needs to be a little more sure of facts, of the contractual position etc, but essentially the requirements are no different. It is to be presumed that the claim is set out and substantiated on the lines set out in Chapter 3 (under 'Presentation') which is not dissimilar to what would be required in arbitration — this with a view to presenting the case as succinctly as possible (and the rejoinder likewise) with a view to avoiding waste of time. The time required must be taken but it is exasperating, and also damaging, if either side cannot at this stage (after perhaps weeks or even months of negotiating lower down the scale) present their arguments clearly or, worse, cannot produce or refer to the necessary documents, records, correspondence etc required for substantiation.

In a claim containing several heads some may be accepted and some rejected. Even in these cases it may not have been a simple 'Yes' or 'No' with any one of them but taken in juxtaposition the balance may have gone one way in one case and the other way in another. There may then remain one or more claims where the proper answer lies in a very grey area. Before going into a meeting where it is expected (or hoped) that a settlement might be reached it is essential first to realize that such a grey area exists, why it exists and what principles are involved in reaching settlement. It is also necessary to know whether compromise is possible, and the financial consequences. One also needs to be reasonably sure that the person leading each delegation (engineer or engineer's representative on one side and director, manager or whatever on the contractor's side) has authority to reach a settlement. Otherwise one may find oneself at the end of the meeting having achieved nothing more than presenting the other side with one's complete case and argument (or rejoinder and argument) to be taken away and analysed for loopholes and weaknesses.

The powers of the architect, engineer and quantity surveyor are as defined in the various

359

Forms. By definition these are what these people may do under the contract. If the matter at issue is extra-contractual it may be necessary to enquire whether, if the employer is not represented, they are empowered to reach settlement. One should go into negotiation with the same attitude as in an arbitration, i.e. that the time has come to put all the cards on the table. It is very probable that, as with an arbitrator's award, neither side will be satisfied with the result but if both sides feel that perhaps it is the best they could have done, then the answer may well be fairly near the right one.

Time and timing

It is a common experience that settlement of claims is unduly delayed. The complaint is most often heard from contractors and sub-contractors, but delayed settlement can also cause difficulty for the employer and A/E/QS. A related problem is that of contractual provisions for payment on account of claims being disregarded. Contracts provide for interim payment, yet to suggest that money should be paid on account in respect of claims is considered by some as heretical — feather-bedding the contractor — and so on.

The effects felt by contractors and sub-contractors, whether due to delayed settlement or lack of payment on account, include adverse cash flow, uncertainty and diversion of effort. The psychological impact was eloquently expressed by a sub-contractor concerned with the electrical/hydraulic mechanism of the domes to the telescopes of the Equatorial Block at the Royal Observatory at Herstmonceux. At one stage he was in great difficulty to establish a claim to the money to which he considered he was entitled and ended one poignant letter as follows:

> 'We are not content to be treated like Thornhill[3] whose supplicant hand can be seen at the end of the Painted Hall[4] or Harrison[5] who eventually had to appeal to the king to get even part of his dues. The six copper-headed virgins we set out to build with such enthusiasm are now sordid, raddled and mercenary pieces.
>
> Yours faithfully'

The unfortunate sub-contractor in that case was, happily to report, given his money without having to go beyond the Board of Admiralty, but it is quite wrong that claims should remain outstanding for months or even years after construction has been completed. Consider for a moment that a contractor has £100,000 owing to him in claims. At 10 per cent per annum (to take a round, simple figure for illustration) that means he will be paying or losing £10,000 per annum whilst he is standing out of his money. If one multiplies the 10 per cent by a factor to bring it in line with interest and overdraft rates over the past few years, if one multiplies the period by anything between two and eight, being the time not uncommonly taken to settle claims, and if one tries to multiply the £100,000 by a factor to represent the real value of claims outstanding in the industry (could that factor be something like 5,000 or 10,000?) one can get some idea of the appalling proportions which this problem possibly assumes.

Employers may perceive an apparent advantage in holding on to money, but unless the contractor is to be driven out of business, the financing costs must be passed on one way or another, in tender prices or claims. If the contractor goes out of business an employer may obtain a short term gain, but the important security of contractual warranties will be lost. The advantages of withholding money have in any event been severely curtailed by the Administration of Justice Act 1982. This introduced the power for an arbitrator or judge to award interest on all monies outstanding at the date of reference to arbitration or commencement of an action in the courts. The power is not limited to amounts which are the subject of an award, it includes amounts paid over before the award, although it does not extend to amounts paid over before the commencement of proceedings. This innovation

3. Thornhill, the artist who painted the hall at:
4. the Royal Naval College, Greenwich.
5. Harrison of chronometer fame.

will make delayed payment much less attractive to employers, but it requires the contractor to commence arbitration proceedings in order to activate the provision.

In many cases, however, the employer is not the cause of delay. Except where the employer becomes involved in dealing with claims, responsibility on that side rests with the A/E/QS. There is a distinction between claims handled by consulting engineers acting as the Engineer under civil engineering forms, and claims handled by quantity surveyors. Consulting engineers rarely get paid extra fees for protracted handling of claims (unless the matter is referred to arbitration) so financial gain cannot be the cause. In some instances, delay is due to reluctance to accept claims which involve the admission of mistakes or failings. That is understandable if unjustified. Or delays may be due, inexcusably, to lack of understanding or failure to deal expeditiously with matters. Where quantity surveyors are responsible for evaluating claims (as under the JCT Forms or GC/Wks/1) the Standard Form of Agreement for the appointment of a quantity surveyor does provide for entitlement to additional payment for investigation of contractor's claims.[6] On the other hand, it is less likely that the quantity surveyor will have been responsible for matters giving rise to a claim. If the A/E/QS does not deal with claims with reasonable despatch, the contractor may need to proceed swiftly to arbitration to obtain satisfaction (assuming he has a justified claim).

The delay may, however, be of the contractor's own making. For example, some contractors apply a 'ratchet' technique, submitting claims piecemeal, accepting what is certified, then bringing in new claims involving the same facts. Concessions are chalked up rather than treated as steps towards settlement. In such a situation, delay may be adopted as a defensive measure until all the claims are on the table. Is such a response unjustified? Or the substantiation submitted by the contractor may be inadequate; it is not for the A/E/QS to do the contractor's job for him. Or the contractor may be holding out, either to try and drive the settlement higher or because those directly involved are unwilling to admit operational or tendering shortcomings, or that profit forecasts have not been reached; the A/E/QS does not have a remit to dole out charity or yield to bullying.

Prompt settlement is almost certainly in the long-term interests of employers, both so that they know their own true financial position much earlier, and so that feedback to the contractor for current management accounting and future tender pricing is speeded up. Realistic tender pricing is, at the end of the day, a key factor in reducing the incidence of claims.

Negotiator's powers

In final negotiations the contractor is usually represented by someone who has power to settle, who is also usually someone with a technical knowledge of construction and construction contracts, and so would expect someone on the other side to be able to argue on level terms.

If negotiations are with the A/E/QS or his representative, there is often a question of his authority to settle. So far as contractual claims are concerned there should be no question; he has the powers conferred on him by the contract and if these have been curtailed it should have been made known to the contractor. If representatives are merely to conduct exploratory discussions, that again should be made clear. It is not helpful to confer authority on a representative, or a line of representatives, to say 'no' unless each is also empowered to say 'yes'.

Under ICE and FIDIC Conditions, the engineer has additional special powers to deal with disputes on any extra-contractual claims that could be referred to an arbitrator under the arbitration clause.[7] These special powers only come into force, however, after a dispute

---

6. These comments are based on the Standard Conditions of Engagement Agreement 2 (1981) published by the Association of Consulting Engineers, and the Standard Form of Agreement for the appointment of a Quantity Surveyor, published by the RICS, October 1983. Where a quantity surveyor is employed by a consulting engineer as sub-consultant, the anomaly can give rise to further complications.

7. See Lloyd H QC 'An expanded power to decide? The effect of two cases on the Engineer's power under Clause 67 of the FIDIC Conditions' (1988) 5 ICLR 326. The Government of Hong Kong General Conditions of Contract for Civil Engineering Works (1985 Edition) contain a similar provision for remission of disputes to the Engineer in Clause 87.

between contractor and employer has arisen and if that dispute is then referred to the engineer under ICE Clause 66 or FIDIC Clause 67. The extra-contractual claim must therefore have been referred first to the employer — otherwise there could be no dispute. Except in that situation, the A/E/QS has no powers to deal with extra-contractual claims without additional authority from the employer.

In all cases it should be made known by both sides what the respective powers of their representatives are. If matters have been debated with, say, the architect over a long period without result, the contractor may be unwilling to debate further with little or no prospect of result and so may wish the employer to be present or be represented. After all he, not the A/E/QS, is the other party to the contract.

On the other hand, in the case of central government departments or local authorities, the presence of 'administrators' and/or auditors and/or treasurer's representatives can cause problems. Their functions are often not clear. If they take part in discussions on matters which are contractual and are therefore by definition within the powers of the A/E/QS to settle, they are in danger of usurping those powers. If they are representing the employer, their powers in connection with the settlement of extra-contractual claims should be made known. Offers made subject, explicitly or implicitly, to legal advice should be treated with circumspection.

That is not to say that the employer should not be represented. It is legally quite acceptable for the employer to be kept informed and to be heard by the A/E/QS, so long as, at the end of the day, the decision is that of the A/E/QS[8] and the decision is not unduly delayed by the process. Such consultation does, however, generate a degree of distrust on the other side. The problem arises because submissions from the contractor are treated as open documents, but communications between the employer and the A/E/QS are kept secret from the contractor. The situation could easily be improved by making it the practice to put to the contractor during negotiations any points raised by the employer.

If there are reservations placed on the authority of negotiators, or they become apparent in the course of negotiations, then the contractor's representative can be expected to take a similar line and reserve his position for reference back to higher authority or his Board prior to clinching an agreement.

Such considerations will assist in restricting numbers participating at meetings to reasonable proportions. The actual numbers will depend to some extent on the complications of the problem, but not all the 'aides' on either side need necessarily be there at the same time, some can be called in when the topic in which they have something to contribute is being dealt with. A team of three should suffice in most cases, with the architect or engineer chairing the meeting and either reaching agreements with the contractor or considering the arguments and submissions before reaching a decision where agreement cannot be reached. The engineer or architect may need the C/W or RE as the person who was intimately concerned with the problem on site and who knows the facts of the matter. He would also usually require a quantity surveyor or other specialist to advise on contractual/valuation aspects. The contractor will probably also need the agent and a quantity surveyor. There should be no question of one side significantly outnumbering the other.

Confidence

Probably, in terms of negotiation, all the foregoing add up to a matter of mutual confidence between the sides: confidence that each wants no more nor less than his rights. Confidence as regards an understanding of the problem and the willingness to seek a solution. Confidence that no better can be done by resort to arbitration or litigation.

GETTING INTO ARBITRATION

It may be that, despite all efforts, negotiations break down. The A/E/QS makes a decision which the contractor (or employer) finds unacceptable and the only recourse is arbitration

---

8. *Panamena Europea Navigacion v Frederick Leyland & Co* [1947] AC 428.

or litigation.[9] For various reasons, most claims on construction contracts must be pursued through arbitration. If there is an arbitration agreement, as there is in most Standard Forms, either party may insist[10] that any dispute is referred to arbitration. Also, in *Northern RHA v Derek Crouch Construction*[11] the Court of Appeal held that a court could not exercise the special powers conferred on an arbitrator to open up, review and revise the decision of an architect or engineer. The effect of this judgment was that claims based on contractual provisions involving the decision of the A/E/QS could only be pursued in arbitration. The judgment has subsequently been partly overturned by statute. The Courts and Legal Services Act 1990 s100 provides (as a new section 43A of the Supreme Court Act 1981):

> 'In any cause or matter proceeding in the High Court in connection with any contract incorporating an arbitration agreement which confers specific powers upon the arbitrator, the High Court may, if all parties to the agreement agree, exercise any such powers.'

The relative merits of arbitration and litigation have been discussed above in Chapter 3. Arbitration offers potential advantages, but it is essentially a consensual procedure. The advantages of arbitration are obtained if the parties co-operate in the choice of the arbitrator, in respecting and complying with his orders, in making use of time and cost saving procedures, and in restricting the scope of the dispute. Within the context of construction contracts, such co-operation ought to be available.

Reference to arbitration

The two prerequisites for a reference to arbitration are that there should be a dispute and that the dispute should be within the scope of an arbitration agreement.[12] If the Arbitration Acts are to apply, the arbitration agreement must be in writing.[13] The arbitration agreement must be between the parties to the dispute — the two parties, in relation to a main contract arbitration, are the employer and the contractor. The A/E/QS is not a party, although the dispute may concern his decision. Nor can a sub-contractor be joined in an arbitration under the main contract unless the parties agree.[14]

Under the ICE and FIDIC Conditions, there is also a pre-condition that the dispute or difference be first referred back to the Engineer in writing for his decision under Clause 66 or Clause 67 respectively. The dispute must then be referred to arbitration within the strict time limits laid down in those clauses, otherwise the decision of the Engineer becomes final and binding on both parties.

If the prerequisites are satisfied, arbitration proceedings may be initiated by either party simply serving notice on the other party to refer the dispute to arbitration. The party who serves the notice becomes the 'Claimant'; the other party becomes the 'Respondent'. Notice must be given within the limitation periods laid down by the Limitation Act 1980 and, subject to statutory powers of the courts to extend time limits,[15] within any time limits laid down by the contract.

The next step is the appointment of an arbitrator. The claimant initiates the process by serving a Notice to Concur in the Appointment of an Arbitrator; usually the Notice will contain a list of three or more persons proposed as arbitrator. The respondent may concur in the appointment of one of the persons named, or counter-serve another list. Agreement of an arbitrator is much to be preferred, but relationships are often soured by this stage

---

9. Litigation is the resolution of a dispute by an 'action' through the court system.
10. Arbitration Act 1950 s4 provides that in the event of a party to an arbitration agreement commencing legal proceedings in a court, the other party may, before delivering any pleadings, apply to the court for the action to be 'stayed'.
11. *Northern Regional Health Authority v Derek Crouch Construction* [1984] 1 QB 644.
12. What constitutes a dispute is illustrated in Case 12.1.
13. Arbitration Act 1950 s32; Arbitration Act 1979 s7(1)(e).
14. Some arbitration agreements or arbitration rules provide for sub-contractors to be joined in arbitrations under the main contract, e.g. JCT 80 Art 5.1 or Clause 41.2 under JCT 80 Amendment 6, or ICE Arbitration Procedure (1983) Rule 7.
15. Arbitration Act 1950 s27.

— it has been commented that mutual distrust between the parties commonly leads to the six people best qualified to arbitrate being ruled out.

In the event of failure by the parties to appoint an arbitrator within a stipulated time (typically one month) of the Notice to Concur, the Standard Forms provide for the President of one of the Institutions (CIArb, RICS, RIBA, ICE etc) to appoint an arbitrator on the application of one party. The 1950 Act s10(2) provides power for the High Court to appoint an arbitrator on the application of one of the parties if the appointing person refuses to make the appointment or does not make it within the time specified or, if no time is specified, within a reasonable time; but the sub-section does not apply if a contrary intention is expressed in the arbitration agreement.[16]

The arbitrator will usually seek the agreement of the parties to his proposed fee charges before accepting the appointment, but there is statutory provision for the courts to fix[17] the arbitrator's remuneration retrospectively in the absence of agreement. Many arbitrators now require an appointment fee to discourage frivolous appointments.

The arbitrator will have jurisdiction only to deal with those matters which are both referred to him in the terms of reference and within the scope of the arbitration agreement. The reference may be extended by agreement. Some arbitration rules also allow, however, for the arbitrator's jurisdiction to be extended by one party unilaterally after the original reference. In some cases, this effectively overrides requirements in the contract. For example in the ICE Arbitration Rules (1983), Rule 4 provides:

'4.1 At any time before the Arbitrator's appointment is completed either party may put forward further disputes or differences to be referred to him. This shall be done by serving upon the other party an additional Notice to Refer in accordance with Rule 1.

4.2 Once his appointment is completed the Arbitrator shall have jurisdiction over any issue connected with and necessary to the determination of any dispute or difference already referred to him whether or not the connected issue has first been referred to the Engineer for his decision under Clause 66(1) of the ICE Conditions of Contract.'

Rule 4.2 has been interpreted by the Courts as permitting considerable leeway in introducing new issues without prior reference to the Engineer under Clause 66.[18]

Pleadings

Once the arbitrator is appointed, the next step is for each party in turn to set out its case and establish precisely the issues in dispute by means of 'pleadings'. Conventionally, in arbitration, the pleadings will comprise Points of Claim, Points of Defence, Points of Reply, Requests for Further and Better Particulars, and Replies to those Requests.[19] The Pleadings may also include counter-claims, with a similar sequence of responses following. The parties may be required by the arbitrator, where there is a multiplicity of issues, to put their pleadings in the form of a 'Scott schedule', in which the sequence of pleadings for each issue in turn is presented as a spreadsheet.

The form of pleadings merits study by all those involved in claims. The discipline of logic and language can be applied at a much earlier stage to establish whether or not there

---

16. Courts and Legal Service Acts 1990 s101(3).
17. Arbitration Act 1950 s19. For the position on the arbitrator fixing fees and conditions after accepting an appointment, see *K/S Norjarl A/S v Hyundai Heavy Industries Co* [1991] 3 All ER 211.
18. *Mid-Glamorgan CC v Land Authority of Wales* [1990] 49 BLR 61.
19. In the JCT Arbitration Rules (1988), s5.3.6 talks instead of a 'statement of case', 'statement of defence', 'statement of counterclaim' etc. The ICE Arbitration Procedure Rule 11 also allows 'statements of case' as an alternative to pleadings. The term 'statement of case' is not defined but appears to envisage specifically that it would not be drafted by lawyers and, more generally, that it would be more narrative in form, possibly give references to cases, even include some evidence: see *Arbitration* 1991 **57**, 146, 147; *Arbitration* 1984 **50**, 209 at pp 216−18.

is a valid basis for claiming or rejecting claims, to identify the real issues in dispute and thereby to focus on the relevant records of fact and contractual arguments.

On the other hand, there is no requirement that pleadings in arbitration proceedings should conform to the style required for High Court litigation. It may be more appropriate in arbitration, for example, to present part of the case in the form of charts or drawings. As a rule, however, pleadings should not contain evidence, but only state the facts to be proved by evidence, together with the points of law and terms of the contract relied upon.

Discovery

Following the close of pleadings, there follows the procedure known as 'discovery'. This comes as a shock to the uninitiated. Each party is required to provide to the other a list of all documents and other records relevant to the matters in issue, which are or have been in his possession, custody or power;[20] and must subsequently allow the other party to inspect and copy the records.[21] The fact that a document is adverse to a party's case does not relieve him of the obligation to disclose it.[22] The only relief is against giving inspection of various classes of 'privileged' documents — this refers principally to communications between the party and his professional legal adviser. A solicitor has a professional duty to ensure that his client complies fully with the duty of disclosure and does not destroy documents likely to be required.

At the stage of discovery, the contractor's tender make-up will become available, as will correspondence between the employer and the A/E/QS. Manuscript comments on letters received (sometimes with scurrilous comments about the sender) are revealed. The truth will generally out.

On the other hand, there is a regrettable tendency to adopt a non-selective approach to copying documents disclosed on discovery. The saving in costs which discovery is supposed to facilitate can appear rather out of touch in relation to construction projects, if a non-selective approach is adopted. The number of pages can run into tens or hundreds or thousands, copied maybe ten times over. It is open to the parties to agree to limit discovery.[23] (Solicitors will rarely suggest limiting discovery since the mindless photocopying involved is a great money-spinner.) It is also in the discretion of the arbitrator to refuse to order discovery of documents which he considers not sufficiently relevant.[24]

Viewing the site

An arbitrator will commonly visit the site for a view. It is one of the advantages of arbitration that the arbitrator may apply his specialist knowledge to interpret the evidence, and a view of the site itself constitutes 'real evidence'.[25] For example, the arbitrator could assess difficulty of access, or the nature of a rock face, or the condition of concrete without the need for expert evidence that a judge requires.

It is desirable, if not essential, that the arbitrator should be accompanied by representatives of both parties when visiting the site. If he were to visit the site unaccompanied (other than with the explicit consent of both parties) or accompanied by one party only, this might provide grounds for his award to be upset for misconduct.[26]

'Without Prejudice' correspondence

The commencement of an arbitration does not mean that it must necessarily proceed through all the stages to a hearing and award. A substantial proportion of cases referred to arbitration never reach a hearing. They are settled along the way as the relative strengths of the claim and defence become apparent and, more particularly, as the bills for legal costs accumulate. It is open to the parties to continue to negotiate as preparations proceed, and the law provides a means by which such negotiations can be carried out confidentially. This is important.

---

20. RSC O24 rrl,2. The same rules apply to arbitration: *Kursell v Timber Operators* [1923] 2 KB 202.
21. RSC O24 r9.
22. *Compagnie Financiere v Peruvian Guano Co* [1882] 11 QBD 55.
23. RSC O24 rl.
24. *GKN Centrax Gears v Matbro* [1976] 2 Lloyd's Rep 555. Some arbitration rules also explicitly empower the arbitrator to limit discovery.
25. Barber, J N 1988 Real evidence and expert arbitrators. *Arbitration* **54**, 34.
26. *Salsbury v Woodland* [1970] 1 QB 324.

Otherwise concessions or offers could be revealed at the arbitration hearing if the negotiations failed. Confidentiality is achieved by heading correspondence relating to such negotiations as 'Without Prejudice', or by agreeing that meetings shall be 'Without Prejudice'. The effect is to protect the contents of the letter or the details of the meeting from disclosure to the arbitrator.

The proper conduct of 'Without Prejudice' correspondence demands a degree of skill. Indiscriminate heading of letters as 'Without Prejudice' can lead to a muddle, particularly when there are cross-references in open letters. It is essential, where a course of 'Without Prejudice' correspondence is entered upon, to maintain a separate and concurrent set of open correspondence. The two sets of correspondence should not be intermingled or confused.

If a party wishes an offer in settlement of a claim or counterclaim to be considered by the arbitrator in relation to costs, a simple 'Without Prejudice' heading would be inappropriate. The correct approach is to head the letter containing the offer as 'Without prejudice save as to costs'. The offer (if it is not accepted) will then be protected from disclosure at the main hearing, but it may be put before the arbitrator in regard to his award on costs.[27] There is a difficulty with communicating the existence of such an offer to the arbitrator. The offer may be given to the arbitrator at the close of the main hearing as a 'sealed offer', not to be considered until the arbitrator has reached his decision, but this leaves a doubt whether the arbitrator has seen the offer before making his award. The better procedure is to ask the arbitrator to issue an interim award first, and then to make a separate award on costs afterwards. It is essential that the parties should tell the arbitrator, before he makes his substantive award, that they wish this procedure to be followed.[28]

Proofs of evidence

Where a witness might be called in an arbitration, the party intending to call the witness will first take a 'proof of evidence'. This is a concise statement by the witness of what he can personally testify to in support or refutation of any contention in connection with the case. Where solicitors are involved, taking proofs of evidence is one of their functions.

Proofs of evidence may be taken at various stages. Preliminary proofs of evidence should be taken from the principal potential witnesses at an early stage to enable the party and its advisers to assess the strength of its case before commencing, or deciding to defend, arbitration proceedings. Not only will the party be able to assess the strength of the evidence to support its case, but also, perhaps, to discover weaknesses.

Detailed proofs of evidence will be required at a later stage for all potential witnesses to be called by a party, to enable the person presenting the case — whether counsel or non-lawyer advocate[29] — to prepare for the hearing.

It is now a common requirement in arbitration, and in litigation before the Official Referees, that written proofs of evidence should be exchanged by the parties some time before the hearing in respect of all witnesses who are to be called. A witness may be excluded if his proof of evidence has not been exchanged. Commonly, the written proof will be treated in arbitration as 'evidence-in-chief', that is, the evidence first given in response to the party calling the witness. The witness will then be cross-examined by the other party on the basis of the written proof. The prior availability of the written proof means that such cross-examination can be more thoroughly prepared, although the scope of the cross-examination is not limited by the written proof. If new matters are raised in the cross-examination, these may be dealt with by the party calling the witness in re-examination. (As a matter of practice, a party calling a witness may not cross-examine or ask 'leading questions' of his own witness, unless the witness is acknowledged to be 'hostile'. Leading questions are questions which

27. *Calderbank v Calderbank* [1976] Fam 93.
28. *King v Thomas McKenna Ltd* [1991] 1 All ER 653.
29. It is common to refer to non-lawyer advocates as 'lay advocates', but that is really a misnomer. Construction arbitrations deal with issues of both law and construction practice. In relation to construction practice the lawyer may be a 'lay' person.

suggest the answer wanted. This is one reason why the contractor will rarely call the A/E/QS as a witness, the employer will rarely call the contractor's employees.)

The amount of work involved in producing written proofs of evidence should not be underestimated, nor should their value in concentrating the minds of potential witnesses on the matters at issue and the proving of the facts. The intrusion of emotions, wishful thinking or personalities soon becomes apparent.

There is no reason why proofs of evidence should not include tables, charts, or drawings if these convey the information more easily than words alone.

Where experts are employed — as they usually are, despite the expertise of the arbitrator — the experts will produce reports. Commonly, the number of experts on each side will be limited by the arbitrator and it will be a requirement that the experts' reports should be exchanged in advance of the hearing. In addition to allowing the parties to prepare their respective cases more thoroughly and minimize the element of surprise, the exchange of information before the hearing may enable the parties to compromise their dispute on an informed basis.

Agreement of facts

Agreement can often be reached, either between the parties or between their experts, as to what certain facts are (weather, numbers of men, availability of plant, what costs have been paid, etc, etc), even if it is for the arbitrator to decide the significance of the facts. A good deal of time and expense can be saved by co-operation in agreement of facts beforehand, rather than ploughing through detail at the hearing while fees of arbitrator, lawyers, experts and other participants are clocking up.

The arbitrator may order that the experts employed by the parties should hold 'without prejudice' meetings to agree matters so far as possible and identify the remaining issues in dispute. It is essential in such situations that each party should clearly define the scope of its expert's authority to agree facts. Experts hold a difficult position. They are employed by a party because their evidence is favourable to that party's case. A party is under no obligation to call any expert consulted in connection with the arbitration, nor even to disclose that such consultation has taken place,[30] so a party may 'shop around'. On the other hand, the expert is under oath to tell the truth — that means, he must answer truthfully the questions which are put to him. He is not, however, required to deal with any questions other than those put to him, even if he has relevant knowledge.

There are sometimes complaints that experts act as the 'hired gun'. It should be clearly understood that expert witnesses are not to act as advocates. An advocate need have no belief in the truth of what he puts forward — he should refrain from expressing any belief. The only requirement is that he should not put forward a statement as true if he has knowledge to the contrary. An advocate is under no obligation to seek such knowledge, and is trained to avoid embarrassing his client. (For example, a barrister asks his client in a criminal case 'How do you wish to plead?', not 'Are you guilty or not guilty?') Expert witnesses, on the other hand, are under oath to give their evidence as the truth, based on their knowledge, understanding and investigation.

The hearing

The law and practice of arbitration hearings have been described in Chapter 3, but some practical points should be emphasized concerning the preparation for, and conduct of, hearings.

Arbitration hearings are an expensive way to resolve disputes — they often bring more benefit to the lawyers, consultants and arbitrators than to either party — but it is the inevitability of a conclusion being reached and the fact that the conclusion is enforceable by law as a judgment that underpins the binding nature of construction contracts.

---

30. An expert's report is protected from disclosure by 'legal professional privilege' if prepared for the party's lawyer in connection with the impending arbitration. The position is unclear where no lawyer is involved.

Having embarked on an arbitration, the parties may hope that settlement will be reached or that the other side will capitulate before the hearing, but such an outcome cannot be presumed. Both parties must therefore prepare for the hearing. The crucial point is that the arbitration hearing is the parties' last chance to present their respective cases. There is no possibility of raising the same dispute again with fresh evidence or arguments — the issues are treated as *res judicata*, that is, matters which have been adjudicated and cannot be disputed again. There is no scope for appeal on questions of fact and very restricted scope for appeal on questions of law. It is therefore essential that the case should be prepared fully and conducted recognizing that it is the parties' last opportunity to put forward evidence and arguments.

Any party putting forward or defending a claim or counterclaim should bear in mind that the arbitrator may be convinced by lines of reasoning other than those which the party's representative personally finds most convincing. The claim may be submitted on alternative grounds. In defending a claim or counterclaim, a party should deal with all the bases of claim, not just those which are most easily dismissed.

A good deal of work may be required during the hearing, not only of the outside lawyers or representatives and experts employed to present the case, but also of the party's own staff. The arbitrator may only sit from 10 am to 4 pm, but the working hours of participants can be twice as long, considering the evidence given each day and preparing for the next day. Participants will commonly be involved in conference with counsel (if employed) or in discussions with the non-lawyer advocate after the day's hearing, and in providing further information or evidence which may be required.

At the end of the hearing, the arbitrator will go away and write his award. Arbitrators do not deliver *ex tempore* awards or reasons as judges sometimes do. Also unlike the judgment of a judge, an arbitrator's award is normally only obtainable from the arbitrator on payment of his fees.[31] The arbitrator has a 'lien' on his award as security for his fees. It follows that the party taking up the award has to pay the arbitrator's fees in the first place, but it will commonly be the party who believes he has won — and therefore expects not to have to bear the arbitrator's fees in the long run — who will take up the award.

ALTERNATIVE DISPUTE RESOLUTION

Various other methods of dispute resolution are available involving the assistance of a third party. These include 'mediation' and 'conciliation'. Unfortunately, the two terms are difficult to define as they are used to mean different things in different parts of the world. The essential question is whether the conciliator or mediator expresses an opinion or merely acts as a go-between. Attempted conciliation or mediation is stipulated or permitted in some contracts as a step before arbitration, as in FIDIC4, ICE6, the ICE Minor Works Conditions, and the Hong Kong Government General Conditions of Contract (1985). The ICE have produced a Conciliation Procedure, which is referred to in ICE6 Clause 66 and the ICE Minor Works Form. In Hong Kong, there is a powerful mediation procedure for use on Government contracts.

Such procedures can help parties to reach agreement and the cost is much less than arbitration. The draw-back is that even if the mediator or conciliator produces proposed terms of settlement, they do not bind the parties directly as does the award of an arbitrator. The terms of settlement only become binding if accepted and agreed by the parties.

Another form of ADR, which has been found successful in the United States and has attracted attention in the UK, is the 'mini trial'. In this process, a neutral assessor sits together with two senior executives — one from each party — to hear presentations by the respective organizations. The neutral assessor can explain any points of principle and assist the executives to reach a settlement. The success of the system is of interest in its own right,

---

31. See Mustill M J, Boyd S C 1989 *Commercial Arbitration*, 2nd edn., pp 234–5. Butterworth & Co, London.

but it also has more fundamental significance. It provides a reminder of the ingredients needed for informed settlement of disputes generally. These are that:

1. There should be someone on each side appointed to deal with the dispute with authority to settle.

2. The person on each side should be fully informed of the facts and arguments which support his own side's case. He should also appreciate and understand the weaknesses of his own side's case.

3. The appointed person on each side should understand the strengths and weaknesses of the other side's case.

4. The appointed persons on each side need to communicate and overcome distrust.

Power, responsibility, integrity and understanding are the vital keys to informed settlement of disputes.

CASE 12.1   REFERENCE TO ARBITRATION

The JCT Form 63/77 provides in Clause 35(1):
'Provided always that in the case of any dispute or difference shall arise between the Employer or the Architect on his behalf and the Contractor . . . then such dispute or difference shall be and is hereby referred to the arbitration . . . of a person to be agreed between the parties, or, failing agreement within 14 days after either party has given to the other a written request to concur in the appointment of an arbitrator . . .'

JCT 80 says in Article 5:
'5.1 In case any dispute or difference shall arise between the Employer or the Architect/Supervising Officer on his behalf and the Contractor, either during the progress or after the completion or abandonment of the Works, as to
1. the construction of this Contract, or
2. any matter or thing of whatsoever nature arising hereunder or in connection herewith . . .
3. excluding any dispute or difference under Clause 19A . . .
then such dispute or difference shall be and is hereby referred to the arbitration and final decision of a person to be agreed between the parties to act as Arbitrator, or, failing agreement . . . to be appointed . . . by the President of the Royal Institute of British Architects.'

Subsequent amendments to JCT 80 (Amendment 4:1987 and Amendment 6:1988) have substituted a new shorter Article 5 with more extensive detail and provisions for arbitration as Clause 41.

GC/Wks 1 Edition 2 provides in Condition 61:
'(1) All disputes, differences or questions between the parties . . . other than a matter or thing arising out of Condition 51 or as to which the decision or report of the Authority or of any other person is by the Contract expressed to be final and conclusive shall after notice by either party . . . be referred to a single arbitrator agreed for that purpose . . .'

GC/Wks 1 Edition 3 provides in Condition 59 for 'Adjudication' and in Condition 60 for Arbitration. Condition 59 provides:
'(1) The Contractor may by notice . . . ask for adjudication on any dispute, difference or question arising out of, or relating to, the Contract during the course of the Works, other than a matter as to which a decision is expressed to be final and conclusive and provided that the dispute etc has been outstanding for at least 3 months.'

Condition 60 provides:
'(1) In addition to adjudication the procedures of arbitration set out in this Condition

will be available to the Authority and the Contractor with regard to disputes, differences or questions between the Authority and the Contractor arising out of or relating to the Contract . . . The dispute etc shall after notice by either party to the other be referred to a single arbitrator agreed for that purpose or, in default of agreement within a reasonable time, appointed at the request of the Authority by the Chairman or Vice President of the Chartered Institute of Arbitrators.'

ICE5 provides in Clause 66:

'(1) If any dispute or difference of any kind whatsoever shall arise between the Employer and the Contractor . . . it shall be referred to and settled by the Engineer . . . Such decisions shall be final and binding . . . unless either of them shall require that the matter be referred to arbitration . . . If the Engineer shall fail to give such a decision for a period of 3 calendar months . . . or if either the Employer or the Contractor be dissatisfied with any such decision, then and in such case either the Employer or the Contractor may within 3 calendar months after receiving notice of such decision or within 3 calendar months after the expiration of the said period of 3 calendar months (as the case may be) require that the matter shall be referred to arbitration . . .'

Clause 66 of ICE5 was substantially modified in the 1986 Reprint, particularly to stipulate the application of the ICE Arbitration Procedure (1983).

In ICE6, Clause 66 has been expanded still further. It provides:

'(1) Except as otherwise provided in these Conditions if a dispute of any kind whatsoever arises between the Employer and the Contractor in connection with or arising out of the Contract . . . it shall be settled in accordance with the following provisions.
(2) . . . a dispute shall be deemed to arise when one party serves on the Engineer a notice in writing (hereinafter called the Notice of Dispute) . . .
(3) Every dispute notified under sub-clause (2) of this Clause shall be settled by the Engineer . . .
(4) Unless the Contract has already been determined or abandoned the Contractor shall in every case continue to proceed with the Works . . . Such decisions shall be final and binding upon the Contractor and the Employer unless and until as hereinafter provided either
(a) the recommendation of a conciliator has been accepted by both parties
(b) the decision of the Engineer is revised by an Arbitrator . . .
(5) . . . either party may give notice in writing requiring the dispute to be considered under the ICE Conciliation Procedure (1988) . . . The recommendation of the conciliator shall be deemed to have been accepted in settlement of the dispute unless a written Notice to Refer . . . is served within one calendar month of its receipt.
(6)(a) Where . . .
(i)   the Employer or the Contractor is dissatisfied with any decision of the Engineer or
(ii)   the Engineer fails to give a decision . . . or
(iii) the Employer or the Contractor is dissatisfied with any recommendation of a conciliator . . .
then either the Employer or the Contractor may within 3 calendar months after receiving notice of such decision or within 3 calendar months after the expiry of (the period allowed for the Engineer to give his decision) or within one calendar month of receipt of the conciliator's recommendation (as the case may be) refer the dispute to the arbitration of a person to be agreed upon . . .
(7)(a) If the parties fail to appoint an arbitrator within one calendar month of either party serving on the other party written Notice to Concur in the appointment of an arbitrator the dispute . . . shall be referred to a person to be appointed on the application of either party by the President for the time being of the Institution of Civil Engineers.
(8) . . . The reference shall be conducted in accordance with the ICE Arbitration Procedure (1983) or any amendment or modification thereof being in force at the time of the appointment of the arbitrator . . .'

It should go without saying that the provisions of the Form of Contract applicable in any given case must be followed meticulously. It will be seen that all the above Forms (and FIDIC similarly) refer to disputes. Obviously, therefore, one needs to be clear about when a dispute exists or has arisen. Consider the following case.

In respect of a contract based on JCT 63/77, the Contractor wrote to the Architect:

Contractor to Architect   *3 December 1979*

> *We refer to Variation Order No 87 which the Quantity Surveyor has measured and valued in accordance with Clause 11(4). We have been involved in direct loss and expense by way of additional overheads due to delay and loss of productivity consequent upon the timing of the Variation Order in question and we hereby claim to be reimbursed the sum of £22,417 in respect thereof.*

If the architect does not reply or if he should reject the claim, is there a dispute? In both cases the answer must be 'No'. In the second case the rejection of itself does not bring the dispute into being (the contractor might accept the rejection). If, however, the contractor reiterated the claim, then there is technically a dispute which can then be cited so as to bring Clause 35 into play. In the first case it may be more difficult to prompt the architect to take some action but there must be at least some follow-up unless the contractor is prepared to allow the matter to lapse. It may be necessary to approach and involve the employer and if this results in refusal then again there must be reiteration before there is a dispute. Should the employer also do nothing, the contractor would then have to give notice that the absence of any reply would be regarded as rejection, and formal request for arbitration would then follow.

Under JCT 63/77, the reference to arbitration is effected by a 'request to concur in the appointment of an arbitrator'. Such request would normally include or be accompanied by the names of three or more persons proposed to act as arbitrator. If the parties are unable to agree on an arbitrator, the contract provides, as a default mechanism, for application to the President of the RIBA to appoint an arbitrator.

The 1987 and 1988 Amendments to JCT 80 have introduced a two-stage process for reference to arbitration. The initial step is a written notice given by one party to the other requiring the dispute to be referred to arbitration. There then follows a second stage of appointment of the arbitrator. The commencement of the arbitration in such situations is considered to be the giving of the notice to refer. The advantage of separating the notice to refer from the request to concur is that the notice to refer may then be shown to the arbitrator appointed without disclosing to him the proposals and negotiations over the appointment.

GC/Wks 1 Edition 2 also provides for two stages of notice to refer to arbitration followed by appointment of a single arbitrator.

GC/Wks 1 Edition 3 has introduced the further possibility of 'adjudication'. It is unclear whether the contractor is bound to apply for adjudication before referring a dispute to arbitration. The use of the words 'in addition to' leaves the matter arguable. There is also a curious anomaly that, in the event of failure by the parties to agree on an arbitrator, only the Authority may apply to the Chairman or Vice-President of the Chartered Institute of Arbitrators to appoint an arbitrator.

In the case of the ICE Conditions, the situation can be somewhat different and care needs to be taken not to get into arbitration inadvertently. Take a case parallel to that indicated above:

Contractor to Engineer   *3 December 1979*

> *We refer to Variation Order No 87. We have been unable to reach*

*agreement as to the rates and prices to be applied in the valuation of the
work executed under this variation order. In consequence you have yourself
fixed rates and prices for the work in question. With these we do not agree
and we are not prepared to accept them. Pursuant to Clause 52(4)(a) we
give notice of our intention to claim higher rates and prices.*

Engineer to Contractor   *2 January 1980*

*I have to acknowledge your letter of 3 December 1979 and to inform you
that I have re-examined this matter very carefully and regret I cannot
agree to increase any of these rates and prices. Please accept this as my
final decision.*

It looks clear enough, but what does it mean in the context of the ICE Conditions? Has
the decision been given pursuant to Clause 52 or does the reference to 'final' in any way
bring Clause 66 into play?

The answer to the former is 'Yes' and to the latter 'No'. Again there is no dispute until
there has been reiteration — this time coupled with a request for a decision *under Clause
66*. The contractor and the engineer can do battle over a protracted period, with apparently
the last word being said on both sides, yet until Clause 66 is specifically invoked the arbitration
'clock' does not start ticking. Both sides need to be quite clear about what is wanted. There
is no point in getting involved in arbitration proceedings unless there is a deliberate decision
to do so. Even if the engineer were to have ended his letter of 2 January with the sentence
'Please accept this as my decision under Clause 66', it would have made no difference because
the dispute did not yet exist (the letter of 3 December is the first intimation of the problem,
not its reiteration). Even if there were reiteration and a dispute existed, the engineer still
could not give a decision as being under Clause 66 because it had not been referred to him
for decision under that clause and by its wording he has no authority to apply it unilaterally.

In *Monmouthshire CC v Costelloe & Kemple Ltd*[32] the question before the Court of
Appeal was whether a notice of the contractor requiring arbitration under Clause 66 had
been given within the three months required by that clause. The court held that a mere
rejection of claims by the engineer did not amount to a decision under Clause 66 and that
after the rejection the contractors were at liberty to make formal reference to the engineer
under Clause 66 of the matters in dispute.

Assuming there has been reiteration and further rejection, let us assume the contractor
writes:

Contractor to Engineer   *3 February 1980*

*With reference to your letter of 2 January, not only is there a lot of
money involved but a matter of principle as well. We therefore require you
to give your decision under Clause 66.*

Now the 'arbitration clock' has started ticking and the engineer has 3 months in which to
reply. If he replies favourably so well and good; that would be the end of the matter. If
he were to accede to part of the claim, there would still be a dispute unless the contractor
accepted the decision. The engineer would have stated his 'decision in writing' and the
arbitration clock would continue. There is no provision for further reference to the engineer
once he has given his decision in writing under Clause 66.

A more difficult problem can arise if the engineer writes:

---

32. *Monmouthshire CC v Costelloe & Kemple Ltd* [1965] 5 BLR 50.

> *I refer to your letter of 3 February and in connection with the matters at issue I should be glad if you would let me have the following information . . .*

Supposing the contractor takes a month to put together the required information plus the necessary explanation, justification or whatever. What has happened to the 'arbitration clock'? Has its advance been suspended or has it relentlessly continued?

The arbitration clock operates in various ways, and its relevance is different for each of the parties and for the engineer.

For the engineer, it imposes a time limit of 3 months for the statement of his decision in writing. It does not, however, prevent him stating a decision after the 3 months has expired, even after notice to refer the dispute to arbitration has been given. Total failure by the engineer to give a Clause 66 decision would no doubt be taken into account by an arbitrator.

For the employer or contractor, Clause 66 creates a three-month window for reference to arbitration. The window may open with the decision of the engineer before the first 3 months has elapsed. Or the window may open at the end of the first 3 months if the engineer has failed to give a decision. Or the window may open later if the engineer gives a decision after the expiry of the first 3 months and the dispute has not been referred to arbitration meanwhile.

In a situation such as described, if the information is minimal and can be supplied forthwith, then the contractor would normally be well advised to provide the information, perhaps with a reminder that a decision is still expected within three months of the original date. Alternatively, if the contractor considers the engineer's request to be unreasonable, he may refuse to supply any further information and insist on a decision on the basis of the information already available to the engineer — unlike Clause 52(4), Clause 66 does not require the contractor to submit additional information required by the engineer.

If the nature of the dispute and the necessary investigation and collection of further information requires more than 3 months and the contractor considers it would help to resolve matters by providing the information, it is probably open to the parties to waive the time limits by agreement, but it is essential that any such agreement should be explicit.[33]

Following this procedure there should be no difficulty about whether or not there is a dispute, whether a decision under the relevant clause is being sought or whether the preliminary steps to arbitration are being taken.

Interim arbitration   All the Forms discussed here provide for interim arbitration (i.e. arbitration before work is complete), in certain circumstances.

JCT 63/77

Clause 35(1) permits disputes under 'Article 3 or Article 4 of the Articles of Agreement or on the question of whether or not the issue of an instruction is empowered by these Conditions whether or not a certificate has been improperly withheld or is not in accordance with these Conditions or on any dispute or difference under Clauses 32 and 33 of these Conditions' to be referred to arbitration before practical completion or determination.

JCT 80

Paragraph 5.2 of Article 5 permits interim arbitration without restriction in regard to specified questions including:

---

33. Such a waiver would be binding as an estoppel without any requirement of consideration.

'whether or not the issue of an instruction is empowered by the Conditions; or
whether or not a certificate has been improperly withheld; or
whether a certificate is not in accordance with the Conditions; or
whether a determination ... will be just and equitable'.

Otherwise, the written consent of the Employer or the Architect/Supervising Officer on his behalf and the Contractor is required, if the reference is to be opened prior to 'Practical Completion or alleged Practical Completion of the Works or termination or alleged termination of the Contractor's employment under this Contract or abandonment of the Works'.

This provision has been retained as Clause 41.3 under Amendment 4:1987 and Amendment 6:1988.

GC/Wks 1 Edition 2

Any matter agreed upon between the parties may be referred to arbitration before completion or abandonment or determination. It means, however, that neither side can force matters to arbitration without the agreement of the other.

GC/Wks 1 Edition 3

Condition 60(2) provides that no reference to arbitration shall be made until after the completion, alleged completion or abandonment of the Works or the determination of the Contract, unless the parties otherwise agree. Adjudication under Condition 59 is not so restricted but requires that the dispute should have been outstanding for at least 3 months. Condition 59(7) provides that 'The decision of the adjudicator on any matter referred to him will be binding until completion, alleged completion or abandonment of the Works or determination of the Contract'.

ICE5

'Any matter arising under Clause 12 or the withholding by the Engineer of any certificate or the withholding of any portion of the retention money under Clause 60 ... may be referred to arbitration notwithstanding that the Works shall not then be complete.'

In the 1986 Reprint, the provisions for interim arbitration were considerably altered. In particular, the time for the Engineer to give his decision under Clause 66 is reduced to one month where a Certificate of Completion of the whole of the Works has not been issued. Clause 66(5)(c) then provides 'Any reference to arbitration may unless the parties otherwise agree in writing proceed notwithstanding that the Works are not then complete or alleged to be complete'.

There is a particular problem attaching to interim arbitrations and that is the necessity to define the dispute and the decisions required from the arbitrator in the context of the work continuing to proceed. So far as the withholding of a certificate or validity of a given instruction is concerned, there should be no great difficulty but in the case of such as earthworks (or any other matter touching upon the construction which is being proceeded with) it may be difficult to define the issues in dispute and/or the monetary recompense being sought.

ICE6

The arbitration provisions under ICE6 are similar in effect to the ICE5 1986 Reprint, although some of the wording has been changed. In addition, ICE6 provides an alternative method of resolving disputes by the use of 'conciliation'.

Index

376